International Congress and Symposium Series
Number 115

Health care provision under financial constraint:
need, demand and resources

Edited by
T. B. Binns
Mary Firth

Royal Society of Medicine Services
London   New York
1988

Royal Society of Medicine Services Limited
1 Wimpole Street, London W1M 8AE
7 East 60th Street New York NY 10022

British Library Cataloguing in Publication Data

Health care provision under financial constraint:
  need, demand and resources: [proceedings of an
  Anglo-American conference held at the Royal Society
  of Medicine, London, UK on 2–4 December 1986]. —
  (International congress and symposium series;
  V.115).
  1. Medical economics
  I. Binns, T. B.   II. Firth, Mary   III. Series
  338.4'73621   RA410

  ISBN 0-905958-47-0

Library of Congress Cataloging-in-Publication Data

Health care provision under financial constraint.

  (International congress and symposium series;
no. 115)
  Proceedings of an Anglo-American conference held
at the Royal Society of Medicine, London, UK on
2–4 December 1986.
  1. Medical care — Cost effectiveness — Congresses.
2. Social medicine — Congresses. 3. Medical care —
Great Britain — Cost effectiveness — Congresses.
4. Medical care — United States — Cost effectiveness —
Congresses. 5. Social medicine — Great Britain —
Congresses. 6. Social medicine — United States —
Congresses. I. Binns, T. B.
II. Firth, Mary.   III. Series. [DNLM: 1. Cost
Control — congresses. 2. Delivery of Health Care —
economics — congresses. 3. Health Policy — congresses.
W3 IN207 v.115 / W 74 H4345 1986]
RA410.A2H44 1987   362.1'0941   87-20697
ISBN 0-90595-847-0 (pbk.)

Phototypeset by Dobbie Typesetting Limited, Plymouth, Devon
Printed in Great Britain at the University Press, Oxford

Contributors

Professor Sir Gordon Robson
> *President, The Royal Society of Medicine, London, UK*

Mr Arthur J. Mahon
> *President, The Royal Society of Medicine Foundation Inc., New York NY, USA*

CHAIRMEN AND SPEAKERS

Professor Alwyn Smith
> *Professor of Epidemiology and Social Oncology, Department of Epidemiology and Social Oncology, University of Manchester and University Hospital of South Manchester, Manchester, UK*

Dr H. David Banta
> *WHO Consultant on Technology Assessment, WHO/Steering Committee on Future Health Scenarios Study on Future Health Care Technology, Health Council, The Hague, Netherlands*

Sir Douglas Black
> *The Royal College of Physicians, London, UK*

Dr Stuart Bondurant
> *Dean, School of Medicine, The University of North Carolina at Chapel Hill, Chapel Hill NC, USA*

Professor Robert N. Butler
> *Brookdale Professor of Geriatrics and Adult Development; Chairman, Ritter Department of Geriatrics and Adult Development, Mount Sinai School of Medicine, New York NY, USA*

Mr Martin J. Buxton
> *Director, Health Economics Research Group, Brunel University, Uxbridge, Middlesex, UK*

Dr Theodore Cooper
> *The Upjohn Company, Kalamazoo MI, USA*

Professor John Corbett
> *Professor of Mental Handicap, Department of Psychiatry, University of Birmingham, Birmingham, UK*

Sir Richard Doll
> *Emeritus Professor of Medicine, University of Oxford, Oxford, UK*

Dr Christopher C. Fordham III
  Chancellor, The University of North Carolina at Chapel Hill, Chapel Hill NC, USA

Professor John Grimley Evans
  Professor of Geriatric Medicine, University of Oxford, Oxford, UK

Sir Raymond Hoffenberg
  President, The Royal College of Physicians, London, UK

Dr John Horder
  Visiting Professor, Royal Free Hospital School of Medicine, London, UK; Past President, Royal College of General Practitioners, London, UK

Professor Michel A. Ibrahim
  Dean and Professor of Epidemiology, School of Public Health, The University of North Carolina at Chapel Hill, Chapel Hill NC, USA

Professor Bryan Jennett
  Professor of Neurosurgery, Institute of Neurological Sciences; Dean, Faculty of Medicine, University of Glasgow, Glasgow, UK

Mr Lawrence S. Lewin
  Lewin and Associates Inc., Washington DC, USA

Mr Robert Maxwell
  Secretary (Chief Executive Officer), The King's Fund, London, UK

Dr Eugene Mayer
  Associate Dean, School of Medicine, The University of North Carolina at Chapel Hill, Chapel Hill NC, USA

Professor Alan Maynard
  Director, Centre for Health Economics, University of York, York, UK

Mr Eric Munson
  Executive Director, North Carolina Memorial Hospital, The University of North Carolina at Chapel Hill, Chapel Hill NC, USA

Professor Herbert Pardes
  Professor and Chairman, Department of Psychiatry, College of Physicians and Surgeons, Columbia University; Director, New York State Psychiatric Institute, New York NY, USA

Professor Mitchell T. Rabkin
  President, Beth Israel Hospital; Professor of Medicine, Harvard Medical School, Boston MA, USA

Professor Uwe E. Reinhardt
  James Madison Professor of Political Economy, Princeton University, Princeton NJ, USA

Dr Arnold S. Relman
  Editor, The New England Journal of Medicine, Boston MA, USA

Sir Martin Roth
  Professor of Psychiatry, University of Cambridge, Cambridge, UK

Dr E. Rosemary Rue

Regional General Manager/Regional Medical Officer, Oxford Regional Health Authority, Oxford, UK

Professor Sam Shapiro

Professor Emeritus, Department of Health Policy and Management; Past Director, Health Services Research and Development Center, School of Hygiene and Public Health, The Johns Hopkins University, Baltimore MD, USA

Professor Rosemary A. Stevens

Department of History and Sociology of Science, University of Pennsylvania, Philadelphia PA, USA

Mr Arthur C. Taylor

Chairman, National Association of Health Authorities; Chairman, Newcastle Health Authority, Newcastle upon Tyne, UK

Professor George Teeling Smith

Director, Office of Health Economics, London, UK

Dr Richard D. Tonkin

President, Research Council for Complementary Medicine, London, UK

Sir John Walton

Warden, Green College, Oxford; Immediate Past President, The Royal Society of Medicine, London, UK

Professor Glenn Wilson

Professor and Chairman, Department of Social and Administrative Medicine; Associate Dean for Community Health Services, School of Medicine, The University of North Carolina at Chapel Hill, Chapel Hill NC, USA

DISCUSSANTS

Mr Howard Brody

University of Michigan, Ann Arbor MI, USA

Dr Gillian Ford

Director of Studies, St Christopher's Hospice, London, UK

Dr Gail Wilensky

Vice President, Division of Health Affairs, Project HOPE, Millwood VA, USA

OTHER PARTICIPANTS

Dr Roger Bulger

University of Texas Health Science Center, USA

Professor Ruth Bulger

University of Texas Health Science Center, USA

Mr E. Byers

The Maudsley Hospital, UK

Dr J. Malcolm Forsythe
South-East Thames Regional Health Authority, UK

Mr J. K. Iglehart
The New England Journal of Medicine, USA

Dr John Lister
The Royal College of Physicians, UK

Professor Isaac Marks
Institute of Psychiatry, UK

Mr G. R. Rodgers
Upjohn Ltd, UK

Mr S. Sieverts
Blue Cross/Blue Shield, USA

Contents

Contents

Acknowledgement

The Royal Society of Medicine, London, the Royal Society of Medicine Foundation Inc., New York, and the University of North Carolina at Chapel Hill wish to thank Glaxo Laboratories Ltd for generously financing the publication of these proceedings.

Welcome

PROFESSOR SIR GORDON ROBSON

President, The Royal Society of Medicine, London, UK

As President of the Royal Society of Medicine, it is a great privilege and pleasure for me to open this meeting. This is the first Anglo-American conference to be held in the new and refurbished buildings. This gives us particular pleasure.

There have been over 20 such conferences since 1971, half of them in the USA. This one was planned in 1983 following a meeting in 1982 on responsibility in the shaping of health policy in the UK and the USA — which I believe was a very successful meeting.

The topics have always been broad, and they must fulfil their function, I suppose, by exerting small pressures which fashion trends in health care.

As President, I have attended one meeting of the Royal Society of Medicine Foundation Inc., in New York, under its President, Mr Arthur Mahon, who is present at this meeting. With Mr Mahon and the Executive Director, Mr William O'Reilly, the Foundation is a thriving concern, and we are enjoying here some of the fruits of this co-operation on both sides of the Atlantic.

This conference has been organized also in association with the University of North Carolina at Chapel Hill, in particular with Dr Christopher Fordham, the Chancellor, Dr Stuart Bondurant, Dean of Medicine, Dr Eugene Mayer, Associate Dean, and Professor Glenn Wilson, Professor of Social and Administrative Medicine.

Among those attending the conference from the UK are many people who I have known in many walks of life, all of whom are very distinguished contributors to medicine. Equally distinguished people are present from the other side of the Atlantic. This conference therefore should produce something of great use, not only in broad brush terms but because all have a considerable part to play in the shaping of the future of health in the USA and the UK.

Opening remarks

CHRISTOPHER C. FORDHAM III

*Chancellor, The University of North Carolina at Chapel Hill,
Chapel Hill NC, USA*

It is a great pleasure to begin this third Anglo-American conference on medical matters jointly sponsored by the Royal Society of Medicine, the Royal Society of Medicine Foundation Inc., and the University of North Carolina School of Medicine.

The earlier conferences have been provocative, informative and pleasant, and I am confident that this effort, timely as it is, will be our best thus far.

The USA shares a multitude of qualities and traditions with the UK—as profound as the commonality of our genes, our civic values and our language, and as trivial as our preoccupation with sports and our inclusion of politics in that rubric—yet we differ on many matters of profound substance.

One of the marvels, perhaps the greatest marvel, of the 20th century is the advance of biomedical science and its ramifications. Almost as dramatic are the increased life expectancy in our two countries, the reduction in the rate of death from most major diseases and the aging of the population. Taken together with the inexorably increasing costs of sickness and injury, medical care issues and choices are among the foremost concerns of our societies. This is abetted in the USA by our expectation of long life and our absolute preoccupation with issues of human health.

We have translated these issues into operational medical care systems in different ways in our two countries.

The UK has emphasized the interdependence of a modern society and, like many—indeed most—other western nations, has taken a collective (that is, governmental) responsibility to assure access for all citizens to equitable medical care. The USA, preoccupied as it has been with individual independence and its economic expression, private capitalism, has chosen to eschew fully collective responsibility and to depend instead upon diverse and multiple methods of access, relying upon individuals to seek out and find care—provided until recently also by individuals.

All this is changing somewhat, as would be expected. In the USA, we have tended to accelerate the process of eschewing collectivism in medical care, despite the recent proposal by Secretary Bowen for a limited form of catastrophic health insurance. There are those, however, who believe that medical care is a special human need and service which should be considered outside the normal framework of commerce; in other words, that medical care is a special part of the debate over the relative merits of independence and interdependence.

It is interesting to reflect for a moment on the fact that in the USA societal preoccupation with the innate worth of independence of the individual, noble as that is, sustains a system which may permit neglect of the individual human being in his or her time of greatest need.

It is our understanding that the UK has also experienced strains in its collective approach to the provision of medical care. Since we in the USA believe our medicine to be, like theirs, so excellent and our delivery of care to be less than fully effective, we obviously have much to learn.

As in past conferences, we can learn much from each other. On behalf of all of us from North Carolina, we profoundly appreciate the opportunity to be here to seek shared insights.

FINANCE IS FINITE: CARING KNOWS NO BOUNDS:
THE CURRENT DILEMMA

1. How high a priority will society accord health care in financial terms?

Chairman:
CHRISTOPHER C. FORDHAM III
Chapel Hill NC, USA

A UK view

GEORGE TEELING SMITH

Director, Office of Health Economics, London, UK

Introduction

I have been asked to predict how much society will be spending on health care, perhaps 30 or 40 years from now. I would have liked to make a global prediction because the health care problems of the Third World are more acute than those of our own countries. However, to deal in reasonable depth with the very many different aspects of the question, I have regretfully confined my discussion to the advanced economies such as the USA, Europe and Japan. I would emphasize that this does not mean that I am unaware of the problems elsewhere in the world.

Developments in the last two decades

Before discussing the future, it is useful to review the developments of the past 20 years. Table 1 shows that each of the advanced countries listed has more or less doubled the proportion of national wealth devoted to health care between 1960 and 1983 (1). In the case of the USA, the percentage of gross domestic product (GDP) spent on health care rose from 5·3% to 10·6%. The increase in the UK was rather smaller, from 3·9% to 5·9%.

These figures emphasize the second point, shown forcefully in Table 1. This is the variation between nations which, to a large extent, is explained in Fig. 1 (2). In general, the richer nations devote a higher percentage of national wealth to health expenditure. There are exceptions, such as Switzerland with a high GDP but a relatively low percentage spent on health. Ireland, on the other hand, spends a larger proportion of its wealth on health than its rather low national income would predict.

It is now clear that the authorities in each case are worried by this increase in expenditure. The fashion in Britain and America, and throughout the rest of Europe and in Japan, is for 'cost-containment' in medical care. This will be discussed in detail later.

Health Care Provision under Financial Constraint, edited by T. B. Binns and M. Firth, 1988: Royal Society of Medicine International Congress and Symposium Series No. 115, published by Royal Society of Medicine Services Ltd.

Table 1

Health as a percentage of gross domestic product (GDP)

Country (1960)	%	Country (1983)	%
USA	5·3	USA	10·6
Germany	4·8	Sweden	9·3
Sweden	4·7	France	9·3
France	4·3	Netherlands	8·7
UK	3·9	Germany	8·2
Italy	3·9	Switzerland	7·8
Netherlands	3·9	Italy	7·2
Denmark	3·6	Denmark	6·8
Belgium	3·4	Japan	6·6
Switzerland	3·3	Belgium	6·2
Japan	3·0	UK	5·9

Source: Organization for Economic Co-operation and Development (1).

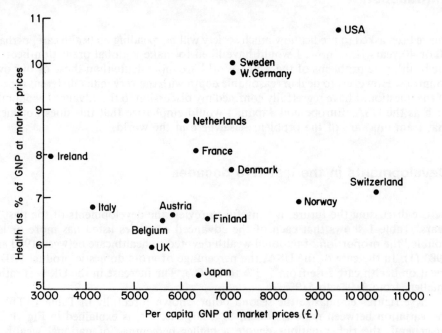

Figure 1. Relationship between health as percentage of gross national product (GNP) and per capita GNP (1983).
Source: Chew (2).

Issues involved in predicting health care expenditure

Against this general background, I have chosen, fairly arbitrarily, five issues to discuss before making my prediction about future levels of expenditure on health: first, the comparative role of a market economy as opposed to that of a bureaucracy in determining health expenditure; secondly, the crucial issue of whether 'needs' or 'demands' should determine the pattern of health expenditure; thirdly, the contradictions involved in the current 'cost-containment' policies; fourthly, what has been described as the 'technological imperative' in health care. Finally, I will examine whether it is possible to determine an 'appropriate' level for health expenditure in our increasingly service economies. Only then will I risk my reputation by predicting how health expenditures will actually develop.

Market versus bureaucracy

When health economics was in its infancy in the 1950s the great debate was between private health care and socialized medicine. The former was characterized by the US system, and the latter by the National Health Service (NHS) in the UK. In Britain, intellectual giants like John Jewkes and Richard Titmuss stood on opposing sides and allowed themselves to descend to levels of triviality in their efforts to prove that their particular preferences had all the virtues and their opponents' system all the vices. When the Office of Health Economics (OHE) came into existence in 1962 it stood aloof from this essentially political argument, and it soon appeared that the debate was sterile. The underlying problem of health economics far transcended the political debate, and it was clear that both socialized medicine and private health care had serious defects. Neither system could close the inevitable gap between available resources and potential demand. Nor was the existence of private medicine by itself a prime determinator of higher levels of medical expenditure in countries like the USA.

However, this was by no means the end of the market discussion. In Europe at least, the next stage was an interesting debate in the 1970s as to whether health insurance had advantages over Britain's essentially tax-funded system of health care. Other European countries, such as Germany and France, depended on either pure health insurance, largely on a private basis, or social insurance, in which health care was financed as part of an overall social security package. Because the bugbear of the British system — waiting lists for hospital treatment — appeared to be absent on the continent, it was argued that health insurance was better able to meet health needs than a tax-funded bureaucracy.

Once again, this particular debate turned out to be sterile. Waiting lists were absent in Europe primarily because the Europeans spent so much more on health care and because they were more affluent, rather than because they relied on health insurance. When the British and European systems were carefully compared there appeared to be no great advantage in raising health care funds from insurance rather than taxation. Thus, yet another apparent solution to Britain's health care problems had to be discarded.

In the 1980s the discussion on both sides of the Atlantic now centres on the potential advantages of what is called an 'internal market' for health care. On the one hand, the theory is that a bureaucratic system such as the NHS is better able to ensure fair distribution of resources between the privileged and the underprivileged. On the other hand, there are inevitably inefficiencies inherent in a bureaucracy where the profit motive is lacking, and it is now argued that these can be avoided by introducing market principles, within the NHS in Britain, or health maintenance organizations (HMOs) in the USA. This debate is continuing, and its relevance to my subject is that even internal market principles within a bureaucracy are likely to exert upward pressure on levels of expenditure. Thus, although the classic market versus bureaucracy argument is largely dead, its reincarnation in the form of arguments for an internal market may be a factor increasing health care costs.

Needs versus demands

One argument central to health economics is whether the health service should be attempting to meet demands for health care, or whether the service should be restricted to meeting proven needs. From an economist's point of view, this question raises a major philosophical dilemma. The economic concept of demand is clear-cut. It is what the customer wants and, in the case of what is sometimes called 'expressed demand', also what he is able to pay for. In a market where there is a zero price, such as with health insurance or an NHS, demand is no longer limited by the ability to pay. This results in the classic phenomenon of 'queuing', as under the NHS waiting lists.

Many epidemiological theorists argue that this problem could be largely overcome if the supply of medical care was restricted only to meeting proven needs instead of demands. From the economist's point of view, this raises the insuperable problem of defining need. No one, for example, *needs* more than one pair of shoes, and people certainly do not *need* a ticket for the opera. A person does not even *need* bread, if biscuits or cake are available instead — as Marie Antoinette pointed out. Thus, need has to be much more arbitrarily defined than demand.

The problem is similar in health care and, as will be discussed more fully later, it has been accentuated by technological progress. For example, in the 1930s pneumonia was described as 'the old man's friend', which provided a peaceful end to a natural lifespan. The most conspicuous contrast to this in the 1980s is the US federal law on end-stage renal failure. For many elderly people renal failure, like pneumonia, occurs as a natural terminal event in a declining life. But in the USA, instead of being allowed to die, the patient must receive treatment at the government's expense. Clearly, in one very real sense, the patient 'needs' treatment, but is such a need a realistic basis for allocating scarce medical resources?

On the other hand, many people with relatively trivial disease or bearable discomfort demand treatment which may not be strictly necessary. As Professor Archie Cochrane pointed out in the conclusion to his Rock Carling Lecture (3), many people expect treatment for the reason that Aunt Agatha gave in T. S. Eliot's *The Family Reunion*:

Not for the good that it will do, But that nothing may be left undone, On the margin of the impossible.

As long as demand of that sort continues to occur in the health services it is likely to go on exerting upward pressure on health expenditure. Neither doctors, politicians, nor economists have made any real progress so far in shifting the basis of medical care from meeting the clear-cut concept of demand to the nebulous and often technically obscure concept of need.

The contradictions in cost-containment

It has already been pointed out that cost-containment for health care has become a fashionable principle. The problem is that it is an exceedingly crude weapon, at least as it has been used so far. For example, in Britain, hospital expenditure is limited under the NHS, and when a department's annual budget has been expended there have been cases when the department has simply been closed down. In other cases, closure for annual redecoration has been extended to save revenue costs by reducing the numbers of patients admitted.

The real danger of measures to reduce costs are illustrated, however, by the study published by Ware *et al.* (4). This showed that in the USA the HMOs were undoubtedly less expensive than fee-for-item-of-service health insurance, but the sick poor also fared significantly worse under the cheaper system. For the healthier and more affluent sector of the population there was no difference in medical outcome.

Thus, there is at least an impression that cost-containment in health care disadvantages the least privileged and most needy sections of society, but if it is justified it will provide a strong social argument against 'cheap' health care and the general application of cost-containment.

The technological imperative

The most impressive evidence that health care expenditure may continue to rise in the future comes from the expectation that medical science will continue to make just as dramatic progress over the next 30 years as it has done over the past 30. At the OHE we have referred to 'the second pharmacological revolution' (5). This will be based on an understanding of intracellular biochemistry, and a consequent ability to control the viral infections, the cancers and the whole range of autoimmune diseases.

It is ironic that when the NHS was first conceived it was assumed that it would reduce medical expenditure by creating a healthier society. What has happened is that medical progress, regardless of the NHS, has greatly extended the scope for therapy. This, in turn, has created an ageing population which *requires* more of the modern medical technology which has become available.

There can be little argument that this trend will continue. A longer and less disabled existence for the population as a whole will become possible, and it will inevitably be associated with rising expectations for medical treatment. In the 1950s the conquest of diseases like tuberculosis brought enormous economic savings, for example, in reduced hospital costs. There will be some similar examples in the future when the control of senile dementia, for instance, reduces the need for continuous nursing surveillance. But, in general, the technological imperative will be another factor increasing potential expenditure on health care over the next 30 years.

An appropriate level in a service economy?

Each of the factors discussed so far has led to the conclusion that a technologically oriented caring society will have to spend more on health care in the future. This runs counter to the fashionable view that cost-containment is desirable and possible. Is there, in fact, a balance to be struck? Can an appropriate level of health expenditure be established?

The late Lord Vaizey often drew attention to the anomaly that the explosion in health expenditure was seen as a major problem, while the corresponding explosion in expenditure on electronic home entertainment, for example, was greeted as an economic achievement. The problem, of course, is that the former is funded collectively, while the latter depends on individual purchases. We do not have to pay for the next man's video recorder, in the way that we contribute to the cost of his hernia or heart transplant.

This is where economists and politicians should have something to offer in measuring and explaining the benefits of health expenditure. The benefits can no longer be quantified by the traditional cost-benefit equations which showed, for example, the savings from the conquest of tuberculosis. They will have to be demonstrated by measurements of the improvements in the quality of life which are achieved by modern therapy. This is a central concern of the OHE in its current activities. It is also a concept which is gradually gaining ground amongst health professionals, politicians and administrators.

Much of the discussion about the way in which rising health expenditure can be justified by improvements in the length and quality of life is still controversial. However, it is vital to answering the question of whether an appropriate level of health expenditure can be established. Obviously, health has to compete with defence and education in the public sector, and with entertainment, travel and material well-being in the private sector. Over about the past decade the case for increased expenditure on health has tended to go by default. The 'consumerist' lobby has successfully denigrated the achievements of the health services for reasons which are sociologically difficult to understand. If the foregoing arguments are accepted, the health industry needs to be much more successful in the future in justifying the social benefits of its activities. Only then will an appropriate level of health expenditure be established in the context of a society where most expenditure goes on services of one kind or another.

Conclusions

There is nothing on the horizon to suggest that the present almost universal belief in cost-containment for health expenditure will in fact prevent a further rise in the proportion of national wealth devoted to medical care.

Indeed, looked at from an economic standpoint, the question seems to be why the rising expenditure has to be perceived as a problem. In Britain, the NHS, as a burden on taxation, is an embarrassment to a government committed to reducing taxes — but that is a political problem not an economic one.

In the USA, the health insurance funds have a tarnished reputation for their inability to curb rising *prices* for health care (as opposed to total expenditure). Competition from organizations such as the HMOs is seen as a solution, but it has been pointed out that perhaps the American public were right in the past to regard the cheaper HMOs as an inferior alternative to fee-for-item-of-service insurance. In health care, as in everything else, it seems that you get what you pay for.

None of this is to argue for economic complacency in respect of *any* of the existing systems of medical care. Every country undoubtedly has wasteful procedures and unmet needs as well as unnecessary activity. As an economist, it is not surprising that I should argue that health economists working alongside other health professionals could probably make a major contribution in reducing inefficiencies and improving performance, but greater efficiency cannot be expected to yield savings which will finance the technological advances in medical care over the next three decades. There seems to be an overwhelming argument that health care will absorb an even higher proportion of national wealth in the years ahead in all the developed countries with their increasingly service-oriented economies. Improvement in quality of life will become more important than crude material wealth, but it will not be any cheaper.

Twenty years ago, when Britain spent less than 4% of national income on health, and the USA little more than 5%, who would have predicted that by the 1980s those percentages would have reached 6% and almost 11%, respectively? I would not be too surprised if the USA was spending 20% of her GDP on health by the year 2020. The British economy is harder to predict, but health expenditure here too will certainly continue to rise. It will probably reach the current US level in the early 21st century.

References

(1) Organization for Economic Co-operation and Development. *Measuring health care 1960–1983*. Paris: Organization for Economic Co-operation and Development, 1985.

(2) Chew RSB. *Health expenditure in the UK*. London: Office of Health Economics, 1986.

(3) Cochrane AL. *Effectiveness and efficiency*. London: Nuffield Provincial Hospitals Trust, 1972.

(4) Ware JE, Rogers WH, Davies AR, *et al*. Comparison of health outcomes at a health maintenance organization with those of fee-for-service care. *Lancet* 1986;i: 1017–22.

(5) Wells NEJW. *The second pharmacological revolution*. London: Office of Health Economics, 1983.

A US view

THEODORE COOPER

The Upjohn Company, Kalamazoo MI, USA

It is a pleasure to participate in this unusual and important conference. Juxtaposing the UK and US views is a novel way to devise solutions to problems shared by both countries. I am delighted to present a US point of view on the current dilemma although I shall not represent the position of the US government, neither do I have an infallible crystal ball. Health as a priority in financially difficult times is of interest to many other persons and groups besides myself, including such prestigious organizations as the American Medical Association, the American Enterprise Institute, the Ford Foundation and others. Their crystal balls are clearer than mine. Nor am I here to represent the Upjohn Company's point of view, or even that of the pharmaceutical industry. The priority of health care concerns the industry and me as a corporate executive, but my remarks should be taken as an amalgamation of my personal perspective, which has been shaped by experience in medicine, academia, government and industry.

The future of health care in the USA

I believe that health care will remain a high priority for the American public. Today's environment has caused a great deal of anxiety for the medical establishment by a short-term restructuring of the health services delivery and reimbursement systems, but in the longer term, health care will not only *survive* as a priority, it will *grow* in importance.

The reason for this growth is rooted deeply in our culture, and cultural values last much longer than debates over such things as prospective reimbursement or how much health care costs should be as a percentage of gross national product. As things stand now, however, the macrocosmic view of health care is out of line with the microcosmic view, as I hope to show.

What has changed in America since the mid-1960s is the perception of health care *costs*, not the health care itself. Then, the ideal of universal access to high quality care was codified in public policy. Today, public policy on health is driven by cost-containment, and in one sense the public has endorsed the shift from fee-for-service, third-party reimbursement to other systems that devalue medical services delivery.

Health Care Provision under Financial Constraint, edited by T. B. Binns and M. Firth, 1988: Royal Society of Medicine International Congress and Symposium Series No. 115, published by Royal Society of Medicine Services Ltd.

Such things as hospital maintenance organization (HMO) enrollments and reduced lengths of stay in hospital show there is a feeling that we are paying too much for what we collectively get out of the system—the key word being 'collectively'.

The macrocosmic and microcosmic views

'Collectively' comes from the macrocosmic view, which assumes that Americans are willing to accept limits in the medical system in order to achieve lower total cost. In the microcosm that is not true at all. In a study done for the Equitable Life Assurance Society in 1983, 46% of the sample felt that total health care costs were too high, but the identical percentage thought that denying expensive technology to terminal patients was an unacceptable way to lower those costs (1). The respondents also opposed the idea of having nurses, midwives and physicians' assistants provide more of the services customarily provided by physicians.

In other words, the American public feel one way about quality and the use of expensive technology when they think about society as a whole, but individuals who are at the microcosmic level feel completely different when it is themselves or a loved one who is sick or dying. This phenomenon, as I said, is culturally rooted, and I would ask that its validity be accepted because there is not enough time to launch into a treatise on fear of death in the American culture. The phenomenon must be valid in any event because why else would Americans be willing to accept increased co-payments and deductibles, on the one hand, and to encourage by legislative decree the spread of expensive procedures such as liver transplants, on the other?

Our policy makers seem to have overlooked how Americans behave as individuals. Professor Richard Pipes, of Harvard University, recently published an excellent article that dealt, in part, with what happens when scientists (or people who like to think of themselves as scientists) become involved in setting national policy (2). Professor Pipes' specific topic was US strategy in nuclear weapons *vis-à-vis* the Soviet Union, but his contextual remarks are also applicable to health care.

He wrote that scientific modes of thinking have influenced Western culture since the 16th century and, in his words:

> Applied to human affairs, this method has produced the 'science of man' or sociology. Conceived in France in the early years of the 19th century, sociology and its theoretical underpinning, positivism, deprecate national culture and history as factors that shape human behavior in favor of abstract conceptions of man, isolated in time and space.

Later in the article, Professor Pipes says:

> It is psychologically as well as intellectually impossible for most [scientists], and especially for the most gifted, to accept the irrational as real.

I realize that these are harsh words, and I do not intend to offend sociologists, who certainly play a useful role in solving human problems, or scientists who, in formulating public policy on health, face daily a tiger of large proportions. I wish only to suggest that sometimes scientific approaches to health care policy—whether it is economics, psychology, sociology or the scientific method in general—can overlook the fact that health care choices are made by people, and people by nature are given to doing irrational things. In the USA, this includes spending huge sums of money for a small gain—a few months of life, a slim hope of a cure, an off chance that one might start feeling better.

It has been suggested that imposed rationing is the only way to bring the macrocosm and the microcosm into line. National-scale efforts to control health-related behavior, however, have always failed in the USA. The Volstead Act (better known as prohibition), designed to affect the availability of alcohol for recreational purposes, is a perfect example. The question in America, then, is not rationing, but rationality.

Effective health care policy will, therefore, allow for changes in the delivery system that reduce the cost of each physician-patient contact, while making those contacts more frequent and accessible and also providing adequate coverage for what have been called catastrophic illnesses and injuries. The question is not whether there will be growth in the amount spent on health care, but rather at what rate the growth will occur. Last year the rate declined to 8·9%, still ahead of inflation but none the less the lowest increase in 20 years (3).

Our goal ought to be having a realistic attitude about assuring quality, controlling the rate of growth in expenditures, developing a favorable mix of services, and creating more uniformity throughout the system. I will describe a few of the ways in which the system is being restructured to achieve this goal.

Restructuring the health care system

Much of the push for change has come from corporations, who pay much of the health care bill through employee benefit plans, and who are also working more with government and the insurance industry to develop cost-effective health care plans. The most visible corporate representative is Joseph Califano, formerly Secretary of Health, Education and Welfare, and now heading the Chrysler Corporation's efforts to decrease its employee health care costs. Mr Califano favors the spread of pre-paid health care to the entire delivery system and would like research to focus on prevention so that half the hospital beds would be eliminated by 1995. He also believes that employer-provided health insurance benefits should be taxed as income and that all plans should charge higher deductibles and require greater co-payments (4).

All his suggestions are representative of efforts to lower cost by reducing use of the medical delivery system. Other trends, such as free-standing surgery centers and walk-in emergency care facilities take more services away from hospitals, which is where the bulk of health care inflation has been centered. Hospitals themselves are looking more towards the 'bottom line'. They are engaging in a number of entrepreneurial efforts such as buying physicians' practices, offering preferred provider services, more home health care and consulting services to one another, and engaging in collaborative purchasing agreements. This means that if an individual wishes to get fee-for-service medical care in a hospital setting without first getting a second opinion, he will have to pay more for it.

It is appropriate to ask how far these trends will extend into the fabric of American medical care. Will we have a uniform national medical delivery system? I think not. Harry Schwartz, writing in *Scrip*, said the following about Mr Califano's suggestions:

> Curiously, he never mentions a fact well known in Washington: nobody of any importance in the Federal Government who is pushing for greater HMO enrollment belongs personally to one of these organizations. HMOs are great—for the other guy. (5)

So we return to the microcosm.

I doubt that we will ever reach a point in the USA where everybody receives the same treatment. At the moment, the public seem willing to accept a two-tiered system. Some people give up freedom of choice for lower costs when they enrol in HMO programs; others do not because they value too highly the freedom to choose a particular specialist, and freedom is a component of what we call quality in health care. Eventually, the highest tier of care may more closely resemble the lowest, but there will always be distinctions as long as some people can afford greater out-of-pocket expenses than others.

The demand component to health care

This restructuring can be viewed as an attempt to create steady demand in the system, with the idea that a levelling of demand will produce a levelling of supply and therefore a levelling of cost. I do not believe that either supply or demand will level out. It is worth repeating comments made by Kronfeld and Whicker, both medical sociologists, in their book on US national health policy (6) which discusses the concept of homeostasis (the maintenance of a steady state) in health care demand.

The authors believe that when homeostasis in health care is applied to society as a whole, a wide range of ethical issues appear. Here again we see the conflict between macrocosm and microcosm which gives rise to ethical issues. The authors raise the question of how the concept of distributive justice fits in with our traditional attitudes toward aging and dying. They ask whether such a large percentage of resources should be spent on people in their last years of life, as is the case now (see 7), or whether those resources should go towards preventive services for the young and healthy.

Kronfeld and Whicker also say:

> In traditional economics, tastes are assumed to be relatively constant and stable. In health, however, controversy exists over the stability of tastes for individual medical care. Partially, tastes depend on the health of the individual, which is variable across individuals and for the same individual across time. (6)

These observations tie together neatly to prove that demand for health care will continue to rise. First, we find it acceptable to spend a great deal of money for very little return, so demand is not tied to traditional pricing structures. Secondly, as individuals, our demand for health care is not uniform and, beyond that, each person's demand for health care changes over time. The young, single person cares much less about reimbursement structures for pediatric care, for instance, than he does when he has a family and his children are sick. That same person at the age of 30 is likely to care much more about treatment of acute diseases than chronic ones, whilst at 70 it is probably more likely to be the other way round.

At this point, I would repeat that I believe that the unit price of medical care will go down, but volume will rise. In this sense, Professor Teeling Smith and I are in agreement. Three other areas support my contention: the number of Americans who have either no health insurance or inadequate insurance, the rising number of elderly citizens, and the effects of new technology.

The uninsured

Estimates of the number of Americans without health insurance vary, although the Robert Wood Johnson Foundation placed the number at 28 million in 1983 (8). The number is now closer to 35 million and millions more are underinsured. This means that too many people are falling outside the delivery system. A thorny problem for many hospitals is treating these so-called 'medically indigent' people. The problem of who treats the uninsured has reached crisis proportions, leading the State of Texas, for instance, to pass a law requiring each of its counties to provide care for the medically indigent, using $70 million in state aid as seed money (9). The law also prohibits the transfer of unstable emergency patients for financial reasons and imposes stiff sanctions against hospitals and doctors who fail to comply.

Texas is a leader in facing a problem that must be dealt with on a national scale. We need a national policy, and one seems likely soon. The whole concept of medical indigents is also an anathema to the American sense of fairness, which is another cultural factor lurking behind the economic models and charts.

If about 50 million people, who, in some sense, are outside the system are brought back into it, the supply of medical services will obviously rise to meet their needs. I agree with Professor Teeling Smith that some policy makers have confused need with demand in health care, but I like to look at it from a somewhat different perspective. A sick person with no health insurance may *need* an expensive operation, but he is unlikely to *demand* it, in the strict economic sense. Thus, as distributive justice catches up with a restructured system, needs will become rights and the supply of medical services will grow.

The elderly

By the end of the century, 13% (about 35 million) of the American population will be 65 or older (10), of whom about 5 million will be over 85. This aging population will need more health care services, which they will get for the simple reason that 35 million people make a strong political power base, one which will be cultivated by the elected officials who will have a great deal of influence on how much is spent on health care and in what fashion.

I also believe that the current restructuring can be extended to deal with an increasing number of elderly patients. We will need to devise insurance packages that cover long-term care, develop more comprehensive medical coverage and make a shift to alternative sites such as the home, community-based services and retirement communities. In addition, I would expect many more physicians to specialize in gerontology. This is logical because if, as has been suggested, there are too many physicians, and there is a rapidly growing patient population, specialty trends can be expected to follow patient population trends.

Technological developments

Finally, the medical system will soon be receiving a steady stream of spectacular technological innovations. These range from cell-specific new drugs to DNA probes to new imaging systems and possibly even to gene therapy. Already considerable attention has been focused on the research that produces these innovations. The attention paid to the development of azidothymidine (AZT) for treating acquired immune deficiency syndrome (AIDS) patients is only one example.

As these products of biotechnology and other sophisticated research methods increase, the expectations of what the medical system can do will rise significantly. That is the last reason why health care will continue to be given high priority. I cannot imagine a time in the USA when we might say to a citizen that we can correct the genetic defect which causes a horrible disease, but we are not going to do it because it is too expensive. That is rationing in its bluntest sense, and I do not think a statistically significant number of Americans would agree with the philosophy behind that statement. In the final analysis, the microcosm rules because when individuals are aggregated they become an electorate, and the lawmakers, those with the power to deny to people such things as gene therapy, either listen closely to the electorate or do not remain lawmakers very long.

Conclusions

Finally, I would like to make a comment that is not confined to the American perspective. Medicine, wherever it is practiced, is the only profession that strives constantly to put itself out of business. Yet for every success, e.g. with smallpox, another problem arises, like AIDS. Therefore, health care will fade as a priority only when there is no more disease on the face of the earth. That is obviously far beyond our current comprehension. In the meantime, we shall continue, as an American colleague put it, 'to strive to have people die young as late as possible'.

References

(1) Louis Harris and Associates. *The Equitable health care survey: options for controlling costs.* New York: The Equitable Life Assurance Society of the United States, 1983.
(2) Pipes R. Team B: the reality behind the myth. *Commentary* 1986 October: 26-7.
(3) Rich S. Health-care spending's share of GNP reaches a new high: rate of increase declines but still outstrips inflation. *Washington Post* 1986 July 30.
(4) Califano JA. America's health care revolution. *Who lives? Who dies? Who pays?* New York: Random House, 1986.
(5) Schwartz H. Who lives? Who dies? Who pays? *Scrip* 1986 July 7: 22-3.
(6) Kronfeld JJ, Whicker ML. *US National health policy: an analysis of the federal role.* New York: Praeger Publishers, 1984: 109-10.
(7) Fisher C. Differences by age groups in health care spending. *Health Care Financing Rev* 1980; 4: 65-6.
(8) The Robert Wood Johnson Foundation Communications Office. *Special report: updated report on access to health care for the American people.* Princeton: The Robert Wood Johnson Foundation, 1983: 8-9.
(9) Reinhold R. Treating an outbreak of patient dumping in Texas. *New York Times* 1986 May 25.
(10) Strategic Technologies Inc. *Changing US health care markets: 1985-2000.* Lincoln MA: Strategic Technologies Inc., 1986: 98-9.

Discussion

Professor Ibrahim

As countries get richer they spend proportionately more on medical care than other countries. However, if social services are included as well as medical care—and social factors are important determinants of health care—would that relationship continue to exist?

Professor Teeling Smith

Yes, it applies to all the caring services — education, social security, social services and health. On the whole, the more affluent nations spend a higher proportion of gross national product (GNP) on the caring services. In the UK, defence has received less. Expenditure on education is falling because of the falling birth rate over the last 20 years. Insofar as we take health out of taxation, the proportion of public expenditure can be held constant, at the same time increasing the amount that is spent in the remaining part of the service.

Professor Wilson

Health care expenditures rose in the USA when the GNP was rising rapidly. I am unaware of any data that would suggest anything but rather uneven and quite slow growth in our economy over the next several years. From where will this new money come for health?

Professor Teeling Smith

I believe that the slow-down in the US national economy is a temporary phase, and that it is unrealistic to suggest that it will go into zero growth for the next 30 years. I still think that the USA has enough brains and brilliance to increase its national wealth over that time.

Professor Wilson

How would you propose to reverse a 10-year decline in productivity?

Professor Teeling Smith

There is a shift from manufacturing to service industry; a reduction in the production of motor cars, for example, because of competition from the Far East, but an increase in video recorders, entertainment and eating out. It is from these that the wealth is coming.

Professor Stevens

The National Health Service (NHS) has been through a major reorganization and there is a new commitment to general managership. What does Professor Teeling Smith think is most inefficient about the NHS as it is now?

Professor Teeling Smith

That is a difficult question! I say with some diffidence to this particular audience that the primary cause of inefficiency is still the recalcitrance of the medical profession which has a tradition of being autonomous and unmanageable. It is all very well to appoint a general manager, but there is little he can do about introducing internal market principles when faced with a consultant who says that he has carried out a particular operation in the same way for 30 years, has no intention of changing now, and who has another 10 years before he retires.

Professor Maynard is the principal exponent of one of the most attractive methods of internal market. This has the general practitioner (GP) as the budget holder within the NHS, who 'buys' services from the most efficient hospital. To take this to its logical conclusion, the district general manager or the GP as budget holder — that is, the 'buyer' of services — could put inefficient hospitals out of business, and they could shut down.

This would be an anathema to many people in the health service, including the unions, and also consumer groups who want their own local hospital, however inefficient it may be.

The full realization of an internal market, buying from the most efficient and most economical supplier, would quickly revolutionize the degree of efficiency in the health service.

Dr Tonkin

Everybody is agreed that the cost of treating disease will inevitably escalate, and we are all worried, of course, about where the money will come from. Is it not therefore essential that we turn our minds more to enhancement of health—which is, after all, preventive medicine—as a means of controlling expenditure?

We are all guilty of using the words 'health care' when we are really discussing 'disease management'. As I often say, in the UK there is an excellent national *disease* service, but we do not have a national *health* service.

Dr Cooper

That concept has received much greater attention lately. As a policy, the difficulty has been to know what we can actually do, and how to implement a programme that is not a further restriction of freedom of choice in the way we live, whether it be diet, recreational activities, enforced exercise, and so on.

I think, however, that the technology that is driving even the care system will eventually produce means to detect disease-susceptible individuals and to enhance disease resistance. I think that some more practical methods, other than behavioural modification, will emerge. The pharmaceutical industry is certainly taking that approach much more seriously at the moment. Looking perhaps as far as 20 years ahead, we think that we see a market in preventive medicine, not only with health care and vaccines.

Professor Pardes

What would Dr Cooper think an appropriate health care policy for the approximately 50 million people who are not fully protected? One of the problems is that providers do not have the same numbers of such people coming to their doors. That creates a special fiscal problem for health care providers who happen to have large numbers of uncovered people coming for health care.

Dr Cooper

As I mentioned, in some jurisdictions an attempt is being made to provide this locally, but a national policy will be required. Obviously, one option is a national comprehensive insurance programme but, in the USA at the moment, this is said not to be a very viable option.

Professor Reinhardt

One approach might be to recognize that there are not one-tier systems in all human service areas in the USA. There are certainly two-tier systems in education, jurisprudence and other areas. Perhaps we should tailor a health care system to that cultural proclivity by having a two-tier system. That would mean a publicly financed health care system that procures health services for the poor from private providers, mainly health maintenance organizations (HMOs), on a competitive basis, and which might embrace as many as 20 or 25% of the American people, leaving the rest of the system in private hands, as it is now.

That would clearly be two-tier, mainly in freedom of choice; it would not have to be two-tier in terms of clinical quality. That sort of system would be affordable, and could be purchased for something like $100 billion. We are spending that already anyway through the federal system, so it is just a question of 're-shuffling' money.

I would finance it in part by making employer-paid health insurance premiums taxable and means-testing Medicare. Medicare, the system for the aged, is inequitable at present, giving too much to the rich aged and too little to the poor aged. It is easily affordable within the amount we spend by giving more to the poor and letting the rich aged pay more.

That sort of system would be very American, in that it has a strong private component which is innovative and will always lead the other system, which could never lag too far behind for political reasons. Yet the publicly financed system, by observing economies, might also point to waste in the private system. This private-public mix might be useful, and lead to a high quality and fair system—at least, what we Americans would call 'fair', which does not mean that everyone gets exactly the same.

Dr Cooper

Underlying part of Professor Pardes' question was the sometimes deplorable way in which certain institutions and providers purposely avoid taking any community responsibility on a voluntary basis. As the burden then shifts increasingly to other institutions, and as everybody begins to watch their profits, this will create further public dissatisfaction and lead to the emergence of a new policy.

Mr Taylor

Professor Reinhardt said that the two-tier system does not — or should not — necessarily involve a two-standard service. What is the reality? I wonder whether history does not show that indeed it would force a position in which there were two quite different standards in the two tiers.

Dr Relman

There is little reason in the USA to believe that a separate publicly funded system for the poor would retain the quality that most of us would consider to be mainstream and acceptable. The history of US health care has been that what is publicly funded for only the poor turns out to be bad medicine.

Although I share Professor Reinhardt's belief that we will have to find some public solution for the care of the poor, I am persuaded that the solution will have to embrace the whole country, leaving options open to those who want to spend more money for the luxuries.

Much saving can be produced by reform of the medical profession. Professor Teeling Smith alluded to British physicians as being part of the inefficiency problem in Britain, and it is the same in America. It is astonishing that there is so little public debate about this. We discuss reforming our financing system, as if this is really the way to make the system behave better. Everyone involved in health care knows that unless the behaviour, thinking and motivation of the doctors are changed we will get nowhere.

I look for a more productive and successful approach to this problem through the medical profession. We have just begun to see what might be done in this direction.

Dr Cooper

If the doctor is to blame, what is the pervasive disease that needs changing? If it is that deep-seated, who will change it? Since the teachers of the future doctors themselves have all the bad diseases, from where will this reform come?

Dr Bondurant

As an educator myself, I would like Dr Relman to elaborate on the precise symptoms and patho-genesis of the disease for our guidance on what we should do to respond to Dr Cooper's query.

Dr Relman

One of the symptoms is the difficulty that we physicians have in assessing the usefulness and effectiveness of what we do. It seems to me that one of the great enemies here is ignorance. Another problem is the way the medical profession is now rewarded. It is paid on a piece-work basis for most procedures. Until we convince the profession to accept a different kind of reimbursement there will be an enormous amount of inefficiency because of the economic incentives involved. To make physicians part of the enterprise by offering them shares in the profits obtained by saving money (which is the fashion in the USA today) is the wrong way to go about it, in my opinion.

Dr Cooper

Do you think that giving a salary will eliminate the ignorance? The incentive can be eliminated, but if doctors are given a salary and no longer work on a piecemeal basis, will that eliminate the ignorance?

Professor Teeling Smith

This is a classic example of the grass always being greener elsewhere. We have a salaried service for our most expensive and most recalcitrant group of physicians, and there is no evidence that this leads to any greater efficiency. We have under- rather than over-provision, for the reasons that I was trying to explain earlier, because we spend so little. There is no question of doctors suddenly becoming efficient when the fee-for-item-of-service incentive is removed.

Dr Relman

I did not mean to suggest that simply changing to salaries would solve the problem. First, we need to seek out and communicate the information that we do not now have, with effective feedback and encouragement. Secondly, we should remove, as much as possible, the economic incentives that are impediments to more rational and socially useful behaviour.

If those two things are done, both in the UK and the USA, we would see a vastly different and much more efficient health care service.

Mr Lewin

With regard both to Professor Stevens' point about efficiency and to what we have just been discussing, Professor Teeling Smith mentioned that the shift from manufacturing to service industry is part of the explanation why we do not see real productivity. In the service industry, at least in the USA, we have not developed effective measures of value of product. This means that we undervalue the productivity that is gained.

This is particularly true of the health care industry. Many of our efforts at cost-containment in the USA are being replaced, especially by private employers, by measures of quality of output and service — which, admittedly, are in their early stages. Has Professor Teeling Smith some information about measuring output, both in aggregate terms and in institutional (small population) terms, that might be instructive for us?

Professor Teeling Smith

As economists, Professor Maynard, Mr Buxton and I have all been centrally concerned with the issue of quality of life. The conventional measure of the success of medical treatment, which is whether or not the patient is kept alive, is inappropriate because, generally, we are talking about very old people, for whom an extra year of life may not be the most important aspect. It is the *quality* of that life that is important.

There is a considerable literature on the measurement of quality of life from doctors and economists in North America (Canada and the USA) and from three centres in the UK (Brunel University, the Office of Health Economics, and particularly the University of York). Instead of saying that the man or woman lives for another 5 years, the quality of survival for those 5 years is adjusted by a variety of economic techniques. This leads to the much debated unit, the quality-adjusted life year (QALY). In a recent article, Professor Maynard's colleague in York, Alan Williams, has given the cost per QALY for various procedures (1). This has caused a stir because, for example, renal dialysis is about 14 times as expensive per QALY as a new hip or a pacemaker.

Those techniques are in their infancy but, as Professor Maynard has said to me privately, even the measurements available now are better than just a hunch judgement. They may be imperfect but they are better than no measurements at all. The medical profession in the UK is beginning to think along these lines.

This comes back to the need to educate doctors. I believe that the question of how they are paid is irrelevant. What is important is whether or not they are trained to *think*. For two centuries doctors have had an authoritarian medical education. If the professor did it, the student did it, without any argument. We have a number of medical schools in the UK now which are training doctors to ask *why* something is done, and what is the evidence that there is any benefit for the patient from doing it. It is potentially an important and encouraging development.

Professor Rabkin

With regard to Dr Relman's point about dealing with the so-called perversity of the physician, I agree that the feedback of information becomes very important. Also, as Professor Teeling Smith said, the willingness to generate that information is increasing.

Secondly, I would like to emphasize that I think it is the system within which the physician operates that is important rather than the method of payment. Physicians are no different from other professionals. Consequently, whether it is doctors, nurses, scientists or artists, the world in which they operate tends to determine their behaviour. Part of that world is economic, and part of it is social. The hospital may function in an efficient and warm way for patients but, regardless of their basic motivation, the workers will not perform well if the system grinds them down.

The important thing is not pre-paid salaries, fee-for-service, or whatever (although those all have specific characteristics), but the nature of the system that is created. This is the major — but not the only — determinant of the way people act and behave.

I would disagree completely that physicians have a peculiar nature that gives them some inherent perversity making them impossible to deal with.

Professor Reinhardt

Could Dr Cooper elaborate on his comment that he thinks unit costs will go down but that volume will go up? In the last 5 years it has been more the reverse. It is hard to know what he means by 'unit', but hospitalizations and length of stay are down, physician visits in total have levelled off or are down somewhat, and unit costs are up. Is it possible now that prices will be depressed?

Dr Cooper

The tendency throughout the world has been to depress prices. In the UK, various new measures through economic legislation, the limited list, parallel imports, and a whole variety of techniques are being used to push down the cost. Although the USA has been relatively immune, I think that the next attempt at cost-containment before nationalizing the system will be in the direction of price management. Whether the first step is setting physician fees prospectively, diagnostic related groups (DRGs) or drug prices, I think that will be the next attempt because it is what has been used elsewhere. An effort will then be made at rationalization. While hospitalizations are down for a variety of reasons, the actual use of the system will begin to increase again as other people come into it. The net effect will still be escalation of expenditure, but the mix will be different.

Dr Banta

My comment was triggered by Dr Relman's use of the word 'ignorance'. I certainly agree that unfortunately we do not know the benefits of our technology, and that of course may be our biggest problem.

I do not think that we do much in medicine which is ineffective, but an enormous amount is done which is not very effective, or not effective in relation to cost. It is interesting comparing the UK and the USA as there is such a discrepancy between the two countries in the percentage of GNP devoted to health, with no evidence so far as I know of detriment to the British population. That suggests to me that in the USA we do much that is cost-ineffective.

I also agree with the general thrust of the comments of both Professor Teeling Smith and Dr Cooper that the amount of resources going into health care will rise, but I am mainly concerned about where that rise will be. With an ageing population the need for care will be very great in the future. I would like to see more attention paid to that part of our medical economy.

Professor Marks

It has been said that if someone discovers a new gene he gets a Nobel prize, but if he discovers a new form of health care delivery that saves labour he gets a picket line. Part of the problem is that we do not teach our medical students the value of delivering health care economically and effectively. The value system needs to be changed: it is as important to know how to deliver health care efficiently as to know the Krebs cycle. It is perhaps in the medical schools that we need to begin this revolution in values before a properly structured health care delivery system can be obtained.

Sir Raymond Hoffenberg

Some time ago I was obliged to make up the word 'criticality' to describe a quality that I think students and doctors should try to acquire—the quality of looking at *all* their actions critically, at the investigations and the treatments that they order—just as Dr Relman was discussing.

I do not believe that it is impossible to teach this. For over 10 years in my unit we have run a regular weekly meeting, at which students, junior doctors and consultants have been present. At random, we have looked critically at the records of patients discharged over the previous 1 or 2 weeks, asked questions about the number of investigations carried out, how many were done as emergencies, the number of treatments, etc.

The result has been dramatic. Overnight, there started to be an improvement, most marked of all in the great drop in the number of investigations, particularly emergency investigations carried out in the middle of the night, and also a very large reduction in the number of prescriptions. Our critics would argue that we have not been doing good to our patients, and in fact might have been doing them harm.

I would like to suggest that there is a much greater need for measurement of outcome when there is this type of critical review of our actions. I believe that we are doing good—but this is a gut reaction, and I do not know whether it is right or wrong.

Professor Reinhardt

What is actually known about health status and quality of life? I was impressed by Professor Teeling Smith's remark that the quality-cost relationship for a pacemaker is actually good. Yet it is my understanding that in the UK far fewer pacemakers are implanted than in the USA. If this is true, I would assume that a higher quality of life is produced in the USA with the pacemakers.

That could be extended to other operations—for example, hernias and other life-enhancing procedures. I had a hernia for 30 years, and I was shocked by how much the operation enhanced the quality of my life.

Is there really good information on the difference in health status produced by the two systems? It is often said that there is no difference in health status—but where is that evidence?

Professor Teeling Smith

The evidence is starting to appear. A research assistant started 2 or 3 months ago at Brunel University specifically to do a 3-year study on the quality of life on pacemakers. It is very difficult, because we are dealing with elderly patients and multiple pathologies, to separate the effect of the pacemaker from rheumatoid arthritis or other diseases from which the patient is suffering. As Sir Raymond Hoffenberg has said, unless we *know* whether or not we are doing good, there remains a question as to whether we are doing the right thing. It is total self-interest on our part, but we believe that economists have a major contribution to make in improving both the quality and the effectiveness of care with these sorts of measurements.

Professor Wilson

I would compound the question by suggesting that if we adjusted our sums properly the differences in the GNP would not be nearly so great as they appear. In fact, I believe I could demonstrate that the USA spends less of its GNP than Canada (with the exception of Quebec).

Mr Lewin

How we measure output and the relationship between that, budget and organization have a great effect on the way decisions are made. Some work we have been doing for the pharmaceutical and device industries in the USA illustrates this. Both before and after the advent of the DRG payment system under Medicare, which creates a strong incentive for hospitals to discharge patients as quickly as possible (it deals with the hospitals as a boundary), there has been an interesting effect in both of these industries.

For pacemakers and hip implants, for example, the interest is not necessarily in the device that will have the longest-term effect, even when demonstrably cost-effective in terms of enhancing the quality of life over a period of years, but rather in terms of unit costs. Thus, hospitals are now seeking to move towards implants and other kinds of procedures (and also drugs) that have the lowest cost, even though the long-term effect may not be the greatest, simply because of the way the incentive system is set up.

It would be thought that an HMO system based on capitated payments would solve that problem, but the difficulty is that most patients stay in an HMO only 2½ years; therefore even the HMOs are not very interested in long-term effects. In the absence of a system that values, either financially or otherwise, these long-term quality-enhancing effects, the decision-making process does not seem to be linked to them, unless of course the ethic of the physician, the nurse and other caregivers overwhelms the financial incentives.

I think we are learning in the USA, but we do not yet know very much about the relationship between financial incentives in these kinds of ethical considerations.

Reference

(1) Williams A. Economics of coronary artery bypass grafting. *Br Med J* 1985; **291**: 326–9.

2. Goals, values and equity in health care. Distribution between population groups, and between acute medicine and long-term care

Chairman:
SIR RICHARD DOLL
Oxford, UK

A UK view
appropriate high technology — a painless prescription?

BRYAN JENNETT

Professor of Neurosurgery, Institute of Neurological Sciences; Dean of the Faculty of Medicine, University of Glasgow, Glasgow, UK

Appropriate high technology — a painless prescription?

What British society wants from its doctors is that they should minimize premature mortality from illness and accidents. For survivors and those whose lives are not threatened doctors are expected to make every effort to reduce disability — physical, mental, personal and social. Ideally, it is hoped that these goals will be achieved by prevention or cure, failing which doctors are expected to maximize the quality of life by effective palliative measures. These range from interventions that can result in many years of good quality life, through less effective measures that only partially relieve disability or temporarily prolong life, to the provision of care and comfort in the final weeks of life.

However, society in Britain also wishes its doctors to deploy the nation's health care resources wisely and economically but without denying, or unduly delaying access to, appropriate care. It is when care is both effective and necessary that it can be deemed to be appropriate. This expectation of society implies that doctors should accept some responsibility for minimizing the inappropriate use of resources. It requires them to resist well-intentioned but ill-informed pressures for the inappropriate acquisition or application of expensive technologies and services. These may come from the public, from patients and their families, from the medical and nursing professions, sometimes aided and abetted by commercial suppliers. Such pressures are particularly prone to build up in relation to dread diseases (e.g. cancer and heart disease) or to life-threatening situations (e.g. renal failure or critical illness).

The ethics of health care

There are those who warn doctors against accepting this assignment as a double agent. They maintain that the doctor's role as adviser to and advocate for his patients

Health Care Provision under Financial Constraint, edited by T. B. Binns and M. Firth, 1988: Royal Society of Medicine International Congress and Symposium Series No. 115, published by Royal Society of Medicine Services Ltd.

(whether as a group or as individuals) is incompatible with his acting as gatekeeper to the health care resources of society. Doctors themselves often invoke ethics as a shield against the threat that cost-benefit analysis be more often made the basis for clinical decision-making. They do so in the hope that under the guise of ethics their clinical freedom will remain sacrosanct. These clinical freedom fighters hope thereby to legitimize their attempts to secure all possible services for *their* patients, regardless of the expectation of benefit relative to the prospects for other patients belonging to other specialists. These doctors want to feel free to ignore the opportunity costs to the health service as a whole when they recommend costly interventions for their patients.

This absolutist, individualistic ethic is in contrast to the utilitarian or societal ethic, which emphasizes justice in the allocation of health care resources in order to achieve maximum health benefits for the community as a whole. The utilitarian approach is most readily accepted at the macro level of dividing resources between sectors of the health service (e.g. hospital *vs* community, acute *vs* chronic hospitals), or between large client groups that are reflected in medical specialties (paediatrics, obstetrics, radiotherapy, geriatrics or psychiatry). Such decisions are made at a safe distance from the bedside of sick persons and far from the pressures of situational ethics. None the less these macro-allocations should depend on data about what aggregate benefits are likely to accrue to various different groups of patients if certain resources are provided. The extent of those benefits will depend crucially on the way in which available resources are deployed by clinicians responsible for micro-allocation between patients.

The use of resources at the point of delivery of patient care even in the UK depends more on the daily decisions of clinicians than on policies put out by health authorities nationally or in regions or districts. A paradox seldom recognized is that, within the annual cost limits, clinicians in the UK enjoy much greater freedom from regulation than do their cousins in the USA. This is particularly evident in high technology specialties where decisions by doctors to investigate or to treat certain types of patient can commit resources of staff, equipment and consumables on a large scale. Some see ethics becoming a battleground for a confrontation between doctors and economists, whereas I believe that they might find common ground in ethics (1). This would benefit both individual patients and society because the inappropriate use of high technology is not only wasteful of resources but it is also against the best interests of patients.

Inappropriate use of technology

Inappropriate use of expensive technology may be of five kinds (2):
   (1) *unnecessary* because the patient is not badly enough affected to justify the diagnostic or therapeutic technology in question;
   (2) *unsuccessful* because the patient is too badly affected to benefit;
   (3) *unsafe* because the risks outweigh the benefits;
   (4) *unkind* because the quality or duration of life after intervention does not justify rescue;
   (5) *unwise* because it diverts resources from activities that would yield greater benefits for other patients.
Not only may inappropriate use of technology expose patients unjustifiably to risk, distress and indignity but it can give technology as a whole a bad name. In his essay, 'Apples of discord', Sir Douglas Black cited technology as one of the major divisive

forces in medicine today in the UK (3). And witness the welcome given in America to the pejorative phrase 'halfway technologies'. An ill-informed anti-technology lobby could do as much harm as enthusiastic technologists if it resulted in policies that denied *effective* technology to many patients who could benefit from it. No country can afford inappropriate technology either on economic grounds or for humanitarian reasons.

In 1979, the Royal Commission on the National Health Service (NHS) stated baldly that acute medicine is increasingly being challenged (4). It is the privilege of royal commissioners to be allowed to write conclusions on tablets of stone without having to show the data that might have led others to draw different inferences. It was easy for a policy analyst confronting a cardiac surgeon in a debate on centres of excellence to claim that 'the people have demanded a switch from acute high technology services to chronic care' (5). But when were the people ever offered that choice? Of course there are frequent calls for more resources for the care of those with mental handicap or mental illness and for better long-term facilities for the disabled and the elderly. It is, however, the politicians who have declared that there is not enough money to meet the demands of both acute and chronic services—leaving it to health authorities to draw the self-evident conclusion that more finance for maintenance medicine means less for the acute hospital sector.

It is relatively easy to estimate the scale of unmet needs for the chronically ill—needs that some believe might be better met outside the NHS by local authority and community care that depends on a different part of public sector expenditure. But what attempt has been made to calculate how much the acute hospital sector can afford to lose without seriously impairing the quantity and quality of care offered to patients whose needs can be met only by this part of the service?

High technology and the elderly

Concern that inadequate provision of chronic care for the elderly stems partly from too generous expenditure on the acute hospital sector has led health departments to recommend reallocation of resources. This policy ignores the appropriate need of many elderly patients for acute high technology medicine. Although supposedly in the interests of the elderly, a policy of severely restricting resources for acute care could prove counter-productive because it ignores the appropriate need of many elderly patients for acute high technology medicine (6). If therapeutic technologies were even more strictly rationed, it is likely that some older patients who could benefit from such treatment might be denied access. This is because when demand for technology exceeds supply a readily available and widely accepted means of selection is advancing age. This is not unreasonable either, because there are several biological features of ageing that adversely affect the probability of a good outcome compared to younger persons with similar severity of illness.

That said, there is in Britain no general moratorium on high technology treatment for elderly patients. Although only 14% of the UK population is over 65 years old, this age group accounts for almost 50% of the patients in acute hospital beds and for 30% of patients in general intensive care units (ICUs). In coronary care units in Britain 60% of patients are over 60 years of age and 20% are over 70 years (7). The over-65s account for 25% of all surgical admissions, 50% of those in urological and ophthalmological wards, and 20% of open-heart operations. Of all admissions to non-psychiatric hospitals of patients over 65 years 43% are to surgical wards. Surgeons in the UK now admit as many patients over 75 years as do general physicians and geriatricians combined (8).

Although selected elderly patients respond well to these various technologies many do not — because critical illness in the elderly is often terminal illness. However, it is clear that British doctors share with their colleagues elsewhere an unwillingness to resist the impulse to embark on rescue procedures even when prospects are bleak because of the severity of illness and the patient's age. They are therefore liable to be caught in what I have called a cycle of commitment — once treatment is started there is reluctance to abandon it even when it has become plain that it can do no good (9).

Rescue *vs* cure

The comfortable philosophy of policy makers and planners that when budgets for acute services are restricted clinicians will choose to use only effective technologies and will abandon all others proves in practice not to be justified. More often, the reaction of clinicians is to respond to the demands of patients who require rescue, no matter how limited the long-term benefits seem likely to be. They therefore have to postpone the treatment of patients whose demands are less pressing but whose prospects of benefit are much greater. In a letter to the Royal Commissioners in the *Lancet* in 1976, I sought to epitomize this dilemma for doctors in the acute hospital sector in the phrase 'it is easier to delay cure than to deny rescue' (10).

This imperative to do something in desperate circumstances is perhaps understandable. As the mysticism of medicine melts away in the glare of the media spotlight doctors find themselves in a dilemma. Although experts seem sometimes now to be suspected rather than respected they are still expected to respond to desperate situations by action. This expectation may be shared by the patient and his family as well as by other doctors and nurses in the institution. There is also some concern that lawyers are waiting to blame a doctor for doing too much or too little, albeit a much less serious threat in the UK than in the USA. There is a cultural gradient in the strength of the imperatives to action in desperate circumstances. It has been said that many Americans seem to consider that death is optional whilst the British are more realistic. This is not limited to western cultures — witness this report from one of my students on his elective period in Papua New Guinea:

> wantoks (= friends and family) of an ill man expect something to be done for him, an operation performed or a drug given. If death follows, it is accepted philosophically only if a heroic procedure has been attempted. Terminally ill patients are not exempt from this expectation and a surgeon's refusal to operate on a hopeless case is rarely accepted graciously.

UK *vs* US use of high technology

Equity in meeting professionally defined health care needs is highly valued in the UK. It is recognized that *needs* are not the same as *wants*, and that sick people and their families often expect or demand inappropriate investigation or treatment, especially when acute illness threatens life. What appears to British doctors to be widespread inappropriate use in the USA of several expensive technologies is commonly defended by American doctors as being a response to consumer demand. However, a comparison of the use of 10 technologies in the UK and the USA, based on data collected by Aaron and Schwartz about 1980, revealed differences that varied widely between one technology and another (11). Although health care spending is about four times as great per capita in the USA there were several technologies that were used frequently in both countries. These included radiotherapy and chemotherapy for potentially curable cancers, renal and bone marrow transplantation, and the treatment of haemophilia with blood products — all of them therapies of acknowledged benefit to most patients who receive them.

By contrast, American doctors used many diagnostic X-ray examinations twice as often, and twice as many films at each examination. Computerized tomographic scanners were six times more frequent in the USA than in Britain, intensive care beds 10 times more numerous per million population, and chemotherapy for incurable cancer was used five times more often. What characterizes these therapies is that all are of dubious benefit in many circumstances. The differences in their rate of use are mostly accounted for by their employment in the USA in situations which many British doctors would deem to be inappropriate — because their use is either unnecessary or bound to be unsuccessful.

Intensive care units

If we consider in more detail the case of intensive care, the 10-fold difference in bed provision between our two countries alone accounts for more than half the entire discrepancy in hospital expenditure on health care between the USA and the UK. Many patients in American ICUs do not need the expensive skills and technologies that these units provide. One US study showed that 70% of ICU patients were not critically ill and that less than 10% of them ever needed an intervention (12). In some American coronary care units half the patients prove not to have had a heart attack but to have been admitted only because of suspicious chest pain. These are examples of the unnecessary use of expensive technology. Prognostic indices to identify which patients are at high enough risk to justify care in an ICU are leading to reduced admission rates in the USA.

Many other patients in American ICUs are terminally ill, often because they are elderly. Indeed, the 5% of patients who die account for 20% of the Medicare and Medicaid expenditures each year. Under the title 'Medicine versus economics', an American health economist recently wrote:

> The potential of modern technology to make dying an expensive business gives scope for almost unlimited expenditure before reaching the traditional "do no harm" stopping point (13).

Reluctance to ration by withholding or withdrawing treatment from the hopelessly ill is a feature of intensive care in both our countries. Although admission triage is probably more effective in the UK, formal 'do not resuscitate' orders are not yet used; in the USA these have become commonplace over the last decade.

Choosing patients for high technology

Limited resources for such technologies are unlikely to be allocated justly unless the basis of rationing is made more explicit (14). An American court recently criticized an ICU that had failed to establish arrangements to ensure that a hopeless patient already under treatment would give way to a newcomer whose expectation of benefit was much greater (15). Reporting this it was suggested that choices between patients competing for costly technologies might be facilitated by an 'entitlement index', based on estimates of the probability of benefit.

Without such an explicit guide doctors find it difficult to ration rationally, even
when it is in the best interests both of the individual patient and of society, because
the demands of economics and of ethics coincide. Given that this is so, the prospect
is not good for wise choices being made between alternative treatments both of which
promise some benefit but have different costs. Sometimes the less costly method is
also the more beneficial as, for example, kidney transplantation compared with dialysis
for the treatment of renal failure. It might therefore seem obvious that the right policy
would be to maximize the proportion of patients whose renal replacement is by
transplantation. Yet there are wide variations in practice between different countries
in the proportion of such patients who are treated by transplantation; for example,
it is twice as great in Britain as in the USA.

The need for technology assessment

The greatest impediment to more appropriate use of expensive technologies is
ignorance of their effectiveness in different types of patient. There is no point in
devoting resources to activities that do not yield commensurate benefits. Nor is it
sensible to strive for efficiency in the delivery of measures that are not effective in
improving patient outcome. Nor is it helpful to agonize over the withholding or
withdrawal of technologies when their use is in any event inappropriate — because
they are either unnecessary or bound to be unsuccessful. There may be no assessment
data available anywhere — because many established and commonly used practices
have never been formally evaluated. More often there are data available but they
are not known to the individual clinician making a decision. Or he may know about
assessment but choose to ignore the findings — either because they conflict with his
reasoned or intuitive beliefs, or because he yields to imperatives to action.

A pressing need is slowly being recognized on both sides of the Atlantic for a comprehensive system of assessment (16). The Institute of Medicine has set up a consortium in
Washington, and in London the King's Fund has included technology assessment
on the agenda of its newly formed Institute for Health Policy Analysis. Sweden and
Holland have set up assessment organizations, and one Swedish university now has
a department of medical technology assessment. It would be good to see university
clinical departments accepting asessment of technologies and the identification of
their appropriate use as legitimate and highly regarded clinical research. However,
there is evidence that the National Institutes of Health in the USA and the Medical
Research Council in Britain hold such studies in lower esteem than laboratory research.

Assessments have to go beyond the limited trials of efficacy that are required before
licensing new drugs. They should include economic and social implications, and they
need to be applied to established as well as to new technologies. It is also important
to ensure that when data are available on assessment that these are translated into
practice. This means not only the dissemination of information but systematic efforts
to encourage clinicians to modify their practice accordingly. One such device is the
consensus conference which has been used since 1977 in the USA, and is now being
adopted in Sweden, Holland, Denmark and the UK.

Economic appraisal

There is good evidence that significant financial savings could be achieved by limiting
the use of expensive technologies to circumstances in which they are appropriate.

Table 1

Unit and aggregate costs in the UK

Procedure	Unit cost (£k)	Units (per year)	Aggregate (£m)
Cancer operation	1	500 000	500
Hip replacement	1·3	15 000	20
Coronary bypass	3	10 000	30
Renal transplant	6	12 000	7·2
Bone marrow transplant	7	200	1·4
Renal dialysis	12	2000	24
Heart transplant	15	30	0·5

Derived from Jennett (2) (with permission).

Table 2

Health authority expenditure (total £500m per year)

Service	Equipment/consumables (£m)	+ staff (£m)
General practice prescriptions	48	—
Hospital drugs	12	—
Diagnostic laboratories	8	23
Radiology (diagnostic)	3·5	8
Radiotherapy	1	2

Derived from Jennett (2) (with permission).

However, economic appraisal may indicate that a costly technology is such good value that provision should be increased, as occurred when economists reported on heart transplantation in England (17). This was found to produce marked improvement in quality of life, and survival rates were considerably better than for several common cancers for which surgery, radiotherapy and chemotherapy are provided without question.

It is also important to consider aggregate costs when deciding about macroallocation — for it may transpire that much more is spent on the frequent use of less expensive items than on procedures with a high unit cost that are relatively seldom used. Thus, the many operations carried out for cancer at low cost account for a much larger proportion of the national technology bill than do organ transplants (Table 1). Also, family doctor prescriptions cost a health authority more than all the diagnostic laboratories and both diagnostic and therapeutic radiology departments combined (Table 2).

Choosing between patients by expected benefit

It might seem obvious that the way to ration health care would be to choose to do that which will probably produce the most benefit for least cost. When health economists recommended this utilitarian approach in the *New England Journal of Medicine* they drew attention to the importance of data about effectiveness (18,19). However, in the same issue an American physician commented that it was dangerous to conserve resources by using the probability of success to choose between patients (20).

He regarded the doctor's role as advocate for his patient to be subverted by what he denigrated as 'probabilistic practice'. What was encouraging was that all the letters published after these three articles disagreed with the doctor and supported the arguments of the economists. What is more, every one of these utilitarians was a doctor.

The critic of probability estimates as a basis for decision-making commented on the unreliability of the data in this field. He seemed unaware that for several conditions predictive models based on large computer banks of data prospectively collected according to strict protocols have made it possible to predict a fatal outcome with considerable accuracy. A good example is the international data bank on severe head injury set up in my department in Glasgow. This now holds data on more than 2500 patients from two Netherlands centres and from centres in Los Angeles and San Francisco as well as from Glasgow. Using a statistical model, predictions were made about the number of deaths in one centre based on data from another. The number of deaths that actually occurred corresponded closely with those predicted (21,22). This study also revealed that outcome depended much more on the severity of illness and the patient's age than on details of treatment. Indeed, statistical predictions can be used as a method for assessing the effectiveness of different therapeutic technologies—according to how much they improve the outcome compared with that expected (23).

Reallocating resources

Before considering the redistribution of resources at the macro level it is important to ensure that reliable data are available about both benefits and costs. Aggregate figures are needed for each side of the cost-benefit equation. Only such data can provide protection against making decisions in response to slogans or special pleading—for particular diseases that are more dreaded than others or for groups of patients who are seemingly more disadvantaged or more deserving than others. Once allocated at this level there should be continuing audit of use at the micro level to confirm that the intended target group of patients are indeed the recipients. It is also important to monitor benefit, in order to be ready to respond appropriately to the next round of demands for more resources.

The aim should be to ensure that appropriate patients have access to effective care without undue delay or cost. My contention is that rationing rationally by limiting the use of expensive technologies to appropriate circumstances could be a relatively painless prescription for more economical and ethical practice.

References

(1) Jennett B. Medical ethics and economics in clinical decision making. In: Mooney G, Maguire A, eds. *Medical ethics and economics in health care*, Amsterdam. Oxford: Oxford University Press, 1987.

(2) Jennett B. High technology medicine—benefits and burdens. 2nd edn. Oxford and New York: Oxford University Press, 1986.

(3) Black D. Apples of discord. *J Roy Soc Med* 1981; **74**: 92–100.

(4) *Royal Commission on the National Health Service*. Cmnd 7615. London: Her Majesty's Stationery Office, 1979.

(5) McCarthy L. Medical ethics needs a third dimension. *J Med Ethics* 1982; **8**: 147.

(6) Jennett B. High technology medicine and elderly. *Int J Tech Assess Health Care* 1987. [in press].

(7) Jennett B. Intensive care for the elderly. *Int J Tech Assess Health Care* 1985; **1**: 7–19.

(8) Seymour DG, Pringle R. Surgical emergencies in the elderly: can they be prevented? *Health Bull (Edinburgh)* 1983; **41**: 112–31.

(9) Jennett B. Inappropriate use of intensive care. [Editorial]. *Br Med J* 1984; **289**: 1709–11.

(10) Jennett B. The way ahead for acute hospital services. Delay cure or deny rescue? *Lancet* 1976; **ii**: 1235–7.

(11) Aaron HJ, Schwartz WB. *The painful prescription: rationing hospital care.* Washington DC: The Brookings Institution, 1984.

(12) Thibault GE, Mulley AG, Barnett CO, *et al.* Medical intensive care: indications, interventions and outcomes. *N Engl J Med* 1980; **302**: 938–42.

(13) Thurow LC. Medicine versus economics. *N Engl J Med* 1985; **313**: 611–4.

(14) Knaus WA. Rationing, justice and the American physician. [Editorial]. *J Am Med Assoc* 1986; **255**: 1176–7.

(15) Engelhardt HT, Rie MA. Intensive care units, scarce resources, and conflicting principles of justice. *J Am Med Assoc* 1986; **255**: 1150–64.

(16) Jennett B. Assessment of medical technologies. *Lancet* 1986; **ii**: 735–6.

(17) Buxton M, Acheson R, Caine N, *et al. Costs and benefits of the heart transplant programmes at Harefield and Papworth Hospitals.* DHSS Research Report No 12. London: Her Majesty's Stationery Office, 1985.

(18) Thurow LC. Learning to say 'no'. *N Engl J Med* 1984; **311**: 1569–72.

(19) Fuchs VR. The 'rationing' of medical care. *N Engl J Med* 1984; **311**: 1572–3.

(20) Levinsky NG. The doctor's master. *N Engl J Med* 1984; **311**: 1573–5.

(21) Jennett B, Teasdale G, Fry J, Braakman R, Minderhoud J. Treatment for severe head injury. *J Neurol Neurosurg Psychiatry* 1980; **43**: 289–95.

(22) Murray GD. Use of an international data bank to compare outcome following severe head injury in different centres. *Stat Med* 1986; **5**: 103–12.

(23) Jennett B. Assessment of a technological package using a predictive tool. *Int J Tech Assess Health Care* 1987. [in press].

A US view

ROSEMARY A. STEVENS

Department of History and Sociology of Science,
University of Pennsylvania, Philadelphia PA, USA

British visitors to the USA are often mystified by apparent anomalies in the US health care system. Meanwhile, Americans are struggling to define and to 'operationalize' equity—specifically, to devise programs or incentives that meet three potentially conflicting goals. The first is to provide at least a basic adequate floor of health services for the whole population; this goal, in principle, is non-controversial. The second goal is to allow individual consumers of health services (and health insurance), as far as possible, as much freedom to purchase medical care as they have to purchase other goods and services. The third is to leave the working of the health service, as far as possible, in private hands. Questions of equity intertwine with each of these missions.

In this paper I want to delineate some of the basic issues and difficulties infusing American debates about equity and health care in the late 1980s. I should like to stress in particular that the notion of equity is slippery. As ideology, the concept of equity is useful for pinpointing inequalities and deficiencies in the system and for rallying reformist interests. For policy, the idea of equity can exist only in a specific framework of politics, organization, power and money. Just as British notions of equity are bounded by the structures and assumptions of the National Health Service (NHS) so American approaches are tempered by the inertia and momentum of health care organizations, the practical trade-offs of everyday life, conflicting interpretations as to who should be served and how, and the immediate agendas of powerful interests. I will look first at some obvious anomalies and inequities in the present US health care system. I want then to raise some fundamental questions about values and goals, and to finish with some 'nuts and bolts' questions of strategy.

Anomalies and inequities: dimensions of debate

Depending on how comparisons are measured, the US system spends between two and four times as much per head as the British system (1). One obvious anomaly lies in the fact that the richer the resources the greater the number of Americans who are apparently denied access to them. An estimated 45 million people are either uninsured or underinsured (2). Private health insurance is almost universally tied to organized

Health Care Provision under Financial Constraint, edited by T. B. Binns and M. Firth, 1988: Royal Society of Medicine International Congress and Symposium Series No. 115, published by Royal Society of Medicine Services Ltd.

workplace arrangements — a historical legacy which, curiously, is rarely questioned, that was born of the selling of voluntary hospital insurance in the depression and of government fringe benefit incentives to business and industry in the 1940s.

Anyone can, of course, buy insurance as an individual, but it is expensive (and a decision that is easy to put off). Not only do large firms usually pay part (sometimes all) of the health insurance costs of their employees, but the cost of premiums of group policies insuring a large number of workers is significantly less than that of individual purchase. As a result, it has become commonplace for large numbers of Americans to gamble with the system: for example, those with part-time or temporary jobs, new employees who are not entitled to health insurance as a fringe benefit, or those between jobs and those who are otherwise unemployed. Both my own children, aged 20 and 22, were uninsured for a brief period this year. More than one-fifth of the population under age 65 has either no automatic protection for medical bills or grossly inadequate protection from private or government programs if they fall sick (3). Equitable access to health insurance has become a major political issue in the USA — exciting federal policy makers, state legislators and major businesses which are, in turn, being pressed to extend their coverage to laid-off workers.

An outside observer looking at US health insurance arrangements who is unaware of the quirks of history might assume that present insurance patterns were a natural outgrowth of the equity assumptions of industrial capitalism, with benefits designed primarily to protect worker productivity — and with little concern about anyone else. However, here we come to another anomaly. The US government is, in fact, heavily involved in guaranteeing medical service provision to selected groups of persons who are unproductive and socially dependent — primarily the elderly and the poor.

Medicare

Through Medicare the federal government oversees an enormous system of transfer payments from the working population, to provide national hospital insurance for the elderly (those 65 years of age and over). The program also covers the disabled and, by virtue of effective interest group lobbying, in 1972 also patients with end-stage renal disease. As a result, it might be said that kidney disease is a 'Cinderella' service (using British terminology). It is, indeed, the one and only chronic condition singled out for US government national health insurance coverage.

I would remark in passing that studies of the relatively high rates of dialysis in the USA compared with Britain rarely point out that these services are financially favored as government policy in the USA in a unique way. Indeed, kidney dialysis is a curiously inappropriate benchmark of the different 'rationing' processes at work in Britain and the USA (4). It would be more appropriate to look, for example, at the distribution of services for schizophrenia, pre- and peri-natal care, juvenile diabetes or acquired immune deficiency syndrome (AIDS).

Returning to the main theme, that there is substantial government involvement in the provision of health insurance to the non-productive sections of the population, in the last 21 years, through Medicare, the federal government has assumed responsibility for a huge national health insurance program of health care which is limited in large part to services for the elderly. Americans tend to take this for granted. Medicare has become an accepted part of social security, but this choice of a priority population is in fact extraordinary. The USA is the only country in the world which has begun a national health insurance program by concentrating on the elderly population. Of Americans over the age of 65, 90% are covered by Medicare hospital insurance, part A.

Virtually all these people also subscribe to part B, which is a federally subsidized insurance program that concentrates on doctors' bills and other professional medical services. As is the case with private health insurance, care is not provided directly but is purchased for patients on a contractual basis from hospitals, doctors and health care systems which are largely under private ownership.

In terms of access to acute care, Medicare makes an important social equity statement. The elderly are now better covered, for hospital care at least, than younger members of the population. In financial terms, the Medicare program is also very generous. In 1984 Medicare spent on average about $3000 (£2000) per beneficiary. Indeed, it can be argued that in purely financial terms the USA is doing more by way of health protection for its elderly than is the UK. Within the USA meanwhile, there are claims that the elderly population is receiving more than its fair share of health care resources, in terms of the distribution of public funds to different population groups, particularly in comparison with children. It is, indeed, easy to argue that the USA has made a set of private and public choices in the last two decades that have 'dramatically altered the age profile of well-being', with gains for the elderly being made at the partial expense of services for children, who have been a casualty of reduced tax expenditures (5).

The internal distribution of Medicare funding is also open to serious criticism, both in terms of allocation to different services and in geographical distribution. Despite its cost, Medicare pays less than half the total health expenses of the elderly, is heavily weighted towards acute medical services and is a long way from being comprehensive. For example, it excludes essential services such as dentistry, hearing aids, meals-on-wheels and basic residential care. Although there are now major efforts to incorporate Medicare patients into organized private health care systems (health maintenance organizations (HMOs)), where a mix of preventive, maintenance and curative services can be provided, and although there are a few experimental programs linking health and social services for the elderly, Medicare is far from being a *health care* system. Its strength has always been in protecting the income and capital of the elderly in the face of huge unexpected hospital bills, and this it does quite well. Nevertheless, after 21 years of reasonable success in income protection of catastrophic illness, with the major exception of patients requiring long-term care, Medicare is finally having to face the slow and difficult transition from a program of health insurance to a more rounded program of health care provision. Costs alone make this transition essential.

Medicaid

Federal and state programs for the poor (Medicaid) pose other organizational, distributional and equity issues in the 1980s. Medicaid's Byzantine eligibility barriers daunt all but the truly desperate, however needy. These barriers include requirements that beneficiaries be children (and their parents), or people who are elderly, blind or disabled as well as poor, and that they meet stringent detailed means tests requirements. The able-bodied unemployed *per se* are not included. Medicaid is indeed a direct descendant of 19th and early 20th century welfare values, with programs targeted to recipients whose poverty was unimpeachable: children, the blind, the disabled or the elderly. It says something for the administrative ingenuity of American systems that the present confusing matrix of Medicaid eligibility requirements and services, which vary state by state and are nowhere comprehensive, is taken so readily as a bureaucratic given, spawning great 'bibles' of administrative regulations.

Medicare's primary contribution is to hospital care of the elderly. Medicaid programs, too, are skewed. They play a particularly important role in medical care of destitute children and in supporting institutional care of the impoverished elderly over and above Medicare benefits. Since many of the impoverished elderly are members of middle-class families who have become impoverished by spending their savings on nursing home care, there is an important middle-class constituency in favor of Medicaid programs for the elderly. Over three-quarters of all payments made under Medicaid are for hospital or nursing home care.*

Medicare and Medicaid together have brought the federal government firmly into national health care policy making: in seeking cost-containment policies, in detailed scrutiny of doctors' behavior through clinical records analysis and policing hospital lengths of stay (to an extent that might well not be tolerated in Britain), and in standardized prospective payment systems. Taken together, Medicare and Medicaid, plus a third major federal program for armed service veterans, strongly emphasize institutional over non-institutional medical care. Hence, almost all the regulatory interest in resource distribution in the last decade has been centered on hospital provision, with little effective government influence over other types of care.

The scope of government involvement in the USA should be stressed. Government funding as a whole represents over 40% of all health care expenditures. In the three major federal programs of Medicare, Medicaid and the Veterans Administration (VA), US government agencies spend more per head than is spent in Britain per head on the entire NHS. Yet services continue to be partial, patchy and far from comprehensive.

Goals and values of American health care

What, then, are the goals, assumptions and values underlying the provision of health care in the USA, and how do these affect the equity questions?

Equity

The first and most obvious observation of the American scene is that there is no mainstream movement toward more egalitarianism in health care. Indeed, present discussions about equity in terms of so-called 'rationing' of health care almost invariably decry the limitations on individual freedom to purchase expensive medical care that might be incurred in a more equal system. The basic concerns in present discussions about distributing scarce resources across the USA deal not so much with the value of righting present day inequities, but alarm at the possibility of creating new ones. The poor are deprived of services only because they cannot pay. Under a rationed system the rich might face arbitrary service restrictions. Hence, the sense of alarm expressed in such phrases as 'tragic choices' or 'painful prescriptions' — and the tendency to project resource decisions directly to the potential impact on fee-paying individuals. Implicitly the fee-paying patient has a right to consume. For those who cannot pay there is no government or constitutional obligation to provide or pay for medical care. As a result, the health care system is inherently and deliberately unequal, favoring those who can afford to pay most or have the best insurance coverage. Lawyers put the issue quaintly but succinctly: 'wealth is not a suspect classification' (7).

---

*In 1984, Medicaid reported expenditures of $11·8 billion on hospital care and $12·3 billion on nursing homes out of a total expenditure of $32·9 billion. These figures exclude the services of physicians attending patients in these institutions, which should be added to the totals (6).

Exclusions and deficiencies

At the other end of the scale the realities of exclusion and deficiency in the American health care system at present provoke relatively little passion or interest, whether in talking about the distribution of health insurance, health status or utilization.

Table 1 shows, for example, that there are obvious correlations between self-assessment of health and family income in the USA, and that whites are much more likely to rate their health as excellent than blacks. Table 2 shows that despite these

Table 1
Self-assessment of health by family income and race, USA, 1983

	% of population[a]		
	Excellent	Very good or good	Fair or poor
Total	40·5	48·3	10·6
Family income			
<$10 000	28·9	49·4	21·1
$10 000–14 999	34·0	51·7	13·7
$15 000–19 999	36·9	52·2	10·4
$20 000–34 999	43·7	49·0	6·9
≥$35 000	52·8	42·0	4·6
Race[b]			
White	42·4	47·6	9·5
Black	28·3	51·5	19·5

[a]Figures include 'unknown' self-assessment of health.
[b]Age adjusted.
Source: National Health Interview Survey, US Department of Health and Human Services (8) (Table 32).

Table 2
Source or place of doctor-patient encounter by family income and race, USA, 1983

	% of visits[a]			
	No. physician visits per person	Doctor's office	Hospital out-patient or emergency department	Telephone
Total	5·0	55·9	14·9	15·5
Family income				
<$10 000	5·9	49·8	18·4	12·3
$10 000–14 999	5·0	52·2	17·7	13·2
$15 000–19 999	4·7	54·2	16·7	16·3
$20 000–34 999	5·0	59·0	13·2	16·1
≥$35 000	5·4	59·6	11·5	18·8
Race				
White	5·1	57·4	13·4	16·2
Black	4·8	44·1	26·5	9·7

[a]Includes source 'unknown'.
Source: National Health Interview Survey, US Department of Health and Human Services (8) (Table 43).

differences the average number of doctor visits per person per year is more or less equal by social group. Moreover, this table also suggests further distinctions in place and type of care, with poorer members of the population and minority groups more likely to see doctors in hospital out-patient clinics and emergency rooms.

Such observations are likely to be seen in the USA as intrinsic features of the US system rather than as major criticisms. Indeed, Britons would be more likely to be outraged than Americans that 15 states refused to cover poor working-class children in their Medicaid program (9), that over one-third of all American children aged 1–14 years are not currently immunized for measles, rubella, diphtheria, tetanus and pertussis (DTP), poliomyelitis and mumps (8), or that the transfer of patients from one hospital to another for economic (rather than medical) reasons has become an accepted commonplace.

Goals of the health care system in the USA

The underlying point here is that the goals of the US and British health systems are quite different—and not merely because one has a national health service and the other does not.

Seven major goals or value assumptions infusing the American health care system are listed in Table 3. Other American critics of the health care system might devise a somewhat different array. However, I suggest that three major points are important to British and other foreign observers who seek to make sense of the American system.

Table 3

Goals and values intrinsic to US health care

---

(1) Protect individual income from the economic hardship of massive medical bills.
(2) Support private enterprise, including the health care industry, through facilitating employment, capital development, industry expansion.
(3) Encourage productivity in the health care system.
(4) Support scientific and technological innovation.
(5) Develop healthy workers.
(6) Aspire to social justice via a minimal floor of medical benefits for all.
(7) Avoid major confrontations.

Involvement of government agencies in health care

First, government agencies have become involved in American health care largely to protect individual income and to support the private health care enterprise. Medicare and Medicaid speak for themselves but, beyond this, government agencies have not generally become involved in funding medical care primarily for the purpose of *health enhancement*. This is obviously an essential point in understanding present discussions of equity. The wording of the President's Commission for the Study of Ethical Problems is frequently cited: namely, that society has an 'ethical obligation to ensure equitable access to health care for all' (10). However, this statement is significant in two respects. It defines an adequate, equitable access in terms of a *minimal* rather than an optimal level of care, thus laying the basis for a two-class or multitiered health care system. At the same time, it limits equity to access to *services*. There is no effort to ensure equity in health status or health care outcomes. In short, there is a policy of equality of access to minimal services but not for equality of results.

A second point intrinsic to my list in Table 3 is that the goals and values listed have not been ascribed specifically to government agencies or the private sector. The history of medical care in the USA has been for a closely intertwined process of policy making. The flavor of legislation tends to be pragmatic rather than based on egalitarian or other ideological commitments. Employers have a major stake in government policy because of the central importance of workplace arrangements in the collection of private and public premiums for health insurance. Indeed, if we do see some form of universal national health insurance in the USA in the next few years—which I think quite likely—it will probably come through joint corporate and government efforts.

The US health care industry

A third point is that the American health care industry is more than an industry in name. It *is* an industry, one of the largest in the USA. It provides income for approximately 8 million workers, and supports subsidiary enterprises in areas as diverse as medical electronics, computer software, major accounting services and investment banking. This industry, which also includes the major purchasers of care (employers, health insurers and government), forms the necessary environment shaping discussions of health care. As a result, equity issues are not limited to questions of the distribution of resources by social class, geography and race. They also include attempts to include principles of justice that take into account the equity interests of major stakeholders; that is, equity for consumers, for decision-makers and, not least, for taxpayers. As a result, there are no simple or obvious directions for resource allocation in health care. Rather, there is an array of potential and negotiable strategies, each addressing part of a much wider picture.

Strategies

The market ethos of the American system makes it difficult, if not impossible, to say no to patients who cannot afford to pay for treatments, if and where these treatments are potentially beneficial. If equity in Britain is seen in terms of politics and the macromanagement of resources, in the USA equity translates, functionally, into micromanagement. Where Britain looks to Resource Allocation Working Party (RAWP) allocations, Cinderella services and regional planning, the US approach is necessarily more oblique. Because I think this is a very important point in considering cross-national US/British comparisons, I will suggest four examples in conclusion.

Shifting to enrollment in health care organizations

One method for considering relative priorities in services and across population groups is to have such decisions made on a decentralized basis within an HMO or similar health care service system. In subscribing to a particular organization, the patient accepts the limitations of coverage in that scheme. These may include rationing services by:
— requiring each patient to have a primary practitioner who acts as a gatekeeper to specialists' services and hospital care;
— requiring second opinions in cases of major surgery;

—excluding coverage of services such as liver transplants;
—limiting services such as long-term psychiatric care;
—time (that is, the length of time it may take to get a medical appointment for all but urgent care);
—encouraging specific forms of patient behavior.

This last point might include, for example, encouragement of self-care and self-diagnosis, consumer education leading to reduced consumption of prescription and non-prescription drugs, acceptance of non-heroic treatments in terminal illness, and perhaps even the ability to tolerate minor levels of pain.

There is already an acceptance of variety in third-party insurance coverage in the USA. By putting the onus on the consumer to choose a particular insurance plan or HMO enrollment, the rights of the consumer for optimal care are, in theory, protected in two ways: first, by giving the consumer the option to enroll in one configuration rather than another and, secondly, by allowing the consumer to purchase services over and above those covered by the insurance organization, assuming such services are available. My purpose here is not to delineate the role and scope of HMOs, which I am sure others will do, but merely to suggest the role of local health care organizations as potentially important rationing agents.

Rediscovering the quality of care

Questions of supply have almost always been linked historically with assumptions about the appropriate quality of care. A second fruitful strategy for considering resource distribution in the USA is the use of quality standards as a subtle mechanism for reducing services.

Out-patient cataract surgery is a case in point. Such surgery has become a major enterprise in the USA, even though surgery there may not be indicated in the vast majority of patients, and the case for surgery may vary depending on the visual needs and lifestyle of the individual patient (11). By suggesting that such surgery may not only be unnecessary but potentially dangerous to patients, the qualitative argument can be used to stem market-oriented behavior by both patients and physicians.

Recent publicity about the success of coronary bypass surgery depending on place of operation extends the qualitative argument one step further. My local newspaper recently stressed, for example, that *where* a patient goes for such surgery may mean the difference between life and death (12). It is only a step from here to formal or informal regulation of patient flow to some institutions rather than others. One recent suggestion was for the development of quality of care ratings for hospitals for services such as cardiac surgery, somewhat similar to the complex financial ratings that are made by national investment services which determine a hospital's credit rating (and which are, in turn, essential in raising funds on the capital markets) (13). Although the language of such recommendations may be designed to encourage consumers to choose hospitals with the best results, a further result may well be on the distribution of such services across the population. I think we are going to see much emphasis on quality of care as an intrinsic element in the equity debates.

Establishing fiscal norms

A third point of leverage is the acceptance of fiscal norms; that is, the regulation of health services through rules and restrictions attached to the third-party payment mechanism. The new standardized payment system for Medicare, prospective payment on the basis of diagnosis related groups (DRGs) is a major example of an attempt to standardize Medicare benefits across regions and areas of the USA. Although DRGs were introduced as a market mechanism, one effect is to proclaim that each member of the Medicare population should have a 'fair share' of available benefits, according to nationally defined rules.

The search for norms or rules is also apparent in the increased attention being paid to 'small area' variations in health service utilization; variations, that is, that appear to be associated with traditional style of practice rather than with the results of care. For example, coronary bypass surgery shows more than a threefold variation in rates of use between Medicare regions (14). More generally, there is discussion of the possible development of rates of use for different procedures—rates which might justly be regarded as 'right', as already there are norms for length of stay by diagnostic group for Medicare patients (15). The logic of industrial regulation is to make medical services increasingly standardized. In theory, then, an equitable system in the USA would be one which provides reasonable access to a standard rate of use of medical care for all members of the population. Note, however, the detailed regulation and narrow consensus that has to be established in order to make such a system viable. That is, of course, one of the problems of micromanagement.

Providing basic insurance protection

My fourth and final example is the evident move toward some basic insurance protection for as large a proportion of the population as possible. This may be funded by the federal government, through the states, by taxes on employers and/or by taxes on providers. Some of these mechanisms already exist. I have suggested that major employers may push for increased government protection of the uninsured. But, whoever pays for the programs, there will need increasingly to be generally agreed specifications of what should be included in basic medical care, to provide an 'adequate' level of care as a matter of equity to the whole population. As a result, those involved in health service research in the USA will be increasingly involved in microanalysis in an attempt to establish acceptable norms around which a more equitable system can be based. I see no way around the fact that at present the USA is heading toward a multitiered health care system, with services varying by ability to pay, although I should like to be proved wrong on this.

Conclusion

My role here has been to suggest that the goals and values of the American health care system are intrinsically different from those of the UK and that questions of equity thus have to be conceived as different. This is more than saying that they have to be approached differently, although this is obviously true. I have also suggested that equity, as a notion, is also different.

Cross-national discussion such as this may help to sharpen our relative perceptions. No one familiar with the paradigm national pastimes of British cricket and American football can fail to appreciate the distinctive array of national values: different definitions of solidarity of purpose, technique, the nature of authority, the money nexus and the role of experts. If Britain is a country which prides itself on fairness,

America is a country that prides itself on rules. It is through the micromanagement of rules within a largely private system that basic changes will be made. Equity in the USA means more and more precision in definition—about insurance coverage, payment, services provided and the quality of care.

I believe we are about to enter an extremely interesting decade in the USA when questions of equity will come to the fore, however disguised as organizational, qualitative or fiscal questions. Two immediate targets will, and should be, the uninsured and children. In the meantime, the balancing act will continue: a complex, shifting dialogue between conflicting notions of what is just.

References

(1) Harrison A, Gretton J. *Health care UK, an economic, social and policy audit.* London: Chartered Institute of Public Finance and Accountancy, 1984. Cited by Carrier J. Health. In: Wilding P, ed. *In defence of the welfare state.* Manchester: Manchester University Press, 1986: 36.

(2) Bazzoli GJ. Health care for the indigent: overview of critical issues. *Health Services Res* 1986; **21**: 362.

(3) Levit KR, Lazenby H, Waldo DR, Davidoff LM. National health expenditures, 1984. *Health Care Financing Rev* 1985; **7**: 23.

(4) Aaron HJ, Schwartz WB. *The painful prescription: rationing hospital care.* Washington: The Brookings Institution, 1984: 37, 49, 55, 57.

(5) Preston SH. Children and the elderly: divergent patterns for America's dependents. *Demography* 1984; **21**: 434.

(6) Levit KR, et al. *Health Care Financing Rev* 1981; **3**: 22.

(7) Miller RD. Rationing health care: the legal complexity and some guidelines. *Topics in Hospital Law* 1986; **1**: 30.

(8) US Department of Health and Human Services. *Health, United States 1985.* DHHS publication no. (PHS)86-1232. Washington: US Government Printing Office, 1986: 68.

(9) Rosenbaum S, Johnson K. Providing health care for low-income children: reconciling child health goals with child health financing realities. *Milbank Q* 1986; **64**: 442-78.

(10) President's Commission for the Study of Ethical Problems in Medicine and Biomedical and Behavioral Research. *Securing access to health care*, Vol. 1. Report. Washington: US Government Printing Office, 1983: 4.

(11) Margo CE. Selling surgery. *N Engl J Med* 1986; **314**: 1575-6.

(12) Anonymous. Bypass surgery may depend on which hospital. *Philadelphia Inquirer* 1986 Oct 12: 3-E.

(13) Greenberg W. Information on quality will fuel competition. *Health Span* 1986; **3**: 6.

(14) Chassin MR, Brook RH, Park RE, et al. Variations in the use of medical and surgical services by the Medicare population. *N Engl J Med* 1986; **314**: 285-90.

(15) Wennberg J. Which rate is right? *N Engl J Med* 1986; **314**: 310.

Discussion

Dr Wilensky

I do not disagree with most of the list of goals set up by Professor Stevens. I have some quarrel with the concept of social justice with regard to the minimum provision of care—both its position on the list and about what is meant by that. I do not believe it is that low on our list. We have great difficulty in the USA deciding what and for whom we mean by 'minimum benefits'. That relates in part to an ambivalence we feel about the poor in this land of unlimited opportunity and to our attempts periodically to come up with concepts of 'deserving' and 'undeserving' poor. How can there be this limitless opportunity and still be various classes of poor people if that sort of distinction is not made?

I am not attempting to justify the distinction, but I think that the struggle with regard to Medicaid, about which Professor Stevens has spoken, is an inability to come to grips with the fact that there are people who are indeed poor, who might need to make use of government services, but who do not fit some sort of definition which makes it obvious why they are there.

I certainly agree with Professor Stevens that we will soon have to face up to that. It is because of the shift that has taken place from what a number of us have called 'implicit' financing to 'explicit' financing. This has become much more popular in the last few years. There is a real focus on the purchase of health care—that is, the private purchasers, in the form of employers, and government focusing on what it is they are buying, thereby emphasizing the lack of resources for those who are not covered by any system. It is as yet unclear how we deal with this—whether by trying to require that employers provide health insurance of some sort for all their workers, or (as in Texas) that state or local areas provide some sort of health care for people who are outside the system.

We will find ourselves pushed in that direction because we have removed the cushion of cross-subsidy—or have at least diminished that as a way to finance care for these populations.

There has been a higher priority for providing minimum care for at least some populations of the poor (although it is difficult to decide whether this is in theory rather than practice). The problem is how to deal with the poor if we are not sure they are deserving, and to define the role of government.

This problem has not been handled in a very clear fashion, even though it is not new but has been obvious since the introduction of social programmes in the USA.

Professor Stevens

It is curious that we are trying to approach 20th century medicine with 19th century concepts—concepts such as charity, voluntary effort and the deserving poor. One of the reasons why Medicaid and some of the other programmes are so confusing is that every so often we want to add another group—for example, we say now that the unemployed are deserving, but we do not want to include layabouts, so we have to make some definitions.

It is finally becoming evident that this approach does not work and that we need to move towards a national programme.

Dr Wilensky

I do not disagree with that—only about where on the list we put the concept of minimum care. I think it should be higher. We are now being forced to recognize much more explicitly the groups of the population that have been left out. I agree that we have been trying to work with ideas which may have been appropriate 20 or 30 years ago or in the 19th century but which are much less appropriate now.

The concept of some sort of minimum is much more a part of the beliefs in the American system. It is difficult to decide what to do because the role of government does not fit neatly into the broad concept.

Professor Reinhardt

In discussing her Table 1, which showed self-reported health status by social class, Professor Stevens made the point that this evokes no social opprobrium in the USA. I do not think that is being fair to Americans. I think it bothers us a great deal that infant mortality among blacks is still twice as high as among whites—although it has fallen quite precipitously in the last decade in both groups. Indeed, in our discussions we often implicitly accuse American health care providers, and attribute those differences to their behaviour—which, of course, is grossly unfair. I say it is unfair because I recall a paper by Walter Holland, in an Organization for Economic

Co-operation and Development publication, listing health status measures in the UK by social class (1). The infant mortality rate varied by a factor of three between the highest and the lowest. That is higher than would be found in the USA.

Suppose I make the hypothesis that, if we were to look at health status by social class in both countries, the disparity in the UK may be wider than in the USA. The question could then be raised as to what opprobrium that evokes in the UK. After all, it seems that 30 years of the National Health Service (NHS) have not brought about much improvement.

I am not sure, first, that the USA is all that different and, secondly, that it is fair to say there is no opprobrium in the USA — the situation does worry many people.

Dr Banta

To extend the argument slightly further, who is to do the kinds of assessments described by Professor Jennett and, specifically, who is to pay for them? Would he agree that the only major source available is national level public funding — that is, taxpayers' public money?

Secondly, how do we control or channel technology? How do we use these results? Does Professor Jennett think that the funder or the payment mechanism is the major control device? He also mentioned education, or dissemination of the results. How would he put that into a national strategy? Should the education be addressed to policy makers, clinicians or the general public — or to all three?

Professor Jennett

There is an extraordinary anomaly with regard to who pays for assessment. In the pharmaceutical industry the assessments, on the whole, are much better and more systematic (although far short of perfect) because they are paid for by the industry, to some extent in response to fiscal requirements (in the UK, the Committee on Safety of Medicines, and in the USA, the Food and Drug Administration (FDA)). It was once said that there is no FDA for surgeons. Of course, that remains true. Very little money is put into research and development in the devices industry, and even less into surgical and other procedures. It is not only surgeons, but also radiologists and physicians who undertake very complicated procedures.

Assessment has to be taken on, in the UK at least, mainly by the main funding agency — in other words, the NHS. With a total cost of £17 billion a year, it would amount to only a tiny fraction of the total — much less than an industry would put into examining its products.

The question of applying the technology — how we get the message over — is a completely different issue. We cannot afford to wait 20 years for the present undergraduates to become wise dispensers of expensive technology. That would be far too long. The idea of some sort of accountability on the shop floor, which we are possibly in sight of under the new management structure, gives some prospect of hope.

The funding agencies such as the National Institutes of Health and the Medical Research Council have to make this kind of activity respectable, both in research and its use, and also respected, so that we are praised for parsimony rather than for spending. This has to become, as Thurow said, 'one of the norms of good practice' (2).

Dr Brody

Professor Stevens raised the issue about quality being a move towards the sort of low-key rationing that would create an increased equity in the USA. I was slightly surprised by that statement because it seems as though we have been using quality as a way to smuggle notions of inequity into the system for some time now. This has occurred to the extent that, if we fail to take into account available resources defining a level of quality of care, in effect a setting is created in which only a limited number can receive that quality.

To take one example, there are widely broadcast standards in the USA for mammograms for screening for breast cancer, but it has not been calculated whether there are enough mammographers or radiologists in the USA to do the required number of mammograms per year if all American women of the relevant age groups receive that standard of quality.

We therefore guarantee that only the most vocal or the wealthiest will get 'quality' care, and ensure that the poor will be unable to get it.

Professor Shapiro

The entire discussion concentrates on national goals and values, as though the federal government in the USA is the only factor attempting to implement or to promote them. Yet we have seen that in the USA there has been a considerable growth in emphasis on decentralization.

If we look at what has been happening in the Medicaid programme, where the states have primary responsibility for setting standards for determining eligibility with some degree of national oversight, we see an enormous variation among the states in terms of the eligibility criteria, leading to a disenfranchisement of many families and individuals from what we might view as a minimum standard of care.

In attempting to address the goals, values and strategies, to what extent does Professor Stevens see the need for a reversal of the efforts that have been made for decentralization in authority in the USA, instead placing a greater emphasis on the federal government?

Professor Stevens

Perhaps I can also return here to Dr Brody's comment. Medicare is a federal programme, and it is becoming increasingly centralized in terms of rule-making. I think it is a moot point whether Medicaid will also become increasingly centralized. If we have a national health insurance scheme, again it could be said that at the ends of the range there are two models. One is prescribing everything centrally — exactly what is covered, for what level of care, and where — a huge bible of administrative regulations centrally diffused. The second (and only other) option is to say that there will be a decentralized service system, with a form of reimbursement — a form of payment system, Medicare, Medicaid, national health insurance — which will overtly buy into decentralized health care service schemes. I think that the issues are still open on these options.

I agree that there is a continuing struggle over the level at which decisions are made; whether we are dealing with increasingly highly specific criteria at the national level (which I think have arisen because of the cost frustrations of Medicare) and, what is obviously a preferable system, how far much more informal, locally based decisions can be taken. I believe that these decisions can only really be made within local health care systems. In part, it depends upon what these systems look like and how effective they are.

This comes back to what Professor Jennett said about the role of the doctor in all these systems. What I find so fascinating is that he focuses on the physician as the critical character in resource allocation, whereas I focus very much on the formal systems, which is where most of the concern has been in the USA. These are the very troubling questions which will engage us in the USA for the next few years.

Professor Pardes

I would like to thank Professor Stevens for introducing a corrective note into our appraisal of the goals of the US health care system. In referring to the ability of the gatekeeper to exclude people from long-term psychiatric care, did she see this as an asset of the system?

Professor Stevens

First, a particular system, a health maintenance organization (HMO) or insurance system, may not cover certain services, such as long-term psychiatric care.

About the role of the gatekeeper, I was not suggesting that the primary physician would say off his own bat that a particular patient would not get service X or Y.

There are two things: first, what is covered within the services provided under a particular system and, secondly, within that system and that coverage, what is the role of the gatekeeper. Some people have undoubtedly looked at the role of primary care physicians in keeping the gate and in making decisions, but to my knowledge there is still relatively little good research about what gatekeepers' decisions actually are in HMOs and what independent effect they have.

Professor Maynard

If I may return to the goals of the NHS: with regard to the efficiency goals, I do not find any problems with Professor Jennett's arguments. The implication of that sort of rationing decision is that we do not provide care for elderly end-stage renal failure patients, and we would also look very sceptically at some neonates.

I am less happy so far about the discussion of the equity issues mentioned by Professor Reinhardt. The gaps in the UK between different social classes, or different income groups, are large. What evidence we have indicates that the relative gaps between these groups are widening. Obviously, the NHS may have little impact on those gaps which may be much more related to income. Certainly, in the NHS it is very difficult to target resources at deprived groups or areas.

That is particularly true when we look at things which Professor Stevens mentioned, such as the Resource Allocation Working Party (RAWP) formula. That contains some inherent contradictions. It has to be remembered that the UK is four countries, each of which has different allocation formulae and different levels of endowment. If we are very simplistic and apply one formula to the aggregated budgets of the four countries, Scotland would lose nearly 20% of its budget, and the Irish over 27%.

Also, those sorts of formulae are applied only to the hospital budget. Our primary care system is not RAWPed and is grossly unequal. RAWP is really only about things like inputs and financial processes.

An important point we should not lose sight of is that the NHS in the UK is avowedly about fairness (whatever that means) and reducing inequality. In many ways, the indicators tell us that those inequalities have not declined in relative terms as much as many people would hope.

Dr Bulger

A fairly profound difference between doctors in the UK and in the USA, which we do not yet fully appreciate, revolves around the issue of informed consent. In the USA, the judges have decided that the patient owns everything about his or her record of medical care. In a sense, we are moving towards the ultimate decentralization in that each person determines his or her care.

If I am not mistaken, in the recent Sidaway case in England, the judiciary decided that the patient only needs to know what is customary and what the doctor needs to convey to that patient in order to care for him (3).

The implications of this difference in the doctor's role in the distribution of technology seem to be extremely profound.

Professor Jennett

This is another of the areas in which the gap between the two countries is narrowing. The Sidaway case was in fact a disputed judgement from the House of Lords (it was not unanimous). Two of the five judges took the view that we should be following America more closely. I think this issue is gathering momentum. Just as our malpractice insurance has more than trebled in the last year, I think informed consent is also on the agenda.

References

(1) Scrivens E, Holland WW. Inequalities in health in Britain. A critique of the report of a
        research working party. *Effective Health Care* 1983; **1**: 97–109.
(2) Thurow LC. Learning to say 'no'. *N Engl J Med* 1984; **311**: 1569–72.
(3) Sidaway *vs* Bethlem Royal Hospital [1985] 1 All ER 643.

CURRENT OVERT CONSEQUENCES OF RESOURCE LIMITATION

Chairman:
GLENN WILSON
Chapel Hill NC, USA

A UK view

ARTHUR C. TAYLOR

Chairman, National Association of Health Authorities;
Chairman, Newcastle Health Authority, Newcastle upon Tyne, UK

Resource limitation

The principle, that beauty is in the eye of the beholder, when applied to resource limitation, implies that what comprises resource limitation is very much in the mind of the person looking at the problem. In the broadest terms we could be examining the whole fabric of society in the UK and the resources available for housing, employment, social services, education and health. However, this wider debate is not my task, and I therefore limit the interpretation to resource limitation in the health service.

I understand resource limitation to mean the constraint on financial resources and the comparatively low proportion of the gross national product (GNP) which is devoted to health care in the UK, a topic already referred to in a previous paper.

The beholders who perceive the beauty divide into a number of categories:
—politicians;
—doctors and nurses;
—health service managers;
—patients and their supporting organizations;
—medical schools;
—the media.

As Chairman of the National Association of Health Authorities (NAHA) and of a health authority which is a teaching authority, I come into several of those categories.

Politicians

Politicians, at any rate those in power, concentrate on showing how the numbers of patients treated, and the numbers of doctors and nurses employed have increased, and also how the resource available to the National Health Service (NHS) has increased (24%, it is said, in real terms since 1979). Opposition politicians concentrate on the shortfall of resource compared with need and demand, and point to waiting lists, ward and

Health Care Provision under Financial Constraint, edited by T. B. Binns and M. Firth, 1988: Royal Society of Medicine International Congress and Symposium Series No. 115, published by Royal Society of Medicine Services Ltd.

53

hospital closures, shortage of doctors and nurses, and shortfall of service provision in the case of popular causes like cervical cytology and breast cancer.

The Government assertion that spending on the NHS since 1979 has increased by 24% in real terms merits examination. It is based on deflating the cash increase to the NHS by the gross domestic product deflator, i.e. changes in prices in the economy as a whole for the period 1978–79 to 1986–87. If, however, the NHS deflator is applied—that is, if the cash spending in the NHS is deflated by a measure of the prices of the goods and services in the NHS itself—and excluding the current financial year (because inflationary pressures have not yet ceased), there is an increase in real terms of 10% over a period of some 7 years. There is a difference. Even this figure can be further reduced to about 6% by taking the hospital and community health services (HCHSs) rather than the NHS as a whole (1–3).

Doctors and nurses

Doctors and nurses will never be satisfied at the amount of resource either in terms of their own salaries or the available facilities to enable them to perform their professional tasks. Groups of professional organizations—the British Medical Association, the Hospital Consultants and Specialists Association, the Royal College of Nursing and many others—draw attention to these shortfalls.

Health managers

Health managers are in an invidious position. They particularly have the responsibility of providing the service at local level and are aware of the mismatch of resource on the one hand and need on the other. Their position in the health service organization precludes them from excessively shrill presentation of the problem, but they are nevertheless subjected to the major pressure at local level. They feel the obligation to hold the line and to maximize the value in terms of service from the resource which is allocated to them.

Patients

Patients, for the most part, are long-suffering and surprisingly docile. They are represented by consumer organizations, by the Patients' Association and by the community health councils. They are the ones who really know where the shoe pinches, and it is little comfort to those on a waiting list of 3 years for a hip operation or 8 years for plastic surgery to be told that there is 24% more money going into the health service than there was in 1979.

Medical schools

Medical schools, hit simultaneously by cuts in the University Grants Committee (UGC) allocations and cash limits in the NHS, find difficulty in realizing their roles which in our system provide for teaching and service commitment to be conducted side by side. Indeed, the pressure upon the NHS in some places imperils the standards of teaching and the loss of clinical academic posts has its impact upon service provision.

The media

Finally the media tend to see no beauty at all but are ready to report all the overt and some of the covert consequences of resource limitation. Thus, long waiting lists, closures of wards in hospitals, threats to London teaching hospitals, shortage of nurses, pressure on accident and emergency departments, and inadequate provision in the community for patients discharged from large institutions, are all good copy which the media do not fail to record.

It is perhaps too early, and we are perhaps too close to events, to assess objectively which of these perceptions is nearest to the truth. Some day, the history of the NHS in the 1980s may be written, perhaps in the light of the outcome in the 1990s, which may give a more objective assessment, but the conspectus I have given does, I think, lead to one conclusion. There is no doubt that as a result of current resource constraints (whatever its real extent may be) resource limitation has indeed become overt. The very title of this paper illustrates it. This is a relatively new phenomenon. Although there has been resource limitation and consequently rationing in the NHS since its inception, during the 1960s and 1970s there was relatively more growth money available than to-day. Therefore, perhaps many people actually believed that everyone who had a need for health care would receive it. Today, most people are aware that rationing is a highly politicized process, sometimes overt, sometimes covert.

Overt consequences

Whatever resource limitation really is and whoever is writing about it, what are the effects or consequences?

Conflicting demands between services

In many places there is a clash between the demands of the acute services, on the one hand, and the so-called 'Cinderella' — or, in modern terms, priority — services, on the other. I refer to the elderly, the mentally ill and the mentally handicapped.

Thus, many of our regional health authorities (RHAs) have instituted a system whereby every district health authority (DHA) in their region must give up 0·5% of its cash allocation to the RHA which then redistributes those funds according to the level of need, as perceived by the RHA, for the priority services throughout the region. Thus, a DHA with satisfactory provision of those services will not see much of its money back — and yet it may have great pressure on its acute services. Consideration of changes in the division of resources in the HCHS budget as between hospital health services and the community health services over the past 8 years for which we have figures illustrates the position (Table 1).

Just over 80% of the HCHS budget is allocated to hospital services, and under 10% to the community services. The remainder of the allocation is spent on ambulance services and headquarters' administration.

Table 1

Division of resources in the hospital and community health services (HCHSs) between hospital and community health services

	1976–77 (£m)	% of total HCHS budget	1984–85 (£m)	% of total HCHS budget
Hospital services	6854·4	82·9	7541·6	83·2
Community services	692·5	8·4	855·9	9·5
Ambulance and headquarters administration	723·8	8·8	664·7	7·3
Total HCHS (excluding joint finance)	8270·7	100·1	9062·2	100·0

Source: House of Commons Social Services Committee (3).

Although the change in the proportions of the HCHS budget allocated to these two sectors appears slight, the change is very significant. The hospital health services have been constrained — especially so, if the growth of the Labour government years is taken out of the assessment of the period. The resources in the community health services have increased by over 20%.

The average annual change in current expenditure over the period 1976–77 to 1984–85 was 1·2% for the hospital health services and 2·7% for the community health services.

Demographic change and high technology medicine

There are clear increasing demands to meet demographic change, on the one hand, and the cost of high technology medicine, on the other, which need additional resource and yet which imperil the continuation of existing services if resource is limited.

Demographic change. As to demographic change, in the Government's expenditure plans 1986–87 to 1988–89 it was stated that one of the Government's main aims was to:
> meet the greater demands for services for the growing number of elderly people, particularly those aged 75 and over. Demographic pressure on the Hospital and Community Health Service (HCHS) is estimated at 1% in 1986–87, falling thereafter to 0·9% in 1987–88 and 0·8% in 1988–89; (4)

Over the period 1979–85 the number of people over 75 years old increased by 450 000 (16%). Government estimates of expenditure per head by age group reveal that spending on those 75 and over is approximately nine times greater than for those aged 16–64.

It has been suggested by Alan Maynard and Nick Bosanquet that HCHS spending on the elderly is being squeezed whilst that of family practitioner committee and personal social services (PSS) is expanding (5). They argue that, overall, those aspects of the HCHS budget which are age-sensitive have declined by 0·1% during the period 1982–83 and 1984–85. Local authority PSS expenditure on age-sensitive services has been rising twice as fast as spending on other services.

High technology medicine. In relation to high technology medicine, from an analysis in the acute sector of the average number of cases treated per year over and above that which demographic factors would have required, and from an estimation of the overall rise in cost per case as a result of a more expensive specialty mix, the

Department has calculated that 0·5% of HCHS resources is absorbed by medical advances.

In the same way that extra cash in the HCHS to cover demographic pressures may not have been spent on age-sensitive services it may well be the case that those areas of the HCHS needing money to cope with medical advance have gone without. Although it is mainly the acute sector which is really affected by technical innovation (if the impact of drugs is ignored), it appears that the acute sector has been very constrained in resource terms in recent years. For instance, in the period 1982–83 to 1984–85 the expenditure on acute in-patient services declined by approximately 1%.

Manpower

Another consequence of resource limitation is pressure on manpower and, in order to achieve targets, distortions are almost inevitable. About three-quarters of the HCHS budget is spent on staff. In 1982, the total number of staff employed in the NHS in England (measured by whole-time equivalents (WTE) not numbers of people) peaked at just under 830 000. Since 1982 there has been a reduction of ancillary staff of 25 000 WTE (a 14% reduction of the total number of WTE ancillary staff in 1982). On the other hand, there has been an increase of medical and dental WTE staff of 2000 (5%), an increase of 4000 WTE nursing and midwifery staff (1%), and an increase of 6000 WTE professional and technical staff (9%) (4).

Regarding manpower targets (now called manpower ceilings), the 14 RHAs were set manpower targets for March 1984. In fact, the RHAs reduced staff by nearly 7000 beyond the target set. Therefore, between March 1983 and March 1984 there was a reduction of nearly 11 000 staff. As the reduction in staff numbers had not affected exclusively ancillary, and administrative and clerical staff, the Social Services Committee (SSC) of the House of Commons became critical of the targets. The Committee stated that during the year the numbers of nursing and midwifery staff fell by over 3000. The Committee made the following recommendation:

> We recommend that, before any further setting of manpower targets or ceilings, the Department undertake an evaluation of their impact at Regional, District and Unit level. (2)

I am unaware of any Department initiative to follow up the Committee's recommendation.

The manpower ceilings have continued. The March 1984 ceiling was maintained for 1985. The March 1986 ceiling was 2000 WTE lower than March 1985, and the March 1987 ceiling is 6500 WTE lower than March 1986. It is anticipated that the March 1987 ceiling will allow some growth in staff because RHAs are expected to start 10 000 below the March 1986 ceiling. The fixing of artificial targets or ceilings inevitably leads to distortion because overall numbers become more important than having the right numbers of the right groups of staff.

Medical education

As already mentioned, there is pressure on the medical schools and the teaching function and its interrelation with clinical services (6).

Universities have experienced a reduction in income of 20% (in real terms) since 1981. They are likely to lose, on average, a further 2% per year, which may result in a total reduction in resources of 30% by 1990. If the planned 2% per year reduction in university funding continues without any protection being afforded to medical faculties, many of the teaching authorities will be placed under considerable strain, and the successful relationships that have been built up between the medical schools and the NHS will be threatened.

Perhaps 25–30% of hospital patient care in teaching authorities is carried out by academic staff, and so any reduction in their numbers can cause operational problems.

The NAHA together with the University Hospitals Association (UHA) have attempted to monitor the effects of the UGC cuts both on the standards of medical education and of patient care (7). During the period 1981–84 there was a net loss of clinical staff which amounted to 152 WTE clinical academic staff, 129 WTE technical staff, and 36 WTE secretarial staff—a total loss of 317 WTE, or an average of just over 12 WTE per school. At a rough estimate, the full complement of UGC-funded clinical academic staff in an average medical school is equivalent to approximately 80 WTE. Up to 1984, therefore, the cuts represented more than the loss of the clinical academic staff of one whole medical school. The resulting knock-on effects of these losses, on numbers of patients treated and expertise lost, should not be underestimated—and the reductions are continuing.

From the outset of the UGC cuts the very particular problems that would be caused to teaching authorities by medical schools freezing posts as they fell vacant were acknowledged. A special plea was made in December 1981 by the then Chief Medical Officer, Sir Henry Yellowlees, to the Chairman of the Medical Advisory Committee of the Committee of Vice-Chancellors and Principals, to point out that medicine has a high rate of staff turnover and that the unpredictable nature of the policy of freezing all posts could have serious effects on the NHS's ability to plan and provide services.

Universities appear to be adopting the policy of freezing all posts as they become vacant. The length of 'freezing' seems to vary but it is common for posts to lie vacant for periods of 6 months to 2 years before attempts are made to fill them—if, that is, the decision is taken not to close the post completely. As the UGC cuts continue and bite deeper, so this policy is becoming more widespread.

The NAHA/UHA surveys showed that departments of pathology were suffering disproportionately from the UGC cuts. The SSC drew attention to this in 1985, and the Government's response in 1986 was to accept that pathology required a strong academic base and to announce the creation of 35 'new blood' posts in this specialty between 1983 and 1986.

Recent anxieties about the adequacy of services in cervical cytology and of services to detect pre-natal and peri-natal abnormalities are instances of the dangers inherent in shortfalls in the pathology services. Six senior posts in pathology have been lost or threatened, and two further professorships have been frozen for lengths of time. It is obvious that the concern expressed by the SSC and the DHSS about the effects of the cuts on pathology has not stopped universities from closing posts. It would seem that the universities cannot give special dispensations, given the continuing financial pressures that they face.

There is also strong evidence in the surveys that the greatest impact is on research and postgraduate education rather than on undergraduate teaching.

Waiting lists

There is no doubt that waiting lists in certain specialties are at an unacceptable length both from a patient's and from a provider's viewpoint. Recent statements of intention by the Secretary of State indicate Government anxiety on this topic.

There are 680 000 on the hospital in-patient waiting list in England and Wales. At the end of March 1985 there were over half a million people waiting for treatment in five specialties. Of the 150 000 patients waiting for non-urgent general surgery, 25% are kept waiting for over 1 year, as are 32% of the 140 000 waiting for non-urgent trauma and orthopaedics treatment, and 24% of the 111 000 waiting for non-urgent ear, nose and throat treatment. Patients waiting for non-urgent treatment in gynaecology and ophthalmology beds fare slightly better, with 16% and 18%, respectively, waiting longer than 1 year (8).

It should be noted that a 'non-urgent' requirement for treatment does not mean that the patient is not suffering quite severe discomfort. An 'urgent' case is one in which the condition is thought likely to deteriorate unless treatment is given more or less immediately.

Capping of services

Another consequence of resource limitation is the capping of services. Thus, pacemaker operations may be limited, as may coronary artery bypass grafts and transplants, because the funds are not available. Many of these operations are life-saving, and therefore restriction of services means imperilling life. This leads to impossible choices and decision-making (to which I shall refer later).

Cost improvement programmes

The obvious way of reducing these consequences with present resource limitation is to maximize the efficiency of the service and the way in which resource is utilized. This has led to the so-called cost improvement programmes (CIPs) whereby health authorities are required to make savings from within their cash allocations.

Finance made available from the CIP is playing a crucial role in helping health authorities to meet the growing demands made upon them. However, there is concern that the CIP is becoming the main source of finance for developing services and in some cases for meeting shortfalls in present allocations.

Savings generated within the HCHS significantly exceed the margin of central Government funding above inflation. For instance, in 1983–84 there was zero growth from Government funding, and savings amounted to nearly 0·5% of total budget. In 1984–85 there was decrease in input volume terms of 0·1%, whilst cost improvements amounted to over 1% of the budget. In 1985–86, centrally financed growth was 0·4%, whereas cash-releasing cost improvements were 1·2% of budget. In 1986–87 centrally financed growth will be at best 0·5%, whereas cash-releasing cost improvements are likely to be 1·5% of budget. In assessing whether cost improvements should continue to take such a dominant role in financing service developments a number of points should be considered.

It was only in 1984–85 that a substantial yield was recorded: approximately 1% of total budget. Therefore, as the CIP has been in existence only a short time in its present form, there is little past evidence on which to base solid predictions concerning future yields. It may be the case that those areas of health authority budgets most likely to produce savings have been tackled and future savings may be harder to achieve.

NAHA's 1985 autumn survey of district health authorities' financial position revealed that approximately 40% of the 148 health authorities responding to the questionnaire had used cost improvement savings to meet shortfalls on their pay allocations (9). Even in the current financial year, when a lower level of price inflation has offset the shortfall on pay allocations, a considerable number of health authorities envisage using cash-releasing cost improvements to protect existing services rather than to fund service developments.

It is clear that more information and understanding must be obtained concerning the CIP if it is to continue to play such a central role in funding the development of the NHS. The following conclusion of the Committee of Public Accounts is very significant:

> We think it is particularly important that the NHS continues its own search to improve efficiency and to provide better value for money. But we cannot emphasise strongly enough that both the NHS and the Department should keep fully to their policy that CIPs should not include savings from cuts in services. We recognise that this is particularly difficult where other central initiatives, such as RAWP [Resource Allocation Working Party] allocations and manpower targets which in some regions are designed to reduce available resources, are operating in parallel with the CIP. And we note that, despite their increasing robust scrutiny of CIPs, DHSS could not give an absolute assurance that service cuts had not been included. (10)

Pay awards

The NAHA's 1986 autumn survey on the financial position of district health authorities revealed that most DHAs had a 4·5% addition for pay award increases allocated to them by their RHAs (11). However, pay awards in the current year have increased the overall wage bill by 6%. Although some health authorities have been able to ride this situation without too much disruption, there are many authorities which will be hard pressed and will have to curtail developments and possibly restrict services. There is also a substantial input of management time involved in making the necessary adjustments in the middle of the financial year.

Problems arising

In accommodating health provision to available resources it is inevitable that choices have to be made, and those choices frequently raise moral, and some would say impossible, issues to decide. If there is to be regard to quality assurance in patient care—as there must—then the assurance of quality and value in terms of life must create very difficult dilemmas for health managers and doctors. For example:

(1) What is the correct balance between the acute services, on the one hand, and the Cinderella services, on the other?

(2) How do we measure the respective values of putting more money into primary care with emphasis on health promotion and screening procedures as against putting the same money into hospital services?

(3) How is the allocation of resources decided as between specialties? How do we measure the value of the hip operation against a kidney transplant or renal dialysis, or transplants against plastic surgery or GP advice about smoking?

Quality-adjusted life year

Recent work by Alan Williams, of York University, has suggested a possible basis for making such decisions (12). In brief, he suggests measuring by how much a health care procedure prolongs the patient's life and improves the quality of life, and what it costs to do so.

The quality-adjusted life year (QALY) is a composite measure of the additional life years and the improved quality of life of those years generated by a given form of medical treatment. From costing out different types of medical treatment it is possible to estimate the cost of producing one full quality of life year.

From the work done by Alan Williams, the researchers at York University have produced cost-QALY estimates for Britain which give the cost per quality life year of different types of treatment. For instance, it costs £20 000 to obtain one full quality of life year from hospital haemodialysis but only £750 per QALY from hip replacement. Therefore, given a budget of, for example, £100 000, it is possible to produce 5 QALYs if the money is spent on dialysis and over 130 QALYs if the money is spent on hip replacement. GP advice to stop smoking costs only £167 per QALY (nearly 600 QALYs could be obtained from a £100 000 budget!).

I cannot say whether QALYs are in fact being utilized by health authorities at the present time or whether they are only a twinkle in the eye of a health economist. They are no doubt an interesting and useful way of costing treatment and assessing outcomes, but whether they can be a basis for decision-making is much more doubtful.

Moral issues

Some of these decisions present moral issues for doctors which can bring them perilously close to breaches of their Hippocratic oath. I am thinking of the sentence which reads:

> The regimen I shall adopt shall be for my patients according to my ability and judgment and not for their hurt or wrong.

I apprehend that refers to the duty to the individual patient and not to the totality of the doctor's patients in QALY terms. If, as happens in some fields, the cost differential between two drugs can be as much as £48 000 per patient per year, one drug being much more effective, on what basis does the doctor make that decision? Or does he pass it (as I believe to be happening) to his general manager and leave the decision to him? If one operation has to be evaluated against another in terms of quality of life, is the doctor fulfilling—indeed, can he fulfill—his Hippocratic duty to every patient?

The need for efficiency

All these problems emphasize the need for efficiency in relation to available resources, hence the introduction of general management with all its associated activities of management budgeting, clinical performance indicators and now, imported from the other side of the Atlantic, diagnosis-related groups and other ideas. But they must not, in my submission, be allowed to detract from the practice of medicine in terms of quality of care and morality of judgements.

Conclusion

We all know — and it is the most commonplace truism of health service gurus — that resource is finite and demand is infinite. The concept of the health service was based on the assumption that good health from the cradle onwards would reduce the cost to the community of providing the necessary service. The reality is that good health care has eliminated many of the killer diseases, with the result that we live longer, we cost more to look after in our later days, we develop more expensive conditions, or conditions which are more expensive to treat and, because operations are available to cure problems, expectations increase requiring that they should be available on demand and free. This perhaps is the great dilemma which accounts for the difference in views which I highlighted at the outset. It is true that we are treating more patients. It is true that there is greater dissatisfaction than ever before in the NHS. Heightened expectations have certainly contributed to this.

References

(1) House of Commons Social Services Committee. *Public expenditure on the social services 1983–4*. HC395. London: Her Majesty's Stationery Office, 1984 (July).
(2) House of Commons Social Services Committee. *Public expenditure on the social services 1984–5*. HC339. London: Her Majesty's Stationery Office, 1985 (June).
(3) House of Commons Social Services Committee. *Public expenditure on the social services 1985–6*. HC387–II. London: Her Majesty's Stationery Office, 1986 (July).
(4) *The Government's expenditure plans 1986–87 to 1988–89*. Cmnd 9702–II. London: Her Majesty's Treasury, 1986 (Jan).
(5) Maynard A, Bosanquet N. *Public expenditure on the NHS: recent trends and future problems*. London: The Institute of Health Services Management, 1986 (Sept).
(6) National Association of Health Authorities. *University funding and the NHS: the 1986 review*. Birmingham: National Association of Health Authorities, 1986.
(7) *University Hospitals Association/National Association of Health Authorities survey of academic medical staffing, changes in the clinical medical schools and university clinical faculties in England and Wales*. London: University Hospitals Association/National Association of Health Authorities, 1985 (Sept).
(8) College of Health. *Inter-authority comparisons and consultancy guide to hospital waiting lists 1985*. London: College of Health, 1985 (Nov).
(9) National Association of Health Authorities. *Autumn survey 1985: the financial position of district health authorities*. Birmingham: National Association of Health Authorities, 1985.
(10) House of Commons forty-second report from the Committee of Public Accounts, session 1985–86. *Value for money developments in the National Health Service: energy conservation*. HC335. London: Her Majesty's Stationery Office, 1986 (June).
(11) National Association of Health Authorities. *Autumn survey 1986: the financial position of district health authorities*. Birmingham: National Association of Health Authorities, 1986 (Oct).
(12) Williams A. Economics of coronary artery bypass grafting. *Br Med J* 1985; **291**: 326–9.

A US view:
the American health care dilemma:
discontent among plenty

ARNOLD S. RELMAN

Editor, The New England Journal of Medicine, Boston MA, USA

The paradox of the US health care system

Health care in the USA today is becoming ever more expensive, at the same time becoming less equitable. It has already been pointed out that the USA spends a greater share of its gross national product for health services than any other country in the world. We spend almost three times as much, per capita, as the UK, and this expenditure continues to increase rapidly despite all efforts at cost-containment. Yet at the same time more and more of our people are losing their access to health services, and the disparity increases between the services available to the rich and the poor.

About 15% of Americans have no health insurance. Another 8–10% have only Medicare or Medicaid coverage, unsupplemented by any other private insurance, which means that they are becoming increasingly vulnerable to the financial risks of injury and disease as their coverage under publicly funded programs is progressively reduced. Under present Medicare coverage, America's elderly are now required to pay out of pocket for health care a much larger percentage of their income than when the program was first instituted some 20 years ago. Medicaid, as Mr Lewin's paper makes clear, does not begin to take care of all the medical and health care needs of the poor, and the extent of its coverage is also being curtailed.

In addition, a reduction in the ability of voluntary hospitals to cross-subsidize the acute hospital care of the uninsured poor has produced a great deal more 'dumping' (i.e. the transfer of indigent patients for other than medical reasons) from private to public institutions. In some parts of the USA public hospitals are receiving increasing numbers of acutely ill or injured patients who, simply because they have no insurance and are unable to pay their hospital bills, have been hastily transferred out of the private hospitals to which they were first taken. This reprehensible practice risks the lives of those with serious conditions, who are not adequately treated or stabilized before their precipitate transfer to another hospital.

To appreciate what is happening to the hospital care of the acutely ill uninsured citizen today we have to remember that, in the past, more than 60% of the free

Health Care Provision under Financial Constraint, edited by T. B. Binns and M. Firth, 1988: Royal Society of Medicine International Congress and Symposium Series No. 115, published by Royal Society of Medicine Services Ltd.

care in US hospitals was provided in the private voluntary institutions, which cross-subsidized their care through the surpluses earned from the insured and self-paying patients. With the advent of price competition and fixed prospective prices, cross-subsidization has come to be viewed as economically unjustified and a threat to a hospital's financial stability. Non-profit hospitals which formerly were willing to accept their share of the poor are no longer as receptive. For-profit, investor-owned hospitals have never considered free care to be their responsibility, and their proliferation over about the past 15 years has added to the dumping problem.

I do not wish to be misunderstood. I am not suggesting that the old days of cross-subsidized hospital care for the poor were very good. There is substantial evidence that they were not. We know that most of the free care in hospitals was limited to emergency and obstetrical services, and that the poor received far less than their proportionate share of the full range of services hospitals have to offer. Free care has constituted about 3 or 4% of all hospital services nationwide, while the poor and uninsured are about 12–15% of the population.

There is no need to expand on this theme. The evidence of inequality and of failure to provide needed services for those who cannot afford to pay is clear, widespread and growing. I will examine briefly some of the reasons for the present paradoxes in the American health care system. Why is there all this shabbiness in the midst of so much wealth? With all that we are spending on health care in the USA, why are we failing to give adequate care to so many of our citizens? What accounts for all the turmoil and change, but so little progress towards equity and cost control?

In my view there are several important factors contributing to the present American health care dilemma.

The myth of the market

Americans are presently under the illusion that health care is a consumer product like any other, and that it can best be distributed like other goods and services in a commercial market. It is currently fashionable to talk about 'the health care market', and to address its problems as if they could be solved by encouraging 'market competition'. The two major payers (the federal government and the large business employers) are ideologically disposed to think about the product they are paying for as a consumer good rather than as a social service. It therefore seems logical to them to encourage price competition among the providers as a means of containing rapidly rising costs and improving the 'efficiency' of what is seen as an over-expanded, wasteful and undisciplined industry.

The industrial market view of health care has also been given considerable impetus by the appearance of large investor-owned corporations beginning about 20 years ago. As more and more health care facilities of all kinds have come under investor ownership, and as the new corporate owners began successfully to apply business marketing and managerial techniques to their health care enterprises, it seemed natural to regard medical care as just another consumer service. But it is not, and to treat it thus is to invite the kinds of problems that the US health care system is now experiencing.

In discussing this subject, some of my non-medical friends are sure to say that the notion of medical care as a business was first exemplified by private fee-for-service medical practitioners. They also point to the increasingly entrepreneurial activities of US physicians who are entering into investment and ownership arrangements that give them a financial interest in health care facilities, resources and organizations, involving far more than simply their own professional services to patients. I believe that the climate of earlier fee-for-service practice, when physicians were in short supply and not — as they are now — obliged to compete for patients, was quite different from the more competitive, profit-oriented business market in which medicine is being practiced today. I acknowledge that the medical profession's ambivalence about the proper economic role of the physician has contributed to the present commercialization of the system. However, I do not think that the coming of the medical care market was a direct consequence of the behavior of the medical profession.

In any case, the point here is that the market model cannot be applied to the medical care system without so many modifications and exceptions that it is of little value as a tool for analysis or prediction. More important, public policy primarily dependent on this model cannot be expected to achieve equity or cost control. The market may be a useful instrument for the distribution of goods and services according to consumer demand and ability to pay, but it is certainly not concerned about equity or the needs of those lacking ability to pay.

Furthermore, price competition alone will not control costs, as recent experience bears out. Price competition in a free market may control prices but not total utilization and expenditures — not unless there are additional imposed constraints. The risks in applying such constraints are, first, that those unable to pay may suffer the greatest exclusion from benefits and, secondly, that profit-maximizing providers may concentrate their attention on the most profitable services and the wealthiest customers. Only if there is a public commitment to redress the inevitable inequities can we expect to see any solution to these problems in a largely market-driven health care system.

The failure of political will

The second factor responsible for the present predicament in the USA is a failure of political will to solve the problem at the level of federal government. I believe that it will be difficult, if not impossible, to achieve a decent health care system in the USA without more regulation and more financial support than our government has so far been willing to provide. The present administration seems committed to the reduction of federal support for, and involvement in, social welfare programs of almost any kind, including medical care. It has no interest in a national health insurance program, particularly because it would probably increase federal expenditures. Nevertheless, I agree with the opinions of other Americans at this conference that reports of the demise of such an idea may be premature. A comprehensive, compulsory health insurance program is clearly not in the wings waiting to go on stage, but it could arrive at the stage door before long, ready for reconsideration. The present market competition scenario has not yet played itself out, but that may well occur not too many years hence, when the human consequences of the growing inequity of our present market-driven system become more widely publicized and political pressures for reform mount. There will probably have to be a change in leadership in the White House before some kind of national health insurance plan can come under serious consideration again, but I am convinced that its time will come. In the meantime, more limited forms of protection, such as 'catastrophic insurance' for the elderly, are likely to receive favorable government action.

More universal and better health insurance is neither a Democratic-Republican nor a liberal-conservative issue. It is a practical question: will compulsory, universal insurance provide better control of costs and quality than we now have, and will it

assure more equitable access to needed services? Even the medical profession may ultimately end up advocating a national health insurance plan of some kind when it begins
to feel its freedom to manage patients threatened by the economic constraints applied
by corporate management, and more clearly perceives present government funding
cutback efforts as a threat not only to patient care but to the profession's own future.

Public indifference

A third explanation of the present problem is the public's relative indifference. At
the moment, public opinion is not sufficiently aroused to insist on any action, although
opinion polls usually show a large majority of Americans favoring universal health
insurance. In my own state of Massachusetts, for example, a referendum question
in the November 1986 ballot calling for such a plan was supported by two-thirds of
the voters. However, it is by no means clear that voters in my state or any other would
accept the increased taxes necessary to pay for such a system.

In any event, the present trend towards *less* public insurance is likely to continue
as long as the US public remain indifferent. Public opinion will begin to change only
when there has been more publicized evidence of the human costs of the present
inadequate treatment of the poor and near-poor. When that happens, the policy
pendulum which has been steadily moving towards privatization of health insurance
and increased individual responsibility for costs, is likely to reverse. Latent public
support for national health insurance has been there for a long time, but nothing
has happened yet because this support has not been politically mobilized. In my view,
it is only a question of time before better health insurance again becomes a major
public issue. My guess is that public ownership of hospitals or public employment
of the doctors, as in the UK's National Health Service, will never command much
support in the USA. Delivery of care mainly in the private sector, with funding mainly
in the public sector, is a much more likely outcome, although optional private funding
will surely remain as a choice.

New technology

Inadequate evaluation and ignorance of costs and benefits

A fourth major factor behind the current dilemma in health care is the rampant
proliferation of inadequately evaluated new technology and a general ignorance of
the relative costs and benefits of many of the tests, procedures and drugs now being
employed in the practice of medicine. Professor Teeling Smith has discussed the
'technology imperative', and I need not elaborate on it. But I should emphasize that
nowhere else in the world has there been a more explosive and varied development
of new medical technology than in the USA, or such commitment by practicing
physicians to the use of all types of technology, both old and new.

This type of practice, motivated by many factors, plays a major role in the continued
rise of per capita health care costs in the USA. Aging of the population and rising
public expectations are also important in generating costs, but an irresistible drive
to use more technology is the key. To the extent that this trend reflects genuine
technical progress and the widening application of ever-improving standards of care,

the technology explosion is both desirable and inevitable. But there is reason to believe that much deployment of technology is redundant, unnecessary or simply bad practice. This kind of inappropriate usage reflects excessive specialization among physicians, lack of adequate primary care, the economic incentives deriving from a piece-work reimbursement system which heavily favors procedures and tests over personal contacts between doctor and patient, and rising anxiety by physicians over malpractice liability.

The importance of technology assessment

I agree entirely with Professor Jennett that careful assessment of the safety, efficacy (comparative as well as absolute) and costs of medical technology is a critical requirement for the development of a rational, cost-effective medical care system. The sad fact is that much of the technology employed in practice has never been adequately evaluated. As a result, physicians are woefully ignorant about much of what they do, and are influenced at least as much by custom, authoritative opinion, advertising, personal clinical experience and economic self-interest as by hard, objective, published data. This state of affairs allows physicians, however well-intentioned, to follow their own biases in their style of practice. The result is that there are large variations from physician to physician and from place to place in the rate of use of various types of technology in the management of similar clinical conditions.

A much larger investment is needed in technology assessment to generate new, reliable information and to reduce the extent of the ignorance and ambiguity with which practitioners must contend. But more clinical trials and more reliable information are not enough. Better education and feedback techniques, more peer review and peer pressure, and ultimately more constraints by third-party payers will be needed to modify practitioner behavior. There will, of course, always be the need for discretion and individual variation in the way different patients with similar diagnoses are managed. No two patients are exactly the same. But what we urgently require is a much larger body of sound, clinically relevant information about the general characteristics of various technologies — their safety and effectiveness under various conditions, and their relative costs and efficacy compared with other available techniques. Without this kind of information, cost control can become arbitrary bureaucracy, but with these sorts of data available it becomes possible to design cost control measures which actually improve the quality of care and minimize the need for rationing.

The role of the physician

Such considerations lead finally to a consideration of the role of the physician. Unfortunately, all is not well with today's physicians. The medical profession in the USA, growing too numerous and too specialized, now finds itself buffeted by forces which threaten its economic future and impede the internal reforms necessary to encourage more socially responsible behavior. The profession needs help and guidance from society, which will have to decide whether it wants its doctors to be private commercial entrepreneurs, corporate employees or personal agents who are paid to serve the interests of their patients first and foremost. Depending on how this question is answered, laws and regulations governing licensure, anti-trust protection, tort liability, technology assessment, peer review, conflict of interest and the support of medical education can be drafted to help the profession better serve the public interest.

Doctors in America currently receive conflicting signals from society. They are expected to regulate themselves, but when they take collective action against incompetent or overcharging colleagues they become the targets of anti-trust litigation or personal injury suits. They are expected to use resources prudently, but get federally approved fees which reward high technology procedures far more lavishly than primary care and preventive services. Furthermore, they may be sued by patients for malpractice if they fail to employ all the technological resources available. They are exhorted to put the patient's interest ahead of all other considerations, but are given increasingly attractive economic incentives to do just the opposite in 'managed care' arrangements which offer them a share of the profits earned by withholding services.

It was only two decades ago that government policy was encouraging the expansion of medical schools and hospitals because of the general perception that we needed more physicians and more acute care facilities. Now the administration has declared that there is a surfeit of both physicians and hospital beds. It offers so far no specific plan for reducing these surpluses other than the competitive pressures of the market.

Summary

The problems with America's medical care are due more to a failure of the system than to absolute shortages of funds. Although the USA presently spends more per capita on health care than any other nation in the world we have been less successful than many others in providing access for all our citizens and in protecting them against the economic ravages of major illness and chronic disability. Present efforts at cost-containment rely primarily on the putative efficiency of the competitive market, but so far we have seen only a continued rise in costs and a further loss of equity.

In my opinion, our problems are not likely to be solved by the market. We will need a change in public opinion, and political pressure on the federal government to assume more responsibility. A successful, affordable universal insurance plan will require effective technology assessment and the co-operation of the medical profession. We will have to devise better ways of reimbursing our physicians that preserve professional morale and clinical autonomy, but which reduce the perverse incentives now driving us towards the excessive and inefficient use of technology, on the one hand, and the under-serving of pre-paid, managed care groups, on the other. This goal will not be easily achieved, and may be approached only in incremental steps, one state at a time. Nevertheless, I believe that a national health insurance plan of some kind is inevitable because nothing less will satisfy the needs and aspirations of the American people.

Discussion

(invited discussant *Howard Brody*)

Dr Brody

My purpose is to be an *agent provocateur* and I hope particularly, by comparison, to make Dr Relman appear an apologist on behalf of the medical profession.

We have heard evidence now from both sides of the Atlantic that there are identifiable human consequences of limited resources in health care which are negative in impact, and which are at least potentially preventable—or at least treatable. I would like to suggest that we might discuss what to do about them. It seems to me that physicians have a moral responsibility to address these problems and to seek solutions—although not physicians alone by any means as everyone has underlined so far.

In the UK the problem may well not be a result of a system failure but an issue of how much resource is available to the system, whereas I agree with Dr Relman that in the USA it is a system problem—and something needs to be done quickly.

What is the position of the medical profession in the two countries to do something and to exert the kind of moral and political leadership which seems to be called for to address these problems?

I would like to suggest that it is immeasurably better in the UK than in the USA and relates to the issue of 'clinical freedom'. Professor Jennett has covered the problem in the UK very well. If we cannot tell the difference between the three statements, 'benefiting our patients', 'we've always done it this way for 30 years, and are going to go on doing it', and 'it's what we feel like doing'; if all three are labelled 'clinical freedom', and physicians fight for clinical freedom, then we are in a very bad position to exert the kind of moral leadership that is necessary here. The British medical profession is in a much better position than the American to do something about this.

What has been the response of the medical profession in the USA to the problem that Dr Relman mentioned? As far as I can determine, it can best be described as 'whining'. If you have something that you can whine about with everyone who offers to dance with you, you finally find that you are the only one not dancing. The American medical profession seems to be in that situation now.

There have been two occasions in the history of the UK when the British government proposed to do something serious about health policy—national health insurance and the National Health Service (NHS), respectively. Each proposition involved physicians but they seemed to take advantage of the situation, and produced a system in which they had a good deal to say about how health care in Britain was to be managed.

In the USA since 1918, each time that new ideas in health care have been proposed American physicians have refused to 'dance', finding something at fault, or some reason for not dancing, after the proposal was made. They would not make any proposals themselves, but just reacted negatively. Finally, the physicians are now alone, everyone else is dancing and ignoring them.

When I came to the UK for the first time in 1984, it was interesting to see the furore over the limited drug list—the proposal that certain drugs would no longer be on the list for which the NHS would pay. There were screams of horror from British physicians that they had not been consulted about it. This was despite the fact that, as far as I could see, there was no evidence that any benefit to any patient would be jeopardized by not paying for certain brand-name drugs, and by insisting that British general practitioners should prescribe generic drugs in their place. It was an outrage that British physicians were not consulted.

In the USA, in 1984 the Tax, Equity and Fiscal Responsibility Act, the law that established the diagnosis related group scheme (which I think is the abysmal failure that Dr Relman has just described), went through Congress in 4 months with no input from the American medical profession, and no awareness on the part of organized medicine that this was happening. The reaction of physicians after it happened was not to be outraged, but to whine.

We can still see this happening today. At least in the community where I work, American physicians do not think that the problem in health care in the USA is either equity, quality of care or limited resources. They think that the big problem is malpractice. What do they do about it? They whine without doing anything positive. If American physicians wanted to do something about malpractice they could either put their own house in order and remove incompetent physicians from their ranks, or they could join forces with other segments of society outside medicine that are being hurt by the liability-tort system. The American medical profession is doing neither of those things and at present I see no prospects for the American medical profession to exert the kind of leadership that would be required to move us in that direction.

Dr Cooper mentioned earlier that the American Medical Association has a 'health policy', a health agenda for the American people. I do not see any positive movement in organized

American medicine towards the kinds of goals that Dr Relman has laid out, and I really wonder from where this will come.

Dr Rue

I was interested in these two papers and the fact that they were put together. It rather seemed as though, with a somewhat negative view of the NHS and a somewhat rosy view of what might occur in the USA, the two concepts of health care were coming quite close together. It could be said that the overt consequences of resource limitation, which are of course cash limits and manpower ceilings, have led to some evidence that we have better value for money, and that we can demonstrate this in the NHS.

I do not know whether people realize the very increased productivity that has occurred through the activities, mainly of the medical profession in this country who have given the lead in showing that there are indeed infinite lengths of resourcefulness to which doctors will go to undertake more work. That is the incentive which drives them, and the rewards which they give themselves in the NHS.

It even leads me to wonder whether the resources are as finite as they seem to be. Although both the manpower and the money are finite, what men and women in the medical profession will do in that situation seems to know no bounds. In the acute sector, in my own region during the last year, very broadly, with a 5% reduction of manpower there was a 10% increase in activity. That is one way of overcoming these problems.

I was interested in Dr Relman's point about there being lack of political (in terms of ballot box) interest in the state of health care in the USA. There was a similar lack of interest in the UK a few years ago when it seemed as though the NHS was being threatened by the politically inspired myth of the medical market place. It appeared that we were going to have imposed upon the NHS some of the features of the industrialized or commercial activities from across the Atlantic which have, as we have seen in this session, a different basis and different goals.

Some of us wondered what would happen, seeing in this threat the seeds of the destruction of the NHS as we know it. We tried to induce a higher political profile, and to make the NHS a topic which was talked about and discussed in electioneering terms. Until this revival, such interest had not been shown since the big public debate in 1948.

I do not quite know where that has led us, but it is very interesting that in this country we took the route, as it were, thoughtfully down that path which Dr Relman feels is needed now in the USA.

Finally, if anyone asks what is the evidence of the relative success of the NHS compared with the expensive system of health care in the USA, I would say that it is the virtual absence of the groups of disenfranchised or excluded patients. We have two categories, one in health care and one in social care, in this country, called the 'difficult to place' person. This is either the patient or the socially deprived person who somehow falls through the system. When I last reviewed the position in my region of 2¼ million people, I knew by name four people who had been known to me for some time, and who were also known personally to a Minister of State, as people whom the specialized system was failing.

There is also another system for primary health care where, of course, every individual has the right to have his own named doctor. Any UK citizen will be able to give the name of his or her own personal doctor — something that is not found in most other countries.

Dr Forsythe

The title of this session is primarily concerned with financial limitations, although Mr Taylor talked about the Government's limit on manpower through the setting of ceilings. We should not neglect the broader problem about manpower. In the UK, demographically, there is now the smallest number of school leavers for a very long time. There are dire consequences in my own region for recruiting to our nurse training schools and of other core staff needed to run a health service. There could be a real crisis in the next few years, not financial but in being unable to provide the form of delivery which we are trying to provide.

In particular, this will raise questions about whether or not we can move from the institutional form of care for the mentally retarded and the mentally ill. Also, the whole question about whether or not we will have to extend the roles of different types of health workers may well become crucial.

I would be very interested to know whether the USA has any potential manpower resource problem in the future in relation to workers in the health care field.

Dr Relman

I do not feel qualified to answer that in any detail, not having studied that rather complex question. Nursing is something of a problem in the USA. The number of nursing students is decreasing, and I think there will be a problem in the future unless some solutions are found.

Professor Reinhardt

It seems slightly odd that there is trouble recruiting when we read, certainly on our side of the Atlantic, of the high unemployment rates throughout Europe. It really means that the educational system is failing the nation. When there is so much unemployment, particularly among youth, it ought to be possible to recruit. The question has to be asked what is wrong with the British economy in general that could lead to such a paradox?

Mr Taylor

In relation to nursing for example, it is calculated that 50% of all girls leaving school at 16 will be required to supply the nursing manpower. It is not simply a matter of recruitment either because there is also a considerable fall-out. All kinds of factors could lead to that — and it may also occur in the USA — but certainly the fall-out rate in the UK identified by the nursing bodies is quite alarming and leads, I think, to the 50% figure required for recruitment.

Professor Pardes

Dr Relman feels that the citizens of the USA want everybody to receive appropriate care. I have some scepticism about whether that is reflected in the way people vote. I would imagine that for all citizens to receive appropriate care some additional resources will be needed — unless he thinks it just requires a redirection of resources. My reading of the American public attitude has been that there is a reluctance to see new taxes, but rather a steady inclination to reduce them. Perhaps that will change over the next few years.

Dr Relman

I mentioned the discrepancy between desire and willingness to pay. As for the desire, I think there is a little question here. Every public opinion poll that I have ever seen that addresses this question specifically, asking the American electorate what kind of insurance coverage they want, produces a majority saying they want broad coverage, publicly supported.

It remains to be seen what kind of price they are willing to pay for that — I concede Professor Pardes' point. Of course, the question of taxation in the USA at the moment has to be viewed in a very broad context. There are many reasons why US voters do not want to pay taxes. I do not think the reasons are specifically directed against taxes to support health care.

If, for example, some sort of meaningful poll could be conducted that asked voters what they wanted their tax money spent on, without increasing taxes, we might find that their priorities for public money spent on health care would be higher than for other things.

Professor Pardes

I would tend to agree. If I may refine the point slightly further, I can think of two instances. First, when the Carter administration came to power, there was at least an exploration to try to establish some kind of universal health care system — although it floundered.

Secondly, Dr Bowen is now suggesting catastrophe insurance. Has Dr Relman a view about that? My impression is that it is in trouble politically in Washington. I am not sure how far that proposal will go.

Here then are two instances, one which ostensibly preceded the greatest intensity of the taxpayer revolution of the late 1970s at the time of the Carter administration, but which politically could not be put through. The second is an initiative generated by this administration, and which I think is also in political trouble.

Dr Relman

The Carter initiative was a near miss—it came very close. What will happen to the Bowen proposal—and what would happen to any proposal now to the Reagan administration to spend more money—is another matter. I view that as an evanescent problem. If there is one thing that we learn from watching the American political process, it is that it never stands still, it is always changing, and what is 'out' this year may be 'in' 4 years from now.

Dr Bondurant

I was interested that both Mr Taylor and Dr Relman have interacted and, in a sense, addressed jointly the resource limitations and the design and operation of the systems for decisions about the allocation of resources. Granted that the two cannot be separated, in terms of the effectiveness of the application of the resources, would they both be brave enough to grade the size of the problem of resource limitation in the two systems at the present time? I suggest putting it on a scale of 1 to 10, with all the other problems in the system, beginning, for example, with lack of fundamental knowledge—then going on to other forms of lack of knowledge. How would they grade resource limitation as a limiting factor among all the others that might compromise our ability to deliver equitable, appropriate health care to the people?

Mr Taylor

That is very difficult. It depends upon whether we are talking at a national, regional or district level. Our system comes down from the Treasury through the Department of Health and Social Security to regions and then to districts. The Resource Allocation Working Party (RAWP) policy was started in 1976. It sets a mythical target of 100% of the entitlement of each region and district, and then tries to move everybody towards 100%. The Thames regions were all far beyond the 100%; some other regions, including my own, were well below. That sort of rationalization is producing a strong reaction, as can be imagined, because it is much easier to get a little more than to give up what we already have. It has been a major problem for the Thames regions around London, who have been under particular pressure. I think this has been recognized by the Government recently—although we do not quite know what that means.

If we are talking about resource limitation at that level, it is a considerable problem and an enormous occupier of management time. If we are going to have strategic plans for the services provided, and administer them with due regard to the equity, if you like, of how those services reach all the people they should reach, it becomes a very difficult task to do that against a moving target of resource allocation. One of the frustrations of our system, as I think those at regional level will agree, is that a great deal of time is spent doing planning work against an expected resource allocation figure which changes, and therefore we have to start doing it again.

I do not say for a moment that it can be avoided in this country. I do not believe that is possible. It is subject to all kinds of winds that blow—economic status, political aspirations, public expectations, and so on. There are all kinds of pressures, so there will never be a straight line that we can count on. It is very difficult to put that in the system priorities.

Dr Relman

I have always believed that money limitation is not the main problem in the American health care system, but the way we spend it. We simply do not manage ourselves very well. It is also a political problem, as I have said, and a growing one.

As an aside, I have emphasized what I think to be the important problem of doctor ignorance. I do not say this in any pejorative sense. We do not have the necessary hard convincing evidence about so many of the things that we do and that we ought to have in order to practise rationally and efficiently. In addition, there is a new kind of ignorance with which we have to deal. As part of the cost-containment programme in Washington our sources of information are beginning to dry up. This is because the agencies and the activities that ought now more than ever to be gathering the kind of hard quantitative information needed about the performance of our health care system are no longer there. That really is a 'catch 22' situation.

Professor Rabkin

One of the consequences of resource limitation is out-of-plan use. In the USA we are seeing growing interest in what is called the 'health maintenance organization (HMO) with choice'. That is, the individual stays within the HMO, but he can also go elsewhere. He will not be penalized, but it will cost more. What has happened in the UK with the use of private health care?

Mr Taylor

A certain amount of private health care is completely separate from the NHS; in other words, there are private nursing homes, and people who work 100% in the private sector and have no part in the NHS. There are also private beds in many of the hospitals. Government departmental approval has to be obtained for the number of beds so designated, so there is an integration, in that sense, between the private and the public sectors.

Because of the pressure on hospitals in the health service, there is now some pressure from the government to use the private facilities by actually buying services from the private sector. It is possible to buy a certain number of hip operations, tonsil and adenoids operations and so on, in order to relieve waiting lists and shortages which may occur in a given district.

That is quite an emotive and politically sensitive matter, particularly in those districts with a Labour party majority and a substantial number of Labour party members on the health authority. There are those in the Labour party who want to see no private medicine, and certainly none integrated into the health service.

There are a number of problems. Although many districts could reduce their waiting lists by contracting out, the facilities are not always in the right place. There is not an even provision across the country. The vast majority of the private facilities are in the south-east of England and not in the north where I come from. A particular operation may not therefore be readily available in some of the districts where it is most needed.

Professor Rabkin

If the resource limitation is not felt by the average citizen to be onerous, he or she might wait until a turn would come within the health service. To the extent that it becomes increasingly onerous, they might be willing to divert money in that direction rather than somewhere else. Is there greater use of private health services today or is it essentially the same as a few years ago? Do the people feel that the limitations are more onerous than they were a few years ago?

Professor Maynard

The size of the private sector is about £600 million. About 1 in 5 cold elective procedures in the south-east are now private as opposed to 1 in 8 in England as a whole. About 4·5–4·8 million people are covered by private insurance. Coverage grew very rapidly during the period 1979–81, then developed what can only be described in American terms as a major cost-containment problem.

The other way of looking at it is to say that the avarice of the doctors overtook the system. Also, utilization rates went up sharply because premiums had not been set very carefully. As a result, the growth of the private sector has been slow during the last 3 or 4 years, and it is down to about 4% in coverage terms.

Dr Relman

Did I understand correctly that the total expenditure on health care in the private sector is very small?

Professor Maynard

It is about £600 million in comparison to nearly £20 billion on the NHS in the UK—so it is extremely small. Some privatization has also taken place in the care of the elderly, the mentally ill and the mentally handicapped. In the usual way that governments operate, it has developed as a result of their inadequacy in framing social security legislation. This has made many people eligible for cash benefits, so there has been a great expansion of private care financed by the social security budget in these chronic sectors.

Dr Relman

Some of my colleagues in the USA have told me that I ought to find out if there is a wildfire epidemic of expanding private services in this country—but that is not the case?

Professor Maynard

There is almost no private sector in primary care. It is very small in the acute sector (excluding elective surgery), and its rate of growth is now low due to the industry's inability to control its costs.

Mr Taylor

The only growth of any significance—and even that is small—is in residential homes in the private sector. This is being fed by supplementary benefit, invalid allowances and so on.

Mr Lewin

The title for this session could well have been rewritten as 'Resource limitation: cause or effect?'. The contrast has been shown very nicely.

I agree with Dr Relman that resource limitation is not a cause of the differences in the US system, but rather an effect—but an effect of *what*? To a very large extent, I think it is a function of two of the points he made, a combination of public attitudes and political leadership.

We are dealing with an area in which the public rarely rise up in a grassroots way and demand radical change. The fact that the political leadership in the USA focuses on priorities other than equal access to care is clearly part of it—I think that did not begin with the Reagan administration but probably at the very end of the Nixon administration and certainly during the Carter administration. What is interesting, and I think fascinating, is why the public have been so unresponsive. It is important to have an understanding of where the American public stand on, and what are their perceptions about, the relationship between health care, poverty and well-being.

This will be discussed later. The one observation I would make now is that, to try to gain that understanding, I have found it helpful to recognize that people divide their thinking about the health care system rather cleanly between the quality of the health care that is available to *them* and the access to health care that they want to be made available to *others*. Many people will argue for a strong health care system in terms of what would be there for *them*, in terms of access, quality and cost when *they* become ill and need the care. A whole different set of priorities, sensitivities and concerns arises when the question is what should be made accessible to *others*.

One of the things that I hoped to find at this conference was a better understanding of the differences between our societies—which, after all, have so much in common—with respect to that question. Is it differences in homogeneity or some of the sociological differences; are there historical differences, or are there some differences related to the delivery system itself?

The argument that I shall make in my presentation is that for some of these answers we need to look beyond the financing system and more towards the organization of services.

I think Dr Relman has pointed us in the right directions, although I would come up with some very different answers. I do not believe that we are even creeping towards national health insurance, although I believe we are moving towards some form of universal coverage which will be sufficiently broad and pluralistic to meet the whole range of goals laid out by Professor Stevens, but will not be as cleanly organized as either the Canadian or the UK system.

PREVENTION: A POLITICAL OR PERSONAL PRIORITY?

1. Can prevention be cost-effective?

Chairman:
SIR RAYMOND HOFFENBERG
London, UK

Introduction

SIR RAYMOND HOFFENBERG

President, The Royal College of Physicians, London, UK

There seem to be three questions that need to be answered about prevention:

(1) Does a particular preventive measure work or not? Some such measures are clear-cut (for example, we know that reduction in smoking would work), but others are perhaps more controversial and therefore need to be considered in a different light.

(2) If a particular preventive measure is known to work, can it be implemented? In the UK, even with such things as immunization, the record is not particularly good. There is obviously also a need elsewhere for known successful preventive measures to be implemented properly.

(3) Can prevention be cost-effective? This itself raises the question of what that phrase actually means. Does it confine itself to consideration of financial cost, in which case reasonably exact figures could probably be put on some preventive measures but not on others? Alternatively, are we talking about cost-effectiveness in terms of extension of life and reduction of suffering and, if so, how are these to be measured? There was some reference to that earlier, in terms of quality adjusted life years (QALYs).

Health Care Provision under Financial Constraint, edited by T. B. Binns and M. Firth, 1988: Royal Society of Medicine International Congress and Symposium Series No. 115, published by Royal Society of Medicine Services Ltd.

A UK view

ALWYN SMITH

Professor of Epidemiology and Social Oncology, Department of Epidemiology and Social Oncology, University of Manchester and University Hospital of South Manchester, Manchester, UK

Some preliminary clarification of terms

In an ideally managed world, both the costs and the benefits of all public policies would be precisely assessed in commensurable terms so that the population or its political representatives might make informed choices as to which policies should be pursued and what proportion of common resources should be devoted to them. We do not live in such an ideally managed world. In most cases, neither the costs nor the benefits are known with any precision; to the extent that they are identifiable, they are rarely expressible in commensurable terms, and reference to the public is usually in terms of rhetoric rather than reason. Many public enterprises delegate their decision-making in a haphazard way to those who work in them. In health services, and especially in the National Health Service (NHS) of the UK, most policy decisions are pre-empted by the health professionals who effectively allocate resources at their individual discretion and defend themselves, if challenged, in emotional rather than economic terms. This might be acceptable if the resources available to the NHS were more than enough to meet the demands made on it. If this were ever the case, it plainly is no longer. Increasingly, the consciousness of restraint on expenditure is prompting questions about effectiveness. So far, these have mainly been directed to issues in respect of which innovation is proposed and to those functions within the NHS that are directed to the maintenance of health rather than to its restoration. Thus, it is the cost-effectiveness of prevention that is in question.

There can be few commonplaces more trite than the often-repeated slogan that 'prevention is better than cure'. Unless the word 'better' be clearly defined, it is difficult to attach much meaning to the claim, still less to assess its validity. It is obvious enough that it is usually better not to incur a disease that can be avoided, provided that all other things are equal, but it is also obvious that they rarely are. Most benefits are acquired at a cost, and the full appraisal of the costs and benefits of prevention would require that both costs and benefits be assigned to those who

Health Care Provision under Financial Constraint, edited by T. B. Binns and M. Firth, 1988: Royal Society of Medicine International Congress and Symposium Series No. 115, published by Royal Society of Medicine Services Ltd.

bear or enjoy them, since benefits enjoyed by individuals may be at a cost to the community and all costs represent benefits foregone.

In practice, it is usually extremely difficult to evaluate both the costs and the benefits of preventive procedures and particularly to express both in commensurable terms. It has generally been found simpler to study the prevention of diseases with lethal consequences, since death has an immediate notional cost and may be expressed in terms of years of life lost when compared with general expectation. If we make the reasonable assumption that all years of life lost have similar value, we have a reasonable initial basis for comparison of different preventive or therapeutic procedures in terms of their cost per life or year of life saved.

The cost of a preventive procedure must include not only the resource costs involved in supplying and delivering the procedure but also any social costs incurred by those upon whom it is carried out. For example, time expended in travelling to and keeping appointments is often difficult to assess, while the costs of complications such as those which may attend some immunization procedures may be particularly difficult to quantify. In cost-effectiveness studies of disease prevention against treatment, the costs of allowing a preventable disease to occur must include the resource and social costs associated with treatment.

Some particular difficulties in the study of prevention

Distinguishing between prevention and cure

One of the many difficulties in assessing prevention is that of distinguishing preventive from curative procedures. The treatment of raised arterial pressure is an example, since the purpose of such treatment is essentially the prevention of the disabling consequences that may arise in people whose pressure is high. Screening for the early stages of processes which may progress to become disabling or life-threatening is particularly problematic. Screening for pre-malignant neoplasia of the cervix may reasonably be classified as preventive, but screening for early breast cancer is difficult to categorize as preventive since the detectable condition is the early established disease.

Preventive measures unrelated to health

Many other procedures that are preventive in effect often lie quite outside the domain of health professional or health service responsibility. The preservation of both international and domestic peace, the assurance of worthwhile and gainful employment to everyone, the provision of a range and variety of food that ensures that what is healthy is identifiable, attractive and affordable, a safe transport system, fit housing and adequate education, are all fundamental and well-established pre-conditions of the public health. Nevertheless, appropriate policies are unlikely to be pursued so energetically in the absence of sustained advocacy from those able to identify their relevance to the public health.

Application of preventive methods to groups not at risk

Another complication is that, whereas it is obvious enough that preventive measures have inevitably to be applied to people who are not ill, it is slightly less obvious that they have often to be applied to many people, sometimes the majority, who would not incur the disease even in the absence of the measures. For example, we aim to immunize all newborn individuals against a range of infectious diseases, many of which would affect only a minority of children even in the absence of protection. Unfortunately, we have no means of identifying those who would contract the diseases if unprotected. A further complication is that it may often be more effective to direct preventive measures against the majority of people who are at no more than average identifiable risk of a disease than against a minority who are identifiably at much above average risk. This 'prevention paradox', as Rose has called it (1), applies to a variety of conditions ranging from Down's syndrome, through alcohol-related diseases to stroke and myocardial infarction, in which identifiable risk factors are approximately normally distributed in the population and, in spite of a sharp association of incidence with risk, a majority of cases occur among those in the centre of the distribution. Thus, for the individuals in a population, it is difficult to represent as directly relevant to them preventive measures which may be highly desirable for the population as a whole.

Assessment of efficacy of prevention

Finally, a particular difficulty in the assessment of prevention is that of being sure either that cases have been prevented or that their non-occurrence is reasonably attributable to the measures for which preventive claims are being made. For example, the incidence of cancer of the tongue has declined in this country, and a case might be made for attributing the decline to improved dental hygiene, but it would be difficult to eliminate a number of other possible explanations for at least part of the decline. The recent decline in mortality from both stroke and myocardial infarction in many countries may possibly be due to changes in general lifestyle, but controversy continues to rage about this question and we may never know the answer.

More difficult questions are raised in relation to the profound changes in age-specific mortality rates that have occurred in this country, as in others, during the past 200 years. Since these changes are quite possibly the most significant in the entire history of the human species, it is both remarkable and disappointing that we cannot attribute them at all confidently to any credible circumstances or procedures. All that we can reasonably assert is that very little of the profound decline in mortality can be attributed to measures specifically designed to bring about such change.

The difficulty can be much greater for diseases whose incidence is variable. Cynics have pointed out that the frequent decline of an epidemic after the introduction of emergency measures must really be attributed to the general tendency for what has gone up to come down. It is rarely feasible to subject preventive measures to randomized controlled trial. The few examples where this has been seriously attempted are nearly all flawed in their design or interpretation.

Is there much scope for prevention?

The scope for prevention is often held to be limited by lack of knowledge of the causes of disease and the determinants of health. There are clearly many diseases whose aetiology remains fragmentary or baffling, but very few for which we know nothing at all of the circumstances in which they occur. The general determinants of health may be said to be specifiable at least in outline, and the requirements for improved health may be stated with considerable confidence. This confidence is not based solely on the findings of medical science or on the experience of medical practice. Doctors are not alone in their centuries-long concern about, and responsibility for, the application of biological science and practical wisdom to the promotion of the welfare of living creatures. Farmers have always been similarly engaged and with conspicuous success. The general principles for public health are not dissimilar from those of animal husbandry. Put at their simplest, they involve the promotion of an appropriate environment and lifestyle, a reduction in the frequency of accidents and a programme of policies and services for securing these desiderata. There is little evidence that the maintenance of a healthy environment and lifestyle and the prevention of accidents are more costly than the neglect of these requirements, and there is some evidence, for example, that if northern Europeans cultivated a diet more nearly like that of southern Europe, there would be economic gains in addition to the probable gains in health.

Addictive substances

Some of the important general requirements for better public health are worth brief consideration although detailed appraisal of their cost-effectiveness may not be possible. A topical issue is the use of addictive substances. There can be little doubt that elimination of tobacco use and substantial reduction in the national consumption of alcohol would represent important preventive measures.

Similarly, the numerically smaller problem of the misuse of prescribed psychotropic drugs, and the even smaller but more publicly disturbing use of such drugs as cocaine and heroin, represent clear targets for preventive action. We know very little of the factors that determine the prevalence of the use of these drugs, and such action as has been taken against them has usually been aimed at influencing their marketing — especially in the case of cocaine and heroin. The factors that dispose people to seek the solace afforded by such substances remain under-researched and poorly understood, and the potential costs of controlling these factors are almost wholly indeterminate. The cost-effectiveness of seeking to prevent their use in the interests of limiting the damage that they do is similarly uninvestigated, but it seems likely that the benefits would be felt in many areas other than public health. It is also difficult to believe that the reconstruction of society in the interests of reducing the perceived need for addictive substances would not be cost-effective.

Work

Work is probably the single most important factor in determining health. Almost all animal species must work to survive, and it is their characteristic organization of work that has permitted human beings to achieve substantial control of the quality and duration of their usual lifespan. Nevertheless, the particular divisions of labour characteristic of industrial societies have determined a substantial variation in the health experience both of workers and of their dependants. A more equitable distribution both of work and of its rewards would undoubtedly bring great improvements in health as well as other benefits. It is also difficult to see how it would cost more than the present distribution which results in many people's health being impaired by excessive and dangerous work, while others suffer from the poor rewards associated with both unemployment and undervalued labour.

Sexual behaviour

Sexual behaviour is one of the aspects of lifestyle that has been incriminated as potentially hazardous to health. In the world as a whole, its principal adverse effect on health is probably due to its responsibility for excessive pregnancy and child-bearing. There are a number of infectious diseases which are characteristically spread by sexual activity—the most dramatically lethal of these at the present time is probably acquired immune deficiency syndrome (AIDS), although cervical cancer is a serious contender. The costs of preventing these diseases are extremely difficult to specify, still less to quantify, and much will depend on how easy it turns out to produce and distribute appropriate vaccines or to treat the infections. The social costs of the behavioural measures currently being advocated for their control have not yet seriously been addressed, and their assessment is unlikely to be either easy or uncontroversial.

Homicide

Homicide continues to be an important cause of loss of human life, and the promotion of mass homicide for political and territorial purposes shows little sign of diminishing. The diversion of resources into preparation for such homicide undoubtedly represents one of the major impediments to the development of public health policies in most countries, and especially in those with a commitment to expensive and obsolescent military technologies. It is difficult to believe that a general commitment to the renunciation of war would be either costly or ineffective in promoting better health.

Waste disposal

Perhaps the most controversial topics in the economics of prevention concern the control of the disposal of wastes. It was in the control of pollution by animal (mainly human) excreta that modern disease prevention first established its credentials, and the heavy costs of providing clean water and safe sewage disposal were justified by a range of other gains apart from those in public health. The control of pollution by industrial wastes has not so far proved so simple or so socially acceptable, and a particularly difficult range of problems arises from the wastes associated with energy conversion. The costs of limiting pollution from internal combustion engines are undoubtedly heavy—as have been those associated with other industrial energy requirements.

The newest problem concerns the use of nuclear energy and the associated release of ionizing radiation, both as a long-term hazard of so far indeterminate effect on health and as an occasional accident with potentially more serious effects. At present, our knowledge both of the economics and of the epidemiology of radiation hazards must be said to be rudimentary and problematic.

Costs and benefits of prevention: the case of cervical screening

Few preventive measures have been subjected to any kind of appraisal of their benefits, costs or cost-effectiveness. In seeking to remedy this state of affairs, it is probably wise to acknowledge that such appraisal is simply not feasible for two important kinds of preventive measure. First, those which are concerned with the general quality of human life or the human environment rather than specifically with health. These include such important issues for health as housing, clean air, wholesome food, general prosperity and the maintenance of peace. The second kind includes all therapeutically intended interventions that have preventive effects, such as the treatment of infectious disease, the rectification of physiological deviations that both incommode their sufferers and threaten their future health or survival, the closure of wounds and the reduction of fractures, and such measures as the provision of obstetric care.

More specifically preventive procedures—usually directed at individuals—are generally more tractable. Some of these are so effective and cost so little that their cost-effectiveness is not usually called in question. Most of the immunization procedures used to protect children from the common infectious diseases fall into this category, although vaccines against some virus infections are extremely expensive and their cost-effectiveness may depend upon restriction of their use to high-risk sections of the population.

Screening for cervical cancer

A preventive measure which has been subjected to fairly extensive appraisal is screening by cytology for the pre-malignant stages of cervical neoplasia. The complexity of its assessment and of the issues it raises make it an instructive example. In most industrialized countries there has been substantial deployment of resources on cervical screening, and in very few has there been unequivocal evidence of a favourable effect. Were it not for the experience of Sweden and Finland, it would be difficult to justify.

When cytological screening for cervical cancer was first introduced, it was welcomed as a particularly important advance in the prevention of cancer and one which might herald a whole series of analogous opportunities to detect and treat neoplasia at a pre-malignant and pre-symptomatic stage. After some 40 years its value remains controversial . Although the screening test is relatively non-invasive and simple to carry out, its delivery as a population screening procedure has turned out to be full of problems. The poor response to invitations to undergo the test has often been interpreted as arising from modesty, apathy or a fear of the discovery of cancer. More recently, it has become clearer that, in common with many preventive procedures, response is a function more of how the service is offered than of the psychology of the clients. Nevertheless, there is evidence from many countries that the test is disproportionately carried out on women of child-bearing age, where it can be included as part of the established examination procedures associated with pregnancy, child-bearing or the provision of contraceptive advice. Those at maximum risk of incurring the disease are beyond child-bearing and are also disproportionately in the less privileged sections of the community where routine 'check-ups' are not yet a cultural norm. Thus, a heavy concentration of screening resources is usually devoted to those at least risk, while those at greatest risk go unscreened.

In most countries where cervical cytological screening has been in use, the incidence of and mortality from cervical cancer has changed very little, if at all. Although there is some evidence that there might have been a rise in incidence had it not been in use, the usual conclusion drawn is that screening has been relatively ineffective. Roberts and his colleagues have suggested on the basis of UK data that some 30 000 examinations are conducted for each life saved and that the resources involved in the exercise make its cost-effectiveness unacceptably low (2). In the UK, the proponents of cervical screening have tended to reply that this is because government policy discourages frequent screening, especially screening of the young, and that what is required is a greater concentration on young women and more frequent screening than the 5-year frequency which official policy commends.

The Swedish and Finnish experience

Two countries in which cervical cytological screening has been associated with a substantial reduction in mortality from cervical cancer are Sweden and Finland. In both cases mortality has fallen by more than 50% over the last two decades. There are, of course, many differences between these two countries and the others (including the UK) where mortality has changed little. They are countries with a high gross national product of which a large proportion (about 10%) is expended on health services and where there has been a political tradition that favours public health as a major social objective. There is a belief that the people of these countries are more compliant in respect of both governmental and professional advice, although little evidence has been advanced to support this. What does seem to distinguish the cervical screening in these countries from most others is that they have achieved regular coverage of the whole adult female population, and that the design of the screening management systems has had high coverage as their objective.

Screening interval

Computer simulation studies of the natural history of the cervical neoplastic sequence and the expected effect of various screening strategies have generally suggested that screening all adult women at intervals of about 5 years would reduce prevailing mortality levels by some 85% (3). These studies also suggest that variations in screening interval around this frequency make little difference, and that the major requirements for cost-effectiveness are full coverage of the adult female population and regular re-examination. Obviously, little effect would be observed if the techniques of taking or examining smears were faulty, or if women in whom pre-malignant abnormality is detected were not referred for appropriate further investigation and treatment. Since the major costs of cervical screening lie in the basic screening, there is little to be said for economizing on further investigation of those found to have abnormal lesions.

Cost-effectiveness of cervical screening

If technically effective screening were carried out at 5-year intervals on all adult women in the age range 20–60 years, 85% of all potential cancers should be detected at a pre-malignant stage and could be treated. In the UK, this would represent a cost-effectiveness of about 1000 examinations per life saved. Reducing the interval to

3 years would result in about 90% detection at some 60% greater cost and a consequent cost-effectiveness of approximately 1600 examinations per life saved. Annual screening would detect about 93% at a cost-effectiveness approaching 5000 examinations per life saved.

The average costs of individual examinations are probably lowest when coverage is lowest and will almost certainly rise as coverage increases, as is usually the case. The marginal utility is difficult to estimate but it will probably be necessary to accept less than complete coverage and a consequent reduction in the proportion of cancers prevented. The point at which the cost-effectiveness of cervical screening rules out the wisdom of seeking a more complete coverage is difficult to evaluate, but there can be little doubt that in a country where coverage is low it makes much more sense to use resources to improve coverage, rather than to use them to increase the frequency of screening among those already being covered. Similar resources would be involved in screening 40% of the population at 3-yearly intervals or 80% at 6-yearly intervals, and the yield of prevented cancers would be almost twice as great from the latter strategy unless that 40% of the population could be identified as those at greatest risk. Although the general characteristics of women at higher risk can be specified, it is difficult to list the individuals involved and complete coverage remains the first objective.

Estimates of the cost of cervical screening are difficult to make and a variety of guesses have been used in the debates on its cost-effectiveness. A figure that is commonly used in the UK is £10 per examination — an amount which is believed to represent all costs directly associated with the examinations as well as those consequential to the discovery of abnormality in approximately 1% of examinations. On this assessment, each pre-cancerous case would cost some £10 000 to detect in a well managed system adopting a 5-yearly screening frequency, but in an inefficiently managed system the cost per case detected may well be as high as £300 000.

How far is cost-effectiveness relevant?

At the outset, an ideally managed world was envisaged as providing for the general assessment of costs and benefits of policy options and for democratic decisions as the basis for policy choice. It is not clear that prevention would receive more favourable emphasis in such a world than in the one we have. There is evidence that most decisions are made on the basis of the values attached to the various options and that these correlate poorly with either their costs or their effectiveness.

Most people want access to treatment or care if they are ill but, although they do not wish to become ill, they tend to assume that they will remain healthy provided that they avoid identifiable gross hazards to health. Most preventive measures available at present require positive commitment to them in a cultural environment which makes that difficult. There would be enormous gains in health if no one smoked, drank alcohol or ate too much, but individuals cannot be expected to make these apparently simple healthy choices while they are so sharply in conflict with cultural norms reinforced by their profitability to those whose influence is greatest.

The issue of the cost-effectiveness of prevention has arisen because the allocation of common resources to what is in the public interest has suffered from competition with what is in the interests of minorities who largely determine the priorities, and because prevention continues to be seen as mainly the province of the same services and the same professions that are responsible for the treatment and the care of the sick. If the maintenance of public health were seen as one of the central objectives of public policy it would probably determine a very different allocation of general resources. No one seems to ask whether the maintenance of law and order or the defence of territory is cost-effective, which is surely because they are seen as imperatives whose costs must always be met. By contrast, the maintenance of public health is seen as an alternative to the treatment of disease and is required to demonstrate that it is just as cost-effective in spite of the difficulty of equating the benefits of health maintenance with those of health restoration.

References

(1) Rose G. Strategy of prevention: lessons from cardiovascular disease. *Br Med J* 1981; **282**: 1847–51.
(2) Roberts CJ, Farrow SC, Charny MC. How much can the NHS afford to spend to save a life or avoid a severe disability? *Lancet* 1985; **i**: 89–91.
(3) Parkin DM, Moss SM. An evaluation of screening policies for cervical cancer in England and Wales using a computer simulation model. *J Epidemiol Community Health* 1986; **40**(2): 143–53.

A US view

SAM SHAPIRO

Professor Emeritus, Department of Health Policy and Management;
Past Director, Health Services Research and Development Center,
School of Hygiene and Public Health, The Johns Hopkins University,
Baltimore MD, USA

A framework

The question, 'Can prevention be cost-effective', can be interpreted as a challenge to prevention which needs to be dealt with only on a technical level. But the issues involved are too slippery for such an approach and we are not likely to get very far without some common understandings. The following is offered as a framework:

Given the nature of the conference, our major concern is with primary and secondary prevention based on actions taken by providers, individually or in alliance with others. Excluded are measures directed at environmental and occupational hazards, most external causes of injury and death, and primary prevention of alcohol and drug abuse. Included are immunizations, early detection of disease which may take various forms, including the periodic health examination, and counseling in personal health practices (e.g. smoking, diet, exercise) aimed at reducing risks for adverse health conditions.

Many factors affect the attitude of providers towards health promotion and disease prevention. Acceptable levels of reimbursement for diagnostic services and added time in counseling may head the list. However, belief in the efficacy of procedures advocated and communication skills would affect the rate of application of preventive measures.

Nor should we overlook the critically important part played by other conditions which influence both effectiveness and costs. Effective links with individuals for preventive care depend upon the population's health care seeking behavior, access to care, attitudes and knowledge. Further, organizational and financial characteristics of the delivery system and the nature of its support services can affect how receptive the population is to preventive measures and the likelihood of reaching high-risk groups; also, whether steps are taken to enhance on-going management and to reinforce advice on personal health practices.

Health Care Provision under Financial Constraint, edited by T. B. Binns and M. Firth, 1988: Royal Society of Medicine International Congress and Symposium Series No. 115, published by Royal Society of Medicine Services Ltd.

A criterion for judging cost-effectiveness is needed, and the one advanced by Doubilet *et al.* (1) for decision-making in medicine has considerable appeal for our wider purposes. One strategy is viewed as

> more cost-effective than another if it is (a) less costly and at least as effective, (b) more effective and more costly, its additional benefit being worth its additional cost or (c), less effective and less costly, the added benefit of the rival strategy not being worth its extra cost.

In (b) and (c) there are three elements: benefits, costs and value judgments which empiricists seek to quantify but which others (e.g. policy makers, program developers) will, in many instances, arrive at on a qualitative basis influenced by more general economic, societal or political considerations.

Cost-containment pressures to hold the line on new services, and increases in the content of existing services which reduce productivity, would act as a brake on the introduction of preventive measures if we depended exclusively on the relationship between health care costs and outcomes. This can be taken as a major message of scholarly reports that have appeared over about the past 10 years and of the recent interesting book, *Is prevention better than cure?*, by Louise Russell (2). The answer offered to the question posed in the title is that, most often, prevention adds to medical expenditures not only in the short run but quite likely in the long run as well. The case is made through careful analyses of past vaccination, screening and exercise programs.

Issues can be raised about the selection of examples, the treatment of uncertainties about measures of risks, benefits and costs, and other technical and conceptual matters. But the heaviest fire the book has drawn can be traced to the title (3). 'Better' implies value judgments which include more than the balance between costs and benefits in morbidity, mortality and quality of years of life. Russell makes quite clear that she is aware of the importance of judgments, but this view is blurred by the far greater attention given to quantifying cost-effectiveness, with the result that prevention, generally, is placed on the defensive.

Status of preventive measures

What is actually going on in the USA with respect to prevention and how strong are the interests in formal cost-effectiveness analysis? It is between 6 and 7 years since the US Surgeon General's report, *Healthy people* (4), appeared and only 3 to 4 years from 1990, the target year for meeting the objectives subsequently identified as achievable through health promotion and disease prevention efforts (5). Also, prevention is very much alive as a public policy goal. It is high on the agenda of government and voluntary health agencies, and strong forces are being generated to enlarge the scope of involvement by health care providers. What distinguishes the present period from the past is the broad front along which activities are being stimulated. A few examples will illustrate the point:

> In 1984, the Office of Disease Prevention and Health Promotion, US Department of Health and Human Services (6), taking a leaf from the Canadian Task Force on the Periodic Health Examination (7), established the US Task Force on Preventive Services*. Its mission is
>
> to develop recommendations based on the best available scientific evidence for the appropriate use of preventive services by health care providers.

*For parallel developments see Task Force reports (8) and Breslow and Somers (9).

Clusters of preventive interventions are being developed for specific age–sex groups, risk categories and conditions, based on the Canadian Task Force's rules of evidence on effectiveness that are applied to information derived from the literature. Criteria for selection of a preventive measure include assessments of the current burden on the individual and society of suffering and costs resulting from morbidity, functional impairment and mortality attributable to the preventable condition.

The Centers for Disease Control have just announced awards to three academically based centers to engage in research and demonstration in health promotion and disease prevention. The National Cancer Institute (NCI) has issued a request for research grant applications (RFA)* designed

to identify and remedy key factors that contribute to avoidable mortality from specific cancer sites in defined populations.

The RFA aims at interventions that affect delivery of health services. Research and demonstration related to primary prevention interventions are covered by other initiatives of NCI's Division of Cancer Prevention and Control.

The Health Care Financing Administration is expected to issue shortly a request for proposals for demonstration programs of 4 years' duration

to reduce disability and dependency [among Medicare beneficiaries] through provision of preventive health services. . . .

Such services are defined as including health screenings, health risk appraisals, immunizations and lifestyle counseling and instruction. Evaluation is directed at determining short- and long-term costs and benefits of providing preventive health services. Alternative methods of payment for these services (e.g. pre-payment, fee-for-service) are to be tested.

Questions can be raised whether the funding and duration of the research and evaluation provided for would be adequate to produce convincing evidence through a number of these efforts. However, for the purposes of this presentation, the important point is that in each instance there is a sharp focus on health care providers and the delivery systems within which they are functioning. Underlying this are the following: first, that we have been experiencing substantial reductions in mortality from highly prevalent chronic conditions and in infant mortality, with health services sharing in the credit; secondly, the observation that large mortality differentials exist in the population which might be diminished through preventive services effectively delivered to disadvantaged groups; thirdly, the possibility that in this period of rapid change in organization and financing of health services, there are new opportunities to reorient providers towards preventive services; and, finally, the sense that a large part of the task is to deliver efficiently what we can prudently conclude works.

Costs are not ignored, but formal cost-effectiveness analysis appears to be relegated, in most instances, to the function of fine-tuning rather than being a tool for larger policy decisions. This should not be too surprising in view of the emphasis on the effectiveness side of the equation, the diversity among payors for health services and what motivates them to foster preventive health care.

It could be argued that prevention, regardless of how the costs are met, is a matter of public concern and subject to scrutiny in a cost-effectiveness model. Indeed, this is the point of departure for many of the publications on cost-effectiveness from academics and the US Office of Technology Assessment (10–13). The reality is that individuals with means can purchase any services offered by providers. The result is high levels of selectivity in who obtain the services and who are left out. Strong advocacy programs of voluntary agencies, such as the American Cancer Society (ACS), and professional societies, as well as public health agencies, seek to overcome

*Request for application.

this problem through education and promotion. However, dependency on out-of-pocket payment decreases the possibility that a preventive measure deliverable by providers will have sufficient penetration to affect the health status of the general population or that it will reach vulnerable subgroups. This does not mean that cost-effectiveness has no role, but that its saliency for public policy action is lessened.

Decisions about coverage of new preventive services by non-governmental health insurance plans do affect large segments of the population, and costs are a major consideration but not in a cost-effectiveness context. More important are competitiveness of premiums and attractiveness of new benefits to the consumer. The potential for savings in the long term is too remote to enter significantly into the calculations. No uniform response can be expected from either the fee-for-service sector of health insurance or pre-paid, capitated systems, and coverage of new preventive services will develop unevenly. This would change, of course, if government or large contractor groups mandated their inclusion, or they became ingrained in professional standards of quality of care as in the case of childhood immunizations and hypertension control.

The situation is different for reimbursement programs funded by government, principally Medicare for the aged and Medicaid for the poor. Inclusion of preventive services has been resisted, because it results in a universal entitlement for large groups of people and could generate substantial new costs. Clearly, here is an arena where cost-effectiveness might be expected to flourish, even in the absence of a fixed budget within which new proposed preventive services would need to compete for resources with existing services. The pressures for cost-containment are severe and, subject to limitations of available data, advocates of change attempt to grapple with cost and effectiveness issues while, at the same time, bringing to bear the weight of societal and political considerations.

There are many examples to draw upon to illustrate circumstances that influence use and non-use of cost-effectiveness analysis in shaping arguments related to preventive measures. I have selected two, pre-natal care and breast cancer screening, with which I have been closely associated for years.

Low birth weight and pre-natal care

What is known and not known about the problem area, low birth weight, and the preventive service, pre-natal care, is detailed in the 1985 report, *Preventing low birth weight*, prepared by a committee of The Institute of Medicine (IOM) (14). Many of the facts can be stated simply. About 6·8% of the children born in the USA weigh less than 2500 g at birth. These infants account for two-thirds of the deaths that occur in the first 4 weeks following birth (the neonatal period), and for one-fifth of the deaths in the balance of the first year, the post-neonatal period (15). Low birth weight infants are characterized by long, expensive stays in neonatal intensive care units, and are at high risk for persistent morbidity and developmental handicaps requiring high-cost care (16), e.g. they average about 2½ days in the hospital by 1 year of age, following the post-natal hospitalization, compared with approximately three-quarters of a day among normal birth weight infants (17).

We can take a great deal of satisfaction from the large decline in infant mortality over the past 20 years, which has reduced the rate by almost 60% to bring it down to approximately 10 per 1000. The disturbing news is that the low birth weight rate has changed very little. Further, the rate varies extraordinarily within the population. Black mothers are at far greater risk than white mothers of having a low birth weight

Table 1

Estimated effects on low birth weight[a] of improvements in pre-natal care and in selected maternal risk factors

Pre-natal care	White		Black	
	Rate (per 1000)	Reduction (%)	Rate (per 1000)	Reduction (%)
Original base rate	47	—	112	—
Rate after elimination of excess risk associated with:				
Non-adequate pre-natal care[b]	40	15	97	12
Non-adequate pre-natal care and maternal risks[c]	34	29	77	30

[a] Single live births, 1981.
[b] Care was begun after first trimester, or was a first trimester start with fewer pre-natal visits than prescribed for the reported duration of pregnancy.
[c] Factors include less than high school education, unmarried status, or high age-birth order risk.

baby (in 1983, 12·6% versus 5·7%), and low educational attainment, teenage pregnancy, and short intervals between pregnancies are associated with increased risk in both racial groups (18). Particularly troublesome is the failure to reduce the gap between high- and low-risk groups.

Although many unanswered questions remain regarding the etiology of low birth weight, the IOM report concluded that enough is known about risks related to socio-demographic, medical and behavioral factors 'to intervene more vigorously to reduce the incidence of low birth weight'. Prominent among the interventions proposed are increasing the 'accessibility of early and regular high quality pre-natal care' and 'strengthening and expanding the content of pre-natal care' (19). The basis for the emphasis on pre-natal care was the favorable interpretation of evidence in the literature (20) and results of analysis of Vital Statistics data for the USA (Table 1).

Reductions of 12% and 15% attributable to changes in pre-natal care may not seem very great but they would surpass the decreases in the previous 10–15 years and the impact on mortality and morbidity would be substantial. Mindful of the fact that public funds would be needed for the disadvantaged in the population who are at high risk for low birth weight pregnancy outcome, estimates of net cost were derived. The target was pregnant women who completed less than 12 years of school and who were on public assistance. Only about half start their pre-natal care in the first trimester compared with about 76% in the total population, and an estimated 11·5% of their children are born weighing less than 2500 g. Improved access to pre-natal care meeting present standards was expected to reduce this rate to 10%, conservatively, and to 9%, optimistically (21). This leaves aside changes in content of care and management discussed in the report and elsewhere (22).

The economic model contrasted (a) reductions in post-delivery costs for care in neonatal intensive care units, rehospitalization of neonatal survivors during the first year, and medical services per year for long-term morbidity among non-institutionalized children; and (b) new pre-natal care expenditures. A summary of the results is shown in Table 2.

The precision of the estimates is heavily qualified because of exclusions from the calculations and uncertainties about some of the figures on which the included estimates are based. Nevertheless, the reasonable conclusion is that even a moderate decrease in low birth weight would result in a significant reduction in costs. This carries

Table 2

Cost savings at different low birth weight (LBW) rates[a]

| LBW rate (%) | LBW infant care costs[b] | | Outlays for additional pre-natal care ($) | Net cost savings ($) |
	Total ($)	Reduction ($)		
11·5	188 231	—	—	—
10	163 683	24 549	12 107	12 442
9	147 319	40 913	12 107	28 806

[a] Data refer to an estimated 12 700 children born weighing under 2500 g to mothers aged 15–29 years, who are on public assistance and who have less than 12 years of education.
[b] All figures are rounded to the nearest 1000 $.

over to other high-risk groups, particularly the poor who have not been eligible for Medicaid.

The social utility of expanding access to pre-natal care for vulnerable populations, supported by prospects of lowering the low birth weight rate and costs, has accelerated efforts to change Medicaid provisions. The result is that the 1987 federal budget recently approved by Congress allows states to provide Medicaid coverage for many women and infants with incomes below the poverty level who do not qualify for welfare or supplemental security income. This is expected to reverse the trend in some states to make Medicaid eligibility more restrictive, at least for pregnant women and their young offspring.

Breast cancer screening

Breast cancer screening is a major candidate for secondary prevention programs because of the morbidity and mortality caused by the disease and the well established efficacy of screening. Briefly, breast cancer accounts for about one-fourth of all cancers diagnosed among women each year. About one in 11 women develop clinically detectable breast cancer during their lifetime. Mortality has remained unchanged for over 40 years, and it has been displaced by lung cancer as the number one cause of death from cancer among women only in the past 2–3 years.

Results of the randomized trials in the Health Insurance Plan (HIP) of Greater New York (23) and Sweden (24) demonstrate that breast cancer screening has the potential substantially to reduce mortality from the disease. Studies in the Netherlands support this conclusion (25,26). The HIP trial has the longest duration and is the point of departure for discussions about promotion of breast cancer screening in the USA. The research was started in 1963, based on random samples of women aged 40–64 years, totalling 30 000 in the study group and an equal number in the control group. Study women were invited for screening examinations, consisting of physical examination of the breast and mammography. Two-thirds appeared for the initial examination. These women were invited for three additional screening examinations at annual intervals. Control women continued to receive usual care. All comparisons were between the total study group (participants and non-participants combined) and the control group of women.

Figure 1 contrasts the cumulative numbers of breast cancer deaths in the study and control groups, and Table 3 shows the reductions in breast cancer deaths and in person years of life (PYL) lost due to breast cancer credited to the screening program (27).

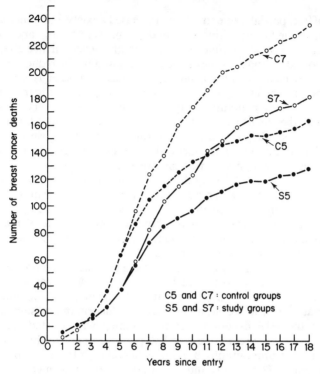

Figure 1. Cumulative number of deaths due to breast cancer by interval since entry: all ages, study and control groups (breast cancers diagnosed within 5 and 7 years after entry).

Table 3

Mortality differentials between study and control groups[a]. The Health Insurance Plan (HIP) randomized trial of breast cancer screening

Differentials[b]	Interval following study entry (years)		
	5	10	18
Deaths due to breast cancer Number (%)	24 (38·1)	38 (28·6)	37 (22·7)
PYL[c] lost due to breast cancer Number (%)	21 (21·3)	188 (29·7)	468·5 (25·4)

[a] Included are deaths among women with breast cancer diagnosed during first 5 years after entry; differentials are similar for cases detected in first 7 years.
[b] Denominators are deaths among control group women.
[c] Person years of life.

Large decreases appeared within a few years after study entry, and impressive gains persisted over the long term of 18 years. Judging from the experience in Sweden, similar decreases in breast cancer mortality may be achievable through screening less often than annually, and with mammography alone, provided that very high percentages of the women appear for screening.

Neither of these studies is producing information on the effect of screening on quality of life. It might be speculated that early detection results in less extensive surgery and adjuvant therapy, thereby improving quality of life. On the other hand, this might be offset, partially or entirely, by increased anxiety and unnecessary surgery caused by a rise in the false-positive cases and diagnosis of breast cancer among some women at such an early stage that the cancer might never surface clinically. These are not trivial considerations but they are overshadowed by the reductions in mortality which serve as the basis for measuring effectiveness. Another risk that loomed as a significant factor in assessing net benefits from screening during the mid-1970s was the radiogenic effect of mammography (28). Conditions are very different today. With monitoring, the absorbed radiation dose to the breast from film mammography is only 0.01 rad, a small fraction of the former levels of exposure.

Recommendations directed at the medical profession and general public for annual screening with clinical examination of the breast and mammography were adopted several years ago by the ACS (29) and the NCI (30). However, it was not until very recently that a serious start was made on the problems of reaching large numbers of women. The lag can be traced to many factors, including the controversy about whether screening should start below or above age 50, the state of readiness of the health care system and providers to engage in mass screening, the high costs of mammography and how they are to be met.

To clarify the cost issue, Eddy (31) has applied a generalized computer-based model to estimate net health care costs and benefits in breast cancer screening for the Medicare population. The parameters are annual screening with mammography and clinical examination of the breast, an estimated reduction in breast cancer mortality consistent with the HIP experience among women who started screening under 65 years of age, and a screening cost of $60 per examination (this is far below the current charges for mammography but it may be too high for large volume, specially designed programs). The results indicate that screening women between 65 and 75 years of age adds one PYL to this population at an average net cost of approximately $26 000. The costs of decreasing the number of deaths by one are about $230 000 each year. With the assumptions used by Eddy, the unit costs for a PYL gained and the reduction in mortality if screening began under age 65 would be lower, but the total dollars required to meet the costs of screening would be considerably higher per 5-year age group because of the larger numbers involved.

The fact that breast cancer screening could not be advocated on the grounds of lowered health care costs has been obvious from the start. The compelling reason for such advocacy, leaving aside economic benefits per year of life saved, has been the social benefit. However, in the practical world of contending with problems of implementation through coverage by private health insurance or governmental programs, high costs will slow the spread of annual screening with the two modalities.

Alternatives that have not yet been examined in cost-effectiveness models based on data now available include less frequent screening, selective screening (32) (i.e. of high risk women), and different ages when screening might start. The main question about age centers on screening women aged 40–49 years, among whom in the HIP study benefits did not appear until 5–8 years after entry and part of the benefits were related to cases diagnosed after age 50. The possibility that screening limited to physical examination of the breast is an acceptable option for women aged 50–59 years is being tested in the Canadian study of breast cancer screening (33).

Conclusion

The two examples discussed make it apparent that there is no general response to the question, 'Can prevention be cost-effective?'. In both instances, a major health problem is involved and strong societal interests are present, but how we approach and weigh the evidence differs.

In the case of low birth weight, major decreases in costs would occur through modest reductions in the low birth weight rate. Expectation of benefits among the poor from increased access to pre-natal care that meets prevailing standards does not come from controlled trials or consistent results from observational studies. However, deficits among the poor are large and, from a social equity standpoint alone, funding to improve access would be justified. The possibility of reduced costs makes the argument more persuasive in the current cost-containment environment.

In the case of breast cancer, cost-effectiveness analysis limited to measures of decreases in mortality and net medical care costs has served the useful purpose of clarifying the heavy investments required for general population screening. However, the fact that hard evidence exists on the efficacy of screening has led value judgments to override cost considerations, to pressure for insurance coverage, and other approaches to increase the probability that large numbers of women will be screened. The difficult task left for cost-effectiveness modeling is to assess the effects of alternative strategies for implementing breast cancer screening.

Neither example should be interpreted as meaning that costs and effectiveness are unimportant. Clearly, these need to be known when new costly services are being considered. However, for preventive services directed at major health problems, the third element, value judgments, will often be decisive even in periods of constrained resources.

References

(1) Doubilet P, Weinstein MC, McNeil BJ. Use and misuse of the term 'cost effective' in medicine. *N Engl J Med* 1986; **314** (4): 253–6.
(2) Russell LB. *Is prevention better than cure?* Washington: The Brookings Institution, 1986.
(3) Sommers KB. Book review. Is prevention better than cure? Russell LB. *J Pub Health Policy* 1986; **7** (1): 124–8.
(4) US Department of Health, Education and Welfare. *Healthy people: the Surgeon General's report on health promotion and disease prevention*. DHEW publication no. (PHS)79-55071A. Washington: US Department of Health, Education and Welfare, 1979.
(5) Centers for Disease Control, Public Health Service, Department of Health, Education and Welfare. *Promoting health/preventing disease: objectives for the nation*. Atlanta: Centers for Disease Control, 1980.
(6) Mickalide AD. *Fact sheet*, US Preventive Services Task Force, Office of Disease Prevention and Health Promotion. Washington: US Department of Health and Human Services, 1985.
(7) Periodic Health Examination Monograph. *Report of a Task Force to the Conference of Deputy Ministers of Health*. Hull, Quebec: Canadian Government Publishing Centre, 1980.
(8) Task Force Reports. *Preventive medicine USA*. (Sponsored by the John E. Fogarty International Center for Advanced Study in the Health Sciences.) New York: National Institutes of Health and the American College of Preventive Medicine, New York, 1976.
(9) Breslow L, Somers AR. The lifetime health-monitoring program. *N Engl J Med* 1977; **296** (11): 601–8.
(10) Weinstein MC, Stason WB. Foundations of cost-effectiveness analysis for health and medical practices. *N Engl J Med* 1977; **296** (13): 716–21.

(11) Bunker JP, Barnes BA, Mosteller F, eds. *Costs, risks and benefits of surgery*. New York: Oxford University Press, 1977.

(12) Warner KE, Luce BR. *Cost-benefit and cost-effectiveness analysis in health care: principles, practice and potential*. Ann Arbor MI: Health Administration Press, 1982.

(13) Health technology case studies. *The implications of cost-effectiveness of medical technology*. OTA-H-126. Washington: US Congress, Office of Technology Assessment, 1980 (August).

(14) Committee to Study the Prevention of Low Birthweight, Institute of Medicine. *Preventing low birthweight*. Washington: National Academy Press, 1985.

(15) Shapiro S, McCormick MC, Starfield BH, Krischer JP, Bross D. Relevance of correlates of infant deaths for significant morbidity at 1 year of age. *Am J Obstet Gynecol* 1980; **136** (3): 363–73.

(16) McCormick MC. The contribution of low birth weight to infant mortality and childhood morbidity. *N Engl J Med* 1985; **312**: 82–90.

(17) McCormick MC, Shapiro S, Starfield BH. Rehospitalization in the first year of life for high-risk survivors. *Pediatrics* 1980; **66** (6): 991–9.

(18) Committee to Study the Prevention of Low Birthweight, Institute of Medicine. *Preventing low birthweight*. Chapter 3: Trends in low birthweight. Washington: National Academy Press, 1985.

(19) Committee to Study the Prevention of Low Birthweight, Institute of Medicine. *Preventing low birthweight*. Chapter 4: An overview of promising interventions. Washington: National Academy Press, 1985.

(20) Committee to Study the Prevention of Low Birthweight, Institute of Medicine. *Preventing low birthweight*. Chapter 6: The effectiveness of prenatal care. Washington: National Academy Press, 1985.

(21) Committee to Study the Prevention of Low Birthweight, Institute of Medicine. *Preventing low birthweight*. Chapter 10: Prenatal care and low birthweight: effects on health care expenditures. Washington: National Academy Press, 1985.

(22) Anonymous. Antenatal care assessed. [Editorial]. *Lancet* 1986; i: 1072–4.

(23) Shapiro S, Venet W, Strax P, Venet L, Roeser R. Selection, follow-up and analysis in the Health Insurance Plan (HIP) of Greater New York Study. *J Natl Cancer Inst Monograph* 1985; **67**: 63–74.

(24) Tabár L, Fagerberg CJ, Gad A, *et al.* Reduction in mortality from breast cancer after mass screening with mammography. Randomised trial from the Breast Cancer Screening Working Group of the Swedish National Board of Health and Welfare. *Lancet* 1985; i: 829–32.

(25) Collette HJA, Rombach JJ, Day NE, de Waard F. Evaluation of screening for breast cancer in a randomized study (the Dom Project) by means of a case-control study. *Lancet* 1984; i: 1224–6.

(26) Verbeek ALM, Holland R, Sturmans F, Hendriks JHCL, Mravunac M, Day NE. Reduction of breast cancer mortality through mass screening with modern mammography. First results of the Nijmegen project, 1975–81. *Lancet* 1984; i: 1222–4.

(27) Shapiro S, Venet W, Strax P, Venet L. *Current results of the breast cancer randomized trial: the Health Insurance Plan (HIP) of Greater New York Study*. Presented at Workshop on Screening for Breast Cancer, International Union Against Cancer (UICC) Project on Screening for Cancer, Helsinki, Finland, April 7–9, 1986.

(28) Bailar JC, III. Mammography, a contrary view. *Ann Intern Med* 1976; **84** (1): 77–84.

(29) American Cancer Society. Mammography: two statements of the American Cancer Society. Reprinted from: *CA — A Cancer Journal for Clinicians* 1982; **32** (4) and 1983; **33** (4). New York: American Cancer Society Inc.

(30) US Department of Health and Human Services. *Breast exams, what you should know*. NIH publication no. 82-2000: 8–10. Bethesda MD: National Cancer Institute, 1982.

(31) Eddy DM. A computer-based model for designing cancer control strategies. In: Greenwald P, Sondik EJ, eds. *Cancer control. Objectives for the nation: 1985–2000.* US Department of Health and Human Services publication no. 2, NCI monographs. Bethesda MD: National Cancer Institute, 1986.
(32) Schecter MT, Miller AB, Baines CJ, Howe GR. Selection of women at high risk of breast cancer for initial screening. *J Chronic Dis* 1986; **39** (4): 253–60.
(33) Miller AB, Howe GR, Wall C. The National Study of Breast Cancer Screening. Protocol for a Canadian randomized controlled trial of screening for breast cancer in women. *Clin Invest Med* 1981; **4**: 227–58.

Discussion

Sir Raymond Hoffenberg

Both Professor Alwyn Smith and Professor Shapiro seem to have answered the question of the subtitle in the negative.

Dr Brody

I raised the question earlier whether there are enough mammographers or radiologists in the USA to screen everyone if these procedures are used. From the American standpoint, the question that might be asked is whether anyone has costed a model of training paraprofessionals to do this work — if, in fact, it would be such a great benefit.

A question from the British side might be the following: given some of the things we have been reading lately about difficulties in showing that general practitioners (GPs) do a good job of preventive screening as part of the primary health care system, is it better in the UK to approach prevention by working through the GP system or to try to go around that system to get prevention by other means?

Professor Shapiro

I may have made it sound easy to introduce mammography screening in the USA. It would be a total disaster if a number of measures were not taken at the same time to ensure that it is practicable to introduce it. One such measure concerns evidence of capability within the radiological profession, ready or anxious to move in on what could be a very lucrative source of income. This goes beyond technical competence. I mentioned very low radiation exposure. This means monitoring the equipment. Equipment can easily go wrong, and the dosage rate can increase 10- or 20-fold in the absence of monitoring.

Even after control for those conditions, in what circumstances would it become economically possible for health insurance companies to move into the field? A number of things are happening in the USA because of the new drives that are under way. There are many communities where the unit cost for mammography has been cut to one-third of what it was only a year ago.

There are many ways of organizing mammography screening. Whether the primary care physician becomes an active participant as a gatekeeper is relevant not only for the UK but certainly also for the USA, if large segments of the female population are to be reached.

Professor Alwyn Smith

The response of the Department of Health in the UK to the suggestion that mammographic screening for breast cancer should be introduced was, predictably, to establish a committee.

That committee has now completed its deliberations, its report is with the printers, and what it says is a fairly well-kept secret. I think it would be fair to say that the possibility has not been excluded of an appropriately measured and controlled introduction of screening into the National Health Service.

Professor Marks

Whether prevention is cost-effective surely depends upon the condition and the methods used. Anything can be proved by selecting particular cases. I understand that if rubella vaccine was introduced for every child in the country, this would prevent the birth of several hundred deaf and blind children. The cost of vaccinating all the children in the country is about the same as that of supporting one deaf and blind child for life. The equation there seems to be heavily in favour of vaccination.

I do not know whether any studies have been made of the effect of aborting cystic fibrosis and haemophiliac fetuses, but I believe that the technology is now well established and surely the balance would be very different there.

To take yet another example, the programmes for smoking prevention in adolescence have shown that, using very inexpensive peer model training programmes, it is possible to halve the amount of new smoking amongst 12-year-olds a year later. Surely, therefore, this has to be argued case by case.

Professor Alwyn Smith

I think that is a fair comment. There is little doubt that some preventive measures are effective and relatively cheap, and therefore I suppose are likely to be cost-effective. The ones quoted by Professor Marks are well established examples. Some studies have been published recently from Mediterranean countries on the control of thalassaemia and on a number of other issues.

The general issue is much more difficult. It is possible to argue that in fact successful prevention, far from reducing the costs of treatment actually increases them — that indeed much of the escalation in the cost of medical care that has taken place during the present century is the direct consequence of the great success of prevention during the 19th century, with its consequent impact on the demographic structure and morbidity of the population.

It is naive to suppose that prevention actually *saves* costs in medical care. It may very well enormously enhance the quality of life in a community. It is in those terms that it has to be judged. I would guard against the often canvassed simple proposition that it would be cheaper to prevent than to treat disease. It may be cheaper to prevent some diseases than to treat them, but to suggest that it is better or cheaper to prevent morbidity in general than to treat it is a very difficult proposition. We have only to look at a simple disease like gonorrhoea. It is obviously very much cheaper to treat gonorrhoea than to prevent it if all the social costs are taken into account.

Professor Shapiro

I agree that the issue of prevention has to be looked at on a specific level and in a specific context. What I liked about the two examples I used was what they illustrated. The first demonstrated that a reasonable assessment of the evidence — not a randomized trial — suggested that, from a financial standpoint, the risks of attempting to change a situation would be likely to have very high rewards, because of the extraordinarily high cost related to each low birth weight infant. In an area of uncertainty, taking those risks seems more acceptable than waiting and attempting to produce substantial hard information.

In the second example it was the reverse. There were substantial costs in trying to introduce breast cancer screening. In those circumstances, there needs to be a higher level of certainty that the condition will be beneficially affected.

Professor Reinhardt

I was impressed by the data on low birth weight and its relationship to infant mortality.

Even if we all knew what is now known about cost-effective prevention, and if physician visits were made available free (as, for example, for polio immunization), to what extent could we assume that mothers would take advantage of the free services? I think that such services are far more readily available now to many people in the USA than might be thought. Secondly, even if the contact were made, compliance might be a problem ultimately.

I am really asking whether part of the problem of the misery at the bottom of the heap in the USA is the fact that we allow people too much freedom to ruin their lives.

Professor Shapiro

A whole session would be needed to discuss that point.

Simply making pre-natal care available, and leaving it at that, would not do the trick, in the opinion both of the Committee and myself (1). There must be some out-reach and community programmes. The set of figures in the bottom row of my Table 1 indicates that a great deal more than just providing pre-natal care is involved in any effort to reduce low birth weight rates. These other factors are much more difficult to grapple with — but even though those figures of 12% and 15% seem small, a lot of money is involved.

Dr Banta

I think that pre-natal care illustrates another problem of the definition of the intervention. The studies that have been done on pre-natal care which I have reviewed all define it in terms of earliness of the first visit and the number of visits. There is no definition of what is actually *done* in those visits. The European Community has commissioned a study of the content of antenatal care, looking at 26 different procedures. There is enormous variation from country to country and from centre to centre in what is actually done. The number of times a procedure is carried out can vary from zero to 20 times in a particular pregnancy. Some of these procedures are probably harmful, and the vast majority of those reviewed have not been shown to be beneficial.

I am concerned that in talking about the cost-effectiveness of prevention the particular intervention should also be defined.

Professor Ibrahim

Dr Relman said earlier that the medical care industry, at least in the USA, is not interested in containing costs. Is it therefore a good idea to sell prevention on the basis of cost-effectiveness? Perhaps we may be barking up the wrong tree.

Dr Bondurant

In addition to focusing the selection of preventive measures on the basis both of the nature of the disease and (as Dr Banta pointed out) of the content of the intervention, would Professor Alwyn Smith enlarge, and Professor Shapiro comment, upon whether or not there is also some power to be gained by sharpening the definition of the population groups which may be served, especially considering the powerful tools of genetics now available? Where we have, for example, coincidental gene expression, such as skin colour and haemoglobinopathies, we can narrow down and improve the efficiency, at least of diagnosis if not prevention, in the case of sickle-cell disease.

With modern molecular biology, restriction fragment linkage analysis and the ability to geno-type populations more precisely than before, is it possible that — to use Professor Alwyn Smith's terminology — by going to the subsets within the medium-risk groups who are truly at maximum risk, rather than to the low-risk groups, we can focus preventive interventions more sharply?

Professor Alwyn Smith

In general, there are two distinct problems. First, is it possible to characterize the high-risk individual? It is for some diseases now and may be for more diseases one day.

If I may take my example of cervical cancer screening, it is possible to characterize the woman who is at maximum risk of developing cervical cancer — it is the woman whose usual marital partner is dirty and promiscuous.

The second problem is, having characterized the high-risk state, can we define, list and gain access to individuals who are defined by that state? I would suggest that is not possible in the case of cervical cancer. There is no practical way of listing women who fall into the category that I have defined. Therefore, we do the best we can. We take one or two proxies for the at-risk state. There has been a great deal of debate about whether cervical screening should be concentrated on particular age bands, and whether the recommended frequency of screening should be varied at different ages. All the evidence suggests that it does not make a great deal of difference. The most efficient use of the resources is probably the most even coverage possible of the age band 20–64 years.

If we could identify, for example, some risk factor which predisposes an individual to respond, say, to raised arterial pressure by developing one of the complications, it might be possible to ask only those who have this additional factor, rather than asking everybody, to lower their blood pressure. At the moment, we do not know what it is. Of course, if we ever do know, it may be as difficult to screen for the risk factor as to apply the preventive measure in a blanket fashion.

We have these two problems: first, the at-risk state has to be characterized and, secondly, we have to compile a list and approach those individuals so defined.

This is done in many ways. One of the examples given is simple and obvious — that is, that sickle-cell anaemia is not looked for in Caucasian people because that would not be profitable. That provides a rather coarse division of the population in relation to an important but rather particular condition.

There is some evidence that whether or not someone gets lung cancer if he smokes may be determined by some susceptibility, but we cannot yet characterize the susceptibility factor nor can we identify the individuals. There is also a little evidence that people who already have chronic respiratory symptoms as a consequence of their smoking constitute a high-risk group, at which it would be particularly useful to direct education.

It is all still quite simplistic, coarse and crude, although Dr Bondurant is probably right, that for the future the use of markers of whatever kind, whether gene probes or other sorts of things, may transform the selectivity of prevention procedures. We are not yet in that position.

Professor Shapiro

I agree totally with Professor Alwyn Smith. If we knew more than we do about risk factors, I think that it would be possible to move ahead with what we call 'selective screening'.

In response to Dr Banta, I think enough is known to say that the content of pre-natal care, as well as programmes before the woman becomes pregnant, are both highly significant factors. The small example that I gave, however, used only the start of pre-natal care and whether or not the prescribed visits were taking place.

Dr Banta

I do not disagree with the study cited by Professor Shapiro, but was just trying to amplify it. I will add that pre-natal care in the USA is defined by the American College of Obstetrics and Gynecology and not based in any way on evidence. In the UK, it is defined by standards that go back decades, based on prevailing practice at the time when pre-natal care was extended to the entire population.

My point is that the content of pre-natal care has not been examined critically. The studies have dealt with it as a package of services, and I am convinced that package contains much that is not effective.

Reference

(1) Committee to Study the Prevention of Low Birthweight, Institute of Medicine. *Preventing low birthweight*. Washington: National Academy Press, 1985.

2. Can health education prevent disease?

Chairman:
EUGENE MAYER
Chapel Hill NC, USA

A UK view

SIR DOUGLAS BLACK

The Royal College of Physicians, London, UK

Introduction

In the UK, as in other countries, there is no consensus view on the matter indicated by the title. The great majority of doctors are so heavily occupied in curing or palliating established disease that they may have given little thought to health education; on the other hand, a substantial number of doctors, including some of the most influential, are strongly seized of the importance of a largely preventive approach to health issues. There is also a strong belief among politicians, sociologists and the intelligent laity (charity compels me to regard the 'and' in that phrase as conjunctive and not disjunctive) that too much attention is being paid to disease and too little to health maintenance—they eagerly welcome the somewhat nebulous concept of 'positive health', and are vulnerable to such slogans as 'health for all by the year 2000'. In view of these differences of opinion, I must make it plain that the views which I am about to express are personal views, and not a summary of UK opinion, which in its variety at least probably does not differ greatly from opinion in the USA.

Questions about health education

The answer to the question, in misleading 'yes' and 'no' terms, depends almost entirely on the gloss which is put on the two key terms—'health education' and 'disease'. If we ask whether some health education prevents some disease, the answer has to be 'yes', but if we ask whether any degree of health education will prevent all disease, the answer surely has to be 'no'. This admittedly superficial analysis perhaps exemplifies a general theme, that if questions are made sufficiently general they may preclude a categorical answer. Other examples of questions which are unanswerable because they are too generally phrased might be, 'does vaccination do more harm than good?', 'do antibiotics cure infections?', and 'is diet important?'. (Our instinct to give an unqualified assent to the last of these examples falters when we contemplate the bizarreries committed by food faddists of various kinds.) An unqualified assent to the question posed would pass for advocacy of the kind of vast schemes of improvement which attract the label Utopianism. As a cautious Scot, I am more

Health Care Provision under Financial Constraint, edited by T. B. Binns and M. Firth, 1988: Royal Society of Medicine International Congress and Symposium Series No. 115, published by Royal Society of Medicine Services Ltd.

attracted to piecemeal measures, each to be judged on its own merits and on the relevance of its probable outcome. I could not hope to express the spirit of my attitude nearly as well as William Blake, when he said:

> General Good is the plea of the scoundral, hypocrite and flatterer; For Art and Science cannot exist but in minutely organised Particulars.

Health education fallacies

Fortunately, there is no lack of 'Particulars' which can be called upon to establish the value of specific preventive measures, so long as we do not fall victim to the two giant fallacies which encumber the general theme—that prevention will abolish disease, and that prevention of disease is necessarily cheaper than treating it. The first of these fallacies was exposed following the post-Beveridge euphoria when politicians, but not I think doctors, cherished the expectation that after a backlog of disability had been dealt with, the cost of health care would diminish—something which does not appear to have happened.

The second of these fallacies persists in the quite extravagant estimation of the value of general health screening. Canadian experience (1) has shown the value of specific measures of surveillance directed towards those groups which are at particular risk—for example, the discovery and treatment of hypertension in middle life, or the examination of neonates for congenital defects. A general screening programme, whether it be conducted by questionnaire or by autoanalyser, throws up by sheer chance apparent abnormalities which alarm the patient, puzzle the doctor, and which, after extensive further investigation, may lead to no useful advice or treatment. The level of compliance to be expected from an apparently healthy person discovered, say, to have a high serum cholesterol is likely to be lower than that in a patient who solicits help because of actual symptoms.

Objective studies of the outcome of general screening programmes are rare, but Professor Walter Holland, of St Thomas's Hospital, was successful in obtaining the co-operation of general practitioners in Bromley for a trial of screening half the patients in their practices on a routine basis (2). At the end of 5 years, no significant difference in mortality had appeared between the screened and unscreened patients. Similar experiences in other places support the view that

> high costs with low yields, high levels of client confusion and unnecessary referral, and disappointing levels of effectiveness as a health education tool have rendered the "shotgun" approach to screening *passé* in the 1970s (2)

—presumably also in the 1980s.

Health education measures

Having hopefully disencumbered ourselves of the proposition that all health education is a free and self-justifying good, irrespective of what it may or may not achieve, there is still value in focusing on those components of health education which have a reasonable scientific basis, and also some prospect of modifying favourably the incidence of specific states of ill-health. The general areas calling for attention are drugs of addiction, including tobacco and alcohol, dietary measures, and exercise. These are for the individual. At the population level, they include information on pollutants in the home, the factory or in the general environment, where the necessary action has to be mainly on a social or governmental rather than an individual basis. Another important subject of health education, directed both at the individual and at society, is prevention of accidents.

For each of these problems, a range of general preventive measures is available, and the overall prospects for prevention have been magnificently set forth by Sir Richard Doll in his Harveian Oration in 1982 (3). Our concern is more limited, to consider what can be achieved by health education, and not by more concrete measures of prevention such as vaccination or the installation of safety devices.

Drugs

Drugs can conveniently be divided into those which are socially unacceptable or illegal (cannabis, heroin, cocaine), and those which are legal and also socially accepted, which may of course not be an unqualified certificate of merit (tobacco and alcohol). In dealing with the illegal drugs, I see the place of health education as limited, except insofar as it can be directed at those who have not yet made the experiment. I cannot believe the drug takers are unaware of the dangers to which they are exposed, and for them the enforcement of the law, especially against the suppliers of drugs, would seem more appropriate than exhortation. There may also be a need to educate legislators against the lunacy of legalizing the use of cannabis.

With tobacco and alcohol, there is more scope for education, and less for legal action, with the important exception of the flagrant and illegal supplying of cigarettes to children. For tobacco, the vulnerable groups to which education should be directed are the young teenagers, since it is easier not to begin to smoke than to give up the habit once begun. For different reasons, teachers and nurses should be at least made aware of the bad influence of setting an example of smoking. There is also a paradoxical increase in smoking with descent in the social scale, and if a way can be found to influence this in the right direction both economic and health benefits would follow. In this country, the campaign against smoking in public places is making slow headway, with occasional victories such as the cleansing of the London tubes but, unlike the USA, in our cinemas we still have the freedom to cough and splutter.

Smokers damage mainly themselves, apart from the money which they waste and the discomfort which they cause to bystanders in confined spaces. The abuse of alcohol has both an individual and a social component. The situation is also confounded by the evidence that the moderate use of alcohol, especially in less concentrated forms, may be of benefit to mood, and perhaps also to health. Again, the general facts are pretty well known, unless suppressed by the confirmed addict, but education directed to vulnerable groups, notably the woman who is pregnant or may become so, should be strengthened.

For those drugs which are legally permitted, the cheapest and possibly the most effective method of health education would be to persuade the legislators to curb more actively than they do at present that dangerous form of negative health education represented by the vast sum spent on advertising and sport promotion.

Other aspects of lifestyle

A cool look at lifestyles across the globe shows that many curious variants both of food and of exercise are compatible with survival. This in itself should suggest scepticism about slogan-ridden campaigns directed against particular foodstuffs or classes of foodstuffs, to which pejorative labels are attached. What to the nutritionist is 'junk' food is to the manufacturer 'convenience' food, and for that very reason may be what the consumer actually buys. Cassius and Brutus died on the same day, but the manner of their death removes them from the witness stand—his lack of obesity would normally have favoured Cassius. It seems likely that the habit of stuffing himself with fibre compensates the African native for the many health hazards which he otherwise faces. Civilization is a Pandora's box which protects us from many dangers and such risks as foul water and decayed food, while at the same time making us unhealthily sedentary. Sensible food and exercise, avoiding extremes, would seem to be a reasonable middle course.

Health education for society

If the knowledge base for health education of the individual is imperfect in some ways, the same applies even more to health education relating to societal hazards, or those which are met in industry. Yet the responsibility for assessing what may affect millions must be even greater than that relating to individuals. It would be tedious, and I would certainly lack the expertise, to attempt to traverse the whole range of health dangers to a population arising from natural disasters, industrial accidents, and the artificialities of modern life, but I may at least indicate the complexity of the problem by reflecting on the type of information and constant education which are appropriate to considering civil uses of atomic energy. A general perspective is needed, to form an information base appropriate to all who are interested. In addition, there are particular information needs for those employed in the industry, for those whose primary concern is with the environment, and for those responsible for legislation and regulation.

Risk and its prevention

In a developed country with a science-based economy, a reliable supply of energy is needed both for industry and for high-yield agriculture, and also of course for domestic use. All artificial processes for generating energy carry risk, coal-mining and oil-drilling no less than nuclear fission. If we define 'actual risk' as the risk associated with the normal operation of the process, we can see that this is pragmatically acceptable in many countries. But two other types of risk have to be considered. 'Potential risk' relates to what might happen, given an accident or human error in the process, and it must always be greater than actual risk, as just defined. 'Perceived risk' is by its nature subjective—an employee will estimate the risk more conservatively than someone unconnected with the industry, whereas an environmentalist may overestimate the risk.

Those employed in the industry need special education to prevent accidents, and to maintain their vigilance at a level which makes human error as unlikely as possible. Can it ever be eliminated entirely? Those responsible for plant design must recognize the inevitability of human error by both perfecting and duplicating automatic controls.

Environmental groups must somehow be brought to appreciate that, however much we aim to conserve energy, there must be a minimum level of energy production if we are to maintain our present population in the land mass at our disposal.

Legislators have to strike the right balance between actual risk and perceived risk. Actual risk may be more important in the long run, but it is perceived risk which brings in the votes.

Conclusion

To return to the point where this paper began, good health education can certainly prevent some disease in the individual, and also clear society of some ill-founded worries, but bad health education can alarm the individual, and encourage governments to make hasty and ill-considered decisions.

References

(1) Task Force. *Periodic health examination*. Ottawa: Ministry of Supply and Services, 1980.

(2) Tilson HH. In: Holland WW, Detels R, Knox G, eds. *Oxford textbook of public health*; Vol. 1. Oxford: Oxford University Press, 1984: Chapter 12.

(3) Doll R. *Prospects for prevention*. London: Royal College of Physicians, 1982.

A US view:
the clinical and public health approaches to prevention: the declining coronary heart disease mortality and behavioral change

MICHEL A. IBRAHIM

*Dean and Professor of Epidemiology, School of Public Health,
The University of North Carolina at Chapel Hill, Chapel Hill NC, USA*

Prevention is an attractive option for maintaining the health of individuals and society in the face of the prevalent chronic diseases and an aging population. The case for prevention has been enhanced by the epidemiological research that uncovered several risk factors of chronic illnesses, especially coronary heart disease (CHD). In addition, multiple efforts have been mounted during the last two decades in the USA to modify such risk factors. Some included randomized controlled trials to determine the impact of stopping smoking, dietary change, cholesterol-lowering drugs, and antihypertensive medications. In the meantime, mortality and morbidity from CHD have gradually but consistently declined since the late 1960s and early 1970s.

The CHD mortality decline has been attributed to changes in risk factors of personal behavior and to medical care interventions. The precise contribution of each of these changes to the decline is uncertain but it can be estimated that lifestyle changes have contributed 50% or more to the decline. The health promotion and disease prevention movement and its important tool, health education, is a major determinant of behavioral change. The impact of health education may be viewed broadly as resulting from the formal type as well as from the media, illnesses of public figures, and advertising.

The decline of CHD over the last two decades and the influence of lifestyle changes on prevention have highlighted once more the clinical and the public health approaches. Each vantage point triggers a series of issues specific to that point. These include classification, method of intervention, outcome measures, and responsibility. A dual approach is desirable to optimize the impact of prevention on health states of populations.

In this paper, the decline in CHD mortality and the role of lifestyle changes are reviewed. The contribution of behavioral change to the decline is estimated. The definitions of health education, health promotion and disease prevention, and their

Health Care Provision under Financial Constraint, edited by T. B. Binns and M. Firth, 1988: Royal Society of Medicine International Congress and Symposium Series No. 115, published by Royal Society of Medicine Services Ltd.

M. A. Ibrahim

potential impact on CHD mortality and other conditions are outlined. Finally, the ramifications and impact of both clinical and public health approaches are put into perspective.

The declining coronary heart disease
mortality and lifestyle changes

Since the late 1960s and early 1970s, death rates in the USA from CHD and stroke
have fallen considerably and steadily (1). This decline has been observed in only a
few other countries. Age-adjusted death rates for heart disease have declined since
1950, but at a steeper rate since the late 1960s for both sexes and all races (Fig. 1).
Although the decline has affected all groups, there continue to be large differences.
For example, the rate in black men is still 20% higher than in white men, and in
black women it is 50% higher than in white women. Similarly, but much more

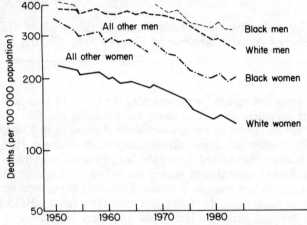

*Figure 1. Age-adjusted death rates for heart disease, according to race and sex: USA,
1950–83.*
Source: National Center for Health Statistics (1) (Fig. 5).

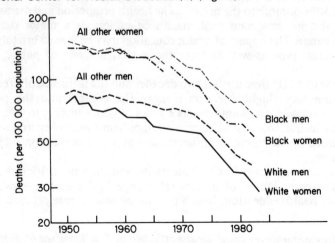

Figure 2. Age-adjusted death rates for stroke, according to race and sex: USA, 1950–83.
Source: National Center for Health Statistics (1) (Fig. 6).

markedly and rapidly, stroke mortality has declined over the corresponding period (Fig. 2). Although the age-adjusted death rates from stroke were very low in 1985 compared with earlier times, the differentials among race and sex groups continue to exist. A recent study (2) that confirmed previous findings documented an overall decline of 28% in the incidence of major coronary events over the period of the late 1950s to the early 1980s. In that study, as well as in others, the decline in incidence rates was higher among individuals of higher socioeconomic status than in others.

Why has mortality declined?

The question is whether the decline is attributable to lifestyle preventive measures, medical care interventions, or both. If both, what is the contribution of each to the decline? If the mortality decline is largely due to a fall in the incidence of the disease, the reasons may lie in preventive measures. On the other hand, if it is due to reductions in case-fatality rates, medical care interventions may be responsible. Even here, however, it should be recognized that the influence of medical care on case-fatality rates may be due to less serious disease resulting from improvement in risk factors achieved as a result of prevention.

Risk factors and lifestyles

Lifestyles and related CHD risk factors include certain dietary habits, physical inactivity, cigarette smoking, and elevated levels of serum cholesterol and blood pressure. About 1964 when the Surgeon General's report on smoking was released (3), more than one-half of men smoked cigarettes on a regular basis compared with about one-third today (Fig. 3). Smoking rates among women remained stable, with about one-third smoking over the entire period of observation. The increase in smoking among women 20 to 24 years old has been offset by a slight decrease in smoking by other age groups.

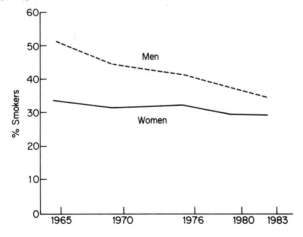

Figure 3. Age-adjusted percentage of persons 20 years of age and over who smoke cigarettes, according to sex: USA, selected years, 1965–83.
Source: National Center for Health Statistics (1) (Fig. 13).

In the 5-year period between the early and late 1970s the age-adjusted percentage of persons 35 to 74 years old with elevated levels of blood pressure has declined in all race and sex groups but more substantially in black women (Fig. 4). Furthermore, the majority of hypertensive persons in the USA today are being detected, treated and controlled compared with only 15% in the early 1970s.

Table 1 depicts the changes, albeit not statistically significant, in the prevalence of elevated serum cholesterol ($\geqslant 260$ mg/dl) for the two periods, 1971–75 and 1976–80, in the four race and sex groups (4). In spite of these small and statistically insignificant changes, alterations in eating patterns have been notable. The intake of foods high in cholesterol and saturated fats such as eggs, dairy products and beef has declined considerably, as well as the mean cholesterol levels among middle-aged men, over the last 10–15 years (5).

As the number of risk factors increases in an individual, so does the risk of CHD mortality. The percentage distribution of risk factors in individuals by race and sex groups and for two time periods (1971–75 and 1976–80) are displayed in Fig. 5. A decrease in the number of people with two or more risk factors and an increase in

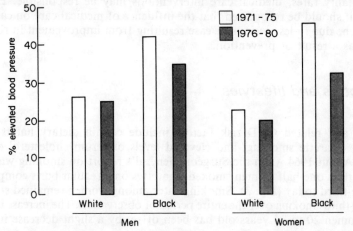

Figure 4. Age-adjusted percentage of persons 35–74 years of age with elevated blood pressure, according to sex and race: USA, 1971–75 and 1976–80.
Source: National Center for Health Statistics (1) (Fig. 14).

Table 1

Age-adjusted prevalence rates of elevated serum cholesterol levels for persons 35–74 years of age, according to race and age: USA, 1971–75 and 1976–80.

Race and sex	Elevated serum cholesterol (rate/100 population)	
	1971–75	1976–80
White		
Men	17·7	19·5
Women	25·9	24·9
Black		
Men	28·2	22·6
Women	23·9	24·3

Source: National Center for Health Statistics (4) (Table B).

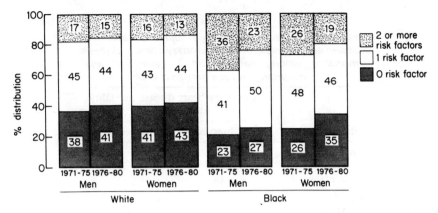

Figure 5. Age-adjusted percentage distribution of persons 35–74 years of age, according to selected number of coronary heart disease risk factors, race, and sex: USA, 1971–75 and 1976–80.
Source: National Center for Health Statistics (4) (Fig. 1).

those with none are noted in all groups, but the changes are more apparent in black men and women.

In addition to the cause and effect relationship suggested by these observations, there were several clinical and community randomized controlled trials which strengthened the belief in such a relationship. For example, Lipid Research Clinics program findings revealed a 24% reduction in deaths from CHD as a result of adherence to a cholesterol-lowering drug and diets low in saturated fats (6). The results of the Multiple Risk Factor Intervention Trial offered additional evidence (7). There was less CHD mortality (but not statistically significant) in men assigned to a stepped-care treatment program for hypertension, counseling for cigarette smoking, and dietary advice to lower blood cholesterol level. That same group of men also showed significant reductions in cigarette smoking and levels of blood pressure and cholesterol.

How much have lifestyle changes contributed to mortality decline?

Now that evidence is compelling that changes in lifestyles have contributed in a major way to the decline in CHD mortality over time, what is the magnitude of their contribution? A thorough analysis indicates that 54% of the decline is attributable to lifestyle changes (serum cholesterol reduction, 30%; cigarette smoking, 24%), 40% to medical interventions (coronary care units, 13·5%; pre-hospital resuscitation, 4%; coronary bypass, 3·5%; medical treatment of clinical ischemic heart disease, 10%; and treatment of hypertension, 9%), leaving 6% not explained, due to errors in estimates (8).

In another analysis (4), the changes in observed CHD mortality reported from Vital Statistics were compared with expected CHD mortality calculated on the basis of changes in risk factors in adults 35 to 74 years old (Table 2). On the basis of risk factor information, expected CHD mortality declined by 13% and 16% for black men and women, and by 7% and 8% for whites, whereas the observed figures were 16% and 24% for black men and women, and 17% and 18% for whites. Dividing the two rates (expected by observed) provides a rough estimate of the contribution to the decline by changes in lifestyles. It ranged from 41% for white men to

Table 2

Percentage decrease in age-adjusted rates for observed and expected coronary heart disease mortality among persons 35–74 years of age, according to race and sex: USA

Race and sex	Coronary heart disease mortality (decrease (%))	
	Observed	Expected
White		
Men	17	7
Women	18	8
Black		
Men	16	13
Women	24	16

Source: National Center for Health Statistics (4) (Table D).

81% for black men. Taken together, lifestyle changes would explain at least 50% of the decline in CHD mortality. This estimate compares favorably with the estimate derived in the previous study by a more thorough method of analysis. It can be safely concluded, therefore, that at least 50% of the decline in CHD mortality may be attributed to changes in lifestyles.

Behavioral change and health education

Since the early 1960s, American health professionals and the public have been informed on a systematic and continuous basis of the risk factors of CHD and ways of controlling them. The message has been advanced through various means, including professional health education strategies and numerous other forms. The latter have included the media, the influence of political and other well-known figures, and advertising.

Definitions

Health education.   The term health education has been used to
represent consciously constructed opportunities for learning which are designed to facilitate changes in behaviour toward a pre-determined goal . . . it is essentially an educational activity involving some form of communication designed to improve knowledge, and develop understanding in skills which are conducive to health (9).
It is widely agreed that health education in the form of imparting knowledge is not sufficient to change behavior. Examples abound, such as those who understand the health effects of cigarette smoking but who continue to smoke.

Behavior modification.   Health education activities must be accompanied by behavioral change in order to accomplish favorable effects. This is a complex area that is in need of further research. In behavior modification,
an individual's behaviour or response is shaped towards some pre-determined outcome by means of positive or negative reinforcement of behaviour, or by reward or punishment

through manipulation of the environment . . . behaviour modification is the end-point in the knowledge, attitude, behaviour (KAB) chain which forms the basis of many early health education strategies (9).

Health promotion and disease prevention.   Concepts related to health education and behavioral change are health promotion and disease prevention. Health promotion may be defined as

the process of enabling individuals and communities to increase control over the determinants of health and thereby improve their health . . . [it] represents a mediating strategy between people and their environments, combining personal choice with social responsibility for health to create a healthier future . . . it starts and ends with the local community (9).

In contrast to health promotion, disease prevention

is normally used to represent strategies designed either to reduce risk factors for specific disease, or enhance host factors that reduce susceptibility to disease . . . [it] is essentially an activity in the medical field dealing with individuals or particularly defined groups at risk.

In the final analysis,

health promotion and disease prevention can be seen as two separate but complementary activities which overlap in a variety of situations and circumstances (9).

Governmental public health education: the Finnish experience

There are several examples of governments taking responsibility for educating the public with respect to health. The Tobacco Act of 1976 in Finland, for example, made health authorities responsible for health education. The Act obligated the state to spend about $0 \cdot 5\%$ of tobacco revenues on health education (10). In addition, a differential price policy was developed aimed at reducing total consumption and promoting brands with lower tar and nicotine. Restrictions were legislated on tobacco advertising and placed an upper limit on the content of harmful substances. Also, labeling of packages and prohibiting sales to minors were required.

Interview surveys during implementation of the Finnish smoking control program revealed changing patterns of consumption and smoking habits among adults (10). Smoking initially declined but subsequently leveled off. In 1975, 40% of adult males smoked, but in 1984 only 33%. The decrease in smoking was especially noted among the better educated. Although in that study mortality from diseases associated with smoking could not be determined because of small numbers, it was clear that health education in its various forms made some impact on the number of smokers. These findings, as well as the social class differential in smoking behavior, are in agreement with US findings.

Media impact

Health education through the media is an important force in changing people's behavior. When the TV news anchor person announced one evening that a leading medical journal had reported that the use of oral contraceptives combined with smoking increases the risk of heart attacks, a very powerful message was conveyed, especially when he went on to say, without equivocation, that women who smoke should not use oral contraceptives, and vice versa.

The impact of broadcast media on changing behavior has been a subject of speculation. Recently, its impact on the rate of suicide among teenagers has been documented. The rates of suicide among American teenagers before and after televised news or feature stories about suicide have been analysed (11). In the week following the broadcasts, the observed number of suicides was significantly greater than the expected number. The difference remained after controlling for several confounding variables. It was concluded that

> the best available explanation is that television stories about suicide trigger additional suicides, perhaps because of imitation (11).

Further evidence about imitative behavior was suggested by comparing the number of completed and attempted teenage suicides before and after televising fictional films. Both types were reported to be significantly greater after the broadcasts than before (12). It was concluded that

> the results are consistent with the hypothesis that some teenage suicides are imitative and that alternative explanations to the findings . . . are unlikely to account for the increase in attempted and completed suicides (12).

The influence of well-known personalities

Another sort of health education message may be imparted by political and other well-known figures. The interest of President Kennedy in mental retardation (and the knowledge by the public of the presence of the condition in a member of his family), the widely publicized conditions of Presidents Eisenhower and Johnson with heart attacks, of Mrs Ford and Mrs Rockefeller with breast cancer, of President Reagan with colon cancer, and of Rock Hudson with acquired immune deficiency syndrome (AIDS), have all contributed to knowledge and behavior about these conditions among the American public, and possibly elsewhere.

Advertising

The power of advertising in imparting knowledge and changing behavior is enormous. Consider, for example, the advertisements on cigarette smoking which depict health, youth, fun, vigor, and sex. Notice that the health message about the harmful effects of smoking is almost invisible in the message portraying the wonderful life associated with smoking. These advertisements must be increasing sales and profits, otherwise companies would not be investing huge sums of money in them. Perhaps health professionals may take the lead from commercial advertising in learning about effective means of changing behaviors. Educational campaigns attempting to change behavior should make use of electronic and printed media in a manner similar to commercial advertising in order to induce the desired effects.

The clinical and public health approaches

The clinical approach encompasses an interaction between the individual and a health care professional on a one-to-one basis. The public health approach, on the other hand, is related to the societal and political concerns of the community. Each approach entails understanding of and concern about disease classification, area of emphasis, type of encounter and method of intervention, outcome measures, and responsibility.

Disease classification

In disease classification, the clinical and individual viewpoint has relied mostly on a dichotomous model that divides the population into well and ill. Health care personnel as well as patients have found that model useful in knowing what to do with the ill. That system of classification has been important in diagnosing and treating illness. However, the public health and societal quantification of health concerns often revolves around measuring a phenomenon as a continuous rather than a dichotomous variable (a normal curve with a 'tail' towards higher values). This raises a classification issue of how to separate the well from the ill. The continuous distribution generally blurs that distinction.

Several methods have been proposed to divide a continuous distribution:
(1) The use of cut-off points beyond which subsequent mortality and morbidity would ensue with greater likelihood.
(2) The use of the statistical concept of standard deviation in claiming that those above 2 or 2·5 standard deviations are 'ill'. Statistically, however, these are unusually frequent rather than abnormal cases.
(3) An approach was devised by Cochrane (13) to perform randomized controlled trials at various pre-determined levels of the distribution to verify whether administering a treatment would do more good than harm. This approach requires the performance of several randomized trials, which may not be practicable. It also requires conditions that would respond to treatment in a known way, which may not be feasible. The approach, however, is innovative and worthy of consideration.

Areas of emphasis

The second attribute of the clinical versus public health approach is the area of emphasis. In the clinical model, the emphasis is on disease prevention, which has been previously defined. Prevention may be classified into primary, secondary, and tertiary. The most prominent primary prevention measure in clinical practice is of course immunization. Secondary and tertiary preventive measures are designed to lessen the burden of illness and improve survival rates.

The area of emphasis in the public health approach is also disease prevention as described in the clinical model, but more importantly it is the area of health promotion. This entails modifying lifestyles through behavioral change to achieve well-being, including emphasis on physical activity, cessation of smoking, maintaining an ideal body weight, eating diets with less saturated fats but with high fiber, and appropriate measures of coping with stress.

Type of encounter and method of intervention

The third characteristic is the type of encounter and method of intervention. In the clinical model, the individual perceives a problem and seeks help from a health care professional. In public health, the approach is more pro-active than reactive in that it is designed to avoid problems. In the clinical model, the encounter is one-to-one between individuals and health professionals. The method of intervention includes periodic health examination, individual counseling and treatment.

The public health model may be viewed from two different time periods. At the turn of the century, environmental problems such as polluted air, contaminated water, and poor housing were important determinants of health. Intervention at that time was to purify the air, chlorinate the water, pasteurize the milk, and provide good sanitary housing — measures that required very little from individual behavior. In addition to these environmental activities, masses of the population were immunized to prevent and control epidemics.

In view of the currently known risk factors, people's lifestyle becomes a major determinant of health. Methods of intervention include mass immunization, media publicity, and health education of large numbers of people. An environmental intervention of current problems would entail, for example, working with industry to produce low-fat, low-cholesterol and high-fiber diets. The latter approach is an environmental measure that only requires the encouragement of individuals to switch to different foods — a simpler behavioral change than that requiring the individual to engage in regular and vigorous physical activity, for example.

Outcome measures

The fourth characteristic is outcome measures. In the clinical model, the severity of illness and survival are of concern. In the public health model, trends of disease and death over time are of interest, such as the declining CHD incidence described earlier. In the clinical model, a single value (of serum cholesterol, for example) in a patient serves as an indicator. In the public health model, the changes in a population distribution of a characteristic provide an excellent indicator. The shift of the population mean for cholesterol towards the lower levels observed in recent years is a good example.

Responsibility for prevention

Finally, the issue of whether prevention is solely an individual or also a societal responsibility surely raises colorful debates. Preventive measures may be grouped into three classes, as those requiring:

(1) Only individual behavior, and therefore entirely the individual's responsibility, of which a good example is physical activity.

(2) Interaction between an individual and a health care professional, and therefore the responsibility of both. These include periodic health examinations, control of hypertension, and immunizations.

(3) Interaction between society at large and an individual, and therefore the responsibility of both. Examples include laws governing the use of seat-belts or speed limits.

Who should pay for preventive measures?

It is widely acknowledged by many countries that medical care is a right and not a privilege, and therefore the cost of such activities is borne by society (through reimbursement by third parties). This is not true for preventive measures. It is perhaps in this area that society must decide whether preventive measures are equally important as medical care procedures. Since the decline of cardiovascular diseases over time can be explained both by medical care and by prevention, it does not make much sense to reimburse former activities and not the latter. The fact that preventive measures have accounted for at least half the decline should justify their inclusion in a comprehensive health care system. Acceptance of the impact of prevention on health states will help society decide on who is responsible for prevention and what priority it should occupy.

Before concluding, it must be emphasized that while clinicians practice the clinical approach, some also practice the public health approach and their informed support and participation in this approach could be useful. Furthermore, the clinical encounter often offers an opportunity for health promotional activities.

In summary, and in order to achieve maximum impact on health states, the clinical approach must be combined with the public health approach. Prevention is both an individual and a societal responsibility and, given its promise, it should be a priority for both.

References

(1) US Department of Health and Human Services. *Health, United States 1985*. DHHS publication no. (PHS)86-1232. Washington: US Government Printing Office, 1986.

(2) Pell S, Fayerweather WE. Trends in the incidence of myocardial infarction and in associated mortality and morbidity in a large employed population, 1957–1983. *N Engl J Med* 1985; **312**: 1005–11.

(3) US Department of Health, Education and Welfare. *Smoking and health*. Report of the Advisory Committee to the Surgeon General of the Public Health Service. PHS publication no. 1103. Washington: US Government Printing Office, 1964.

(4) US Department of Health and Human Services. *Health, United States 1983*. DHHS publication no. (PHS)84-1232. Washington: US Government Printing Office, 1984.

(5) Stamler J. Nutrition-related risk factors for the atherosclerotic diseases — present status. *Prog Biochem Pharmacol* 1983; **19**: 245–308.

(6) Lipid Research Clinics program. The Lipid Research Clinics Coronary Primary Prevention Trial results: I. Reduction in incidence of coronary heart disease. *J Am Med Assoc* 1984; **251**: 351–64.

(7) Multiple Risk Factor Intervention Trial Research Group. Multiple Risk Factor Intervention Trial: risk factor changes and mortality results. *J Am Med Assoc* 1982; **248**: 1465–77.

(8) Goldman L, Cook EF. The decline in ischemic heart disease mortality rates. An analysis of the comparative effects of medical interventions and changes in lifestyle. *Ann Intern Med* 1984; **101**: 825–36.

(9) Anonymous. Health promotion glossary. *Health Promotion* 1986; **1**: 113–26.

(10) Leppo K, Vertio H. Smoking control in Finland. A case study in policy formulation and implementation. *Health Promotion* 1986; **1**: 5–16.

(11) Phillips DP, Carstensen LL. Clustering of teenage suicides after television news stories about suicide. *N Engl J Med* 1986; **315**: 685–9.

(12) Gould MS, Shaffer D. The impact of suicide in television movies. Evidence of imitation. *N Engl J Med* 1986; **315**: 690–4.

(13) Cochrane AL. The history of the measurement of ill health. *Int J Epidemiol* 1972; **1**: 89–92.

Discussion

Dr Brody

I believe there have been studies in the USA examining the public's response about the extent to which lifestyle changes should be a factor in the financing of health care. There would be some popular support for a programme that charged smokers more for their medical care if they developed one of the diseases related to smoking. In effect, this would be a way of trying to enforce lifestyle change by financial penalty.

Given Professor Ibrahim's definitions of health education, and the way it is linked directly to change in behaviour — not offering people options but saying what they *ought to do* — is this a logical outgrowth of health education from his perspective?

Does Sir Douglas Black think that there would be problems with such a scheme, and that it would be yet another way of overtaxing the lower socioeconomic groups? These groups are less able to modify behaviour when given health education, so that a financial penalty would basically be a way of increasing the tax burden on the poor for the health system.

Sir Douglas Black

The problems about charging the 'victim', as it were, are, first, that it is unjust but, secondly — much worse than that — it is impracticable. People would be in the situation of 'enjoy now, pay later' — and they might die before they could pay, which would be unfortunate from the state's point of view as well as from the individual's. (Incidentally, I heartily endorse Professor Ibrahim's point that there is not a fixed distinction between individual and population responsibilities.)

On the same theme of disincentives, instead of having a percentage of tax revenue given to health education it might have been more prudent to have a fixed and agreed sum. Otherwise, health educators would have an interest in tobacco sales, which subconsciously might be unfortunate.

Professor Ibrahim

As Dr Brody has pointed out, the problem with incentives is that the poor will be taxed more than the rich because the changes will occur more in the well educated than in the less educated. In the USA, I understand that some insurance companies already give preferential rates to non-smokers. I do not know whether this goes beyond smoking, and whether preferential rates are given to people who exercise or eat certain kinds of foods, and so on.

I do not think that we have yet reached the point at which health education would be provided and people told that they *must* do certain things. That is behaviour modification. We probably have to stop at providing health education. This is very much the same as providing a form of treatment, in that it is provided and paid for whether or not it works. I suppose health education could be provided, but why should we demand that it produces a required change more than is expected from usual interventions?

Professor Pardes

If the intention was prevention it would be unlikely to have much effect, but if it was punitive perhaps there would be an effect, although I am not sure that is desirable.

Sir Douglas Black alluded to a study which split the practice population of general practitioners (GPs) and followed them for 5 years (1). First, were there any changes in morbidity? Secondly, what would have been the expected mortality? I have no sense of the numbers involved. It is hard to gauge how significant it is that there was no difference, without a standard or expected death rate and a size of population on which to make a judgement.

Sir Douglas Black

The total population size would be about 10 000 or 15 000. This was a group of GPs rather than a single practice. I think that tests of significance were applied. Questions about morbidity are almost impossible to answer because of lack of an adequate database. There are three indices in use:

(1) The GP Survey, which is a small sample, but which has diagnostic precision.

(2) The General Household Survey, which is a large sample, and asks questions about morbidity. This gives larger numbers, but has no diagnostic precision.

(3) A 9000-person survey of morbidity, which has shown the rather interesting result that anything that happens in relation to differential mortality between the social classes is mirrored — and indeed often exceeded — by morbidity. This is the best sample so far.

I think that there would be no hard information on morbidity in the Holland study (1). He has analysed the results only in terms of mortality. The material should be available in the GPs' records to allow that analysis, but of course there is a gap between actual and perceived morbidity, and also between the great mass of morbidity that never gets as far as a doctor's surgery and that which is actually recorded.

Dr Tonkin

With regard to smoking advertisements, does Professor Ibrahim feel that many of our presentations to the public are counter-productive? The cigarette advertisements do not advertise smoking; they just correlate it with totally irrelevant things like sex, mountain streams, strength and motorcycles. In the UK, these advertisements must carry 'Government health warning' but, unlike us, the advertisers know that the human animal is singularly counter-reactive to instructions. One of the powerful effects is that the ordinary person reading the warning asks why the government should tell *him* what he should do. Perhaps the fact that the warning is printed ever larger means that the tobacco industry is capitalizing on this. We should perhaps take a lesson here from the industry. The only really good *medical* advertisement that I have seen showed three men looking at a very pretty girl, saying 'Ah, but she smells like an ashtray'.

I understand that in the USA about 14 multinationals have committed a very large sum of money — some tens of million dollars — to institute personal counselling within the workplace. It is well recognized, of course, that a comforting spouse at home reduces the risk of coronaries. I think industry recognizes that a similar counselling service in the workplace might double the prevention rate for both coronaries and breast cancer. Industry does not usually invest large sums of money unless it is reasonably sure to get returns, and the idea of person-to-person counselling seems an excellent one.

This point was made by Professor Kenneth Pellitier of the University of California, San Francisco, in a recent talk in London about this initiative from industry. I wonder whether other people know about it.

Dr Bondurant

It certainly is true that US industry is making very substantial investments in counselling programmes and other things — in the aggregate, I suspect much larger even than tens of millions of dollars. One result is that offices have been created within personnel departments of the larger industries and people with various credentials in health promotion have been recruited. One of the problems is that there is no generally accepted credential, so a number of people are being employed by industry whose experience is, at best, limited and shaky.

Another result is that several companies have been formed exclusively for the purpose of servicing industries on contract with health promotional programmes for their employees. These are very competitive groups, and they make exorbitant claims. Many of us are concerned that, sooner or later, some of the industries that have invested heavily in health promotion will discover that the claims that were made cannot be substantiated in terms of actual savings to the industry.

Therefore, I would say that the question is still open as to whether or not the volume of investment by US industry in health promotion endeavours at the present time will prove to have been prudent or premature, given the entrepreneurial and competitive nature of the characters involved. I am influenced by the fact that some of them are quite suspect.

Professor Ibrahim

I agree that the question remains open. However, I would think that industry should be able to measure the impact of those programmes. Productivity or days of absence from work are easy measures with which to find out whether or not such programmes are working.

As I understand it, even in industry we again come to this link between social class and education. Many of the people who participate in such programmes will be the white-collar executive-type workers rather than the others.

Mr Mahon

In New York City the United Way system has now introduced a programme called 'Health Guard'. United Way goes to the various corporations, industries, banks, insurance companies, etc. to raise funds. A series of about 15 seminars is held, generally at lunchtime. The employers provide the facilities, sometimes with a lunch.

Since the American Cancer Society, the American Heart Association, the local hospitals and agencies that provide care for the ageing are the recipients of the United Way funds, they have volunteered to provide the lectures without any cost to the employers. They are well attended, and have been very successful in the New York area. In Virginia, the national headquarters for United Way in the USA, people are currently being trained to do this throughout the country. The wide reach of United Way in the USA should bring a great deal of public education to the workplace.

Dr Mayer

Is there any assessment — any evaluation — associated with that?

Mr Mahon

I think so far it is just observation and word of mouth because it has been developed only during the past year. The people with whom I have spoken have said that it has been a very great success. Employers are delighted with it. They were accustomed to see the United Way people coming to raise money once a year, and now they find there is a presence all the year, and that something is being brought back to the workplace as well as taken away.

Mr Lewin

Probably the most sophisticated programme in the USA is Johnson and Johnson's 'Live for Life' programme. This has been substantially evaluated and assessed, showing that the long-term benefits or outcomes cannot be measured. They are therefore examining more short-term programmes to discover how many people have been successful in losing weight or in stopping smoking and so on.

Incidentally, there is some resistance to health programmes because it is not possible to measure outcomes. Those companies that we surveyed were adopting 'wellness' and health promotion programmes not so much because they thought there would be any substantial savings, or even because they thought there would be improvements in productivity, but rather because these programmes, through their general popularity, have become employee-bonding methods. They are very popular, they become social activities during the lunch hour and so on. It is realized that there *may* be a long-term benefit, but probably no really measurable result.

Another interesting effort is by the state of Utah in which discounts have been provided on premiums for state employees who neither smoke nor drink. This is heavily reinforced in Utah because most of the population are Mormons. It has been widely accepted in what is essentially a middle-class population. It is not so much an increase in premiums as a decrease — a kind of discount.

Sir Douglas Black's data about the relatively poor impact of health education by social class seem particularly poignant. We hear much about this. Does he or Professor Ibrahim know of any additional research that might explain whether there are conditions that are amenable, and whether the nature of the response is known? Is it simply that middle-class methods are being used which are known to work with middle-class populations, and which need to be adapted, or are there other factors which ought to be understood as a matter of public policy?

Sir Douglas Black

One of the pioneers of industrial medicine, Thomas Legge, said at the turn of the century that any measures intended to prevent accidents in the workplace must be such that the worker cannot turn them off. This, of course, is a historical anecdote from the days when people were paid by piece-work. Nowadays, it would be less applicable, although I think it has some relevance. I do not know how it would be translated into health education, except in the rather negative and puritanical sense that there should not be off-licences and cigarette shops anywhere near the factory floor.

The failure of health education to reach social classes IV and V is most notable with regard to heart disease, where I think the failure of penetration and subsequent action makes a real difference.

Professor Ibrahim

This whole area of changing behaviour by social class is an obvious area for research. We use middle-class methods, and perhaps do not reach the people we want to reach. The less educated, lower socioeconomic classes have so much on their minds, in terms of employment, housing, taking care of their children, and just day-to-day survival, that health promotion or disease prevention takes a fairly low priority. We need to understand that and perhaps approach the subject in a different way.

Professor Rabkin

We have been working with Johnson and Johnson at my institution, Beth Israel Hospital, in Boston, and have instituted a Live for Life programme within the hospital as an employee benefit, primarily because it affords another opportunity for connections, for employee-bonding, rather than for measurable benefits. I am sure that Johnson and Johnson would love to find indices, whether absent days, productivity or something like that, but that will be much more difficult.

It is indeed true that although this is a classless benefit, the entry-level workers are much more diffident about participating than the others. It takes some time for them to feel comfortable in the same environment.

Professor Stevens

If, indeed, we are dealing with concepts of statistical risk rather than identifying high-risk groups, in some respects the whole enterprise does not match what the medical profession and medical educators have trained physicians to do. Is health education really part of medicine? We have heard much about how health education is education, marketing and communications. At the same time, a certain uneasiness is being revealed about the role of the medical profession in this.

If one of the goals is to achieve small shifts in behaviour from large numbers of people through prevention and health promotion; if we recognize the enormous effectiveness of communications, the media and marketing, and huge changes in their effectiveness as requiring completely separate skills from medical skills; if, again, we look at the whole army of people in industry, in education, in the workplace, in psychology, and in organizations such as Weight Watchers, who are all doing 'health promotion' to a greater or lesser extent—what then is the role for physicians?

Are there places in both countries where there are new programmes which bring some of these communications and marketing (media) skills into the medical arena, seeking to define health promotion as communications and as education, taking it away from health promotion in terms of traditional forms of public health, or even health promotion linked with health services research and evaluation?

Professor Ibrahim

Perhaps Dr Bondurant, as Dean, could say something about the efforts in North Carolina. In my opinion, it is unfair to require physicians to know, or even to be educated, about health promotion and disease prevention at the community level when so many advertising and communication skills are required. This is a profession in itself. If I have a heart attack I would prefer to go to a physician who knows how to treat my heart rather than how to communicate health education measures.

However, the two approaches are complementary. In the University of North Carolina we have developed a centre of health promotion where the medical school, the school of public health as well as other health sciences' schools—dentistry, pharmacy and nursing—complement one another and work together. The public health professional and the physician work hand-in-hand to combine the two approaches to make an impact on the population.

Sir Douglas Black

The reason why we do not use the media more is because they are so very expensive. Our antagonists use them a great deal; we need more money to compete.

Is this a job for doctors? I remember a slightly acid comment in the *New England Journal of Medicine* to the effect that for communicating health information the skills of patience, good communication, and so on are needed—and that there are people who possess those skills, called 'teachers'. I am not sure that is necessarily true. I do not think it is a job entirely for doctors, but they have a vital part to play in the individual situation, as Professor Ibrahim mentioned.

Dr Bondurant

As a dean, perhaps I should elaborate briefly on Professor Ibrahim's comment. The Faculty in the School of Medicine, Chapel Hill, has addressed at some length the question of whether or not the physician should have a significant role in education. A fair summary of its conclusions would be that the physician has a role to play, certainly not the only role and not necessarily the dominant one. The one-to-one patient encounter in the context of a routine examination, a well-baby clinic and so on, or in the care of a specific illness, if, say, some of the 'receptors' are unoccupied and there is opportunity for health promotional education, is somehow different from other kinds of context.

With that in mind, the curriculum committees in the medical school have examined what curricular content in health promotion should be inserted in each of the different clinical courses of instruction. These are beginning to be put in place. In some departments, of course, this is very 'old hat'. Paediatrics, for example, has had health promotional considerations as a part of the clinical instruction in well-baby clinics for a very long time. The paediatricians are taking the lead in showing others—even the surgeons, for example, in accident prevention—what kinds of instruction can be useful for the medical student to have in order to communicate health promotion to patients.

Another aspect of this that has proved interesting is that our students discovered that they were not as effective in instructing their patients as they would like to be, especially in the paediatric age group. A number of volunteer school teachers have been recruited locally to teach them how to teach and communicate effectively. There has been a project for a number of years for students to go into the schools to teach health promotional courses to 7th graders, and to perfect their communication skills. This would not be the only source of that kind of information, but would help to give the paediatricians of the future an opportunity to influence 7th graders.

Professor Jennett

On the question of non-doctors having an important input in this regard, we succeeded in obtaining money for health promotion lecturers in the medical school at Glasgow, both in dentistry and medicine. It has been extremely difficult to find and appoint the right people.

Having persuaded the doctors that we might take some non-doctors, I then could not persuade the professors of sociology and education to agree that the people we wanted to appoint were sufficiently good sociologists or educationalists.

This is the familiar and very difficult problem of the old multidisciplinary set-up with basic scientists and clinicians, who are too 'heavy' for light work and too 'light' for heavy work.

Sir John Walton

Would Professor Ibrahim or any of the US participants like to comment on what they see as the value of the health education newsletters that are produced by various universities and professional organizations, which I gather are increasing their circulation in the USA?

Professor Ibrahim

I do not know what is their formal impact. I suppose they do a little good, but I am not sure how much.

Dr Mayer

For what it is worth, the Harvard health letter is the only document that is read by every one on my staff.

Dr Rue

I want to take up Sir Douglas Black's point about the message being uncertain. The fact that it is uncertain does not mean that the medical profession should therefore opt out of the discussion. It is just as valuable to share with the public, who need to know — and give evidence that they want to know — what the profession feels certain about and what it feels uncertain about. In the National Health Service (NHS) we have used that kind of analysis to select some targets for programmes which we think are worth supporting and we have invested some money into them. We are giving priority to areas where we think the evidence is harder than most, if not absolutely conclusive, recognizing that we are investing for a fairly long-term future.

Of course, what will happen is partly unpredictable. Whether or not behaviour is influenced by investing in health promotion programmes remains to be seen — but that itself is very interesting. As behaviour changes, we also need the kind of programme that can monitor what is happening. I see it as a responsibility of the medical profession to participate in this.

In the UK the specialty of community medicine has become responsible for health promotion. It is very largely responsible for guiding some of the NHS programmes. The Royal College of Physicians of Edinburgh has set up a health promotion unit. There is agreement, in principle, that the Faculty of Community Medicine at the Royal College of Physicians in London should set up a health promotion unit, and this is being developed.

One of the difficulties is appointing the right people to coordinate some of the skills mentioned, and to direct them towards the targets that we are trying to reach. Many doctors have not been trained in this, as has been pointed out already.

Sir Douglas Black

I think that it is a most important part of health education to convey the idea that doctors, like other people, have to live with uncertainty. We have to be honest and say that we do not know everything.

Dr Horder

Certainly we do assume that health education is part of the role of the GP (or primary care doctor) in the UK. There is some evidence that the relationship of the GP with patients, together with the contact provided by a recent illness, makes an opportunity which should not be missed, and which can supplement the education from the media. Messages are best if they come from two or more directions.

A number of medical schools are now doing more than in the past towards the teaching of 'communication', as a training for that role.

Professor Ibrahim

If I may close on a personal note, having chosen the field of public health over a quarter of a century ago, I am totally delighted that health promotion and disease prevention have occupied a conspicuous part of the programme of this conference.

Reference

(1) Tilson HH. In: Holland WW, Detels R, Knox G, eds. *Oxford textbook of public health*; Vol. 1. Oxford: Oxford University Press, 1984: Chapter 12.

CAN THE HEALTH CARE SYSTEM CONTROL THE
DEMANDS OF NEW TECHNOLOGY?

1. The cost-effectiveness of technology development

Chairman:
SIR JOHN WALTON
Oxford, UK

A UK view

MARTIN J. BUXTON

Director, Health Economics Research Group, Brunel University,
Uxbridge, Middlesex, UK

Introduction

Internationally, health care systems face the problem of an excess of technically feasible, and at least marginally beneficial, health care interventions that cannot be afforded within the sums that societies (individually or collectively) are willing and able to pay for health care. It is generally accepted that even if all health care that is positively harmful to the patient or provides *no* positive benefit can be eliminated, the remaining beneficial possibilities will still exceed the resources available. Technology development seems simply to add to the problem. This is true even in those societies such as the USA where relatively large proportions of large per capita national products are spent on health care. The problem is all the greater in a country such as the UK that chooses to spend rather more modest proportions of its much smaller per capita national income on health care.

However, whilst the UK and the USA share this underlying common problem, its manifestation seems very different. The health care system in the USA, like many others with a system of insurance-based individual entitlements, is preoccupied with *cost-containment*. It seeks ways of reducing the total cost of health care. Cost-containment is not the real problem in the UK, however. Here the problem is one of benefit maximization of obtaining the best value from the resources devoted to health care. To achieve this, we need both information on costs and benefits (or cost-effectiveness) of health care interventions, *and* a system for translating such information into appropriate patterns of health care expenditure.

The UK system and technology adoption

The UK system is already highly effective in containing costs. The overall level of public expenditure on health care is determined neither by the health service consumers, nor by the health service suppliers, nor indeed is it a function of explicit rights to specific treatments. It is of course a political decision, just like the decision

Health Care Provision under Financial Constraint, edited by T. B. Binns and M. Firth, 1988: Royal Society of Medicine International Congress and Symposium Series No. 115, published by Royal Society of Medicine Services Ltd.

on defence spending. Cash limits are set for expenditure in the next year that allow for an agreed level of price and wage increases, and these are not automatically increased if, in fact, the costs of care increase in excess of the allowance. The resultant controllability of health service expenditure is impressive. Not since 1976–77 has the actual out-turn expenditure on the 'hospital and community health services' exceeded the pre-determined cash limit. In 1985–86 the provisional out-turn showed, typically, a 0·1% underspending (1).

The family practitioner services (including general medical and dental practitioners and pharmaceutical services) which account for approximately 20% of total public expenditure on health are *not* (as yet) cash limited. Nevertheless, the systems for settling doctors' pay and pharmaceutical prices (the Review Bodies on Doctors' and Dentists' Remuneration, and the Pharmaceutical Price Regulation Scheme) together permit very close control of expenditure under these heads. The health service cost explosion, as far as the UK is concerned, is a very carefully controlled detonation.

In fact, expenditure on acute in-patient care, the area most obviously affected by technological developments, rose by a total of only 3·6% in real terms during the 9-year period from 1976–77 to 1984–85 (2).

Given this overall constraint, it is not surprising that observers have noted the striking differences in the extent of the use of certain technologies in the UK and the USA (3). The differences can of course be interpreted to suggest over-provision in the USA rather than under-provision in the UK (4). Indeed, both levels could be optimal for the countries concerned (5). The pattern of provision in each country should reflect a set of value judgements (individual or social) about the relative benefit that can be achieved with available resources in alternative uses, both within the health care sector and between health care and other competing sectors.

Incentives and mechanisms influencing technology use

Rather than making comparisons about levels of technology adoption, it is perhaps more useful to consider the nature of the incentives and mechanisms that influence the adoption and diffusion of technology.

One of the biggest problems of the tightly cash-limited system is that, in itself, it offers no incentives to maximize output by adopting techniques that may reduce unit cost. A technology that, for example, permits a reduction in length of stay, whilst reducing unit cost, is likely to increase the total cost of the ward, specialty, or hospital, by freeing beds for additional cases. Overall cost reductions can only be achieved by reducing capacity at the same time—closing beds and/or reducing staff. Such actions are both administratively difficult and politically sensitive. Hence, the all too realistic anecdote of the health authority treasurer in the UK living in perpetual fear of his consultants suddenly taking health economics to heart, becoming much more efficient, increasing throughput, and vastly overspending the hospital's budget.

The absence of competition between hospitals reduces the adoption of technology to attract customers but public pressure, often aroused by particular clinicians, is important in leading to the local introduction of 'popular' technology. Indeed, public subscription and charitable foundations have played a prominent role in providing the initial capital costs of new technologies, thus exerting leverage on authorities to take on the subsequent costs of running the equipment, expanding the service and later replacing the capital (6,7).

Performance indicators

Increasingly, 'performance indicators' are being used to generate competition by example, and political and administrative pressure but, in that these tend to be almost totally input oriented, with very crude measures of effect (cases, out-patient visits, etc.), they are no guarantee of cost-effectiveness. Costs, as measured in such crude indicators, can be reduced by transferring costs elsewhere — to other parts of the health care system or to the public care sector. Early discharge, for example, can reduce measured cost per case, even if the true cost per case is increased by a subsequent need to re-admit. For example, between 1974 and 1984 the number of deaths and discharges per bed (for all specialties) in the National Health Service (NHS) (England) rose from $13 \cdot 1-18 \cdot 4$. For surgical beds the increase was from $31 \cdot 1-39 \cdot 8$. Over the same period the number of day cases increased by 77% (8). Such changes are cited politically as improvements in cost-effectiveness. Unfortunately, there are not the data to establish whether they represent a real reduction in cost, an increase in effectiveness, both or neither.

Private costs

The pressure on the UK system discourages consideration of private costs. The obviously inefficient use of patients' time reflects the fact that there are few incentives to take this into account. The small private sector in the UK undoubtedly benefits from this, by offering a service much more geared to consumer (patient) convenience.

Determining priorities

In terms of alternative uses of scarce resources for different services to different patient groups, the process of determining priorities is very much a political process. For many years Department of Health and Social Security policy has indicated to local health authorities the priorities that should be adopted — particularly a shift in emphasis from acute care to care for priority groups such as the elderly, mentally ill and mentally handicapped (9,10). The process of central indication of priorities has more recently been reinforced by the process of regional and district reviews which provide an opportunity to establish that such priorities are being observed. In addition, specific numerical targets have been set for a number of services such as treatment of renal disease but, as yet, priorities have been influenced only marginally by questions of cost-effectiveness.

Possible directions of technology development

Diagnostic technology

Much public attention on technology has been focused on capital-embodied technology, particularly diagnostic technology that involves large-scale capital investment such as computerized axial tomography (CAT) and now nuclear magnetic resonance (NMR) scanning. These will no doubt continue to figure large in the public perception of technology. Such technologies have tended to encourage centralization and specialization. To minimize their institutional costs high throughputs are required, thus reducing the capital cost per patient (although this may simply transfer costs to the patient in increased travel time, work loss, etc.). Their effectiveness depends on the extent to which the improved diagnosis can lead to improved treatment or at least to less invasive diagnosis. Their high capital cost means that usually specific (and potentially controllable) decisions are made on location. A number of evaluation studies have been carried out in this field.

Human skills

A second area of technology development is that of human capital—embodied technology—particularly new surgical skills, for example, in the field of transplantation. These developments are restricted to certain locations which have the necessary support facilities, but in themselves do not usually involve the explicit decision-making (and scope for regulation) associated with the purchase of specific major items of capital.

New locations and types of health care

However, the technological developments that pose more fundamental challenges to the health care system are perhaps those that may release the provision of care from existing physical locational constraints. For example, the development of 'kits and sticks' pathology testing may shift the locus of initial diagnostic care and subsequent monitoring away from the large hospital (and its pathology laboratory) to the individual general practitioner (GP) in his surgery or to small convenient peripheral hospitals (or indeed to the patient's home). The same trend could be encouraged by a continuing shift away from traditional surgery—both in terms of increased use of drug-based alternatives, and the substitution of such practices as percutaneous transluminal coronary angioplasty (PTCA) or the use of lasers in conjunction with endoscopy without the need for general anaesthesia. Finally, the development of informatics and expert systems may be able to provide the general doctor with the effective diagnostic and treatment skills of the highly specialized consultant. Indeed, more highly automated processes for diagnosis and testing may offer the chance to provide much health care using technical facilities rather than traditionally skilled manpower.

Whilst it is possible, at least tentatively, to identify possible technological directions, it is quite impossible to draw any broad conclusions as to their likely cost-effectiveness. It is important to set up early warning systems about *possible* impacts of technological change and illustratively to explore possible scenarios (11). Each technology will need to be evaluated and its specific impacts on costs and effectiveness identified. However, if sensible decisions are to be made about such possible far-reaching technological changes as those summarized above, the concepts of cost and of effectiveness will need to be broad and fairly sophisticated.

Measuring cost-effectiveness

Quality-adjusted life year measurement

Currently in the UK there is a resurgence of interest in using cost per quality-adjusted life year (QALY) as a basic measure of cost-effectiveness. The recent interest has been spurred particularly by the wide publication of work by Alan Williams (12,13). In principle, QALYs can provide a common measure of cost-effectiveness for a wide variety of interventions, thus enabling the relative *value* of alternative ways of spending (marginal) health service resources to be directly compared.

The concept has been developed and applied in North America, notably by Torrance and colleagues, at McMaster University (14), and Weinstein and colleagues, at Harvard (15). The underlying logic of this measure of efficiency is becoming more widely accepted, and the potential value of, and scope for, systematically using such information to help to establish priorities for resource allocation are enormous. There are, however, still a number of practical problems in the calculation and subsequent interpretation of costs per QALY.

Measurements of cost

As has already been indicated, we need broader measures of cost than are typically available in the health service. Choices of technique or technology impose costs on others than the health service institutions — notably the patient and his or her family. Data on such costs need to be collected as part of the process of evaluation. In addition, the cost estimates need to be locally relevant, and appropriate to the particular nature and timing of the decision. Detailed studies have shown considerable variation in cost for the same procedure in different institutions (16). It has also been shown how rapidly the costs of new techniques change as experience is gained and organizational arrangements adjusted to them. Thus, cost data are not only location-specific but also time-specific.

Finally, the costs that are included must be appropriate to the decision context. For example, the costs that are appropriate to a decision whether or not to double the size of a programme by introducing a second centre include costs that might not be relevant (namely, costs that might not change) if the size of the programme were to be doubled within the existing centre.

Effectiveness of cost measurements

While such caveats on the cost side are important, the major challenges still lie in improving our processes of measurement and valuation of effectiveness. Effectiveness in health care is not simply a technical issue but a social judgement. Unless a technology is superior in all dimensions, statements about its relative effectiveness will involve making value judgements about trade-offs between accessibility and quality of care, of risk and benefit, of survival and quality of life. The implications of this are only just beginning to be discussed in the UK. For example, the issue of risk in medicine and,attitudes to it is topical (17), and public involvement in consensus development conferences is beginning to make professionals more aware of patients' views and attitudes (18).

The great merit of the cost per QALY approach is that it is based on a set of specific and explicit assumptions. The effect of this, however, is to highlight how weak is our informational basis on the relative values of different health states. For the purpose of valuing imperfect health states, the UK work on QALYs has used work by Rosser and colleagues (19) who obtained respondents' values for a two-dimensional matrix of health states using psychometric scaling techniques. The US and Canadian work has tended to use standard gamble or time trade-off techniques directly to value health states actually experienced or described in brief scenarios (14). Only recently has there been any attempt in the UK to compare these approaches empirically and to try to explain the considerable differences in values that these alternative techniques appear to create (20). Only if a significant research effort is put into this general area will we be able to answer a number of pertinent questions, such as:

(1) Are the values produced by different methods inconsistent?
(2) Do they depend upon the age of the subject or of the patient group concerned?
(3) Is there a simple linear relationship with time in the particular health state?
(4) Does society consider 0·1 increase in QALYs to 100 people to have the same value as 10 QALYs to one individual?

This final question raises a more fundamental issue, whether cost per QALY as an efficiency criterion is a sufficient basis for resource allocation decisions, or whether there are additional equity considerations. If so, what explicit form should they take?

Using cost-effectiveness information on new technologies

The value of cost-effectiveness information, be it in the form of cost per QALY or less condensed descriptive material on costs and benefits of technologies, lies in an ability to act upon that information; to use it to influence policies so to maximize the social benefit from health care expenditure. Thus, unless cost-effectiveness studies are to be seen merely as a fascinating academic exercise, there need to be policy mechanisms that can achieve the priorities they may indicate. It is not appropriate to attempt to review here the range of policy instruments available in the UK or elsewhere but an illustrative example may be informative.

The example of heart transplantation

Major studies looking at the costs and benefits of heart transplantation were carried out recently in the UK and the USA (16,21). These used comparable, but not identical, analytical techniques and came to broadly similar conclusions. In both studies, the evidence, despite the absence of a randomized control group, pointed to a substantial improvement in survival for transplanted patients and very good quality of life. The costs of the transplant programmes were high, but less than had been expected (less than a number of more routinely accepted therapies), and they were seen anyway to be falling whilst survival continued to improve. What is interesting is the policy responses.

In the UK, the decision has been to continue to restrict earmarked funding to a very limited number of centres and to continue to discourage other centres from starting programmes. Thus, in 1986, just three centres in the UK are carrying out heart transplants—the original two centres of Harefield and Papworth Hospitals and a new unit at the Freeman Hospital, Newcastle upon Tyne. (Incidentally, that hospital in 1985, like the other two a few years earlier, started its programme using a charitable donation.) Thus, the UK decision discriminates between locations and, by setting a fixed 'earmarked' sum of money, restricts the level of activity in them. Cost-containment is paramount, but cost-effectiveness considerations have influenced the pattern of priorities.

In the USA, the decision had to take a different form. There, Medicare has accepted coverage of the procedure to eligible beneficiaries (defined according to specific patient selection criteria) in institutions that meet certain criteria 'aimed at identifying facilities with the necessary experience and expertise' (22). The US Department of Health and Human Services estimates that up to 10 transplant centres will qualify to perform heart transplants, and that up to 65 transplants will be covered by Medicare in the first year. Thus, the cost-effectiveness study in the USA has been fed into a specific decision process—but, of course, separate decisions have and will continue to be made by the various insurers, and Medicaid may or may not follow the Medicare lead. The resultant level of activity and the number of institutions involved cannot be predicted. Cost-effectiveness has influenced at least a part of the system but, even within that part, cost-containment is in no sense guaranteed.

As ever, it would be unwise to generalize from the particular, but this example highlights the need for a specific decision context for cost-effectiveness information to be used, and the very different implications of responding to such information with different policy mechanisms. Much more work is needed to identify the various policy mechanisms of regulation or incentive, and to see how they can best be related to the results of cost-effectiveness studies.

Cost-effectiveness and technology development: the need for a strategy for the future

Knowledge about the cost-effectiveness of alternative technologies is by no means a costless commodity. A strategy needs to be developed to make sure that scarce analytical resources are also used to good effect. An examination of the cost per QALY league tables being published in the UK at the moment shows that their most striking characteristic is their various notable omissions. Why are there no comparable figures for liver or bone-marrow transplantations? What of the various expensive cancer therapies? What of the effectiveness of the various recently introduced diagnostic techniques? Strong policy action in relation to the included procedures seems rather arbitrary given the major omissions.

There are therefore strong calls for more evaluation. The evaluation of all expensive medical technology has been recommended (23), but there are problems of timing, of funding, and of appropriate organizational structures. A policy is needed, but it has to be realistic. All too often evaluation lags behind the development of technology so that it is out of date before it is published. Funding is patchy and apparently uncoordinated.

Organizationally, studies are difficult to mount. Recently in the UK there has been renewed discussion of the problems of mounting randomized controlled trials for new technology. Challah and Mays (24) described their problems with and eventual failure to mount a prospective randomized controlled trial of extra-corporeal shock-wave lithotripsy, and cite ethical resistance as one of the main obstacles. The logic of allocating resources by a criterion such as cost per QALY is that it is necessary to show not that the treatment is more effective than its alternatives but that it is more cost-effective, but once the former statement is known to hold it may be difficult to mount a trial to establish the latter. A situation could well arise in which treatment was denied to many as a resource allocation decision, in the absence of data from a trial — a trial deemed unethical because it would deny the treatment to trial participants.

Also, in the non-clinical fields, there is a reluctance to set up experiments. The national nature of the NHS and its central direction mean that there are too few natural experiments and a tendency to be unwilling to construct experimental situations. It is quite amazing that the recent major change in managerial arrangements in the UK was made without initial pilot studies for evaluation. More encouraging, however, was the recent breakthrough in the setting up of pilot studies of the effect of changing the remuneration pattern of dentists for dental care to children (25).

International exchange of information

One element of the evaluation strategy should be a policy of international pooling of cost-effectiveness information and international co-ordination of evaluation. We need to identify which elements of evaluation, for which technologies, need to have been carried out locally and which are internationally transferable. We need to identify ways of introducing greater comparability either in the evaluation protocols themselves or by being able to 'translate' results from one setting to another, or to compare relative effectiveness when it has been determined using different measures. At present, a small number of technologies are internationally over-evaluated with uncoordinated studies in a number of countries, whilst other technologies seem to receive no attention at all.

Conclusion

In the UK we have a system that holds great potential for systematically basing national and local priorities on well-calculated cost per QALY data. The UK system can effectively exclude certain technologies because their cost per QALY is too high. The NHS can in principle cut back on cost-ineffective existing technologies and substitute more effective new ones. It can transfer funds between specialties, from acute to non-acute sectors, or from hospital care to GP-based services.

What is needed is a commitment to cost-effectiveness evaluation and a strategy that ensures that the necessary research to improve the basis for measuring and valuing effectiveness is funded and carried out and, at the same time, that appropriate evaluations are carried out in contexts in which specific policy decisions can follow.

References

(1) Her Majesty's Treasury. *Cash limits 1985–86: provisional outturn.* Cmnd 9851. London: Her Majesty's Stationery Office, 1986.
(2) House of Commons Social Services Committee. Fourth report: *Public expenditure on the social services*; Vol. II. HC 387-II, Session 1985-6. London: Her Majesty's Stationery Office, 1986.

(3) Aaron HJ, Schwartz WB. *The painful prescription: rationing hospital care.* Washington: The Brookings Institution, 1984.

(4) Jennett B. *High technology medicine—benefits and burdens.* 2nd ed. Oxford and New York: Oxford University Press, 1986.

(5) Klein R. Rationing health care. [Editorial]. *Br Med J* 1984; **289**: 143–4.

(6) Stocking B, Morrison SL. *The image and the reality: a case study of the impacts of medical technology.* Nuffield Provincial Hospitals Trust. Oxford: Oxford University Press, 1978.

(7) Buxton MJ. *Heart transplantation in the UK: the decision-making context of an economic evaluation.* Health Economics Research Group discussion paper no. 1. Uxbridge, Middlesex: Health Economics Research Group, Brunel University, 1986.

(8) Department of Health and Social Security. *Health and social services statistics for England*: 1986 edition. Table 4.3: 70–1. London: Her Majesty's Stationery Office, 1986.

(9) Department of Health and Social Security. *Priorities for health and personal social services in England.* London: Her Majesty's Stationery Office, 1976.

(10) Department of Health and Social Security. *Care in action: a handbook of policies and priorities for the health and personal social services in England.* London: Her Majesty's Stationery Office, 1981.

(11) Commission on Future Health Care Technology. *Health care applications of lasers, the case of coronary artery surgery.* The Hague, Netherlands: Project on Future Health Care Technology, 1986.

(12) Williams A. The value of QALYs. *Health and Social Services J* 1985 July 8; Centre Eight Supplement: 3–5.

(13) Williams A. Economics of coronary artery bypass grafting. *Br Med J* 1985; **291**: 326–9.

(14) Torrance GW. Measurement of health state utilities for economic appraisal: a review. *J Health Econ* 1986; **5**: 1–30.

(15)Weinstein MC, Stason WB. Foundations of cost-effectiveness analysis for health and medical practices. *N Engl J Med* 1977; **296** (13): 716–21.

(16) Buxton MJ, Acheson R, Caine N, Gibson S, O'Brien BJ. *Costs and benefits of the heart transplant programmes at Harefield and Papworth Hospitals.* Department of Health and Social Security Research Report no. 12. London: Her Majesty's Stationery Office, 1985.

(17) O'Brien BJ. *What are my chances doctor? A review of clinical risks.* London: Office of Health Economics, 1986.

(18) King's Fund Forum Consensus Panel. Consensus development conference: treatment of primary breast cancer. *Br Med J* 1986; **293**: 946–7.

(19) Kind P, Rosser R, Williams A. Valuation of quality of life: some psychometric evidence. In: Jones-Lee MW, ed. *The value of life and safety.* Amsterdam: North-Holland, 1982: 159–70.

(20) Buxton MJ, Ashby J, O'Hanlon M. *Valuation of health states using the time trade-off approach.* Health Economics Research Group discussion paper no. 2. Uxbridge, Middlesex: Health Economics Research Group, Brunel University, 1986.

(21) Evans RW, Manninen DL, Overeast TD, *et al. The National Heart Transplantation Study: final report.* Seattle WA: Battelle Human Affairs Research Center, 1984.

(22) Department of Health and Human Services. Press release. Washington: US Department of Health and Human Services, 1986 June 27.

(23) Council for Science and Society. *Expensive medical techniques.* London: Council for Science and Society, 1982.

(24) Challah S, Mays NB. The randomised controlled trial in the evaluation of new technology: a case study. *Br Med J* 1986; **292**: 877–9.

(25) Department of Health and Social Security. *Primary health care: an agenda for discussion.* Cmnd 9771. London: Her Majesty's Stationery Office, 1986.

A US view

H. DAVID BANTA

WHO Consultant on Technology Assessment,
WHO/Steering Committee on Future Health Scenarios Study on
Future Health Care Technology, Health Council, The Hague, Netherlands

Mankind always takes up only such problems as it can solve.   (Karl Marx)

Introduction

Fiscal constraint in the US health care system is becoming a familiar issue, as it is in a number of countries. The cost of health care and the increasing share of national resources that it uses have become a national policy issue. The costs of the Medicare program (the national health insurance program covering the elderly and disabled) have increased even faster. In 1983, the US Congress passed a law that radically changed Medicare's method of payment for in-patient hospital services, from a cost-based system to a prospective payment system (1). One goal was to control technology through changing the financial incentives in the system. This sweeping change indicates the serious attention paid to the problem in the USA.

At the same time, insurance companies, industry, and health care institutions have instituted programs attempting to control costs. Despite this activity, costs continue to rise. In fact, health care expenditures expressed in constant dollars rose more rapidly after 1980 than they did in the late 1970s (2).

Present trends

During the last 20 years the portion of national income in America and Britain devoted to medical care has increased. A number of factors explain this, but medical technology* is surely one of them. Estimates in the USA (4) indicate that medical technology, taken in the aggregate, accounted for about 16% of the increase in per

---

*Medical technology is the drugs, devices, and procedures of medical care, and the support systems in which they are delivered (3).

Health Care Provision under Financial Constraint, edited by T. B. Binns and M. Firth, 1988: Royal Society of Medicine International Congress and Symposium Series No. 115, published by Royal Society of Medicine Services Ltd.

capita personal health care expenditures during the period 1977–82. For hospital care, the figure was 24%. It is this increase in technology per unit of service, or in service intensity, that has attracted the attention of policy makers.

The increasing cost of technology is not surprising. There has been an explosion of biomedical knowledge since 1950, but it is probably the electronic devices and machines of medicine that have contributed most to costs. Clinical laboratories have been automated and now require huge capital investments. Medical imaging devices, such as computerized tomography scanners, have revolutionized diagnosis, but at great cost. Respirators, cardiac monitors, and rapid blood analyses have all contributed to costs, but especially when combined in intensive care units, which are estimated to account for up to 20% of the cost of hospital care (5). In the USA, analyses have shown that the primary reasons for rising costs of hospital care are surgery for people admitted for myocardial infarction, delivery of a baby by Caesarean section, respiratory distress syndrome of the newborn, and the provision of intensive treatments for other critically ill patients, especially including small newborns and the elderly (6,7).

The aging of the population raises particular concerns. The USA now has about 27 million people aged 65 and over, making up almost 12% of the population (8). In 1900, only 4% of the US population was elderly. This change is a particular concern because elderly people have more chronic illnesses and use more health care. Cardiovascular disease, cancer, arthritis, dementia, fractures, dental disease, and many other problems are more common in older people. The cost of a stay in the hospital for an elderly person in the USA is almost twice that for the non-elderly population, because of greater use of specific technologies but also because of longer lengths of stay (9). The rate of surgery was found to be 60% higher in the elderly than in the population as a whole.

Future trends in society

The population will continue to age. By 2010, projections indicate that the USA will have more than 39 million people aged 65 and above, and they will be almost 14% of the population. After 2010 the increase will be even more dramatic, as 'the first wave of the baby boom cohort becomes the elderly boom of the future' (8). While this aging indicates falling death rates, and thus is a technological success, disease rates and health care needs can be expected to continue to increase, at least for the next decades. At the same time, quality of life is an increasing concern, and improving functioning will become more and more of a goal for the health care system. Increasingly, the idea of 'life at any cost' is being questioned.

Purely medical interventions involving high technology could become relatively less frequent. Rates of certain surgical procedures are already falling. More efficient diagnosis could save resources. Lasers might make out-patient surgery more frequent, and might partially replace such expensive procedures as coronary artery bypass grafting (10).

On the other hand, problems of functioning caused by chronic disabilities will become much more frequent. Many of these can be addressed technologically. For example, problems with walking, reaching and handling things, and turning the head are frequent in older people (11). Urinary and fecal incontinence are more common in the elderly. These problems can be addressed by prostheses and other newer technologies.

For the health care system, problems of both physical and social functioning seem certain to become more prominent in the future. Modern society seems more and more characterized by isolation and alienation. Traditional social institutions such as the church and the family no longer give people adequate support for their problems of daily living, so people turn to health care institutions. In the future, as today's young become tomorrow's elderly, patients seem certain to be less tolerant and more demanding. With increasing educational levels and knowledge of health and health care, people will know their rights and will be more critical of the care that they receive.

The biggest problem, perhaps, is that in this time of increasing needs and increasing technological means to meet the needs, available resources will fall. As life expectancy has risen, birth rates have fallen. The teenage population of the USA is expected to stabilize at close to 25 million, while the elderly population will reach close to 60 million in 2025 (8). This means that a smaller proportion of the population will have to pay for the care of those who are dependent (unless rather revolutionary changes in present social patterns are assumed).

Development of medical technology

One problem for policy making with regard to improving the cost-effectiveness of technology development is that governmental policies have relatively little impact on technology development. Public funds are invested primarily in basic research. Once research findings indicate that a technology is feasible, the applied research and targeted development are done primarily by industry or academic clinicians.

Drugs and devices are developed by industry in processes almost entirely hidden from the public eye. Governments are not trying to interfere in these processes. Indeed, given present economic problems, governments are trying to encourage industry by removing constraints.

Medical and surgical procedures are developed largely by academic clinicians. These develop incrementally, for the most part, so it is difficult even to discern an innovation.

In general, little is known about the development of medical technology. Policy making in this area is fraught with difficulty. One very important problem is that changes in policy may harm the processes of technology development because of lack of understanding of the present system and the implications of proposed changes.

The pace of technological change seems certain to be rapid in the future, and may even accelerate (12). In part, the rapidity of change is fostered by health care needs such as those described. In part, it reflects large investments in health-related and other types of research and the corresponding development of knowledge and technology.

Many new diagnostic tests will become available because of the new biotechnology and monoclonal antibodies. Medical imaging will also continue to advance and will provide much new diagnostic information. Lasers will become universal in surgery, and will be used to treat a wide variety of medical problems both as part of a surgical procedure and as part of an endoscope or blood-catheter system. Artificial organs and prostheses will become available to compensate for diminished functioning of most parts of the body. Computers will continue to spread in both clinical and administrative applications. In particular, computers and telecommunications will lead to much more sophisticated patient monitoring systems, both for health care institutions and the home.

The problem is that these advances are mostly cost-raising. The paradox is that definitive preventive and curative tools lead to an even older population, with increased chronic problems.

Solutions?

How can we afford to meet the population's needs? My answer is that we must be much more explicit in our decision making. We have to make choices. We have to understand the implications of our actions. We may not be able to have a great influence over what industry develops. But we *can* refuse to buy it. The issue is selection.

The basis for selection is then a critical question. The basis has often been policy pressure, who makes the most noise, fads, or impressions of what might be useful. I propose that we should rely more on policy-oriented research. In general terms, it means what has come to be called 'technology assessment' (13). Technology assessment means examining the short- and long-term social consequences of the application of technology. As it has come to be used in the health field, it generally means examining the safety and efficacy of a specific technology or alternative technologies. Increasingly, such analyses include financial costs. Examining costs and effects simultaneously is generally done in the health field by cost-effectiveness analysis (14).

Quality-adjusted life year

An example of what I mean has been provided by Professor Alan Williams (15). He suggested that above a certain amount of cost per benefit, a service should not be provided. He thought that a reasonable cut-off point might be gross national product per capita. The figure for Britain is about £4000. Williams calculated cost-effectiveness ratios, based on quality-adjusted life years (QALYs) (Table 1).

Table 1

Cost-effectiveness ratios of various procedures based on quality-adjusted life years (QALYs)

Procedure	Cost per QALY gained (£ sterling)
Cardiac pacemaker	670
Hip joint replacement	750
Valve replacement (aortic)	950
Coronary artery bypass surgery (with left main artery disease)	1040
Kidney transplant	3000
Heart transplant	5110
Coronary artery bypass surgery (for angina pectoris)	11 400
Hospital dialysis	14 000

Under Williams' proposal, heart transplant and hospital dialysis would not be done at all in Britain, and coronary artery bypass surgery would be done only for certain indications.

The specifics of this proposal are not important, but the underlying ideas are. First, we must assume that a country will reach (or has already reached) a limit on how much it is willing to spend for health care. Secondly, we have to accept that choices between competing goods must be made, and that some choices must be foregone. Thirdly, we have to believe that rational analysis is a reasonable guide (although not the only factor) in making difficult decisions.

Of course, the data are lacking to do all the required analyses. That is no argument for not starting. Another objection that might be raised is that the proposal raises many social questions, such as whether we will allow certain groups to die. This only shows that numerical analysis cannot be the only factor in a decision — social and political concerns cannot be ignored.

If such a proposal were seriously considered or implemented, I think that one action is essential: the public must be informed. These decisions are not technical decisions. They are moral and political decisions. The public must understand the issues and support a more explicit approach. One strength of such a method, however, is that it could allow more public input to decision making.

Conclusions

The problem in trying to develop cost-effective technology is that there are few ways that society can constructively influence technological developments. Thus, I would argue that we should stop debating whether or not research is cost-effective. Let us assume that the development of knowledge is a good thing, and work with industry to try to indicate what we think we want for the future, but let us concentrate our efforts on developing better decision-making structures for health care.

A number of countries have begun to use technology assessment as an important part of their decision-making process. For example, in the Netherlands, the Sick Funds Council has commissioned cost-effectiveness analyses of certain organ transplants and of *in vitro* fertilization as a basis for deciding whether or not to make the service routine.

The policy structures that influence technology use are weak in most countries, and are often irrational and even counter-productive in terms of cost-effective technology. We need to examine existing policies with a view towards promoting more efficient and appropriate technology.

References

(1) Office of Technology Assessment. *Medicare's prospective payment system*. Washington: US Government Printing Office, 1985.
(2) Reinhardt UE. *How 'money illusion' may have saved the American health sector from starvation (so far)*. Draft paper submitted to the National Leadership Conference on Health Care, Washington DC, Oct 3 1986.
(3) Office of Technology Assessment. *Assessing the efficacy and safety of medical technologies*. Washington: US Government Printing Office, 1978.
(4) Office of Technology Assessment. *Medical technology and costs of the Medicare program*. Washington: US Government Printing Office, 1984: 48–50.
(5) Russell LB. *Technology in hospitals: medical advances and their diffusion*. Washington: The Brookings Institution, 1979.
(6) Scitovsky AA. Changes in the costs of treatment of selected illnesses, 1971–81. *Med Care* 1985; **23**: 1345–57.
(7) Showstack JA, Stone MH, Schroeder SA. The role of changing clinical practices in the rising costs of hospital care. *N Engl J Med* 1985; **313**: 1201–7.
(8) Office of Technology Assessment. *Technology and aging in America*. Washington: US Government Printing Office, 1985: 3.
(9) Office of Technology Assessment. *Medical technology and costs of the Medicare program*. Washington: US Government Printing Office, 1984: 43–5.

(10) Commission on Future Health Care Technology. *Health care applications of lasers, the case of coronary artery surgery.* The Hague, Netherlands: Project on Future Health Care Technology, 1986.

(11) Orleans M, Orleans P. High and low technology: sustaining life at home. *Int J Tech Assess Health Care* 1985; **1**: 353-63.

(12) Commission on Future Health Care Technology. *Anticipating and assessing health care technology*; Vol. 1. General considerations and policy recommendations. The Hague, Netherlands: Project on Future Health Care Technology, 1986.

(13) Banta HD, Behney CJ. Policy formulation and technology assessment. *Milbank Mem Fund Q* 1981; **59**: 445-79.

(14) Office of Technology Assessment. *The implications of cost-effectiveness analysis of medical technology.* Washington: US Government Printing Office, 1980.

(15) Williams A. *Economics and the rational use of medical technology.* Paper presented at conference on the economics of medical technology, Valkenburg, Netherlands, Sept 2-4 1985.

Discussion

(invited discussant *Gail Wilensky*)

Dr Wilensky

Both Mr Buxton and Dr Banta look at the issue of cost-effectiveness analysis and what we usually regard as technology assessment as an important strategy, although for somewhat different reasons. Mr Buxton described the differences accurately, which is to say that, in the UK, there has been much less concern with cost-containment *per se* because of the nature of the budgetary process. The concern is, therefore, one of maximizing the benefits. In the USA, on the other hand, there has clearly been major concern with cost-containment.

The notion that the USA has been solely concerned with cost-containment is probably slightly less true than it was. A number of us who go from conference to conference, write papers or talk with people in the policy community, are realizing that quality of health care is the emerging issue—if, in fact, it has not already emerged—on the American health scene. Conferences are springing up left and right on the issues of quality of care, how to measure it and how to disseminate information on it. None the less, the concern among people who have spoken about technology assessment in the USA has been primarily of the nature of a cost-containment strategy. The issue is not so much whether or not cost-effectiveness is a good idea. Few people could be found to make a cogent argument that we would be better off not having informed decision-making of some sort.

The issue, which I should like briefly to explore, is who makes that decision and how that information is used. This is likely to be very different in the two countries. Mr Buxton accurately described the ability to make use of this information in the UK in a much more ready manner—that is, there is a centralized system, with budget making, the allocation of resources and the right to certain kinds of equipment all decided in a much more centralized manner.

He has highlighted some of the difficulties of cost-effectiveness analysis, which are mainly its timing, its funding and the way in which the policy is actually implemented. These are very serious. He has correctly noted that it frequently happens that by the time the evaluation is done the technology has changed in such a major way as to question the relevance of that study.

That is obviously not always true but, as pointed out by Dr Banta, the incremental nature of technologies makes a formal assessment something of an ephemeral exercise in all too many cases. That, of course, makes it very difficult to use as a significant decision-making apparatus.

The other problem is how to implement the information for policy making. As I mentioned, the UK can do this in a way that is different from the USA. In the USA I think it is much less clear how serious we are about using cost-effectiveness analysis.

The heart transplant example, which Mr Buxton used in his paper, in fact points out an interesting difference—but not quite in the way that he indicated. He commented that the information from the heart transplant studies was that, although the costs were slightly higher than initially anticipated, the benefits were quite substantial. None the less, the decision in the UK has been to have access to this particular technology on a very limited basis, at only three (perhaps four) centres. In the USA, on the other hand, Medicare has adopted heart transplantation as one of the services that it will now provide in some circumstances for some eligible beneficiaries.

The point that is of interest in the USA, however, is that this major decision-making process was much more traumatic for Medicare and Medicaid, the government programmes, and followed the coverage by the private insurance companies. Much of the trauma that was gone through had been bypassed by the private insurance companies. The government programmes in this case followed the decision making rather than led it. I am not sure how often that may be the case.

I think that the issue for the USA will be much more a matter of 'what is the government responsible for providing or funding?'

Professor Reinhardt discussed earlier the notion of multitiered health care—or was he suggesting that we will have a system in which we will make a choice that if a technology cannot be made available for everyone then it will not be made available for anyone?

I think that is very unlikely, given our history in the USA. It would take a very different attitude from that shown in the past. The struggle with the end-stage renal disease programme indicated that it was not really possible for either the federal or the state government to produce a rationing system that was acceptable either as rational or equitable. Finally we brought it into the federal system and made it available to all those who needed it medically.

I do not know whether or not that would be done today if we knew how much it would cost—but I sense that it would. I do not think that in the USA we have reached a position where we will not make available a technology that has so much medical benefit.

What is less clear to me is whether or not we may get to the point of saying that the minimum benefit package—that which is guaranteed for all people—will be all that is medically available, or whether we will begin to make some choices which allow individuals through their health insurance to supplement, if they wish, what is available to everybody.

I am not sure that is the direction we will take. I do not think that I can see in the USA a very strong likelihood of limiting the availability in general of new technologies for the population. That seems inconsistent with our strategies in most other areas.

Finally, I would like slightly to modify the title of this session. My answer to the question of the title, 'Can the health care system control the demands of new technology?', is probably yes, if we want it to badly enough. I do not think we will in the USA. There ought, however, to be a following phrase in the title—and that is 'should it?'.

Dr Relman

In the USA, we sometimes have difficulty in distinguishing between the new and the useful. Therefore, any new development tends to gather momentum. It is assumed by many people, especially the general public, that any new development in medicine—any new technology or technique—must be good. There is a great rush to apply it, a great public expectation that it should be used. People who suffer from the condition to which the technique might be applicable are eager to try it—so eager, in fact, particularly if they have a bad disease like metastatic cancer, that they may be willing to pay privately huge sums of money for any experimental and frankly unproven treatment which is available on demand for a price. Efforts by medical journals, for example, to slow down the immediate dissemination of information and application, at least until there is some evidence that the new technique is successful—or, at least, is not deadly—are frowned upon and viewed often as impediments to progress.

This attitude is fuelled, not only by public expectations and the assumption that anything new is better than anything old or than nothing at all, but also by the increasing involvement of industry. Having made investment in the research and development, industry is obliged to have revenues to pay for it. Therefore industry wants rapid dissemination.

These two forces, the public assumption that new is obviously better and the economic imperative that says that new has to generate profit, and therefore must be marketed and applied, in my opinion result in an enormous prematurity and over-exuberance in the application of new technology in the USA. This is often called 'progress' but, in the cold judgement of experience and practice, and with the passage of time, it turns out to be simply a passing fancy.

I believe that with most of what we call 'new technological development' we are caught up in a system which results in enormous waste. I say that with all due respect to the point made by Dr Banta that bureaucracy, government and the establishment ought to get out of the way and allow new technology to develop as rapidly as possible.

This is why I believe that a more disciplined evaluation, and a more scientific approach to the practice of medicine would pay tremendous dividends. Cost may not be the most important factor, but rational, safe, effective medicine of itself—whether or not it costs less—seems to me to be an extremely valuable objective for which we ought to be striving.

Mr Buxton

I agree with Dr Relman. One point that comes out of a number of the observations made by both Dr Banta and myself is that technology assessment evaluation is not a one-off process. If technology is dynamic, evaluation has to be dynamic. It has to cope with change. It should also involve some monitoring, both to change our view, as the situation changes, about the desirability or otherwise of the particular intervention, and also to confirm whether policy is having the intended effects.

Dr Banta

I also agree with Dr Relman, but would make two reflections upon it. First, more than 10 years ago, if I asked people whether they were sure that their new technology was beneficial they more or less took the attitude, 'prove it is not'. It seemed to me that, if somebody advocates a technology and says that it works, he ought to prove it. I see a change in attitude now, which I think is one of the most hopeful signs in the USA.

Secondly, there is the question of utilization—alluded to by Dr Relman, but not really emphasized. For me, it is not a question of effective or ineffective technology, but that an effective technology becomes available and is then used for an increasing number of people with decreasing effect. I do not know whether cost-effectiveness can deal well with that issue. I know of no policy anywhere which has dealt well with that. I think that is our biggest challenge and problem.

Mr Lewin

I think that many people in the pharmaceutical industry would wonder whether products that have been developed are rushed to market quite as quickly as Dr Relman would suggest. In the USA especially, there are probably slower, more deliberate processes for bringing products to market. Whether the same is true of procedures is not certain, as Dr Banta pointed out. We do not look as closely at medical and surgical procedures as at devices and drugs.

Utility of cost-effectiveness analysis depends very much on who is the decision maker and wherein lie the fiscal accountability and financial incentives. If the kind of cost-effectiveness analysis that has been discussed here is done for policy makers, particularly in the UK where there is a much closer affinity between fiscal accountability and decision making, those kinds of judgements are particularly useful. I think we find them much less useful in the American system. This is because the ultimate decision makers view cost-effectiveness not so much in terms of cost-containment or benefit maximization but rather as revenue maximization.

When I sit with physician groups, hospitals, or indeed industrial commercial firms, it is clear that they examine cost-effectiveness data more often from the standpoint of how their ability to maximize their own revenue will be affected, and whether the cost-effectiveness analysis that has been done will in any way interfere with or support that.

The problem that we face in the USA, certainly much more than in the UK, is this diffusion of responsibility—which, of course, also has many advantages. I would therefore be much less sanguine about the way in which cost-effectiveness analysis on technology will affect policy. In the final analysis, I believe that we need to worry less about how to make precise decisions regarding the adoption of individual technologies at the policy level than about working more effectively to fashion incentive and payment systems that create those incentives internally, so that there is more affinity and less conflict. I think this is what Dr Wilensky was also saying—if not today, on other occasions.

Sir John Walton

Despite Dr Relman's arguments, one of the problems we always face in the early stages is knowing *which* advances will be the winners. Gastric freezing is a good example quoted by Dr Banta. In the UK, for instance, a large amount of money, time and effort was devoted to showing that hyperbaric oxygen did not work in the treatment of multiple sclerosis. The problem is that we do not always know at the beginning what will work until it has been evaluated.

Mr Sieverts

It seems to me that we often do ourselves a disservice by concentrating on the dramatic, very expensive technologies. Indeed, those have not been nearly as much of a problem, in terms of public policy and costs. When they are very dramatic and very expensive I think the truth comes out fairly quickly. Whether deliberately by policy or simply because of market forces they tend to sort themselves out. Extracorporeal shock wave lithotripsy is an example of that. Cool heads quickly realized that there are only so many kidney stones in the population. We have not seen a proliferation of that technology in the USA, even though the system could have permitted it in much of the country.

The same is true of heart transplants. Dr Wilensky is quite correct in saying that it was not government forces but private insurance companies (primarily Blue Cross and Blue Shield) that laid out guidelines very early on. These stated that heart transplants would be paid for only in certain circumstances and in certain kinds of institutions that met some criteria. That was quite sufficient in much of the country to regulate the development and proliferation of heart transplants.

It is far more interesting and far more important from a cost and value standpoint to look at the other end of the scale in new technologies. The issue there is not a binary question whether it is good or bad, but how will it be used? The system in the USA for paying doctors—a system which I think will remain for as far into the future as I can see—pays them for piece-work services. The doctors try to establish different prices for different kinds of services, and then expect to be paid at those levels.

If we look at some of the technologies which are being primarily furnished through fee-for-service medicine, it begins to be clear that, in a system with that kind of incentive, the issue is not so much whether the technology is a good thing but rather how can we have any assurance that it is being used appropriately.

In the metropolitan area in which Mr Lewin, I and some others here live and work, there is the fascinating example of what in the UK is called nuclear magnetic resonance (NMR), and in the USA, magnetic resonance imaging (MRI), proliferating in the hands of private physicians in a ring around the District of Columbia—because the District of Columbia has attempted to 'regulate' (that is, to prohibit) the installation of MRI facilities. Thus, we now have seven of them in the suburbs, all going full blast. We are providing health coverage for probably three times as many people as do Medicare and Medicaid in that region, and are being faced with a flood of claims at $600 or $700 each. We attempt to regulate that by limiting the parts of the body that can be imaged, and by desperately taking any possible advice.

Even that is not the best example. By far the best examples are the commonly available technologies, such as arthroscopy and endoscopy. It is quite possible for a physician who believes himself or herself to be entirely ethical to make an enormous living doing arthroscopic or endoscopic procedures without any assurance being available that these are being used appropriately—using appropriateness in the way shown earlier.

I know that Dr Banta has been concerned with this in the past — he referred to it briefly earlier. What kind of advice has he for policy makers in dealing with that very real circumstance in the USA?

Dr Lister

Following on from what Dr Relman said, the relative poverty of this country has protected us a little from having too quick an introduction to some of this new technology. This is particularly true of the computerized tomography (CT) scanner. We did not have so many head scanners, so were able to have whole-body scanners.

Apart from the 'heavy' equipment (the term used for this kind of activity in Europe), I was very interested in what Mr Sieverts said about the lower level of technology. I was particularly going to mention endoscopy. This has become a huge industry in the UK, creating enormous problems not only in the private sector where it is very lucrative on a fee-for-item-of-service basis, as has been mentioned, but also in district hospitals where everybody has to have an endoscopy unit. Surgeons will not operate on people who are bleeding from the stomach until somebody has looked to see the ulcer. It inhibits people from thinking about the clinical causes of bleeding from the stomach. I would be very interested, like Mr Sieverts, to hear what Dr Banta would say about the evaluation of this sort of procedure, particularly endoscopy.

Professor Marks

There are three other areas which I would like to enter into the debate. First, the area of computerized interviewing and diagnosis, which has made some progress in the area of mental health, and whether some mileage is to be obtained from that in other areas of medicine.

Secondly, the development of self-help technologies has recently made some remarkable gains. For example, there has been a ninefold increase in efficiency, in terms of therapeutic time required for the treatment of phobic and compulsive rituals. What kind of scope is there for that in other fields of medicine? We can also think of the possibilities for self-treatment of hypertension with the development of the ability to self-monitor blood pressure.

Thirdly, what about the future for training technologies? Quite a few training packages have been developed in the field of psychiatry which seem to give us the ability to cut down the time needed to train people.

Dr Banta

On the question of computers, in the foreseeable future (20 years' time perhaps) I think that we will have essentially one system tied together. This will mean that somebody will be able to oversee what is going on in practices. At the same time, there will be much more data available for saying what is effective practice. How that information is to be used in a regulatory, financing kind of scheme is something about which we ought to be thinking.

Professor Pardes

When we talk about technology prolonging life and 'creating' older people who will then have more cost-consuming illnesses, to what extent has the improved function of the individual been looked at as an offset against those projected higher expenses?

Mr Buxton

I am sure Mr Sieverts is right that, in the end, it is not the high profile technology that is most important. The problem is that people cannot be persuaded to fund research into the low profile technologies. To be fair, I think the reason why it is difficult is because the policy makers cannot see how they could do very much about it even if they had the results. Certainly national funders do not see much scope for influencing individual behaviour.

I am not saying that it is easy, but I think that it is possible to do that sort of evaluation, particularly if cost-effectiveness is tied into a sort of medical decision-making context — for example, if we ask what are the different approaches, how much advantage will be given by extra information and will it lead to different outcomes?

It is technically quite feasible. There are examples in the literature — but no one seems to want to fund it, I think for the reason that it is not clear how the results will be used.

Dr Banta

I do not know of any global analysis with regard to improved functioning for elderly people. Of course it is possible to point to some dramatic examples, such as hip joint replacement. My feeling is that Professor Pardes' point is correct, but I do not know the answer. In future a big issue for society will be home care, and how to support people at home.

In terms of small or big, and which is most responsible or most concerned, the literature is conflicting. We started out with a concern about 'big'. After the Sun Valley forum in the USA everybody talked about 'small-ticket technology'. Now studies from Showstack (1) and Scitovsky (2), from California, have again focused attention on big. These studies show that, at least in California, Caesarean section and other instrumental forms of childbirth, intensive care (particularly for neonates) and terminal care for the elderly are three of the biggest contributors to cost at the moment. I know nothing about it in the UK; I am very confused about the situation in the USA.

I do not see fee-for-service as necessarily bad. I have tried to think about the incentives that are built into any payment system. In theory, there could be a fee-for-service system that really encourages what has been determined to be highly beneficial. The odd thing is that the payment for these high technology procedures, such as endoscopy, is so far away from the cost of delivering them. Thus, the cost or fee for 15 min of effort, say, talking to the patient is very low, whereas the fee for spending the same 15 min doing an endoscopy procedure is enormous.

I see these kinds of incentives that are built into the fee-for-service system in the USA as very destructive, but not that the fee-for-service system itself is necessarily bad.

References

(1) Showstack JA, Stone MH, Schroeder SA. The role of changing clinical practices in the rising costs of hospital care. *N Engl J Med* 1985; **313**: 1201–7.
(2) Scitovsky AA. Changes in the costs of treatment of selected illnesses, 1971–1981. *Med Care* 1985; **23**: 1345–57.

CAN THE HEALTH CARE SYSTEM CONTROL THE
DEMANDS OF NEW TECHNOLOGY?

2. The cost-effectiveness of hospital vs community care

Chairman:
ERIC MUNSON
Chapel Hill NC, USA

A UK view:
can the health care system control
the demands of new technology?

JOHN HORDER

*Visiting Professor, Royal Free Hospital School of Medicine, London;
Past President, Royal College of General Practitioners, London, UK*

Introduction

Looking at the title of this conference and then at the subject allotted to me, the question to try to answer seems to be the following: if hospitals played a smaller part in medical care, would it cost less but remain equally effective? To answer this question I must seek evidence from reliable studies, concentrating if possible on the UK.

No one foresees a time when financial constraints will end. Conflict between the expanding potential of medical science and a limited national budget seems likely to go on for a very long time, so any chance of avoiding the pain of rationing—of withholding care from people who have a right to it—has to be seized.

Within our health service the cost of hospital care is at least three times as great as that of services outside, most of which come under the title of family practitioner services (1-3). On average, the cost of looking after a patient in hospital for one day in 1985 was £55, compared with a maximum figure of £18·50 outside—three times as much (4). These are, of course, extremely crude averages, even though they take indirect monetary costs into account. I shall have more to say about them. Nevertheless, they are the basis for considering whether the part played by hospitals could be smaller and whether this would be a way of releasing money to provide worthwhile care for people who are not now receiving it.

Two further questions are immediately suggested:

(1) Is it realistic to think that hospitals could play a smaller part?
(2) If so, would there be gain or loss in effectiveness?

First, *could* care be transferred out of hospital? Obviously there are many patients who need hospital care because the medical techniques or the nursing they need could be provided in no other setting. Conversely, there are many others for whom hospital care would be a ridiculous excess—think of acute meningitis, on the one hand, and the common cold, on the other—but between these extremes there is a middle group of patients and problems. There are surgical operations which can be done on an

Health Care Provision under Financial Constraint, edited by T. B. Binns and M. Firth, 1988: Royal Society of Medicine International Congress and Symposium Series No. 115, published by Royal Society of Medicine Services Ltd.

out-patient or an in-patient basis. There are many contexts in which the length of in-patient stay is an arguable quantity. The needs for in-patient admission of children, of elderly people and of those with psychiatric problems are all the subject of debate. What about the need for repeated attendance in out-patient clinics? What is the right setting to keep an eye on people with diabetes mellitus, hypertension and other chronic disorders?

The middle group is large and varied. Indeed, as a general practitioner (GP) (or family physician) I am constantly making decisions in this middle ground. Can I cope with this patient myself or do I need specialist advice? Can this patient be nursed at home or will she need admission simply because there is no one to look after her?

It is this middle group on which I shall focus and for which I need to examine any worthwhile studies about relative costs and effectiveness in hospital and outside.

I shall need to consider hospital in-patient and out-patient care, and care in a neighbourhood centre. In this country that last term implies a general practice, although we now talk of 'primary care' in order to include preventive activities and professionals other than doctors.

On this side of the Atlantic it is important to look for studies which compare in-patient and out-patient care, on the one hand, with general practice or primary care, on the other. In the UK in particular, this distinction is clear-cut and contains within it the distinction between care provided by specialists and that provided by generalists.

In the USA it may be more relevant to compare in-patient care, on the one hand, with out-patient and neighbourhood care, on the other. The last two are linked by the term 'ambulatory care', implying care given either from hospital out-patient departments or from a doctor's private office. Both specialists and generalists move between the three settings far more than they do in this country.

In examining the evidence I have taken these differences into account, but before saying anything about the evidence there are essential points to make about costs and effectiveness.

Costs and effectiveness

The broad statement that it costs at least three times more per day to look after a patient in hospital than at home conceals a bewildering number of variable factors. Some of these variations are wide enough to be able, in combination, to change the situation so much that home care may cost more than hospital in a minority of cases. Patients vary in their degree of dependence, and therefore need differing amounts and forms of home care. Costs may vary according to whether a problem is short- or long-term. Capital expenditure may or may not need to be taken into account. So-called indirect costs include loss of earnings by the patient or by a close relative providing essential care. Such a relative, caring perhaps for a mentally disturbed old person, might herself break down and require hospital treatment. There are indeed so many variables that someone like myself, lacking any training in economics, has to rely on the expertise of others even in deciding which studies to trust (5).

A further point is that human costs or burdens, particularly those incurred by relatives and neighbours, are difficult to quantify. They are therefore easily omitted from the equation by anyone looking at people in the mass, but they are of great importance to individuals.

Effectiveness, too, is a word which conceals much. I would like to follow Freidson (6) and Donabedian (7) in suggesting that there are both technical and interpersonal aspects to the assessment of effectiveness. Thus, the outcomes include not only items such as mortality or change in symptoms and signs of disease, but also those such as expressed satisfaction or dissatisfaction — but to say only that is to oversimplify a complex subject.

Nevertheless, I must answer my main question whether, if hospitals played a smaller part in medical care, this would cost less but remain equally effective — and also look for reliable studies.

The evidence

I have examined 43 studies which make relevant comparisons, and many others which touch on the problem. A paper by Berk and Chalmers (8), in the *New England Journal of Medicine* in 1981 seems particularly important, not only because the authors reviewed 109 studies reported in 134 papers written between 1965 and 1979 but even more because they set very high standards of judgement. For example, they accepted only randomized controlled trials, insisted on a full calculation of indirect costs, and required exacting statistical criteria for the assessment of technical and interpersonal outcomes. Perhaps it is not surprising that they finally accepted only four of the original 109 studies as offering appropriate evidence to permit decisions for action (9–12). They reached the general conclusion that the data to support the substitution of ambulatory for in-patient care had still to be collected.

The four winners in Berk and Chalmers' paper were all in the surgical field and they all came from this country. Two studied patients with hernias and varicose veins. They both found the cost of ambulatory care to be lower and clinical (technical) outcomes to be equal. The third and fourth studies, about the treatment of varicose veins and haemorrhoids, respectively, found ambulatory care to be cheaper but less effective. These studies fall into the area which I believe will be covered by Dr Rabkin, so I shall describe in a little more detail one paper which has appeared more recently from Australia in a different field, psychiatry. I quote it as the sort of study I had hoped to find.

Hoult (13) compared the cost of care for 60 patients with severe mental illness treated in hospital with 60 treated outside, at home if possible but, if not, in a temporary boarding house. All had acute psychotic illnesses — acute in the sense of urgency and seriousness. Allocation to the two groups was strictly random and the study continued for a year. The results were clear-cut. Care outside hospital cost 26% less and was more effective, as judged on 13 out of 14 criteria. This study resulted in a policy decision by the government of New South Wales to aim to develop community-based teams for psychiatric care. (Berk and Chalmers (8) mentioned seven other randomized controlled trials of psychiatric treatment which show ambulatory care to be more effective, but which fail to examine costs.)

Surgery and psychiatry are two areas in which a small number of papers of high standard can be found. Another concerns the care of the elderly. There is also a cluster of studies focused on the care of patients with myocardial infarction, and others on terminal care and on the surveillance of diabetics in out-patient departments or in neighbourhood centres. In each area some of the studies are concerned with keeping patients out of hospital altogether, others with early discharge*.

Anyone reading these papers is bound to realize that they challenge commonsense ideas. Any assumption that home care obviously costs less without being less effective now looks blurred — 'muddy', as one health economist puts it. We certainly have

*A full bibliography is available from the author on request.

to agree with Berk and Chalmers' verdict that there is still a need for more and better data.

Nevertheless, there is more evidence today than there was in 1981. Adding it together, I conclude that the obvious assumptions have not been disproved. Overall, transfer of care from secondary to primary *does* seem to offer hope of reducing costs without loss of effectiveness, provided that it is done in a selective way. The policy certainly deserves further exploration.

In reaching this conclusion independently, I am much reassured by finding a similar conclusion to have been reached by Drummond *et al.* in a survey of recent studies (14). He writes:

> Community care does represent a feasible, acceptable and lower-cost option in many situations, although more research is undoubtedly required.

One finding which stands out uniformly and sharply in almost all these studies is that the great majority of patients prefer to stay at home and at work, provided that this is possible and involves no threat to their future health. They express more satisfaction with home than with hospital care in almost all the studies where this point has been assessed.

My conclusion obviously provides only the most general guide for action. Space does not allow me to be more selective and specific — except to say that the evidence badly needs to be subdivided and examined in different contexts. For example, I mentioned three different sorts of comparison found in the literature of differing relevance in our two countries. Another example is a small group of patients, whether among the elderly or those with a psychiatric or a surgical problem, for whom home care will prove more expensive, less effective, or both. They clearly need to be identified, even if they are not numerous enough to overturn my general conclusion.

Further analysis of the literature must consider separately different forms of comparison between in-patient, out-patient and neighbourhood care — and, for that matter, also day-hospitals and nursing homes. It must consider separately the issues of keeping people out of hospital altogether and of early discharge, and questions which bear on psychiatric cases separately from those which bear on surgical cases — and so on. I do not have time to pursue any of these important subdivisions.

One last word about the studies is that the more attention is paid to these subdivisions the nearer we move to the boundary of the administrator's field — the field of groups and general policies — and begin to approach the ground familiar to me as a GP, the ground where individuals differ. Whatever the general policy, the final decision needs to be made in discussion with individual patients and their families by a person who knows and is trusted by them, and who includes in his assessment and decisions as broad a range of facts relevant to the individual as can be assembled.

Since policies and their application to individuals overlap so much and relate to each other so closely, the final conclusion which I want to draw out of this excursion into health economics is the obvious need for administrators and doctors to educate each other.

A digression

In making this very rapid survey of cost and effectiveness, I have had to trespass as an amateur into a new and difficult field. It would have required a very considerable body of evidence to have persuaded me that home care costs more than hospital care, that it is never equally effective in dealing with similar problems, or that no possibility of transfer exists. Along with many other people in the UK and in the USA, I have

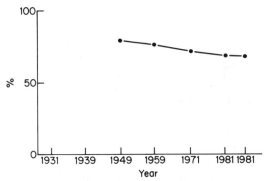

Figure 1. General practitioners as percentage of total fully trained doctors (UK).
Sources: Department of Health and Social Security (15); Central Statistical Office (16).

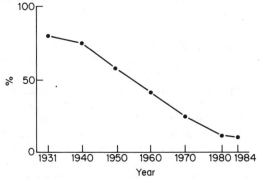

Figure 2. General practitioners and part-time specialists as percentage of total physicians in active practice (USA).
Sources: Stevens (17); Eiler (see 18).

been trying throughout my career to strengthen medical care outside hospital, by advocating the continuing need for generalists in medicine, for integration, for simplification and for the on-going responsibility of personal doctoring. This has meant swimming against the tide at a time when the advantages of specialization, high technology and hospital care have been very evident, and when it has been these which have been attracting money, brains and influence. In examining the studies of cost and effectiveness, I have had to watch my own bias. I leave them with a feeling of great relief that the evidence does not in fact disprove and require me to abandon the assumptions and beliefs which have driven me since I chose to be a GP.

Increasing the effectiveness of care outside hospital

I would now like to return to more familiar ground by saying something about what we are trying to do in the UK—to improve the cost-effectiveness of care outside hospital—that is, primary care, within which GPs play a central, but by no means the only, role.

I shall start by pointing to some existing features in our system which favour primary care and increase its effectiveness, all of which happen to reveal contrasts with the USA (if that vast and varied country may be spoken of as one unit).

162   J. Horder

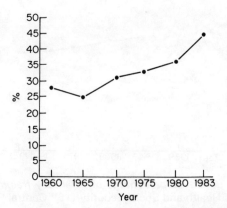

Figure 3. Career choice, final year medical students (UK): general practice first choice.
Sources: Last and Stanley (20); Ellin, Parkhouse and Parkhouse (21).

First, the ratio of GPs to specialists has not changed very greatly in the last 50 years (Fig. 1). This contrasts sharply with the USA where our colleagues have had to swim even harder against the tide (Fig. 2).

The second feature is that 98% of the UK population is registered with a chosen GP, combined with the fact that there are now almost no areas where such doctors are in short supply, at an overall rate of 1 per 2000 people.

The third feature is the unwritten rule that patients consult a general doctor before they consult a specialist, even when the latter is necessary. This is an important tradition which contrasts, for instance, with practice in France, where even 10 years ago 30% of patients consulted specialists direct (19). It depends upon people seeing the advantage of having a personal advisor and advocate, and also on specialists seeing the advantage of a protective gatekeeper who helps them not to waste their special skills on inappropriate cases, as happens, for instance, in countries where primary care is weak or absent.

Under our arrangements, specialists lose the prestige of acting as a valued consultant if they do not require a letter of referral from a GP, or if they hold on to patients unnecessarily. Indeed, there is no financial gain, while GPs have no financial advantage by admitting patients to hospital, although they may offload work in that way. I want particularly to stress this tradition of referral as a way of strengthening primary care. Maxwell (1) suggests that it may be the key variable in the cost of a whole health care system, because it both controls access to specialists and avoids duplication. In his study of 10 countries, those which allow direct access to specialists prove to be those where costs are highest, and vice versa.

The fourth feature is that GPs in this country are not very interested in hospital privileges. Most of them actually prefer to treat people in their own homes if they can. For this reason home visits continue and are available at night and at weekends, if needed. GPs do look after patients in hospital in country districts. In cities they mainly do hospital work for the purpose of further training or as a separate special interest. The divide between practice inside hospital and outside is more pronounced than in the USA. In the UK the more ambitious GPs do not seek to specialize, but rather to shine among their own colleagues in family practice. Interest focuses on defining the specific role of the generalist, and specific postgraduate training takes place largely outside hospital.

I am describing features of our system which already strengthen primary care and limit the dominance of specialization. The last one, which seems particularly important for the future, is, I believe, unique to the UK. General practice has changed from being a career which few medical students aimed to enter as their first choice to become today much the most popular choice (Fig. 3).

The future

Important changes are being discussed at the moment (22). We want to develop more and better team-work between doctors, nurses, social workers and administrators — and with the informal carers who carry the main burden when illness starts. The work of this team has to develop further in the direction of prevention (a subject I have neglected because it has been covered earlier). Team-work is now essential, but not at the expense of comprehensive and continuous personal responsibility.

We want to reinforce the technical effectiveness of the primary care team by a less hurried style of practice and by sharing more of the care with specialists. We see this already in antenatal care, and in the fact that one in five psychiatrists now spends significant amounts of time working in the setting of general practice (23).

We want to strengthen the motivation of all members of the team to do work of higher quality — through forms of continuing education which are rooted in their own clinical problems, performance review voluntarily undertaken, increased accountability to patients, and perhaps by relating pay more closely to recognized features of good practice (24).

We certainly see the primary care doctor of the future as needing personal qualities and training no less demanding than any other branch of medicine, if he or she is to act as an integrating force in a field illuminated by very diverse sorts of knowledge and subject to constant change.

Will all this cost more? Probably yes, but any increase will be small compared with the rising costs of hospital care which account for about 60% of all National Health Service (NHS) spending. Further primary care savings are possible, notably in prescribing. Meanwhile, hospital savings can be expected, as shown by the studies described above.

Conclusion

In the last part of this paper I have described what I believe to be the most important elements in what we are trying to do to improve the cost-effectiveness of primary care outside hospital, so that it can accept more responsibilities.

Can it be claimed that this system of medical care is *more* cost-effective than another? Within the UK it is difficult to set up alternatives for comparison. Internationally, the NHS is a cheap system overall, but one which is now falling behind in some important respects (25). However, there are few comparisons which refer to primary care and which are valid (26,27). Is it reasonable to draw some parallels between the system here and some of the health maintenance organizations in the USA where there has been a striking reduction in the level of hospital admissions compared with fee-for-service practice (28)? An incentive to admit to hospital seems to have been removed. This incentive has always been absent from our system, and Dr Paul Beeson, in an article about the NHS intended for American readers, particularly noted this as well as our economy in the use of specialists (29).

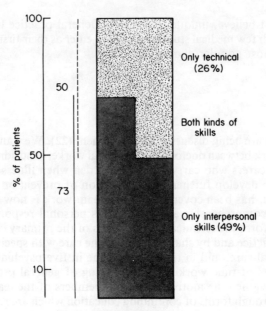

Figure 4. Attributes of a 'good' doctor: patients' views of the balance.
Source: Sussman et al. (31) (see 30).

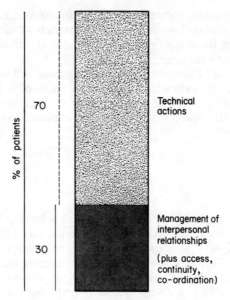

Figure 5. Attributes of a 'good' doctor: the balance as revealed by the actions of physicians (internists).
Adapted from Sanazaro and Williamson (32) (see 30).

What emerges most clearly from my excursion into territory new to me is the same message as I once saw on the wall in a patient's house. It read: 'Home is the place where we are treated best and grumble most'. Most patients want to be treated at home. They understand the technical advantages of hospital less clearly than doctors and nurses. They put less store on them compared with interpersonal aspects, as composite diagrams from American sources demonstrate (Figs 4 and 5).

My subject has compelled me to discuss costs and effectiveness. I want to end by expressing anxiety lest concentration on these two aspects of medical care and the search for measurements, which they both imply, might lead policy makers to think that they are all that matters. What is in my mind may be illustrated by recalling a telephone call about 1971 from a doctor patient who was going through a depressive episode. I no longer remember his first words, but I remember answering that I was afraid that I did not know what else I could do—to which he quickly replied that he did not want me to *do* anything, he just wanted me to be there. How can the effectiveness of that sort of thing be costed or measured?

Acknowledgements

I am grateful for valuable comments to Nick Bosanquet, Professors J. Butler, F. H. Hull, B. Jarman and G. Shaper, and to my wife, Dr Elizabeth Horder.

References

(1) Maxwell RJ. *Health and wealth. An international study of health care spending*. Lexington MA: Lexington Books, 1981: 82–3.
(2) Acheson D. Variations in hospital referrals. In: Teeling Smith G, ed. *Health, education and general practice*. London: Office of Health Economics, 1986: 21–3.
(3) Office of Health Economics. *Compendium of health statistics*. 5th ed. London: Office of Health Economics, 1984: Table 2.6.
(4) Jarman B. Personal communication, 1986.
(5) Drummond MF. *Principles of economic appraisal in health care*. Oxford and New York: Oxford University Press, 1980.
(6) Freidson E. *Patients' views of medical practice*. New York: Russell Sage Foundation, 1961: 50–6.
(7) Donabedian A. *The definition of quality and approaches to its assessment. Explorations in quality assessment and monitoring*; Vol. 1. Ann Arbor MI: Health Administration Press, 1980.
(8) Berk AA, Chalmers TC. Cost and efficacy of the substitution of ambulatory for inpatient care. *N Engl J Med* 1981; **304**: 393–7.
(9) Adler MW, Waller JJ, Creese A, Thorne SC. Randomised controlled trial of early discharge for inguinal hernia and varicose veins. *J. Epidemiol Community Health* 1978; **32**: 136–42.
(10) Ruckley CV, Cuthbertson C, Fenwick N, Prescott RJ, Garraway WM. Day care after operations for hernia or varicose veins: a controlled trial. *Br J Surg* 1978; **65**: 456–9.
(11) Chant ADB, Jones HO, Weddell JM. Varicose veins: a comparison of surgery and injection/compression sclerotherapy. *Lancet* 1972; **ii**: 1188–92.
(12) Russell IT, Devlin HB, Fell M, Glass NJ, Newell DJ. Day-case surgery for hernias and haemorrhoids; a clinical, social and economic evaluation. *Lancet* 1977; **i**: 844–7.
(13) Hoult J. Community care of the mentally ill. *Br J Psychiatry* 1986; **149**: 137–44.
(14) Drummond MF, Ludbrook A, Lowson K, Steele A. *Studies in economic appraisal in health care*; Vol. 2. Oxford and New York: Oxford University Press, 1986: 201–51.
(15) Department of Health and Social Security, England and Wales. *Health and personal social services statistics for England 1985 (and previous years)*. London: Her Majesty's Stationery Office, 1986.

(16) Central Statistical Office, UK. *Annual abstract of statistics* no. 122. 1986. London: Her Majesty's Stationery Office, 1986: 66–7 (Table 3.32).

(17) Stevens R. *American medicine and the public interest*. New Haven CT and London: Yale University Press, 1971.

(18) US Department of Health and Human Services. *Health, United States 1985*. DHHS Publication no. (PHS)86-1232. Washington: US Government Printing Office, 1986: Table 63.

(19) Guidevaux M, Colvez A, Michel E, Hattom F. *Les malades en médecine libérale*. Paris: INSERM, 1975.

(20) Last JM, Stanley GR. Career preference of young British doctors. *Br J Med Educ* 1968; **2**: 137–55.

(21) Ellin DJ, Parkhouse HF, Parkhouse J. Career preferences of doctors qualifying in the United Kingdom in 1983. *Health Trends* 1986; **18**: 59–63.

(22) Secretaries of State for Social Services, United Kingdom. *Primary health care. An agenda for discussion*. London: Her Majesty's Stationery Office, 1986.

(23) Strathdee G, Williams P. A survey of psychiatrists in primary care: the silent growth of a new service. *J R Coll Gen Pract* 1984; **34**: 615–8.

(24) Royal College of General Practitioners. *Quality in general practice*. London: Royal College of General Practitioners, 1985.

(25) World Health Organization. *World health statistics 1984*. Geneva: World Health Organization, 1984: 32.

(26) Marsh GN, Wallace RB, Whewell J. Anglo-American contrasts in general practice. *Br Med J* 1976; **1**: 1321–5.

(27) Epstein AM, Hartley RM, Charlton JR, Harris CM, Jarman B, McNeil BJ. A comparison of ambulatory test ordering for hypertensive patients in the United States and England. *J Am Med Assoc* 1984; **252**: 1723–6.

(28) Manning WG, Leibowitz A, Goldberg GA, Rogers WH, Newhouse JP. A controlled trial of the effect of a pre-paid group practice on use of services. *N Engl J Med* 1984; **310**: 1505–10.

(29) Beeson PB. Some good features of the British National Health Service. *J Med Educ* 1974; **49**: 43–9.

(30) Donabedian A. *The methods and findings of quality assessment and monitoring. An illustrated analysis. Explorations in quality assessment and monitoring*; Vol. 3. Ann Arbor MI: Health Administration Press, 1985: 11–5.

(31) Sussman MB, Caplan EK, Haug MR, Stern MR. *The walking patient: a study in outpatient care*. Cleveland: The Press of Western Reserve University, 1967.

(32) Sanazaro PJ, Williamson JW. A classification of physician performance in internal medicine. *J Med Educ* 1968; **43**: 389–97.

A US view

MITCHELL T. RABKIN

President Beth Israel Hospital;
Professor of Medicine, Harvard Medical School, Boston MA, USA

Defining cost-effectiveness

While Dr Horder has taken a broad and experienced look, I hope to focus on selective aspects of our subject, cost-effectiveness of hospital vs community care. That title unnerves me, in part because of a recent admonition in the *New England Journal of Medicine*. Doubilet *et al.* (1) cautioned on the use of the term 'cost-effective' if not coupled with appropriate documentation of the associated costs and benefits. For some authors, cost-effective may mean simply cost-saving and not take into account the resulting benefit. For others, it means effective despite the cost. A closer approach might be that a strategy is cost-saving with an equal or better health outcome, but this choice would exclude a program that does not save money, or one that reduces costs greatly yet leads only to a small decline in effectiveness.

Doubilet *et al.* prefer a definition appropriate to the domain of health, which takes into account both cost and effectiveness and examines the trade-off between them. Thus

> . . . one strategy is more "cost effective" than another if it is (a) less costly and at least as effective; (b) more effective and more costly, its additional benefit being worth its additional cost; or (c) less effective and less costly, the added benefit of the rival strategy not being worth its extra cost (1).

They caution that the comparison of cost-effective ratios does not necessarily direct us to the desired strategy, in part because we must consider the trade-offs between patient health and monetary costs. Their example is of one treatment A, which yields a life expectancy of 1 year and costs $100, comparing that with treatment B, which costs $1000 but yields a life expectancy of 5 years. The cost-effectiveness ratio of treatment A is $100 per year, superior to the ratio of 1000 over 5 or $200 per year for treatment B. Since few would prefer A over B, to live 1 year rather than 5, they conclude that, while it is valid and important to consider which medical decisions are best based on cost-effectiveness criteria, the rendering of medical decisions on both health and monetary considerations '. . . is a difficult task . . .' as well as '. . . one that raises serious ethical issues' (1). Dr Horder has pointed out the difficulty, noting that the 1981 report of Berk and Chalmers (2) could cite only four of 109 relevant studies in 134 papers reviewed that seemed to provide enough data on both cost and efficacy to allow

Health Care Provision under Financial Constraint, edited by T. B. Binns and M. Firth, 1988: Royal Society of Medicine International Congress and Symposium Series No. 115, published by Royal Society of Medicine Services Ltd.

statistically valid conclusions. Of those, two suggested that the substitution of ambulatory for in-patient care would save money but provide a slightly poorer clinical outcome, while the other two showed cost-saving with ambulatory as effective as in-patient care. Beyond the bases of logic and ethics, the authors point out also that the notion of costs of illness differ, depending on whose costs they are—those of the patient, the hospital, the insurer, or the economy as a whole. Thus, the results may be viewed favorably by one party but not by another. Hospital usage, therefore, and its substitution by ambulatory care, is a moving target.

Hospital usage

In the USA wide variations in hospital usage by comparable populations has led to exploration of the determinants of hospitalization. The experience of Kaiser-Permanente, a classical staff model Health Maintenance Organization (HMO), has revealed that typical US in-hospital days could be halved without decline in measurable indices of health. Thus, when the figure of 1200 hospital days per 1000 insured was bandied about as a national norm, Kaiser was recording about 600. Today, among the working population, the figure may be 450 days per 1000 or lower and is widely replicable. Among the elderly, the move from fee-for-service for physicians and cost reimbursement for hospitals to the capitated risk-reward option of the HMO at the Fallon Plan in Worcester, Massachusetts, for example, has led to a halving of hospital days, from 4200 to 2200 per 1000.

How is this done? In 1978, Luft (3) found total health costs—including both premium and out-of-pocket costs—to be 10–40% lower for enrollees in HMOs than for a comparable population with conventional insurance. He attributed the differences to hospitalization rates, which were about 30% lower in the HMO. Interestingly, he found no evidence that HMOs reduced selectively the admissions deemed less than necessary; rather, the data suggested lower admission rates in all categories. The *Lancet* article by Ware and colleagues (4) (cited earlier in this meeting) did suggest, however, that the HMO experience might not be as helpful for the low income patient in ill health.

Cost-sharing

A recent study from the Rand Corporation demonstrates another economic influence. While the Kaiser-Permanente patient has little to pay out-of-pocket, other insurers require larger co-payments. Siu and colleagues (5) looked at the medical records of more than 1000 adults in several health insurance plans. In one arrangement all the services were free of cost to the patient, but in another series—pooled because there was no difference within its subgroups—the proportion of costs paid by the patient was 25, 50 or 95% up to an annual maximum expenditure of $1000. Those with free care registered 126 medical-surgical admissions per 1000 person years, for a total of 830 hospital days. Among those who cost-shared the rate was 96 medical-surgical admissions for a total of 640 hospital days, about 75% that of the former group. Again, it was particularly interesting that the percentage of admissions judged inappropriate was the same in both groups. It could be concluded that while cost-sharing decreased overall the number of admissions, it did not have a selective impact on those admissions deemed inappropriate.

Geographic variations in hospitalization rates

Before economic influences are assigned sole primacy as determinants of hospital utilization, it should be noted that certain qualities are presumed to be intrinsic to the physician and others intrinsic to the procedure. The variations in medical care among small areas studied by Wennberg and Gittelsohn (6) have been suggested to be related to the degree of medical consensus concerning the indications for hospitalization and for use of relevant surgical procedures, which is, in part at least, related both to individual physicians and to the local medical culture.

McPherson and colleagues (7) found support for this view from an examination of seven common surgical procedures in areas of New England, UK and Norway. A larger study from the Rand Corporation by Chassin and colleagues (8) recorded major variations in the use of medical and surgical services by the Medicare population across the USA. Where variations were smaller, there was generally medical consensus over indications, but the authors concluded that there were additional, albeit arcane, reasons yet to be uncovered to explain the data.

There are national differences too. McPherson (9) has pointed out some differences between our two countries. For example, the 1974 length of stay in hospital for repair of an inguinal hernia averaged 7·3 days in England and Wales, falling to 5·8 days by 1980. In the USA, lengths of stay were 5·8 and 5·0 days, respectively. Today, of course, many hernia repairs are performed as ambulatory procedures, perhaps related to technical advances in part and also to evolution of attitudes of both physicians and patients. Within the USA, geographic cultural variations are seen in the contrasts of the east and west coasts, for example. For comparable populations, hospital stays appear shorter in California by about 1·5 days compared with New England. Total hospital days are not quite so far apart, however, because California doctors hospitalize patients more frequently. It is asserted that when a physician moves from one coast to the other, his or her pattern of behavior becomes co-opted over months to that typical of the new location.

Other factors affecting hospitalization

Other factors may influence the incidence of hospitalization or the length of stay, and thus total hospital days. Merrick and colleagues (10) studied carotid endarterectomy in five California Veterans Administration medical centers. They found a wide range by hospital in the percentages of inappropriate, equivocal and appropriate surgery. Among other issues, they question whether the overall numbers of cases at any one institution might make a difference in the eagerness to operate as well as in the results of surgery.

Social factors have an impact as well. Who has not experienced the elderly individual becoming deeply depressed upon hospitalization, and then medically falling apart? Sikorski et al. (11), reporting in the British Medical Journal on a rapid transit system for patients with fractures of the proximal femur, emphasized that

> . . . hospital is not the place for the elderly and that removing these people from their home environment is destructive.

Examining the outcome of hospitalization for acute illness in the elderly, Lamont and colleagues (12) concluded that routine discharge planning for elderly patients admitted for acute illness or injury would facilitate prediction of the level of care required following discharge, with earlier seeking out of the often limited community resources to provide that post-discharge care.

The availability of transportation, home nursing care and social service resources tends to facilitate earlier discharge and may forestall rehospitalization, as emphasized by Wright *et al.* (13), reviewing obstetric care for patients in an HMO and those in a fee-for-service practice. Interestingly, they found a shorter stay for HMO patients as well as lower Cesarean section rates, but no difference in outcome for child or mother.

Other studies have found home care services to be ineffective. Looking at 12 studies of programs for chronically ill populations, Hedrick and Inui (14) found that home care services appeared to have no impact on mortality, patient functioning or nursing home placements. In some instances, home care was associated with an increase in ambulatory care utilization up to 40% with the cost of care increased up to 15%. These findings were little different from those reported nearly 10 years earlier by Hellinger (15) that

> . . . both out-patient care and nursing home care can substitute for hospital care, but a complementary relationship between out-patient and nursing home care indicates that the additional coverage resulted in greater, not less, expenditure by Medicare.

On the other hand, in a study coming out of Boston's Beth Israel Hospital (16), which examined the use of an alternative system of care for an elderly and chronically ill population in nursing homes in the inner city, there was little doubt that on-site evaluations of patients by nurse practitioners were clearly preferable, in both clinical and financial terms, to the earlier practice by which the nursing home had sent patients to a teaching hospital emergency unit for evaluation of each episode of acute illness. As a result, the number of hospital admissions, length of stay and overall cost of care declined.

Clearly, such social organization has its impact. Agustin and colleagues (17) described the reorganization of ambulatory services in a New York City hospital, Morrisania, by which a neighborhood family care center replaced the conventional out-patient clinic. They reported a significant decrease in admission rates for serious disease—diabetic acidosis, severe hypertension, congestive heart failure, cerebrovascular disease and severe asthma. These improvements appeared to be associated with moderate savings in health care dollars as a result of an increase in ambulatory care and emergency room visits which cost only about half as much as the savings from hospital days avoided.

Quality and efficacy of care

Equally interesting is the sociology within the hospital, as it influences the quality and efficacy of care. Knaus and colleagues (18) studied the treatment and outcome of over 5000 patients in intensive care units (ICU) at 13 tertiary care hospitals. They found that one hospital had significantly better results, with 41 deaths instead of the 69 predicted, while another hospital had 58% more deaths than predicted. They concluded that the differences were related more to the interaction and co-ordination of each hospital's intensive care medical and nursing staffs than to the unit's administrative structure, the specific therapy used or the hospital's teaching status.

In the hospital with the best results, there was a full-time unit director, and the director and staff together forged the decisions both on patient therapy and on admission and discharge of patients. There was 24 h in-unit physician coverage, also a consistent senior charge nurse, continuity of nursing care and no problems with nurse staffing. The worst unit revealed no full-time director, with decisions on patient therapy, admission and discharge being made by the attending physician alone. There was no 24 h in-unit physician coverage, no consistent senior charge nurse, no continuity of care or primary nursing, and there were major problems with adequate nurse staffing.

During the study, the authors observed in this problematic ICU that

. . . admitting physicians and unit nursing staff communicated poorly. No policy was established for routine discussion of patient treatment . . . frequent disagreements about the ability of nursing staff to treat additional patients occurred, and there was an atmosphere of distrust. (18)

By contrast, the top-ranked hospital

. . . relied on carefully designed clinical protocols implemented by senior level in-unit physicians . . . had the most comprehensive nurse educational support system . . . targeted not only to the staff nurse as a care giver but also to the charge nurse as a manager. Excellent communication between physicians and nursing staff was on-going to ensure that all patient care needs were met. . . . A similar degree of respect extended to other physician and nurse interactions. (18)

Our own hospital-wide experience at Boston's Beth Israel Hospital over the past decade confirms the major importance of primary nursing to empower the nurse at the unit level, fostering that professionalism which supports those collegial relationships and makes for better quality of care, better gratification among staff and, most likely, greater productivity in patient care (19).

It can be inferred from this potpourri of studies that the determinants of hospitalization, length of stay, the decision to discharge, and the quality of care rendered are many and varied. While individual aspects can be studied, the place of each must vary from situation to situation. As a result, it is singularly difficult to arrive at universal conclusions on cost and effectiveness in the in-patient vs ambulatory setting.

The future for hospitalization

Where does all this take us? It seems to me that the wisdom of Dr Horder's conclusion on the value of the generalist is secure; it continues to make good sense. There will be much more to come, however, of the data and the techniques by which some questions can be resolved on more specific aspects of the hospital/ambulatory care interface. Significant cost reduction in hospital appears to have been effected by economic systems such as the pre-paid capitated HMO in the USA and by the rationing of resources carried out in the UK. Whether further tightening of those economic clamps is appropriate seems unlikely, but new diagnostic and therapeutic technologies, and a willingness on the part of clinicians to dispense with time-honored but unproven 'rules' about hospital care, will probably diminish further both the incidence and duration of hospitalization. Those indices will also be influenced by the effectiveness of the organization of caregivers, nurses, physicians and others within the patient care unit, and by the availability and co-ordination of out-of-hospital resources to substitute for hospital days rather than supplement them. Overall, the cost of care may further decline even while the cost per day in hospital continues to escalate.

The impact on tomorrow's physicians of changes in hospitalization

As the chief executive officer of a Harvard Medical School teaching hospital, I must be concerned not only with delivery of care of the highest standard but with providing the best possible arena for medical education, that is, with the challenge of educating tomorrow's physicians for this dramatically evolving world they will encounter. Let me share some concerns which arise out of the changes we have just been exploring on the in-patient unit, changes resulting from the foreshortening of hospital stay and the movement of patients from in-patient to ambulatory care. Actions have consequences and it is inevitable, therefore, that steps taken in the interests of control of costs will have additional impacts beyond those desired. Just as cost-effectiveness cannot be considered as a matter of cost alone, cost control cannot be viewed in so isolated a fashion as to ignore the downstream consequences of actions taken in its name.

Earlier discharge, admission on the morning of surgery, more stringent requirements on the justification for admission all make for increased intensity of in-hospital illness on the average. That means not only increased use of resources but also increased pace of work for the resident physician, increased stress on the job, greater time demand for work performance and productivity, and less time available for reflection and personal study by the resident physicians in training. The psychology of the in-patient unit has shifted too. With sicker patients, or rather, with more patients in the sicker phases of their illnesses, and with earlier discharges, the opportunities for gratification — seeing clearly that he has truly done well for the patient both by professional and by personal standards — are less available to counterbalance the mounting stress on the physician (20). Furthermore, to the extent that an in-patient admission appears related primarily to the carrying out of a complicated diagnostic or therapeutic procedure, the focus tends to shift towards technology disembodied from the person and away from the exquisite responsibility and privilege of the doctor-patient relationship (21).

More significant, perhaps, is the qualitative change in what we once labelled the 'patient material', that is, in the specific nature of the illness with which the house officer contends. There is a narrowing of the spectrum of illness on the in-patient unit as well as a shift in intensity.

Medical education and training

Education in clinical medicine calls not simply for a disembodied awareness of the pathophysiology of a disease. The mastery with which we hope to endow the resident physician requires an experiential familiarity with as full a spectrum of the illness as is practicable. To the extent that we truncate the resident's involvement in that broad spectrum, by shaving days off both ends of the in-patient experience, we are altering both the subject matter of that education and its quality.

Let us look at a few specifics. Pre-operative physical examinations and tests in anticipation of admission must often be done by others than the house staff who will be assigned to the actual in-patient admission. For some medical patients there are pressures for the admitting internist to schedule essential diagnostic procedures and critical consultations well in advance of the patient's arrival, and thus in advance of the resident's work-up. Such alterations in the nature of the process of in-patient care create major qualitative disruptions in the resident's experience, altering the education to be derived.

In many teaching hospitals, there is also a sharp change in pace. Where census has not declined parallel to the drop in in-patient usage there are more admissions, a growth in market share — a happy event to the business office perhaps, but a tightening of the noose on the department chairman and the house staff since, in most cases, there has not been an increase in house staff numbers to compensate. If we consider the surgical house officer, for example, at Beth Israel Hospital, about 40% of in-patient surgery is same-day admission, so the resident's experience is often a hurried and harried pre-operative check. The real contact becomes that with an operative field, not with a person. How does that truncated experience relate to the awareness the surgical resident needs when he or she is in practice? To the extent that most trainees will spend much of their careers dealing with many of those things we have extruded from the in-patient experience, how valid does today's teaching hospital in-patient unit remain as the primary and traditional site for graduate medical education? Is the way we deploy residents today losing educational relevance and, if so, to what do we move for training?

A century ago, training was accomplished largely through apprenticeship, but when hospitals evolved from places of care (or, perhaps, places to die) to places of cure, there were specific interventions of diagnosis and therapy to be learned. This was a capability best acquired through actual management of patients in hospital, and the internship and then residency emerged as effective vehicles for the needed graduate medical education. The enlarging armamentarium of in-hospital interventions created a requirement for personnel to manage the admitted patients, and there was a convenient juxtaposition of house staff in the role of hospital professional with the same house staff in the role of learner, acquirer of experience, and seeker of mastery in the enlarging complexities of medicine.

It was a fortunate happenstance in the past that the set of activities which provided the patient management tended to overlap the set of activities which led to the needed learning. Furthermore, the pace of work was such that time could be taken in the day's schedule for discussion and reflection with peers and senior physicians, and also for house staff teaching of medical students on the wards. Today, however, the two sets of activities—the provision and management of care, on the one hand, and the educational experiences important to the mastery of clinical medicine, on the other— are increasingly divergent. That loss of congruence, coupled with the change of pace and its assault on the time needed for discussion and reflection, may now be moving the traditional teaching hospital in-patient experience out of its time-honored role as the locus of fundamental curriculum for graduate medical training, at least for the first year or two beyond medical school.

Actions and their consequences

Actions have consequences, and where the system in which interventions are made is as complex as health care, uncontemplated consequences often emerge. In the UK there have been the advantages of a national strategy to create a co-ordinated system, the National Health Service (NHS). In the USA there are multiple voices:
- Medicare, with its federal mandate of limiting payment to temper its own expenditures;
- Medicaid, which responds to the largess of each of the individual states;
- the business community, now recognizing its power as a major payer and generating increasing leverage, on the one hand, and yet, on the other, searching for opportunities to increase its own revenues and profits by doing more business with the health sector;
- teaching hospitals loath to temper their role in research scholarship, which is perhaps the ultimate approach to cost control, and loath to decimate teaching and training the physicians of tomorrow;

—and, of course, the patients, who will be the ultimate judges of what we do.

Was it H. L. Mencken who stated that America can always be counted on to do the right thing—after it has exhausted all the other possibilities? Unfortunately, we are not there yet.

Presenting their studies on variations in hospital use, Chassin and colleagues opined:

> Whatever the actual explanation for our results, data like these will be employed increasingly by groups such as peer review organizations that are pursuing cost-containment. Policy makers seem ready to equate high use with inappropriate use. Such an assumption is both uninformed and dangerous. It is uninformed because at present we have no clinical data that would allow us to judge the difference in appropriateness of the use of any particular procedure between high-use and low-use areas. It is dangerous because such an assumption will surely result in policies that restrict access to care. Thus, if the assumption is wrong, patients will suffer. (8)

There are two sides to the story, of course. In his latest book (22) former Health, Education and Welfare Secretary, Joseph A. Califano, Jr, recounts how he helped Chrysler cut over $100 million in its health insurance and care payments, eliminate real abuse and fraud on the part of some providers of care and, overall, benefit the health care of employees, retirees and their families. We cannot deny there is further work to be done in tempering some of today's health care costs, at least in the US.

In a recent and thoughtful essay titled, *The destabilization of health care*, Eli Ginzberg wrote:

> My greatest concern is that we have been pursuing contradictory policies that are adding to our problems . . . continued destabilization must be slowed and then reversed if we are not to undermine what has proved to be a highly satisfactory and effective system of care for most Americans. (23)

Conclusion

We may seem to have gone a distance from the original question. However, just as our review has pointed out the multiplicity of factors which weigh on the choice or necessity of in-patient versus ambulatory care and upon the wisdom of such decisions in the individual instance, we must aim for a perspective as thoughtful and far-seeing as possible. The overall issue of health care of fair quality at fair cost is surely no less complex or less meaningful than the considerations we have only begun to voice here.

References

(1) Doubilet P, Weinstein MC, McNeil BJ. Use and misuse of the term 'cost effective' in medicine. *N Engl J Med* 1986; **314**: 253–6.
(2) Berk AA, Chalmers TC. Cost and efficacy of the substitution of ambulatory for inpatient care. *N Engl J Med* 1981; **304**: 393–7.
(3) Luft HS. How do health-maintenance organizations achieve their 'savings'? *N Engl J Med* 1978; **298**: 1336–43.
(4) Ware JE, Jr, Brook RH, Rogers WH, *et al*. Comparison of health outcomes at a health maintenance organization with those of fee-for-service care. *Lancet* 1986; **i**: 1017–22.

(5) Siu AL, Sonnenberg FA, Manning WG, *et al*. Inappropriate use of hospitals in a randomized trial of health insurance plans. *N Engl J Med* 1986; **315**: 1259-66.

(6) Wennberg JE, Gittelsohn A. Variations in medical care among small areas. *Sci Am* 1982; **246**: 100-11.

(7) McPherson K, Wennberg JE, Hovind OB, Clifford P. Small-area variations in the use of common surgical procedures: an international comparison of New England, England, and Norway. *N Engl J Med* 1982; **307**: 1310-4.

(8) Chassin MR, Brook RH, Park RE, *et al*. Variations in the use of medical and surgical services by the Medicare population. *N Engl J Med* 1986; **314**: 285-90.

(9) McPherson K. Length of stay and health outcome. [Editorial]. *Br Med J* 1984; **288**: 1854-5.

(10) Merrick NJ, Brook RH, Fink A, Solomon DH. Use of carotid endarterectomy in five California Veterans Administration medical centers. *J Am Med Assoc* 1986; **256**: 2531-5.

(11) Sikorski JM, Davis NJ, Senior J. The rapid transit system for patients with fractures of proximal femur. *Br Med J* 1985; **290**: 439-43.

(12) Lamont CT, Sampson S, Matthias R, Kane R. The outcome of hospitalization for acute illness in the elderly. *J Am Geriatr Soc* 1983; **31**: 282-8.

(13) Wright CH, Gardin TH, Wright CL. Obstetric care in a health maintenance organization and a private fee-for-service practice: a comparative analysis. *Am J Obstet Gynecol* 1984; **149**: 848-56.

(14) Hedrick SC, Inui TS. The effectiveness and cost of home care: an information synthesis. *Health Serv Res* 1985; **20**: 851-80.

(15) Hellinger FJ. Substitutability among different types of care under Medicare. *Health Serv Res* 1977; **12**: 11-8.

(16) Master RJ, Feltin M, Jainchill J, *et al*. A continuum of care for the inner city: assessment of its benefits for Boston's elderly and high-risk populations. *N Engl J Med* 1980; **302**: 1434-40.

(17) Agustin MS, Goldfrank L, Matz R, *et al*. Reorganization of ambulatory health care in an urban municipal hospital. Primary care and its impact on hospitalization. *Arch Intern Med* 1976; **136**: 1262-6.

(18) Knaus WA, Draper EA, Wagner DP, Zimmerman JE. An evaluation of outcome from intensive care in major medical centers. *Ann Intern Med* 1986; **104**: 410-8.

(19) Clifford JC. Professional nursing practice in a hospital setting. In: Aiken LH, Gortner SR, eds. *Nursing in the 1980s: crises, opportunities, challenges*. Philadelphia: JB Lippincott, 1982: 101-19.

(20) Rabkin MT. The SAG index. *N Engl J Med* 1982; **307**: 1350-1.

(21) Buchanan JR. Educational impacts of new care systems. *J Med Educ*. (in press).

(22) Califano JA. *America's health care revolution. Who lives? Who dies? Who pays?* New York: Random House, 1986: 11-35.

(23) Ginzberg E. The destabilization of health care. *N Engl J Med* 1986; **315**: 757-61.

Discussion

Dr Relman

I was impressed by the information about the career choices of British medical students given to us by Dr Horder in his excellent presentation. I contrasted that in my mind with the situation in America. It says something, perhaps significant, about the differences between our two attitudes towards health care. In Britain the fact that 70-80% of physicians are general practitioners (GPs), but that general practice as the first choice of senior medical students has been slowly rising from 20% or 25% to 45% only recently, must lead to the conclusion that most British medical students are disappointed, at least initially—*only* initially, one would hope—in the choice of their medical career.

In the USA where, depending upon how they are defined, there are 70 or 75% specialists, almost all (95%) medical students get their first choice of career. It would be absolutely unthinkable and intolerable if half the graduating medical students did not get what they wanted. It would be considered un-American and quite unacceptable—but here, in the UK, it is accepted that, for good and sufficient reasons, not all medical students can get what they want.

Dr Horder said that 60% of the expenses of the National Health Service (NHS) is in the hospitals. In the USA, I think that the total amount spent in the hospitals, as a fraction of the total health care bill, is around 40%. Nevertheless, 75–80% of the doctors in the USA are specialists, practising specialized medicine, and only 20 or 25% practise general medicine. That demonstrates that much specialized medicine is practised outside the hospital. Almost all ophthalmology, dermatology, endocrinology and so on can be done outside the hospital.

If I understand correctly, in the UK all consultant activities in the NHS are in the hospital. Would money be saved if the consultants were allowed, on NHS time, to practise their specialties outside the hospital?

Dr Horder

I do not feel competent to answer that question. It would certainly go hard against strong tradition in the UK—but that is not the point being raised.

Professor Teeling Smith

Very interesting developments are going on about the possibility of exactly what Dr Relman is suggesting. It would be unrealistic to say that it is actually *happening* to any extent yet in the NHS, but it is being discussed. For example, the idea that a diabetician very largely does not need hospital beds. The important thing is that he needs to see his patient with the GP.

This is based on a sample of one. A diabetician told me recently that he is extremely keen to see the development of diabetic centres for treatment out in the community, not based in the hospital, where the diabetician would visit regularly, and the GPs would come in with their patients. The assessment of the diabetic patient would be done in these non-hospital settings. There is a very real discussion going on in the NHS on exactly the sort of thing that Dr Relman mentioned. I believe that it would be cost-effective. I hope that Dr Horder would agree.

Mr Taylor

It is also happening in paediatrics to some extent.

Dr Horder

We would care very much about it being done with the GP, not as a rival service with direct access to the specialist. This is a GP point of view.

Dr Lister

There is potentially an enormous discussion here which cannot possibly be covered. I would, however, like to respond to some of Dr Relman's points.

First, there are many reasons for the primary choice of so many medical students being for general practice. Dr Horder has given a very attractive view of general practice. He and his College are responsible for a great deal of the improvement that has arisen in general practice. Of course there is an evolutionary process going on, shifting the emphasis in care from hospital to community. In both countries over the last century the hospital has been regarded as the centre for medical care for people who are really sick. This is changing, for the reasons that we have heard. First, the trend in practice with reduced bed stay and out-patient procedures, driven also by the economic factor. Therefore, there are the two factors at play, that out-patient or community care may be more appropriate, and that it may be cheaper. There can be argument about both of those.

If there is to be community care, there must be a good primary care service. That is what has been developed in the UK, and that is where so much investment has gone.

Dr Horder would be the first to agree that it is not all as he has outlined, because there are areas where it is not good. Inner cities are still a great anxiety.

Our strict referral system is very difficult for other people in many countries to understand. Dr Fordham said to me that many people give primary care in the USA. That does not happen in this country. GPs are really the only people who give primary care, and they are the gatekeepers to the expensive hospital care service.

There is one disadvantage about this excellent development of general practice. There is a slight danger that we are developing two professions in the UK — general practice and hospital medicine. We thought that had been stopped many years ago with the postgraduate centres, but now — as Dr Horder said — much of the education of GPs is taking place outside hospitals. It is extremely important that we come together again.

There are several reasons for students choosing to go into general practice. First, we are in a mess with our career structure in the hospitals. Attempts have been made to solve it for many years. There is now a new initiative, just being looked at.

Training for general practice takes 4 years from the time of graduation. At the end of that time, the doctor can have a certificate saying that he has trained for general practice, and he can compete for a post of principal in general practice. He may not get it 4 years out of medical school but he may do so fairly soon afterwards. Once obtained, there are better career prospects, a much better lifestyle in many ways, and a more certain income at an earlier age. When they go into a practice, GPs earn a lot more than hospital consultants.

Dr Relman

What about the average relative incomes over the whole career? Is there the difference in Britain that there is in the USA?

Dr Lister

The point is that consultants in hospitals probably no longer catch up, which used to be the case.

After the compulsory one-year 'pre-registration', when they become fully registered, people aspiring to a hospital career have to do 3 years of what is called 'general professional training', followed by 4 years' higher training. They will probably not get a consultant post until 10 years after graduation. In fact, the average age for consultant appointment is still about 37 or 38 years. They have worked very hard, and their basic salary is much lower than that of GPs.

We are very worried about this. We have to compete with general practice. The balance has to be restored in some way or other. In the academic field, recruitment is worse now than in the NHS.

Finally, we are trying to develop 'shared care' in appropriate cases, of which diabetes is a very good example.

Professor Wilson

As I understand the numbers, I do not think that US and UK hospital costs can be compared because the specialist expenses in the UK are in the hospital costs. There is a very great difference when we begin to compare those figures.

Sir Martin Roth

My comments relate to that part of Dr Horder's talk referring to hospital vs community care in respect of psychiatric patients, in particular to the trial of acute psychotics in hospital and community settings.

There are very important unanswered questions in relation to that comparison of a relatively small number of patients, and a few points to be made. First, I do not know how compulsory admission was dealt with in these two systems. Presumably, it was not possible in the community option.

Secondly, account has to be taken of the fact that certain relatively rare complications of acute psychiatric disorders have to be allocated a disproportionate weight, because of the grave consequences that they carry. For example, suicide is a rare outcome of an acute psychotic illness but its implications are far-reaching for the patient's immediate relatives and perhaps for other individuals. It cannot be given weight in an investigation covering a limited number of patients because there will not be enough casualties to make a statistical comparison possible.

Thirdly, violence. This is rather rare in psychotic patients. It is becoming more common with drugs compounding the effects of psychoses. Even one violent act or murder by a psychiatric patient has a very large effect upon community morale in a wide segment of the population.

There is also the problem of first admission, which was touched upon by Professor Rabkin. It is of critical importance that the first admission is done with care, in good order, over an adequate period. If it is hurried, there are cumulative consequences of an adverse kind at a later stage. The first admission is so vital for settling the diagnosis which may, in turn, influence the course and management of the patient subsequently.

Chronic mental disorders have been a big issue all over the advanced world. Everyone is trying to empty and shut the chronic hospitals. On the whole, the consequences have been unsatisfactory and often disastrous. I would regard the Italian experiment as an unmitigated disaster. In families saddled with schizophrenic patients sent home to small homes, parents have killed their schizophrenic children and have then committed suicide. There has been a whole succession of these incidents in Italy—an extremely tragic little piece of the iceberg protruding above the water, because the amount of suffering inflicted has been enormous. The statistics about the experiment are worthless because patients were readmitted to the chronic wards and called 'guests' instead of 'patients'. There were all sorts of other consequences with which I need not deal.

Although I do not believe that psychiatry provides a completely adequate or satisfactory model for medicine as a whole in respect of the matters being discussed, I believe that we will have to reconstitute the chronic psychiatric hospitals. A new kind of hospital will have to be created. It is not possible in the community, in small boarding and lodging houses, to provide the abundance of services that are needed in order to keep mental health, mental vigour and interest alive in large numbers of individuals. Hospitals like Glostrup, in Denmark, created in a large general hospital setting, could do that. They could provide occupational therapy, musicians and artists. All sorts of facilities could be concentrated in one place, instead of the enforced isolation and invalidation of patients who have been sent into the community with, I think inevitably, inadequate resources and facilities to support them there.

This raises the next point, which is also valid for medicine. Where, in the future, is research in psychiatry to take place if we have the revolving door system? Where will we study schizophrenia, depression and mania in their long-term course? How will we evaluate the effects of different treatments when patients are scattered in dozens of boarding houses around the city?

The research units in teaching hospitals in the UK have disappeared in almost every instance. Originally, they were supported by the Medical Research Council. The general hospital units cannot provide the space or the facilities for conducting scientific inquiries. These are urgently required in psychiatry.

I believe that the rapid pace of the revolving door policy is also inimical to research in medicine. Where are the many forms of research, the course and outcome, and the clinical trials, to take place in general medicine?

Finally, the point made by Professor Rabkin in relation to teaching. The admission of patients for truncated periods has a disastrous effect not only on the students but also on the resident doctors in hospitals which are supposed to set an example in excellence of care—that is, the teaching hospitals. Admitting patients in one door and discharging them through another within a matter of 4 or 5 days also has a very unfortunate effect upon the exposure of undergraduate students to clinical experience, and the kind of teaching that can be given by those who are supposed to provide it.

CAN THE HEALTH CARE SYSTEM CONTROL
THE DEMANDS OF NEW TECHNOLOGY?

3. Has alternative or complementary medicine a place?

Chairman:
SIR DOUGLAS BLACK
London, UK

A UK view

RICHARD D. TONKIN

President, Research Council for Complementary Medicine, London, UK

Definition

It is generally accepted in the UK that there are five major complementary therapeutic systems: osteopathy, chiropractic, homoeopathy, acupuncture and herbalism. There are, however, many others, and the Research Council for Complementary Medicine does not feel it is scientific to prejudge the situation by assuming any exclusions. In consequence, it encourages research proposals on any socially acceptable methods or techniques which lay claim to a beneficial therapeutic effect.

Has complementary medicine a place?

The question whether or not complementary medicine has a place in health care is indeed difficult to answer, if only because of the present dearth of valid research evidence on which to base a judgement. This being so, I propose to base my conclusions on a consideration of the nature of disease and illness as it exists in the West today and the interrelationships of these two states with both patient and therapist.

I will start by being unequivocally dogmatic, and later go on to be deliberately provocative. The answer in my considered opinion is *no* for 'alternative' medicine and an equally categorical *yes* for 'complementary' therapies—selectively, of course, and with limitations. However, both these qualifications apply equally to the subdivisions of orthodox medicine. Nobody regards drug therapy, psychotherapy and surgery as alternative therapeutic methods in competition with one another. Until we pension off the misleading adjective 'alternative' and accept the essentially complementary nature of all the different forms of therapy, the situation will remain confused, riven by prejudice, preconceived misconceptions and damaging antagonisms.

Health Care Provision under Financial Constraint, edited by T. B. Binns and M. Firth, 1988: Royal Society of Medicine International Congress and Symposium Series No. 115, published by Royal Society of Medicine Services Ltd.

Health needs are unmet by orthodox medicine alone

Perhaps it would not matter so much if orthodox medical practice was not falling short of meeting the current demand in both quantitative and qualitative terms.

Insofar as the quantitative aspect is concerned, we in the UK have little option at present but to leave the financial arithmetic to politicians who continue to foster the fantasy in people's minds that it is possible for them to be 'cured for free on a shoe-string'. One day politicians may eventually recognize that this unrealistic misconception is partly, and I would even go as far as to say largely, responsible for the dire straits in which our National Health Service finds itself floundering today. It is a fantasy if only because relatively few sicknesses of mankind are in fact amenable to being cured by external intervention alone.

Another unfortunate consequence of fostering this fantasy is the impairment by implication of the patient's confidence in his or her inherent self-healing capability. In the end, this is the operative factor underlying anybody getting better from anything. In this simple truth lies a partial answer to the problem we are discussing at this meeting. Doctors may justifiably claim some credit for facilitating or accelerating recovery, and occasionally for forestalling death, but let no therapist, be he orthodox or complementary, delude himself that his ministrations are exclusively responsible for the restoration of his patient's health.

It is now generally agreed that the majority of patients seeking the aid of their general practitioner (GP) are indeed suffering — but only from an imbalance of homoeostasis or, if you prefer the term, from non-specific illness, systems dysfunction, or indeed any of the many other descriptive designations of what is essentially a question of disordered physiology. This majority of sufferers — from illness as opposed to disease — do not necessarily need expensive high technology, even for diagnosis let alone treatment, nor are they necessarily best served by the prescription of costly drugs, not a few of which have an inherently harmful potential.

Such patients are far better served by the application of a generous measure of knowledgeable and sympathetic counselling, backed up by some action or activity designed to activate their self-healing capability. In more scientific terminology, this means 'catalysis' of their in-built bio-regulatory mechanisms. This is the domain of psychoneuroendocrinology, and psychoneuroimmunology (1).

In making the foregoing statement, I am by no means implying that complementary therapies are devoid of any specific action, or that they operate solely by way of a placebo effect, augmented by a strong doctor/patient relationship. On the other hand, neither is the converse true, that the original holistic concept of patient care as practised in both our countries at the turn of this century has been entirely submerged in the overwhelming demands placed on orthodox practitioners by the spectacular advances in scientific technology.

Such is the outline of my argument in favour of actively encouraging recruitment of complementary practitioners as colleagues in the task of coping with the overall problem of ill health in the community today — of course, only with the exercise of appropriate quality controls and ethical constraints. Herein lies an urgent need for research.

Does complementary medicine work?

The next consideration is the more practical one of whether these other methods actually work.

Even the British Medical Association, in its recent and substantially condemnatory report on the subject, conceded that

> it is possible that alternative medicine does provide some help for patients with their experience of illness (2).

Surely, this is the very essence of patient care, the core of any therapy and the primary objective of all workers in the field, whether they be ancillary assistants, social workers, nurses, complementary practitioners or orthodox scientifically qualified doctors? It is, of course, an undoubted bonus if the therapeutic method itself has a specific effect over and above the influence of its use in the hands of an experienced therapist, but the specific effect is by no means an essential element in restoration of health in the vast majority of cases of illness. Thus, no therapy should be condemned solely on the grounds of, as yet, the absence of existence of proof of a specific effect—especially as the important qualifying phrase is 'as yet', for a variety of fairly obvious reasons. Not the least of these is that insufficient research of an adequate calibre has been carried out in the complementary field, although there are already sufficient studies available to substantiate the probability of a specific action in many areas. The most widely known example is the use of acupuncture in anaesthesia and the disclosure of its effect in catalysing endorphin release. More recently, Reilly has revealed that homoeopathic remedies can be significantly more effective than a placebo, utilizing hay fever as the model for his study (3).

I have every confidence that a steadily increasing volume of research evidence will now be forthcoming to confirm the usefulness of an increasing number of the various different therapeutic systems and techniques. In this respect, that is, of usefulness in practice, the competence and integrity of the therapist is of greater importance than the specific validity of the method he chooses to use. Even if complementary therapies are revealed as only equally effective as, rather than superior to, allopathy in the management of non-specific illness, there are other important criteria which could render them preferential for wider use, such as being either safer or cheaper. In respect of the safety factor, it is worthy of note that 5–15% of hospital patients are now claimed to be the subject of iatrogenic illness (4,5). What a tragic twist of fate and an appalling waste of money. Of course, such figures are open to challenge, but even if the incidence was only one half of 1% it represents many people and takes no account of innumerable unrecorded sufferers at home.

Economic aspects of complementary medicine

The economic aspects involve manpower as well as money. Present national health services are not only strained to the limit, they are overwhelmed. This impasse can never be solved by money alone since, in truth, neither the manpower nor the materials exist to come anywhere near meeting the prevailing demand. It is obvious that without radically modifying our approach there is not the slightest hope of catching up with the existing requirements, let alone of meeting future needs.

Change and challenge

I regret to record that our profession has proved itself unresponsive to this challenge, and continues to maintain a disappointing degree of resistance to any ideas of change.

In fact, remarkably few doctors have recognized the profound alteration in the nature of the problem facing us, an alteration inherent in the dramatic reversal of the ratio between disease and illness that has progressively come about over the past half century. In the mid-1930s two GPs, George Scott Williamson and Innes Pearse, carried out a survey of 3911 patients in Peckham (6–8). They found that 90% were the subject of some organic condition, ranging from a mild iron-deficiency anaemia, through valvular heart disease, diabetes and tuberculosis, to cancer. As I mentioned before, only a minority of patients seeking the aid of their GP today are suffering from any disease entity requiring specific therapy. Yet the costly quest for an organic diagnostic label for the remainder continues unabated, as does arbitrary prescribing of equally costly remedies for these cases, which are sometimes inappropriate and, at worst, harmful. Coincidentally, this fruitless search for the non-existent organic pathology is seriously detrimental to those who do suffer from specific disease because it swamps the limited facilities of which this minority stands in immediate need.

A considerable number of practitioners of other far more cost-effective methods have intimated their willingness to share the load as colleagues, were it not for the persistent cloud of mutual suspicion that continues to overshadow the scene. There is a significant similarity in the antagonisms between the various religious factions which, as in medicine, share a common aim. Yet each has, through the ages, persisted in claiming a monopoly of the truth and, in consequence, each has stood out as an exclusive alternative. Now at last many creeds are beginning to recognize the irrationality of such a stance and the advantages to their flocks of becoming complementary partners in their task of caring for the soul. It would be gratifying if our profession could succeed in setting up a parallel example of this ecumenical trend in the field of caring for the body and mind, to the mutual benefit of all concerned.

Financial constraints

So much for a consideration of the generalities of the question whether complementary therapies have any place to play in the management of illness. What is the answer to the addendum to that question—'. . . at a time of financial constraint'? Again in my opinion the answer is unequivocally *yes*. In fact, what at first sight might appear to have prospects of being an additional financial burden could paradoxically prove in the long run to be a solution in disguise.

If the present and continuing demand on therapeutic services is to be met in this country, a considerable increase in the total number of therapists is obligatory. However, the cost of training a conventional doctor is now standing around £75 000–80 000. Complementary therapists carry the expense of their specialized education personally. I am not discussing the rights or wrongs of this situation, merely indicating another possible area of considerable saving, in this case of capital outlay.

Secondly, the prospects of economies in the field of medication are also substantial, even though impossible to compute with any accuracy. Quite apart from the obvious benefits of substitution of less costly herbal or homoeopathic remedies where applicable, especially in geriatrics, less apparent but equally significant savings would result from a reduction of the prevailing unacceptably high incidence of iatrogenic pathology which is such a tragic waste of resources, to say nothing of the discomfort and distress borne by the patients themselves.

Finally, to select an example from the opposite end of the therapeutic spectrum, namely surgery. Wider use of the now well-established non-invasive therapeutic techniques in the management of hypertension and angina (9,10) could well result in halving the number of coronary artery bypass operations that are carried out today and be transmuted into a reduction in the much publicized waiting list for hip replacements.

Incidentally, it should also be more widely appreciated that coronary artery bypass is associated with a high incidence of post-operative neurological morbidity (11,12). In the Newcastle study, 8% of patients had important neurological disability at the time of their discharge from hospital. Overall, the harmful effect of excessive enthusiasm for high technology procedures almost certainly exceeds that of delayed diagnosis of organic disease by complementary practitioners, which is so often quoted as a major risk factor in this field. Moreover, it could be claimed that errors of commission are more culpable than those of omission.

My claim is that a vastly more cost-effective service would almost certainly be the outcome of combining the available skills of all orthodox 'health operatives', lay as well as professional, together with those of complementary practitioners, each and every one being complementary to the others and working in mutual harmony instead of confrontational discord.

Summary

Today's health care services stand in dire need of rationalization, with a predominant emphasis on the enhancement of health running parallel with the technological management of disease, and including greater involvement of the individual patient in both activities. I foresee complementary therapies having an ever increasing part to play. The economic benefits would be considerable, and sharing the clinical overload would go a long way towards enabling the conventional family practitioner to revive his original highly respected role of friend, counsellor and healer, in parallel with the demanding technological exercise of disease detection and control.

Indeed, a mutually reciprocal working partnership between orthodox scientific medicine and complementary therapists could even result in the transformation of our present national disease service into a national health service in actuality as well as in name.

As a preliminary, however, research into all aspects of the various complementary practices is essential to provide the basis for development of the quality controls and ethical constraints which are mandatory for protection of the public from the inherent risk of exploitation.

References

(1) Solomon GF. The emerging field of psychoneuroimmunology. *Advances* 1985; **2**: 7–19.

(2) British Medical Association. *Alternative therapy: report of the Board of Science and Education*. London: British Medical Association, 1986.

(3) Reilly DT, Taylor MA, McSharry C, Aitchison T. Is homoeopathy a placebo response? Controlled trial of homoeopathic potency, with pollen in hayfever as model. *Lancet* 1986; ii: 881–6.

(4) Trunet P, Le Gall J-R, Lhoste F, *et al*. The role of iatrogenic disease in admissions to intensive care. *J Am Med Assoc* 1980; **244** (23): 2617–20.

(5) Justiniani FR. Iatrogenic disease: an overview. *Mt Sinai J Med* 1984; **51** (2): 210–4.

(6) Editorial. An experiment interrupted. *Lancet* 1986; ii: 422–3.

(7) Williamson SG. Peckham: the first health centre. *Lancet* 1946; i: 393–8.

(8) Pearse IH, Crocker L. *The Peckham experiment. A study of the living structure of society.*
New ed. Edinburgh: Scottish Academic Press, 1985.

(9) Nixon PGF. Consensus meeting: coronary artery bypass surgery — is it enough? *Quality of Life and Cardiovascular Care* 1986 Spring: 125–32.

(10) Patel C, Marmot MG, Terry DJ, Carruthers M, Hunt B, Patel M. Trial of relaxation in reducing coronary risk: a four year follow up. *Br Med J* 1985; **290**: 1103–6.

(11) Shaw PJ, Bates D, Cartlidge NE, Heaviside D, Julian DG, Shaw DA. Early neurological complications of coronary artery bypass surgery. *Br Med J* 1985; **291**: 1384–7.

(12) Shaw PJ. Neurological dysfunction following coronary artery bypass surgery. [Editorial]. *J Roy Soc Med* 1986; **79**: 130–1.

Discussion

(invited discussant *Gillian Ford*)

Dr Ford

Had there been a view from the USA it might have been possible to contrast the attitudes of the two countries.

My impression is that in the USA the patient is regarded as the client of the doctor, whereas in the UK I think we still have the remnants of the paternalist attitude of 'I know what is best for you — don't ask any questions'.

It could be suggested that our technical ingenuity and competence far outstrip our ability to handle various human situations, such as working as a member of a team or with other disciplines and other professions, communicating with individuals, patients and members of their families, and with groups and populations. We have heard about how the health education message has to be relevant and understood — but we seem to make rather a hash of getting that message over.

Dr Tonkin has demonstrated that it is important to communicate because it harnesses the body's ability to heal itself. This is what is meant, surely, by good whole-person medicine. Holistic medicine is about listening to and treating the whole person, a knowledge of that person's circumstances and manner of life, nevertheless treating people with respect which leaves them with a measure of control over what is happening.

Is this what is being taught in medical schools? Can it be taught better? Can it be reinforced both in the immediate postgraduate and in the following graduate years?

We have discussed the priorities and the pressure of teaching many things during the undergraduate years, including the need both to evaluate and to take into account what people in other disciplines and other professions are doing.

I think there is hope. There is advance in this field. Two practical things are happening in the UK at the moment. First, the need for individuals to see how they behave as they deal with patients is certainly recognized, and the methods are there to make that message plain — methods such as role playing and video tapes. They show, do they not, what barriers we put up between ourselves and the person to whom we are talking?

Secondly, multidisciplinary learning experiences give the opportunity to know what pressures are being faced by members of other disciplines and other professions as they deal with patients and families. That is certainly something which is being explored in the hospice world.

The hospice movement, which is quite lively on both sides of the Atlantic, had very different origins. In the UK, it arose from neglect of patients. Patients who were dying of cancer were left to moulder in an end bed in wards, hardly spoken to — let alone listened to. In the USA I think its genesis was rather different. The feeling there was that perhaps people were being overtreated, and that far too much was being done.

Professor Rabkin

In the USA I think that we see a range of approaches. On the one hand, there are podiatrists who, in some states, are opting to do triple arthrodeses, sometimes with some success. On the other hand, there are certainly hospice movements and a growing field of psychoimmunology, among others. The prominent call here, as I think Dr Tonkin put it, is not to deny the possible utility but, at least in academic medicine, to try to understand why and how some of these things work.

Secondly, in hospital it seems to me that, a least in the USA, nursing is of very great importance. Hospitals are really nursing institutions, institutions of nurture 24 h a day, providing the arena in which occasional perturbations are created by physicians — some of those perturbations for good, others not. The nurses create the basic skeletal structure. Depending upon the nature of nursing within a particular institution, the whole caring nature can be dramatically influenced. When we think about all the forces brought to bear upon healing we must think first and foremost about nursing.

Dr Banta

Of the five types of complementary medicine that have been listed, it is my understanding that in the USA osteopathy and chiropractic are more or less accepted — perhaps not by the medical profession, but in the sense of being licensed and paid for. Homoeopathy almost does not exist. Acupuncture is accepted more or less, depending upon the circumstances. In fact, my sister is a licensed acupuncturist in Baltimore. Herbalists exist, but more in, for example, Latin American areas than in any sort of widespread way.

I would add two more. Firstly, energy medicine. Although some people call homoeopathy a form of energy medicine, I am referring to a whole variety of techniques to do with energy and imagery which is very prevalent in some areas, particularly California of course. Secondly, clinical ecology, which I think is rather widespread across the country, although in a rather random fashion. This is the belief that low-grade allergies produce rather chronic and disabling complaints, and that manipulating diet can deal with them. I know some quite good physicians who accept that belief.

I would perhaps quarrel slightly with one statement made by Dr Tonkin. I did not find the British Medical Association (BMA) report condemnatory (perhaps I should say considering the source) (1). It is a remarkably progressive document, bearing in mind that it comes from the union of the medical profession. I have already used it in the Netherlands. The typical argument that I find in the medical profession is that we know complementary medicine does not work. The BMA report says that it does not fit their medical paradigm — which, of course, is true. The report goes on to say that none the less it should be evaluated, and if it works it should be incorporated. To me, that is a very progressive stance, coming from the medical profession.

Professor Pardes

I share the concern that there may be much in some of the complementary therapies that is not given adequate examination. Certainly orthodox medicine does a sufficiently mediocre job with enough conditions that we should not be too comfortable about what we offer.

Amongst Dr Tonkin's array of suggestions, evaluative research is itself an investment. How would he sort out the question of which therapies to evaluate, and what would be the criteria for even initiating an evaluation?

When I was director of a National Institute of Health we were repeatedly criticized for not giving sufficient attention to megavitamins and their potential benefit for schizophrenia. Whatever studies had been done by the medical profession had shown them to be of no value, yet any number of anecdotal stories indicated their utility. We said that we would take any applications for research submitted — but none came in.

Therefore, we should ask who should stimulate such research, and what should be the criteria on which a decision is made to invest in it?

Dr Tonkin

First, I think the question of dietary regimes, ecology and allergies only shows that we already regard much of this as complementary — because this is the hinterland between. I have always regarded these areas as well within orthodox medicine.

Secondly, the question of evaluation is the whole problem, because there have not been the facilities for research in this field and there is no evidence on which to base any judgement. We felt that the action to take was to set up an organization, the Research Council for Complementary Medicine, which is essentially an enabling organization. It is obviously not possible for its small membership, all fully occupied elsewhere, to tackle this research which needs to be based in academic institutions with access to all the other disciplines.

In the past, it has always been claimed that the research must be done in the field. However, in the complementary field, particularly in the main systems that I have named, the facilities, patients, equipment and, above all, people do not exist. In our medical schools there is an intermediate echelon of doctors in training — the registrars and senior registrars — part of whose job it is to undertake research, to learn under the wing of professional researchers. Thus, there is a basis for doing research. This does not exist in the complementary field. We originally found that research projects coming to us were quite unacceptable because they were not structured correctly.

Also, when we are trying to research in this area the intangibles of 'getting better' or 'being ill', the standard paradigms of double-blind controlled trials are not always applicable. We have tackled this by having an internal series of seminars to discuss methodology. The Medical Research Council has agreed, and is now split-funding with us a research fellowship in methodology. We feel that much modern research methodology, although highly applicable in specific areas, is not even adequate for orthodox medicine. This whole subject needs examining in much greater detail. We hope eventually to be able to produce adequate research tools with which to evaluate this very much vaguer field of restoration of health.

Dr Relman

First, the status of osteopaths and chiropractors in the USA is quite different. It is true that they are both licensed, but the osteopaths in the USA are trying to integrate themselves into the corpus of traditional medicine. They stand apart only when it comes to reserving to themselves the right to give credentials to their own people, to educate them and so on. In terms of the way they practise and how they want the public to regard them, however, they are trying to pass as regular doctors. They are licensed as regular doctors, they work in the same institutions, and publish in the same professional journals — they use the same paradigm, if you like. Osteopathy is regarded, perhaps unfairly, as second-class regular medicine.

Chiropractors are also licensed — I think in all states — and they are reimbursed by third-party payers, but they are not trying to be part of the medical establishment. Nobody regards them that way. In fact, most people in the USA outside chiropractic look askance at their claims. Chiropractors are recognized as being very good at dealing with the common musculoskeletal causes of back pain when that back pain is not caused by anything serious. It would, however, be a dreadful mistake for someone to go to a chiropractor with a ruptured disc or a neoplasm, or if his back pain was due to kidney disease or cancer of the pancreas. They have a different status to osteopaths.

I agree with Dr Tonkin that it is both easy and correct to criticize regular medicine because it has plenty of shortcomings. We have not maintained a breadth of view of what we ought to be doing. We tend to be super-specialized, narrowly focused on our techniques. I agree with Dr Ford that there is much room for improvement in the way in which we deal with the humanistic aspects of contacts with our patients.

Having said that, it seems to me that the remedy is to improve, to reform, but not to jump out of the 20th century view that all the clinical phenomena in mankind take place in the same three-dimensional space, in the head and in the rest of the body, and ultimately have to be investigated in any way we can rationally. We should not have two standards either of rationality or of evidence.

I am delighted to hear that there is such concern for the methodological problems of getting the evidence in complementary medicine. In the USA, there is virtually none. Chiropractors make claims based on no evidence—as do both osteopaths and herbalists—that is, no evidence that will stand close inspection. If there is an inclination in the UK to seek out the evidence, I think that is extremely healthy.

Dr Tonkin

Both these points are absolutely correct. It is quite unacceptable that it should be 'alternative' medicine. This is why I started my presentation with a didactic statement. Dr Relman is saying that there is a place for osteopathy, and we all agree that it is complementary as long as we can contain it within that field. Secondly, it has to be evaluated—there is no question about that.

However, when we come to the subject of this meeting, economy and cost, there is a considerable economy in employing other methods within their limitations, after they have been strictly defined, with proper accreditation and registration so that the public can be protected. In fact, this also hands back to the orthodox practitioner greater facility to deploy to better effect the technology about which we have been talking.

Mr Munson

Everything suggested by Dr Relman, Dr Banta and Professor Rabkin as being the US view of what is happening in alternative and complementary care has been occurring in spite of the millions of dollars being spent by the American Medical Association (AMA) to prevent it happening. That is most accurately reflected in the last couple of years in its attempts to reject the efforts made by the Joint Commission on Accreditation of Hospitals. As the Joint Commission has sought to become more egalitarian in medical staff organization, so the AMA has increased its lobby budget.

Secondly, even as that is done, it is interesting to note that the American Hospital Association and the AMA are now locked over the issue of hospital governance in its purest form, particularly as it relates to the role played by the medical staff in that governance structure.

Both those trends or issues are being played out in America today, and are in large measure a reflection of the competitive threat of some of these alternative and complementary modes of care.

Reference

(1) British Medical Association. *Alternative therapy: report of the Board of Science and Education*. London: British Medical Association, 1986.

PROVIDING FOR SPECIAL NEEDS
AND VULNERABLE GROUPS

1. An overview

Chairman:
ROSEMARY A. STEVENS
Philadelphia PA, USA

A UK view

E. ROSEMARY RUE

*Regional General Manager/Regional Medical Officer,
Oxford Regional Health Authority, Oxford, UK*

Introduction

It is possible to take a very broad view of special needs for health care and to identify vulnerable groups at every level of society. The World Health Organization has recognized the vulnerability of whole populations in the developing countries and has set out a framework for meeting their special needs in *Health for all by the year 2000* (1).

The principles on which health care should be based in Europe have, however, been developed from the same declaration, and in the National Health Service (NHS) the approach to health care, involving equality of access and comparability of standards, is well understood.

Assuming that a health care system is established, however modestly resourced, in a western country all those concerned with the planning and provision of services will sooner or later be faced with the difficulty of competing claims and unmet needs in variously assorted user groups.

Experience within the NHS is useful to review and forms the background to this paper.

Identifying and updating special needs and vulnerable groups

The NHS planning system (2) has developed upon a framework of care groups. Each district uses its resources to provide services relating to these groups and makes forward plans on the basis of trends and projections of need for such services. The groups are not very strictly defined and not similarly based. There is overlap between them, but this does allow for the needs of the population served to be studied from various planning perspectives to provide total coverage. Some regional variation in the scope of each care group exists and the subsidiary groups differ between regions. The groupings have developed from the practical experience of the NHS in its attempts

Health Care Provision under Financial Constraint, edited by T. B. Binns and M. Firth, 1988: Royal Society of Medicine International Congress and Symposium Series No. 115, published by Royal Society of Medicine Services Ltd.

to provide equality of access for those in need. In the groups there is a basis of comparison across the country which assists in the assessment of standards of health care.

At present, the main planning groups are as follows:
— acute hospital services
— maternity services
— services for children
— services for the elderly and elderly mentally infirm
— services for the mentally ill
— services for the mentally handicapped
— services for the physically handicapped and rehabilitation services
— primary and community health care services
— services for prevention and health promotion
— services for the terminally ill

NHS planning is based on a 10-year strategic projection, reviewed 5-yearly, with short-term programmes of 1–2 years concerned with implementation. In this system, planning groups can be combined, subdivided or changed at different rates in different localities so that some sensitivity towards local situations is retained.

Priorities in health care

From time to time aspects of services—whole groups or their components—are brought forward for special emphasis in the implementation of plans. It may be that a major medical or scientific advance demands a reappraisal of services or additional financial investment. More often the identification of a priority group relates to a changed philosophical or socioeconomic attitude to the delivery of care. More commonly still it is political or other public pressures which demand a period of high profile for the group of services concerned. Rarely, there is a change in the population served—a demographic change or change in morbidity—which requires a response from planning in terms of changed priority.

There has been for several years in the NHS an objective of improving the standards and status of services for the non-acute care groups (3). A higher priority has therefore been given to the elderly and those with mental illness, infirmity or handicap. This priority has been effected through higher and earlier investment of capital and provision of revenue for staffing in the priority groups than in the acute services. The intention behind the accordance of priority was that, while services for all groups advanced, the priority groups should advance more rapidly.

The concept of priority in health care is useful only if it is limited. Political enthusiasm has led recently to the NHS being asked to give priority to such a large number of services and activities that the relative importance of main groups for planning and development has been obscured. A current list of nearly 50 topics for the attention of management has been compiled, some clearly related to health care needs, others less obviously so. The most recent priority is an onslaught on waiting times for surgery, with some individual surgical procedures being singled out for special resourcing. Desirable as these improvements may be, the effect is a reversal of agreed priorities. Inevitably, there will be a reassessment at local level and the effects nationally will have to be re-examined.

Meanwhile there are problems in determining the extent to which resources should be directed towards the extremes of a modern health service. At one extreme are the very rare health needs for which specialized and usually expensive services are required.

In the NHS these are covered by a system of regional (subnational) or supraregional (national) planning and development. At the other extreme are the disadvantaged groups which tend to be large, needing systematic, reliable service networks, and whose less attractive requirements tend to become progressively less well met. The constant vigilance of the NHS planning system and its comprehensive coverage is the best protection devised for these groups, and perhaps the greatest achievement of the NHS when international comparisons are made.

Regional and supraregional specialties (4)

Each NHS district provides a range of specialist services which cover the common requirements of general practitioners (GPs) for consultation and of the population for specialist accident and emergency services. Some specialties or aspects of specialties are provided on a multidistrict basis, often as a single service for the whole region. Others are provided for several regions or on a national basis. The scale of provision relates to the rarity of the need for the service, the rarity of the skills available to provide the service, and the complexity and expense of the equipment or procedures required. One objective is to avoid excessive duplication of investment in expensive services.

More important from the patient's point of view is the agreement reached between doctors in the region to refer cases to the specialist centres in order to avoid dilution of specialist skills and to maintain the highest standards in the care of rare conditions. This is particularly relevant to the development of scientific advances in medicine. An immediate tendency for multiple centres to spring up is avoided and some control is exercised over the introduction of new techniques — the competence of each new team is assured. Without interfering with the professional freedom of doctors to adopt new methods, the introduction of new specialties occurs through a gradual and agreed devolution through the service. While some specialties remain regionally organized for many years, others tend to progress from national to regional to district scale as appropriate.

The organization and development of regional specialties is not the same as the development of special interests or centres of excellence such as occurs in teaching hospitals but which may appear anywhere in the service within the range of specialist medicine. Doctors are free in the NHS to refer patients to any consultant, and the special interests of individual consultants and their teams, especially in teaching centres, are known and exploited in this way.

Examples of current regional specialties are neurosurgery with associated neurosciences, radiotherapy and renal transplantation. Supraregional specialties currently include heart transplantation, centres for choriocarcinoma and spinal injuries. An example of a supraregional specialty which is devolving gradually is bone marrow transplantation.

Planning and providing for regional specialties

The basis for the recognition and establishment of regional specialties and their subsequent development is professional advice, provided in the NHS through the statutory network of advisory machinery. The doctors concerned have the opportunity through this machinery to alert the health authority to the emergence of a medical or scientific advance and to ascertain whether there is a need to centralize the skills and resources to obtain the best results. In an established regional specialty the trends and developments, and the feasibility of devolving the service to more local centres are the subject of similar advice.

A strong medical advisory input is also made to the question of the priority of the new specialty or of major developments in an established specialty, but the health authority has to take much wider advice on this point — from other professionals, GPs and community health councils — and must consider the priority in the context of the total needs of the service.

Resourcing an agreed development in accordance with the priority afforded to it is a familiar NHS problem. Funds for buildings, equipment and staff have to be found, and the availability of staff to recruit and train from a limited manpower pool assessed. Financial resources for all regional specialties are projected over the 10-year planning period in a broad categorization alongside the care groups described above and certain other identifiable demands. A planned financial investment programme thereby places constraints and relative priorities upon aspects of the total services provided in the region. The effect is to produce a small queue for developments in regional specialties from which the top priorities are financed each year. Last year a planned regional development in genetics was wholly displaced by a programme for dealing with the arrival of acquired immune deficiency syndrome (AIDS).

Costed short- and long-term programmes set out the pattern for the future, and these are updated in the light of professional advice at regular intervals. It has to be confessed that there is very great pressure on available resources from the direction of regional specialties which are particularly susceptible to change and unforeseen advances.

Planning and providing for vulnerable groups

In health service parlance, the term 'vulnerable' refers more often to the disadvantaged in a social sense than to the rare and scientifically interesting groups described above. The priority care groups, identified after much consultation within the NHS and with the public, each appear in costed short- and long-term programmes for each district and region. Plans are not approved by the Department of Health and Social Security unless differential improvements in favour of these groups are undertaken, and the annual ministerial review process serves as a check on progress being made. Account has to be taken of the very high usage of acute (i.e. non-priority) services by the elderly, and this effect causes some problems in monitoring exactly where resources have been directed. There is no doubt that the care of the elderly is an increasingly overwhelming NHS activity. Expenditures on services for the mentally ill, infirm and handicapped is more easily accounted for, and development of these services more easily identified as separate activities.

From time to time, small groups of individuals in need or aspects of services can be identified within or across main care groups as being either relatively neglected or able to benefit from recent advances. The problem of alcohol abuse is an example of such selection for special consideration. Not only is this problem seen as relating to several care groups, but the interface with the much larger component beyond the NHS is also recognized. A concerted attempt to plan in conjunction with many non-NHS agencies is made in such circumstances.

Progress

The NHS offers a fairly balanced service overall, and there is considerable confidence in the standards of care achieved. It has suffered somewhat in its development from changing priorities in the face of limited resources and long planning lead-times. The priorities of the first (1961) capital building programme have not yet been achieved even where these could still be confirmed as appropriate to a pattern of service for the 1980s. Some recent advances have not been fully exploited for lack of resources, and similar difficulties affecting universities have made it impossible for academic clinical departments to give a lead. There is, however, a high level of understanding of the possible way forward and a model somewhere in the NHS for most specialist services. It is to be expected that developments, however well-planned, will be uneven and the greatest problem is obtaining a service outcome which is seen to be fair.

References

(1) *Report of the International Conference on Primary Health Care*, Alma Alta, USSR, Sept 6–12 1978. Geneva: World Health Organization, 1978.
(2) *The NHS planning system*. Department of Health and Social Security Circular HC(82)6. London: Her Majesty's Stationery Office, 1982.
(3) *Care in action*. London: Her Majesty's Stationery Office, 1981.
(4) *Regional strategy and regional strategic plan* (extracts). Summary of regional specialty information. Oxford: Oxford Regional Health Authority, 1984.

A US view:
problems posed by the
US health insurance 'system'

LAWRENCE S. LEWIN

Lewin and Associates Inc., Washington DC, USA

Introduction

There is probably no better way to contrast how health care is financed under the British and American systems than to examine the financing of care for low-income pregnant women and children. Doing so not only reveals the differences in financing and organization of the delivery system, but it also provides an insight into some of the underlying social and political beliefs and values that produce these differences.

This paper is a descriptive commentary on the American 'system', and is divided into three major parts:

(1) A description of the various ways in which health care for low-income persons in the USA is financed, and how care is provided for those without health insurance.

(2) A focus on the particular problems and health care needs of low-income pregnant women and their children.

(3) A discussion of the choices that policy makers in the USA are facing as they seek to extend appropriate services to this population when there is no opportunity to achieve universal health insurance coverage for them.

Clearly, low-income pregnant women and children are not the only vulnerable, significantly underinsured populations in the USA. The homeless, many acquired immune deficiency syndrome (AIDS) victims, and the mentally ill are all seriously at risk of not having adequate access to needed care. By focusing on pregnant women and children, I do not mean to imply that they are the only ones in need, but I do believe that they represent a group for whom enhanced access to health care is widely understood to be cost-effective. As a result, their continuing plight reveals much that is significant about the US 'system'.

Health Care Provision under Financial Constraint, edited by T. B. Binns and M. Firth, 1988: Royal Society of Medicine International Congress and Symposium Series No. 115, published by Royal Society of Medicine Services Ltd.

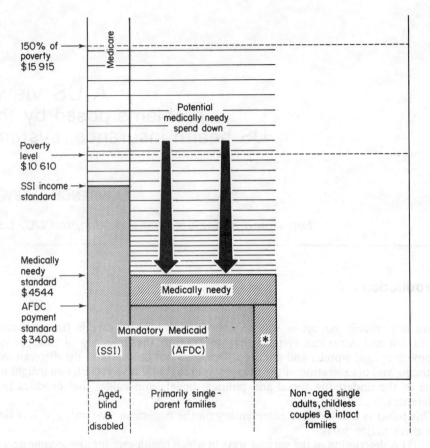

Figure 1. Medicaid and the poor in Florida (income levels for a family of four in 1984).
*Children in intact families and unemployed parents (optional categorical groups).
AFDC = Aid to families with dependent children.
SSI = Supplemental security income.

Health insurance coverage for low-income persons in the USA

Health insurance coverage in the USA has variously been categorized as a patchwork quilt, and as a membership club open primarily to employed persons (particularly in medium and large companies), the elderly, and the 'worthy' among the very poor. While one does not need to be poor to be uninsured in the USA, the high cost of medical care makes the absence of insurance an especially acute problem for the poor and near-poor (generally defined as up to 150% of the federal poverty guideline (which, in 1986, was approximately $18 000 for a family of four).* This group of uninsured poor and those whose illness results in catastrophic expenses are commonly referred to as the 'medically indigent'. In 1984, approximately 35 million Americans under the age of 65 lacked health insurance, private or public, of whom about half were below 150% of the poverty line (2).

*According to the 1977 National Medical Care Expenditure Care survey, 71·5% of those without insurance at least part of the year had incomes in excess of 125% of the poverty line (1).

Table 1

State monthly aid to families with dependent children (AFDC) payments for a family of four, as a percentage of the monthly federal poverty level, 1984

Based on data comparing 1984 AFDC monthly payment levels to the monthly federal poverty level, the states and the District of Columbia can be ranked as follows:

Rank[a]	State	%[b]	Rank	State	%[b]
1	Alaska	91	27	South Dakota	42
2	California	73	28	Virginia	42
3	Connecticut	73	29	Maryland	42
4	Wisconsin	72	29	Wyoming	42
5	Vermont	70	31	Oklahoma	41
6	Minnesota	69	32	Idaho	41
7	New York	67	33	Ohio	40
8	Hawaii	64	34	Delaware	40
9	Washington	64	35	Indiana	37
10	Rhode Island	62	36	New Mexico	37
11	Michigan	57	37	Missouri	36
12	Massachusetts	52	38	Arizona	33
12	Oregon	52	39	Florida	32
14	North Dakota	51	40	Nevada	32
15	Maine	51	41	West Virginia	29
16	Montana	50	42	Georgia	28
17	Nebraska	49	43	Kentucky	28
18	Iowa	49	44	Louisiana	28
19	Texas	49	45	North Carolina	26
20	New Jersey	49	46	Arkansas	22
21	Pennsylvania	49	47	Utah	21
22	Kansas	48	48	South Carolina	20
23	Colorado	48	49	Tennessee	18
24	New Hampshire	46	50	Alabama	17
25	Illinois	43	51	Mississippi	14
26	Washington DC	43			

[a]States with the same payment are assigned the same rank, rankings being based on the actual dollar amount of the payment.
[b]Rounded to the nearest whole point.
Sources: State Vital Statistics Office. Some data gaps filled by National Center for Health Statistics unpublished data. Rankings by Childrens Defense Fund (4).

Public coverage

The coverage picture, revealed in Fig. 1, graphically portrays who has the benefits of public insurance and who does not. Dealing first with the most widely covered groups, Medicare benefits are extended to virtually all those aged 65 and over, disabled persons under age 65 receiving social security or railroad retirement benefits because they are disabled, and persons suffering from end-stage renal disease. Medicare, which currently serves over 28 million elderly, provides extensive hospital in-patient coverage but, while many are covered, the benefits are less comprehensive than many elderly persons believe. Patient co-payment requirements under the program have grown in recent years, and there is little coverage under Medicare for out-patient prescription drugs and long-term care services. A study last year by the House Select Committee on Aging projected that by 1990, if current coverage trends continue, 55% of nursing home costs will be paid directly by the elderly, along with 52% of physician costs and 66% of the costs of drugs and other care, including home health care. This can be compared with the 15% of acute hospital care paid for out-of-pocket by patients (3).

It should be noted that 70% of elderly Americans purchase private insurance to supplement their Medicare benefits. Medicaid, the largest government health program for the poor, also supplements Medicare coverage for some low-income persons receiving cash benefits under the supplemental security income program.

Medicaid was primarily designed to provide medical services to certain low-income individuals and their families. As a joint federal, state and, occasionally, local effort, the share of program costs paid for by the federal government varies according to a formula based on states per capita income and ranges from a minimum of 50% for wealthier states like California to a high of 77·5% for poor states like Mississippi and Arkansas.

As Fig. 1 shows for the example state of Florida, all persons eligible for cash benefits under a state's aid to families with dependent children (AFDC) program qualify for coverage under Medicaid. Children and adults covered by Medicaid by virtue of eligibility for AFDC must be single-parent families, except where states include families with unemployed parents and children 18 years of age who are regularly attending school. Income eligibility for AFDC, and therefore Medicaid, is set by each state and varies greatly. Table 1, prepared by the Children's Defense Fund, shows each state's eligibility standard for AFDC as a percentage of the poverty level (4). Thus, for the year 1984, a woman with two children in the state of Indiana must have an annual income (after certain deductions) below $3072 to be eligible for Medicaid. In addition to AFDC recipients, other pregnant women and children under the age of 6 must be covered by state Medicaid programs if they meet the AFDC income threshold. Coverage for these latter groups became mandatory only in recent years.

States have the option of providing coverage for Medicaid only to certain other AFDC-related groups known as the 'optional categorically needy', and receive federal matching funds (the shaded area, Fig. 1). This includes families with unemployed parents, and older children living in two-parent families whose income is at or below the state AFDC payment standard but who cannot qualify for AFDC because neither parent is absent.

State Medicaid programs may also cover the 'medically needy'. These are categorically related (e.g. AFDC) individuals ineligible for cash assistance whose income is greater than the payment level the state sets for an AFDC family of the same size. Each state that elects the medically needy option (36 by 1986) sets its own eligibility level, but it cannot exceed 133⅓% of existing AFDC levels, except for those with high medical expenses who can 'spend down' to the eligibility threshold (arrows, Fig. 1). Despite recent expansion in state adoption of the medically needy option, there is a large and growing gap between the number of people theoretically eligible and those actually enrolled and using services. The impetus to enrol patients in Medicaid often comes from hospitals and nursing homes for acute care services. There is less effort with respect to primary and preventive care.

Since 1981, states have been allowed increased flexibility in determining eligibility, reimbursement, and coverage under Medicaid. For example, the Omnibus Budget Reconciliation (OBR) Act, 1981, gave states the option of implementing medically needy programs to indigent pregnant women and to children without extending cash assistance and without providing a full-scale medically needy entitlement to parents and the aged and disabled.

Because Medicaid varies so significantly by state, similar kinds of needy persons in less generous states do not have equal access to the program. In addition, because Medicaid is limited to existing welfare categories, large numbers of needy persons

21–64 years of age are ineligible for Medicaid unless they are disabled or in families with dependent children. These omissions reflect an inclination to limit health care as a public good only to those deemed worthy, or considered incapable of otherwise helping themselves or their children.

The rate of growth in Medicaid expenditures has slowed in recent years, due to a variety of factors. The economic recession of the early 1980s forced many states to reduce or restrict eligibility and limit access to some services. Many states took advantage of some of the new programs and management opportunities authorized by the OBR Act as a way of holding down costs. Even though the federal government and the states have taken steps to restore some of the earlier cutbacks and add new eligibility groups, the proportion of the poor and near-poor covered by Medicaid has declined from 63% in 1975 to 46% in 1985. Today the program covers only about one-third of poor children, who constitute 40% of all poor Americans.*

Another major trend in Medicaid payments has also contributed significantly to the program's shrinking ability to serve the poor: an increasingly larger proportion of the program's finances are allocated to the elderly and disabled. Today, skilled nursing home care alone is the largest component of the Medicaid budget, accounting for 43% of all Medicaid outlays in 1984.[†]

There are a number of state-run, publicly-funded efforts such as the Title V maternal and child health, and crippled children's service programs that are targeted to needy mothers and children. In 1981, as part of the OBR Act, Congress folded these and other related programs into the maternal and child health block grant. At the time, their funding was reduced by approximately 20%. The supplemental food program for women, infants and children (WIC), not part of this block grant, focuses specifically on the nutritional health of pregnant and lactating women, and of infants and children up to 5 years of age. WIC appears to be a successful model. Several studies have concluded that fewer babies of low birth weight are being born to women who participate in WIC programs (5).

While Congress increased the funding for these programs in 1983, large numbers of women and children still do not receive the services they offer. In the case of WIC, for example, only about one-third of those eligible are actually enrolled and served.

Private coverage

It has been estimated that over half of those who are uninsured in America are employed (6). This group consists of workers in small firms, the self-employed and part-time workers who do not receive health insurance as part of their compensation package. Of the 17·2 million persons uninsured throughout 1980, three-quarters, or some 13 million were *employed* or dependents of employed persons.

The number of children among this age group has a troubling aspect. Data show that in 1983 over one-quarter of all uninsured children lived with at least one insured parent. Recent growth in the number of uninsured children of insured parents has been attributed in part to increased employer cost-sharing requirements. Most employers require employees to pay all or most of the extra premium for family

---

*This percentage is based on the number of persons who received Medicaid services at some point during the course of the year. An even smaller proportion of the poor and near-poor population (about one-third) were enrolled for the services at a given point in time during the year.
[†]This excludes intermediate care facilities for the mentally retarded which account for an additional large percentage of Medicaid expenditures.

coverage. Families are apt to forego family coverage if they believe that their medical expenses for the children are likely to be less than premium cost-sharing and deductible requirements. This is particularly true if the family's after-tax income is in the bottom half of the income distribution.

Being without insurance does not always mean being without access to health care services. For example, states have a variety of programs that attempt to close some of the gaps left by Medicaid. Many states operate either state or local level provider reimbursement programs for certain low-income populations not eligible for Medicaid or the other federally-supported programs. Unlike Medicaid, a state or county medical indigency program can target the specific populations and services covered. States can limit their overall budget outlays by setting appropriations ceilings or low payment rates for providers. Some states and counties provide funds for low-income individuals with specified medical conditions, such as neonatal intensive care patients, crippled children, shock-trauma and burn cases.

Most states or local governments operate or support public hospitals, clinics, health centers and related programs that serve the poor and uninsured, usually with some kind of income-related fee schedule. Local governments frequently provide lump-sum payments to such public facilities and maintain considerable influence over the type and level of services offered, access, and provider selection. However, one-third of the nation's 100 largest cities lack a publicly mandated, tax-supported provider of indigent hospital care. In the cities where they do exist, public hospitals provide a proportionately greater share of care to the poor than do private institutions. According to a study conducted by the Urban Institute, public hospitals provide close to 65% of all charity/bad debt care — care for which there is no direct third-party coverage (7).

As part of their community mission, voluntary private hospitals will extend care to some uninsured patients without expectation of payment. The costs for such unsponsored charity care amounted to an estimated $5·7 billion in 1984 or about 4% of total expenses (8). Today, there is increasing evidence that burgeoning price competition among hospitals is making it more difficult for them to continue this charity function — indeed, many are finding ways to reduce uncompensated care burdens. The not-for-profit and public hospitals, which provide the overwhelming majority of such charity care, suffer a distinct competitive handicap in the face of increasingly aggressive price competition from investor-owned and other not-for-profit hospitals providing significantly smaller volumes of charity care.

By far the greatest portion of hospital unsponsored charity care is for acute in-patient services. This fails to meet the more serious medical care deficit faced by most poor uninsured mothers and children, namely unrendered and deferred primary and preventive care. While there are fairly good data on total unsponsored charity care rendered by hospitals, little is known about how much charity care is provided to the uninsured by physicians and other providers outside hospitals and, indeed, about the amount of out-patient charity care provided by hospitals. The impression gained from the several household surveys that have been conducted is that physician-provided charity care for primary and preventive services is limited and very much subject to the physician's discretion. There is some anecdotal evidence that many physicians will provide charity care to former patients who are temporarily unemployed and without insurance, but there are also indications that physicians are becoming increasingly restive about growing and maldistributed charity burdens.

While some level of health care services for the medically indigent poor does exist, lack of adequate insurance coverage has been shown to represent a major barrier to access to care. Data collected in the 1977 National Medical Care Expenditure Survey (NMCES) revealed that the low-income uninsured in poor health made only half as many physician visits as those on Medicaid and had 50% fewer hospital stays (1). Given the overall lower health status of the poor, who have been shown to have higher rates of almost all types of illnesses, financial barriers to access take on an added significance.

Thus, for a significant portion of low-income persons the US health insurance system can be described as both inadequate and inequitable. In both these respects, it reflects not only deep divisions but also a pervasive ambivalence in the body politic as to whether health care should be viewed as a public good and assured to all without regard to income, or as a consumption good whose allocation, like clothing and recreation, should be a function of purchasing power. This deep-seated and long-standing ambivalence over publicly-funded social welfare programs has always been exacerbated by a fear that the availability of public support will induce long-term dependency. This ambivalence shapes both the structure of the current system and likely prospects for the future. While few would argue that the current system is an optimal approach for financing care for low-income Americans, given today's political and economic climate there is every reason to believe that any improvements will continue to be of the incremental 'gap filling' variety and that major steps towards universal health insurance coverage are not likely in the foreseeable future.

If comprehensive reforms are not likely, what options are there for the growing numbers of poor mothers and children who find themselves outside the current system of coverage? How might their needs most appropriately be met, and what are the prospects for improved access, especially for primary and preventive care?

Health service needs of low-income pregnant women and children

Health services research provides ample evidence that we are incurring significant societal and human costs that can be directly related to deficiencies in the US health insurance system for low-income pregnant women and children. To a considerable extent, this results from the fact that while the uninsured are unlikely to be denied acute in-patient or emergency care when they need it, the same cannot be said about primary and, especially, preventive care services. These non-acute, non-emergency services are especially sensitive to patient out-of-pocket expenses, and are less likely to be accessible to, and used by, low-income uninsured patients. Several studies, most notably the RAND Corporation health insurance project, have demonstrated that low-income persons are significantly less likely to visit a physician if they must incur out-of-pocket expenses, even at relatively modest levels (9).

Many of the major conditions prevalent among low-income pregnant women and children are especially responsive to primary prevention (avoiding the disease or condition), to secondary prevention (significantly ameliorating its future course or consequences), or to treatment designed to limit the discomfort or damage.

Barbara Starfield's article, 'Motherhood and apple pie: the effectiveness of medical care for children', is an especially useful synthesis of the large body of research on this issue, and offers some pointed examples of why primary and preventive care are particularly cost-effective for these groups (10).

Low birth weight

Low birth weight (fetal weight $\leqslant$ 5 lb) is a major risk factor for adverse pregnancy and post-neonatal (28 days to 1 year) outcomes. It is popularly believed that the provision of early or regular pre-natal care, especially for high-risk mothers, can help reduce the risk of low birth weight. The data show that while pre-natal care provided late in a pregnancy or not at all is associated with adverse outcomes, there is mixed evidence about the ability of pre-natal care *per se* to prevent low birth weight. There is more evidence that early pre-natal care can increase gestational age (i.e. the duration of the pregnancy). Early pre-natal care does help to identify women whose nutritional habits, physical condition, and possible substance abuse place them and their fetus at increased risk. In general, the effect of pre-natal care on pregnancy outcomes is positive, while its absence has little to commend it, but there remains much to learn about the optimum content and manner in which to deliver such care.

Neonatal and post-neonatal mortality

The literature on neonatal mortality clearly indicates that appropriate medical intervention can reduce neonatal mortality and, if targeted on disadvantaged populations, reduce the sizable differential in neonatal mortality rates that exists between the poor and non-poor. While much of the direct effect results from tertiary care in neonatal intensive care units, pre-natal care, especially for low-income women, significantly improves access to these sophisticated services when they are needed. Moreover, there is strong evidence that the reduction of abortion, family planning and primary care services increases the mortality risk and widens the disparity between the poor and non-poor.

Post-neonatal mortality and morbidity are, however, considerably more sensitive to access to and use of primary care services since they result, to a great extent, from infectious diseases and accidents. In a particularly illuminating study, Jack Hadley reported an association of lower post-neonatal mortality rates with medical expenditures and pediatrician-to-population ratios (11).

Early screening and treatment of pediatric congenital hypertension and phenylketonuria

These conditions, which are significant risk factors for mental retardation, can be successfully (but expensively) treated if diagnosed early and reliably, and if treated promptly. Comparisons of the fragmented US testing, follow-up and treatment programs with the more systematic, centralized and universally available programs in the UK reveal the latter to be more effective.

Bacterial meningitis and diabetes

These very different diseases are less systematically studied but, in both cases, once corrections are made for improved reporting, the evidence is that early diagnosis and treatment are positively associated with reduced mortality and morbidity. The same is true for asthma, epilepsy, appendicitis, gastro-enteritis, lead poisoning, and rheumatic fever, among others.

In all the above cases the advantage to the patient and to society of timely preventive and primary care interventions seems clear. It is equally clear, both from health outcomes data and from what we know about the effect of health insurance shortfalls, that the opportunities for successful interventions for these conditions have been and will continue to be missed to the extent that financial obstacles remain to seeking and obtaining primary care.

Moreover, there is ample evidence that the delivery system itself is part of the problem, in part because it is oriented primarily to treatment rather than prevention, and also because most caregivers are bound by the medical model and are ill-equipped to deal with the more complex and frustrating social and behavioral problems to which both maternal and child health are so sensitive. There is even growing evidence that the cost-effectiveness argument is beginning to win converts also among fiscally conservative groups whose interest in 'families' has drawn their interest to this group.

What, then, are the prospects for remedying these missed opportunities and, if additional but limited resources were to be made available, how might they best be deployed?

Policy choices for extending coverage

Notwithstanding the fiscally constrained character of the 1980s, there has been considerable interest in the highly leveraged opportunities (e.g. those with potentially high yielding benefits) to improve pregnancy outcomes and child health. The debate over *what* to do has centered largely around whether to expand health insurance coverage to cover more, if not substantially all, pregnant women and children, or selectively to fund efforts that rely on designated and 'committed' provider groups with a particular commitment to serve low-income women and children. The latter strategy relies on dollars flowing to institutional grants or provider groups, the former on voucher or vendor payments where dollars follow patients. It should also be noted that hybrid approaches have emerged in some cases where state Medicaid programs have contracted with maternal and child health programs to provide such care. A particular feature of the committed programs is that they are more likely to be interested in, and organized to address, the particular social and clinical needs of low-income women, including out-reach, patient education and management, substance abuse treatment, and follow-up.

Relying on insurance mechanisms, especially if they are linked to universal entitlement, has unmistakable appeal and is likely to take two forms. The first would be expansion of Medicaid or some other form of public insurance that requires (or highly rewards) states which significantly increase income eligibility levels at least for poor pregnant women and children. Congress recently took a significant step in this direction by allowing states to obtain federal matching dollars for pregnant women and young children with incomes up to the poverty level. Whether many states will respond to this incentive remains to be seen, however, and is viewed by many as doubtful. Similar proposals have been made for decoupling Medicaid eligibility from AFDC for other populations as well, in part as a way of minimizing the cost of extending medical benefits (12).

However, even if fully extended to the poverty line, Medicaid would still leave large numbers of near-poor women and their children without health insurance coverage for primary and preventive care. Many in this group have a family member who is employed. Most people believe that any significant expansion of coverage of this target population is highly unlikely without the second insurance expansion strategy, namely, a mandating of insurance coverage by state governments at least for pregnant women and children (13). On a much smaller scale, some employers, Blue Cross plans and foundations are experimenting with special insurance products that offer affordable (usually subsidized) coverage to the low-income, non-Medicaid eligible children of employed parents, but these efforts are likely to work only if they remain small enough for the subsidy to be well hidden or diffused.

The insurance approach, which has been incorporated in several unsuccessful legislative initiatives, has many appealing features: universality, simplicity, and avoidance of the inequities that result when access to care depends on the charitable intent and discretion of the caregiver. But it also has some major disadvantages, first because it is likely to be extremely expensive. Before the provision of any new services could be started what is currently provided voluntarily would have to be costed. Moreover, because Medicaid payment rates for physicians are currently very low in many states, most patients have difficulty finding physicians willing to serve them. Since the same physicians are unlikely to serve similar patients unless payment rates increase, an effective program would have to increase Medicaid payment rates for those already being served as well as for new patients.

In the private sector, a mandating of insurance coverage could have the effect of encouraging some employers to drop insurance altogether rather than bear the increased costs of covering women and children. The actual experience to date with this threatened response to mandated benefits, mostly with respect to mental health services, is a bit murky. It is uncertain whether the dire predictions of insurance withdrawal are realistic, but mandating coverage in most cases shifts the cost to the employee in the form of lower wages, or to the employer and, of course, eventually to the consumer which, for marginal companies, could prove to be fatal.

The most important question is whether an entitlement/insurance approach will result in increased *use* (not just access) of the kinds of services that this population in particular needs. The research literature makes it abundantly clear that behavioral changes that reduce self-imposed risks, such as smoking, alcohol and drug abuse, sexually-transmitted diseases, poor nutritional habits, and proper parenting practices, are important determinants of good pregnancy and child health outcomes. These risk factors are particularly prevalent among low-income persons who also suffer serious environmental deficiencies, together with a variety of chronic disease conditions such as heart disease, hypertension, asthma and diabetes (14). For effective prevention and treatment all these conditions require an intensive form of patient management and an ability to cope with complex social and behavioral problems.

Thus, before seeking the commitment of large sums via expanded insurance programs, it is prudent to ask whether physicians and clinics accustomed to caring for persons with middle-class lifestyles will be effective in dealing with persons who require effective case management and special supports and who are living in conditions that aggravate their problems. This issue remains critical, even if payment rates could be raised enough to interest providers in these low-income patients in the first place. In addition, should the current over-supply of physicians produce enough interest to improve access, there still remains the question of whether the nature of the services offered would be cost-effective in terms of desired outcomes. Finally, experience in the field with refugees and other low-income groups has demonstrated that the availability of even the appropriate services is not productive unless there are effective out-reach, enrollment, referral and follow-up services.

An example of one aspect of this problem became apparent in two states that have recently contracted out the management of their Medicaid programs to health maintenance organizations (HMOs). In both cases, the HMOs were confronted with a financial incentive to keep the cost of care below prevailing community averages, but had no concomitant incentives regarding health outcomes. As a consequence, when they developed their network of provider contracts they refused to include a variety of existing maternal and child health clinics whose costs were high for average deliveries because of the social and case management services they were providing along with traditional medical care. The loss of Medicaid patients and revenues threatened to close the clinics, depriving other needy patients of these important services.

The alternative to an insurance mechanism for financing these services is to funnel grant and contract funds to selected providers of care, usually clinics or organized groups of physicians and mid-level professionals, who can demonstrate both the commitment and the appropriate range of services for achieving the desired pregnancy and child health outcomes. Many such programs already exist as a result of both private and public funding (15).* The domestic social budget reductions of the 1980s have hit these programs especially hard, and the slowed decline in infant mortality rates occurring at about the same time suggest that there may be a relationship (13). Despite the difficulties, dedicated maternal and child health programs, and community health centers that serve the same populations have provided both the care and the experience which can serve as the basis for a direct grant or contracting program. The focus of these programs goes beyond pre-natal care and purely medical strategies and includes nutritional programs and post-partum efforts by public health and visiting nurses, the latter proving effective in the USA as well as in more developed forms in the UK and Israel.

Institutional grants to designated providers are, of course, also not without their disadvantages. First, their numbers are few and not necessarily in the right locations, so that access problems are certain to remain. Secondly, while many of these programs have displayed uncommon dedication to their mission, many have become deeply embroiled with local political battles and are often short on solid management talent. They often find themselves with a narrow band of political support but are, on balance, politically vulnerable. In this regard, they share the risk of many direct-funded programs that in the absence of proper financial incentives they will become highly inefficient. In an era in which efficiency and competitive viability are common tests, these concerns must be faced.

Despite these shortcomings, direct grants to dedicated programs are likely to attract growing interest as a means of solving the health care needs of low-income pregnant women and children, and may become even more important as larger portions of state Medicaid programs are subjected to 'managed care' standards.

Conclusion

It must seem rather bewildering to observers from Britain, Canada and other industrialized nations why the USA has chosen such a complex approach to the financing of so important a service as health care, an approach which seems to be difficult to change even where alternative services are so obviously cost-effective.

Why the USA has in the past rejected, and for the foreseeable future will almost certainly continue to reject, a national health plan (e.g. the UK) and a national health insurance scheme (e.g. Canada) has been extensively debated and is beyond the scope of this paper. What is more likely to be acceptable and achievable in the USA is some form of universal health insurance coverage, highly pluralistic in nature, and with most coverage continuing to be employment-related.

*Discussion with Sara Rosenbaum, Childrens Defense Fund, Washington DC.

Where there is strong favorable sentiment for expansion of financing, as there is for mothers and children, the political process and some limited private efforts have yielded small and grudging progress, although the gains achieved pale in comparison to the growing need. The limited nature of this success cannot be attributed solely to fiscal constraints. There are at least three important underlying forces also at work.

First, the strong anti-government sentiment that has been so powerful a force in American politics for the past decade. Privatization and limitation especially of federal government regulatory and financing programs have imposed a virtual moratorium on the government playing a major role in transforming health care into a public good. This moratorium has allowed the American health care system to gain experience with the advantages and limitations of more market-driven approaches. Much in fact has already been learnt, and the economic squeeze that is being placed on many providers is already producing the 'scream' level that signals diminishing returns in some areas. But the experiment with competition has certainly not run its course, and without effective means of fashioning economic incentives to reflect health outcomes the more competitive environment is unlikely to benefit vulnerable populations.

A second factor is the latent volcano of intergenerational politics. Well-organized groups with powerful electoral constituencies, such as the elderly, have proven far more successful than others in securing political and financial support for their health care needs. The political imbalance has been reflected in the health care financing structure, athough it must be said that many of the health care needs of the elderly are also unmet.

Finally, beneath the surface remains a deep-seated ambivalence in the American body politic about the financing of services for the poor. Some of this reflects the recent attention being given to arguments that welfare programs increase dependency. With respect to maternal and child health programs there also appears to be a concern that additional dollars spent for education and pre-natal care, despite their more than three-to-one cost-benefit ratio, may not produce the desired results unless more effective mechanisms can be found to identify, reach, engage, educate, motivate and support high-risk mothers and their children. For this reason, further experimentation with models that effectively focus and deliver a range of social as well as medical services appears to be a sound policy choice in concert with continuing efforts to expand insurance coverage.

References

(1) US Department of Health and Human Services. *1977 National Medical Care Expenditure Survey*. Hyattsville MD: National Center for Health Services Research, 1977.

(2) Swartz K. *Interpreting the estimates from four national surveys of the number of people without health insurance: a summary report*. Project report no. 3442–03. Washington: Urban Institute, 1985 (April).

(3) House Select Committee on Aging. *America's elderly at risk*. Committee publication no. 99–508. Washington: US Government Printing Office, 1984 (July).

(4) Johnson K, Rosenbaum S, Simons J. *The data book: the nation, states, and cities*. Washington: Children's Defense Fund, 1985: 22.

(5) Schramm WF. WIC prenatal participation and its relationship to newborn Medicaid costs in Missouri: a cost/benefit analysis. *Am J Public Health* 1985; **75**: 851–7.

(6) Monheit AC, Hagan MM, Berk ML, Farley PJ. The employed uninsured and the role of public policy. *Inquiry* 1985; **22**: 348–64.

(7) Hadley J, Feder J, Mullner R. *Care for the poor and hospitals' financial status: results of a 1980 survey of hospitals in large cities.* Working paper no. 1444-02. Washington: Urban Institute, 1983 (Jan).

(8) *Final report of the special committee on care for the indigent.* Chicago IL: American Hospital Association, 1986: 48.

(9) The RAND Corporation health insurance experiment for children. *Pediatrics* 1986; **75**: 969-71.

(10) Starfield B. Motherhood and apple pie: the effectiveness of medical care for children. *Milbank Mem Fund Q* 1985; **63**: 523-46.

(11) Hadley J. *More medical care, better health?* Washington: Urban Institute, 1982.

(12) Blendon RJ, Rogers DE. Cutting medical care costs. Primum non nocere. *J Am Med Assoc* 1983; **250**: 1880-5.

(13) Huhes D, Johnson K, Simons J, Rosenbaum S. *Maternal and child health data book: the health of America's children.* Washington: Children's Defense Fund, 1986.

(14) Southern Regional Task Force on Infant Mortality. *A fiscal imperative: prenatal and infant care.* Publication no. 4242. Washington: Southern Governors Association, 1985.

(15) Rosenbaum S, Johnson K. Providing health care for low-income children: reconciling child health goals with child health financing realities. *Milbank Q* 1986; **64**: 442-78.

PROVIDING FOR SPECIAL NEEDS
AND VULNERABLE GROUPS

2. Specific problems:
rehabilitation and care of the elderly

Chairman:
SIR MARTIN ROTH
Cambridge, UK

Introduction

SIR MARTIN ROTH

Professor of Psychiatry, University of Cambridge, Cambridge, UK

It used to be said that old age is no bad thing when the alternative is considered. This aphorism has acquired a somewhat hollow ring as people look at the chronic wards in which old people are confined, at the vegetable-like existence of many with chronic mental disease due to degenerative disorder in the brain and, in particular, patients with Alzheimer's disease, for example.

I draw attention to this only to make the general point that we deal with a crisis, not only in relation to the care of the aged, but one that overspills into the care of every kind of disorder. Everywhere, the aged and the problems they create, the chronically ill aged in particular, strain the health and welfare services, causing them to burst at the seams.

Nowhere are independent, free enterprise and national health supported care systems more sharply contrasted than in the case of services for the elderly in the USA and the UK.

Briefly, the manner in which this situation has arisen is as follows. In the UK, the special services for geriatric care have their starting point in the experiments undertaken in the old workhouse hospitals by a few pioneers like Margery Warren, who brought life and hope into the chronic wards which contained elderly people and chronic sick in workhouse accommodation.

Thereafter, discoveries in both medicine and psychiatry showed that the disorders of old age, which in many cases were regarded as being entirely due to senility and degenerative change associated with ageing, were in fact related to diseases unconnected with ageing which could be controlled, and in some cases cured, by medical intervention.

It is paradoxical that the result of this was the creation of a specialty of geriatrics in the UK because many of the diseases we recognize in old age are merely versions of conditions that occur in early life. Undoubtedly, this advanced the quality of care for the elderly chronic sick. Psychogeriatrics has also provided a splendid example of quality of care both in university departments and in the National Health Service.

The situation is very different in the USA where departments of geriatric care are confined largely to universities. Geriatrics does not exist as a specialty elsewhere, but the care of the aged and chronic sick is undertaken largely by means of special injections of funds from Medicare and Medicaid.

This contrast between the two systems can yield much valuable information.

Health Care Provision under Financial Constraint, edited by T. B. Binns and M. Firth, 1988: Royal Society of Medicine International Congress and Symposium Series No. 115, published by Royal Society of Medicine Services Ltd.

Introduction

SIR MARTIN ROTH

Professor of Psychiatry, University of Cambridge, Cambridge, UK

A UK view

J. GRIMLEY EVANS

Professor of Geriatric Medicine, University of Oxford, Oxford, UK

Introduction

The elderly have suffered much from being recognized as a definable group in society. In the benevolent ambience of 1870s Prussia, the definition of old age as starting at 65 established a worker's right to a pension. A century later, in socialist Britian, old age is used to define a group of citizens who are deprived of the right to work, whose enforced poverty subsidizes the affluence of others, and who are offered second-class health masquerading as specialized services.

The elderly have, of course, shared in the economic and social advances of post-war Britain, although to less extent than have people of younger ages (1). Their deprivations are only relative, but the ambiguities of their place in society are indicative of wider issues and present for our inspection some disturbing properties of the national environment that the British have been creating for themselves.

The origins of modern care for the elderly

In thinking about care for the elderly in Britain the frame of reference differs from that in the USA. The boundaries of specialist medical services for the old include a larger tranche of acute care than is customary in the USA and the non-institutional component is more available and structured than is general there.

The place today perceived for the old in the British health and social services system can only be properly understood in a historical context. The National Health Service (NHS) inherited in 1948 a tripartite system of hospitals and associated facilities. In broad terms, there were the old lunatic asylums which became the new mental hospitals, there were the old charity hospitals which became the new district general and teaching hospitals, and there were the old workhouse hospitals which became the new geriatric hospitals. The charity hospitals had the important privilege of being able to choose whom they would admit and developed policies of proffering care only to the acutely ill and those with treatable conditions. They favoured the 'deserving' rather than the feckless poor. The workhouses were not originally

Health Care Provision under Financial Constraint, edited by T. B. Binns and M. Firth, 1988: Royal Society of Medicine International Congress and Symposium Series No. 115, published by Royal Society of Medicine Services Ltd.

conceived as health facilities. They were founded to provide one form of relief to the indigent but, because potent causes of indigence are old age, chronic illness and disability, they came to develop sick wards that evolved into hospitals for the chronically ill and disabled, for the poor, for the socially incompetent, and generally for the cases that the charity hospitals refused to take. The workhouse hospitals had essentially no right to refuse admission.

The fact that care of the elderly continued to be seen as growing out of, and for many years centred on, workhouse provision coloured the public and administrative perception of their needs. The problems of the new residents of the workhouse hospitals were assumed, like those of their predecessors, to be social rather than medical and due to irreversible age-related degeneration rather than to treatable or manageable illness. There was also inheritance of the Victorian principle of 'lower eligibility' in workhouse provision. This principle, made explicit in the debates on poor law reform, was that workhouse provision must never become better than the worst conditions that prevail outside, for fear that the degenerate poor would lose all incentive to better their state by their own efforts. The new geriatric services also inherited the workhouse imposition of having to take whatever was presented to them.

The response of the well-meaning to this dismal inheritance was to create a separate system of health provision for those old people who found their way into the ambit of the workhouse hospital. This was a psychological necessity for the staff of the hospitals seeking self-respect, but the overt aims were to improve the quality of care for those who were permanent residents, and to provide effective rehabilitation services to prevent unnecessary long-term dependency. This, what we might now call the 'traditional' model of geriatric care, was an enormous achievement and developed principles of medical and nursing care for older and disabled people that have diffused widely throughout the health services. Not least among these early developments was the reaching out from the hospital into a specialist involvement in community care through a variety of patterns of home visiting, day hospital and respite care. This model of geriatric care, in addition to being focused on long-stay and rehabilitative care, had the significant constraint of having the choice of patients referred to it determined by others, particularly doctors in other specialties who were usually ignorant of what functions the geriatric services could provide. This had a number of undesirable consequences, including the inappropriate or mistimed referral of patients and the lack of feedback to the medical and nursing teams on the acute wards about the longer-term outcome of their interventions.

The separatist model of care

The next logical development of geriatric services was therefore to seek to bring the acute care facilities used by older people into the control or under the influence of those who provided the rehabilitation and long-term care. At this point, care for the elderly began to explore two different practical approaches which have evolved into two different philosophies of care. A few centres had inherited large numbers of geriatric beds in workhouses that for one reason or another evolved a general hospital function and facilities. In such settings it was possible to develop the 'separatist' model of geriatric service through an arbitrary age definition of the elderly and the development of acute medical services for them in parallel with those of other ages (2). The essential arbitrariness of the age chosen to define the elderly is revealed both by the lack of any biological basis for the distinction (3) and by the fact that the age of definition varies from centre to centre depending entirely upon the number of general hospital beds controlled by the geriatricians and hence the number of 'elderly' patients with whom they can cope.

The integrated model of care

In a few centres where the inheritance of general hospital beds by geriatricians was limited but the need for the elderly to have unimpeded access to acute beds was recognized, an alternative approach, the 'integrated' model, was developed. In this model the acute medical care of elderly people is provided in the same wards as that for younger adults, but with the physicians responsible for the rehabilitation and other specialist services for the elderly taking part in the management of those wards. This provides the elderly patient with access to a full range of medical specialist skills rather than just those of the geriatrician which may or may not be relevant to her needs.

The philosophy of integration goes much deeper than the mere sharing of ward facilities between geriatricians restricted to the care of old people and other specialists. In the integrated model, the physicians with special responsibility for the elderly play a role alongside their fellow general physicians with other specialist interests and responsibilities, such as cardiology, in providing services to young adult patients as well. This has the potential advantages of removing the pejorative and depressing label of 'geriatric' from elderly people, and of shifting the conceptual framework of physicians from planning for artificially separate, but numerically variable categories of patients with general medical needs into thinking about the general medical services as a whole. Other advantages of the integrated model have been rehearsed elsewhere (4,5).

Which model to choose for the future?

That the crucial element in successful medical services for the elderly is access to general hospital beds under co-ordinated management with a full range of specialist geriatric services has been argued on both theoretical and empirical grounds (6). This interpretation has not so far been disproved although, in the best Popperian tradition of science, it is potentially disprovable if false. If it is true, the conventional thinking in which the elderly and the services they need are treated separately from other adult patients may impede appropriate development of services. When, a few years ago, the government proposed that more hospital resources should be devoted to the growing numbers of elderly people, the specifically identifiable 'geriatric' services of long-stay and medium-term rehabilitation services were not those most in need of attention. What elderly patients most generally lacked was adequate access to acute services experienced in their care.

It is of interest that surgeons have not perceived a need for a separatist approach to the organization of hospital facilities for the elderly. This is in keeping with the view that the separatist philosophy is a historical accident, in that few of the old workhouse hospitals had emergency surgical facilities.

Until recently the choice between integrated and separatist models has been a matter of opportunity and philosophy. There is now a potential danger facing the elderly in separatist models of care. Separatist models are attractive to administrators because it is easy for them to calculate what resources are being devoted to geriatric medicine. Unfortunately, separatist models are also attractive to administrators because, as a relic of their workhouse origins, geriatric departments are traditionally funded and staffed at lower levels than the general acute departments which form the basis of integrated models. Although there are balancing factors, including the fact that, other things being equal, integrated models require fewer beds than separatist services, administrators may see separatist models as being cheaper. The new danger of the separatist model is that administrators may also see separation of geriatric departments from departments for younger adults as a device that will inhibit the access of elderly people to expensive innovations in modern medicine. Geographical separation of general acute and geriatric wards, compounded with the psychological separation of their staff, will inhibit the exploration of the applicability of new medical and elective surgical developments to older patients. Evidence from the USA, where rationing of medical care is traditionally on the basis of ability to pay rather than age, shows that, particularly in the field of cardiac investigation and treatment, older people can benefit greatly from such interventions when intelligently and humanely deployed. The fear is that the enthusiasm with which the Welsh Office has embraced the principle of separatist geriatric services as a national policy owes more to cold-blooded accountancy than to altruism (7).

Allocating resources to the elderly

Having challenged the hidden rationale behind conventional thought about medical services for the elderly, it is appropriate to consider ways in which changes in emphasis in health resource allocation might come about. In a democracy the first proper consideration is politically mediated demand by the elderly themselves. In the USA the last decade or so has seen increasing economic well-being of older people. The proportion of citizens aged 65 and over who fell below the poverty line diminished from 25–14% between 1970 and 1982, and this improvement in direct income has been strengthened by an increase in indirect benefits from sources such as Medicare (8). These improvements in the lot of the American elderly have been brought about largely through political activism by the elderly themselves. The triumph has been to convince American politicians that older citizens are prepared to vote rationally and self-interestedly rather than according to party political loyalty.

In Britain, by comparison, the elderly seem politically supine, and such advocacy as they enjoy comes largely from charities and health and social service professionals who for one reason or another have espoused their cause. Such advocacy is of limited efficacy since politicians have little difficulty in persuading the public that people who run charities are muddle-headed and unbalanced idealists, while the professionals can always be accused of self-interest. Indeed, one of the greatest difficulties the British geriatrician labours under is the lack of any organized demands from the people he is trying to serve. A significant aspect of this problem is probably the term 'geriatric' with its inherited implications of hopeless drooling senility. Who in his right mind is going to volunteer to identify himself as a 'geriatric'?

The reasons for the political invisibility of the British elderly are undoubtedly complex. In part, it is because they have been so effectively excluded from the structure of active society that they lack even the basic means of making themselves heard. On one of the few occasions when large numbers of elderly people converged on the Houses of Parliament to lobby members not one national newspaper or television channel even mentioned the event. A more fundamental reason, however, is that the elderly are entangled in an informal social contract. The political sting of the British elderly has been extracted by free bus rides, food parcels at Christmas, and the octopodal tentacles of a welfare system based on service provision. In return for such gifts the elderly are expected to donate gratitude and silence. A welfare system based on income support, whatever its faults, would produce a very different kind of elderly citizen. Moreover, as the preamble to the last White House conference on ageing makes clear, the Americans regard the elderly as having responsibilities and duties as well as rights and privileges (9). If you have responsibilities you develop a sharp interest in securing the wherewithal to discharge them.

A further problem in the plausibility of any political challenge the elderly may mount to the *status quo* lies in the polarity of British politics. No doubt switching from voting Democratic to voting Republican in the USA would not be undertaken lightly, but I suspect it would be less of a challenge to the self-image of an elderly person than voting for Mrs Thatcher after a lifetime of allegiance to the Labour party. The *Realpolitik*, however, is clear. A Tory government is not likely to do much for people who announce that they are going to vote Labour whatever happens and, more to the point, neither is a Labour government. Unless the elderly can convince politicians that their votes are for sale, they might as well stay by the fireside, for the common image of old age is as a time of rigid attitudes when old habits and allegiances do not change.

Theoretical basis for allocation of resources

If we raise ourselves above the dust of practical politics and attempt to consider the place the elderly would occupy in a rational world, we discover a significant lacuna at the heart of the British social system. In a rational world, the allocation of resources to a defined group of society has to be founded in some definable theoretical system. There are three distinguishable levels of discussion that need to be considered: ideology, ethics and jurisprudence. The British heresy is to fail in distinguishing these separate issues of debate. Eminent writers try to settle issues of priorities in health care as if ethics could exist without ideology, and as if the practicalities of legal drafting could substitute for both. Ideology is concerned with the fundamental concepts about the nature of things. Ethics is the study of the logical consequences of that ideology. Jurisprudence, in the present restricted context, is concerned with enforcing selected ethical principles in society. Not all ethical principles can be enforced by legal means, and others should not be since the laws to do so would cause greater evils than those they seek to remedy.

Medical ethics

Many writers on medical ethics fail to distinguish between ideology and ethics, sometimes disingenuously or with the aim of trying to represent ethics as a science. Whatever the motivation, it can be worrying to see presented as axioms what are merely corollaries of questionable and sometimes concealed premises. In a debate reported in the *Journal of Medical Ethics* (10), Kennedy, introduced as a professional in medical ethics, gave apparent approval to a principle of age discrimination in making ethical decisions involving young and old patients. This was in front of an audience containing medical students. Would they think to distinguish in what Kennedy had to say between logical consequences of ideological principles that are the basis of national culture and expressions of feelings arising from the unexamined premises underlying age discrimination?

Ideology

The British distaste for defining ideology is reputedly of historical origins. The religious conflicts of the 16th and 17th centuries suggested to our forebears that the best way of living together in peace in a small country is to avoid ideological issues in government as well as in conversation. There are at least two unfortunate consequences of this eirenic settlement. We have little defence against moral absolutism because we have never explicitly proscribed it, and we have no agreed strategic basis for the direction of national development. One attempt to avoid the ideological issues in health resource allocation is to invoke economics as the ideological underpinning of society. There is actually a long history of attempts to beg ideological questions by the use of economics to settle the problems of allocation of health care resources. Probably the longest established in Britain is the 'years of life lost' paradigm in which the availability of means of life-prolonging intervention in disease is weighted according to the life expectancy of the individual being considered. Various refinements of this approach have been developed, but they all inevitably discriminate against the elderly whose life expectancy is lower than that of younger patients. Avorn (11) has reviewed economically-based measures proposed for health resource allocation which discriminate against the old.

Among the underlying ideological assumptions in many of these approaches is the idea that since all citizens must be regarded as equal, 5 years of life of person A will be five times more valuable than 1 year of life of person B. One crucial question here is 'valuable to whom?'. The usually undeclared answer is the state. This becomes more overt in those measures of health care effectiveness which weight years of working life more than those of post-retirement life. Is the ideology of Britain really so Fascist, in the sense of subordinating the will of the individual to the purposes of the state, and thus embracing the Fascism of both the left and right wings of the political spectrum? I hope not, and I think not. English idealism, the explicit statement of the implicit basis of the settlement of our religious wars, is based on respect for the uniqueness and the sovereignty of the individual. The implication of this is that only the individual is entitled to put a value on his life, and that the lives of different individuals are incommensurable in an absolute sense. They cannot be compared in value directly nor is it valid to apply differential weightings in attempts to bring about comparisons.

Quality-adjusted life year

The most recent economic meteor to rise above the horizon of common knowledge is the quality-adjusted life year (QALY), a concept whose origins go back more than a decade in the USA. This is a great advance on earlier measures in that it embodies measures of actual outcome of interventions in terms not just of survival but of quality of life. It can also incorporate risk of undesirable outcomes such as operative death. As Williams has shown, it is possible to compute the cost to the health services per QALY obtained by different procedures, and this produces some results that may not be intuitively obvious (12,13).

One problem which arises is who should assess the quality of life that goes into the equations. Some British economists seem to be proposing that samples of the general public should be used to put values on different states of health and disability that can then be used by administrators to allocate resources. Yet, as Sackett and

Torrance showed, the value an individual puts on the treatment facilities for a disease depends greatly on whether he has the disease himself (14). We also know that in changing societies such as ours there are important cultural differences between the young and the old. Can those who have known only the post-war world understand the values of someone who knew the 1920s and 1930s? The defect in the QALY concept, as some propose its use, is that it can be merely a refinement of the years of life lost if cost per QALY is weighted by expectation of life. Used in this way, it embodies purely a provider's perception of the health services, and yet for health services more than anything else it is the customer's view which surely should prevail. Both perspectives could perhaps be embraced in a concept of cost of change in quality of life per person for particular procedures.

Building from first principles

With Western hauteur we mock those emergent states who spend money on developing modern hospitals dispensing the most advanced surgical care while their general population labours under a burden of potentially eradicable infectious disease or subnutrition. Curiously, the idea that we should build our own health services in a hierarchy of need receives little consideration. Yet the provision of basic nursing services, and of acute general medical and surgical assessment facilities would be universally accepted as the necessary basis of any health system, regardless of any demonstration that such services materially alter the natural history of the diseases with which they deal. If these develop in response to levels of demand, and if we liberate ourselves from the tradition of age-associated discrimination, much of the problem created by the 'elderly' will no longer be seen to exist. Clearly, development must be under the constraints of efficiency surveillance, but the techniques for this are now available (albeit insufficiently widely deployed on a routine basis), and certainly the record of the hospital service in improving the efficiency of use of resources over the last two decades is praiseworthy.

Rehabilitation

The provision of rehabilitation and elective facilities is more problematical since the question of effectiveness as well as efficiency has to be raised. What immediately strikes the mind in times of growing financial difficulty is that little in the rehabilitation services for the elderly has been rigorously demonstrated to be effective. The day hospital, for example, is a much-valued dimension to care in most geriatric services, but no one has ever shown that it achieves anything that could not be more cheaply brought about by other means. Perhaps more fundamentally, one of the principles of good care is that no one should pass into a mode of high-dependency care until all possible alternatives have been properly explored by an expert multidisciplinary team. This exploration includes a trial of rehabilitation. Thus, in conventionally run geriatric services, expensive rehabilitation resources are deployed not only to assess but to treat all old people reaching the service, although only a proportion will respond significantly.

Triage approach to rehabilitation

An alternative approach would be to develop a system of triage in which patients
would be sorted early in their illness, for example, into three groups:
(1) Patients who will get better spontaneously.
(2) Those who will not respond to rehabilitation.
(3) Those who will respond if adequate treatment is given.
The last group should then receive more intensive rehabilitation than is possible when
the time of the staff is being diluted by work on patients who will not benefit. There
have been research trials of some forms of rehabilitation which have embodied
procedures of initial triage of this kind but their methods have been arbitrary and
unvalidated (15,16).

Triage procedures used in this way present considerable difficulties. The process
necessarily involves the conversion of continuous probability distributions into
discontinuous categories, which raises both technical and ethical problems. In those
geriatric services blessed with easy access to nursing home beds in the private sector
it may well be found that non-validated triage processes are already in use.

It is not until there has been a systematic evaluation of rehabilitation services that we
can make any rational decision about the resources it is reasonable to allocate to them.
Again, I suspect that the separation of rehabilitation services for the elderly from those
for other age groups has long outlived its usefulness and is now counter-productive.
Geriatric rehabilitation has the virtue of being organized so that it is universally available,
but it consists largely of providing an ambience in which spontaneous recovery can
take place. It is almost self-consciously 'low-technology' in approach and could well
benefit from more sophisticated input from bioengineering and prosthetics specialists.
None the less, I suspect that the triage procedures used in the studies cited earlier are
probably near the mark in suggesting that rehabilitation is objectively relevant for only
a small percentage, perhaps 10% of elderly patients reaching hospital. If triage
procedures are to be introduced as a matter of policy into rehabilitation services, they
will need to be co-ordinated with a comprehensive policy for the long-term care of
patients who are too disabled to benefit from rehabilitation. At present, planning for
long-term care of such patients at both a national and a local level is in total disarray.

Elective procedures

It will be in the third tier of health services, the elective, non-life-saving procedures,
that the greatest difficulties are experienced in allocating resources. There is probably
no substitute for that old British institution, the queue, although recent suggestions
that selection from the queue by lottery would be socially equitable are intriguing.
The medical profession has never been particularly adept at managing waiting lists,
and systems of priority based on severity of disability could in principle be made
more objective than they often are. It is here that the concept of quality of life and
its expected change through intervention would be most relevant.

Conclusion

Attempts to distribute health resources according to age lead to inappropriate patterns
of care and take society in a direction that the majority of the nation would consider

undesirable. It will be preferable to liberate ourselves from the incubus of history and to stop thinking of the elderly as a special or even definable social group. We should rather be concerned with developing systems of care in which the needs of each individual are assessed and the appropriate care provided, rather than systems in which the range of care is pre-determined by some only indirectly relevant biological characteristic such as age. Care systems should be developed in a hierarchical manner with priority given to emergency generalist services with associated rehabilitation facilities. The latter are in need of urgent evaluation and redesign embodying triage procedures with a comprehensive policy for long-term care of patients who cannot benefit. The third tier of care, the elective non-life-saving procedures, cannot be expected ever to satisfy demand, and prioritized queuing seems inevitable. It is inequitable for relief of suffering expected by any particular procedure to be weighted by age or expectation of life.

In a democracy, priorities in health care should be set by the elected representatives of the people. It is certainly no proper business of doctors to withhold effective care from patients on the basis of age alone. There are allegations that this is occurring in Britain, and perhaps this is one area where the law might usefully take an interest.

References

(1) Abrams M. Changes in the life-styles of the elderly 1959–82. *Social Trends* 1983; **14**: 11–16.
(2) Horrocks P. The case for geriatric medicine as an age-related specialty. In: Isaacs I, ed. *Recent advances in geriatric medicine* 2. Edinburgh: Churchill Livingstone, 1981: 259–77.
(3) Evans JG. The biology of human ageing. In: Dawson AM, Compston N, Besser GM, eds. *Recent advances in medicine* 18. Edinburgh: Churchill Livingstone, 1981: 17–37.
(4) Evans JG. Integration of geriatric with general medical services in Newcastle. *Lancet* 1983; i: 1430–3.
(5) Parkhouse J, Campbell MG. Popularity of geriatrics among Newcastle qualifiers at preregistration stage. *Lancet* 1983; ii: 221.
(6) Evans JG. Institutional care. In: Arie T, ed. *Health care of the elderly*. London: Croom Helm, 1981: 176–93.
(7) Welsh Office. *A good old age: an initiative on the care of the elderly in Wales*. Publication no. HD/L/01 & 02. Cardiff: Welsh Office, 1985.
(8) Preston SH. Children and the elderly in the US. *Sci Am* 1984; **251** (6): 44–57.
(9) *White House Conference on Aging*. Final report; Vol. 1. Washington: US Government Printing Office, 1982.
(10) Kennedy I. Commentary 4. *J Med Ethics* 1984; **10**: 206–8.
(11) Avorn J. Benefit and cost analysis in geriatric care. Turning age discrimination into health policy. *N Engl J Med* 1984; **310**: 1294–301.
(12) Williams A. Economics of coronary artery bypass grafting. *Br Med J* 1985; **291**: 326–9.
(13) Teeling Smith G. *Measurement of health*. London: Office of Health Economics, 1985.
(14) Sackett DL, Torrance GW. The utility of different health states as perceived by the general public. *J Chronic Dis* 1978; **31**: 697–704.
(15) Sheikh K, Meade TW, Brennan PJ, Goldenberg E, Smith DS. Intensive rehabilitation after stroke: service implications. *Community Med* 1981; **3**: 210–6.
(16) Rubenstein LZ, Josephson KR, Wieland GD, English PA, Sayre JA, Kane RL. Effectiveness of a geriatric rehabilitation unit: a randomized clinical trial. *N Engl J Med* 1984; **311**: 1664–70.

A US view:
life after cost-containment: perspectives on meeting the health care needs of older people

ROBERT N. BUTLER

Brookdale Professor of Geriatrics and Adult Development;
Chairman, Ritter Department of Geriatrics and Adult Development,
Mount Sinai School of Medicine, New York NY, USA

Increased survival in a changing world

We welcome the unprecedented increase in survival, specifically the 25-year gain in life expectancy that we have achieved in the USA, the UK and the entire industrialized world in less than a century. Thanks to striking reductions in infant, childhood and maternal mortality rates, this gain, which is nearly equal to what had been attained in the preceding 5000 years of human history, is one of the great human triumphs (1). Because of a lower mortality rate in late life, 5 of the 25 years (20%) are from base year 65. I regard this as a transforming historic event that requires new approaches, as well as new policies and priorities that will affect our culture, attitudes, education, work and retirement arrangements, and health and social services. Our new challenge now is to generate wealth to match the proliferation of health and longevity.

In the USA we are going through a cycle—a period of contraction that started with the Organization of the Petroleum Exporting Countries (OPEC) price increase in 1973, but was then orchestrated politically and ideologically. I call this period the politics of uneven austerity, which adversely affects the most vulnerable in our society, the victims of 'voodoo economics'. An increased arms race, decreased social spending and decreased taxes have pushed vulnerable groups like children and old people into conflict with one another. But children and old people are not natural enemies. There is a unity of life. The aged of today were the children of yesterday, and the children of today will be the aged of the 21st century, so the focus must be not only on the aged of today but also on the aged of tomorrow. Our 'baby boomers', 70 million strong now, will number 55–60 million in the year 2020. Our last baby boomer could die between 2056 and 2066. Without appropriate planning and rational policies, this generation will be at risk. At risk today in the USA are the over-75 year olds, especially women and minorities.

Health Care Provision under Financial Constraint, edited by T. B. Binns and M. Firth, 1988: Royal Society of Medicine International Congress and Symposium Series No. 115, published by Royal Society of Medicine Services Ltd.

Both needs and resources must and will rise now because the numbers of older persons will rise. So long as social democracy flourishes, so will the political influence and consumer voice of the elders and their adult children. There will be life after cost-containment.

The demands of patients and families are not unlimited, as has been suggested. In my 30 years as a physician, I have not seen many patients who want to be ill, or want to have their bodies worked on with injections, intubations, and so on. Of course, there are instances of hypochondriasis, but frequently the message of hypochondriasis is anxiety and despair of not being heard. In fact, older persons actually underestimate pathology, under-report symptoms, and delay treatment. As we know from the National Institute of Aging's Baltimore longitudinal study on aging, hypochondriasis is not associated with healthy aging, despite the stereotypes (2).

While the demands of patients and families are limited, there are rising public expectations, including a collective desire for cures of cancer, further longevity, and a vigorous, prolonged life. The desire to live beyond 100 years is reported by 45% of Americans. There is a deep-seated affirmation of the primary value of life. There is a 'longevity lobby' of wealthy and powerful people who, having it all — except a guarantee of longevity — wage an active campaign for funds for life-extension research. As the brilliant comedian (or tragedian), Woody Allen, said,

> I don't want to achieve immortality through my work . . . I want to achieve it through not dying.

We have the resources in the USA generously to support health care that promotes vigorous longevity, we have the wealth, we spend the highest proportion of gross national product (GNP) on health in the world, but we have not thought through the way we spend these resources, and we do not have a national health policy. Health is not a constitutional or statutory right in the USA. Thirty-five million of our people are uninsured; millions more are underinsured. We have not solved the growing issue of long-term care. In fact, caregiving has become a national issue in the USA. Cost-containment, diagnostic related groups and resource utilization groups have made family caregiving an especially critical issue. Families are confused and frightened, uncertain about how much to rely on hospitals and nursing homes. In the USA, there are 2·2 million caregivers caring for 1·6 million seriously impaired people over 65 (1982 data). Of these caregivers, 72% are women, especially adult daughters, 44% of whom are employed outside the home. To assure family stability, support not presently available in the USA must be given. This means the use and mobilization of community support, the development of specific, universal entitlements, provision of home care, assistance with legal problems of the aged, confrontation of bioethical problems and elder abuse, and the creation of special forms of communication and transportation.

After cost-containment

Our only apparent health policy is the failed policy of cost-containment. Via the free market and prospective payment, costs continue to rise, as Professor Reinhardt points out, and there is no measurable increase in quality of care (3). De-hospitalization has become a serious and painful problem for older persons and their families. We have not dealt effectively with issues of access, quality and cost. The cost-containment effort has helped force us to ask questions and sharpen up somewhat, but organized and academic medicine still show very little pro-active leadership, especially regarding the great demographic transformation we are witnessing.

Let me be perfectly clear. I do not counsel imprudence and extravagance. We need to be careful with expenditures. In fact, physicians can help to transform our health care system by putting their own house in order. We need to control the greed of some doctors who induce demand, e.g. a neurology group that routinely orders computerized axial tomography (CAT) scans, EEGs and so on, independent of clinical evaluation. At the same time, we need to be affirmative about the health care enterprise. Wassily Leontief, the Nobel-prize economist, has said that perhaps we do not spend enough of our GNP on health (4). Given the other choices we have in society, we could certainly spend more. Moreover, worldwide and national economic conditions can and do change. Brian Abel-Smith, Professor of Social Administration, London School of Economics and Political Science, questions the 'gloom about the present'.

It is easy,

he says,

> to get the problem out of perspective and to blame the wrong victims. The fundamental cause of the current gloom is not the demographic prospect, but the stagnation of the world economy (5).

Because of the increase in life expectancy, there has been a shift forward in health costs from the earlier to later years, from acute to chronic illness. This does not mean, by the way, that older persons do not have acute illness and do not require acute care, but the danger is to blame the survivors for burdening our health care system. This is a subtle form of ageism. Again, it is not the demography, but the world economy, the world's wealth as we inherit and create it, which is at issue. Moreover, there is little reason to focus exclusively on the human services sector without consideration of the larger context, specifically the trillions spent on arms around the world which is really an indication of our failed attempts at peaceful conflict resolution. Global military spending makes up a tragically large portion of the economic 'pie'. This pie is ever-expanding, according to conservatives like Julius Simon (6). We have a long way to go before we exhaust the world's resources. Scarcity should be attributed to the inequitable allocation of resources and our failure to make a continuing commitment to research and development to ensure continuing progress, that is, the yeast to expand the pie. We still have access to the human imagination, which is the ultimate resource. And research, the fruit of that imagination, is the ultimate service and, perhaps, the ultimate cost-containment.

We need, first, to understand the facts of the demographic transformation and, secondly, to have a vision of what we want for our own and others' old age, based on a realistic portrait of the characteristics and needs of older patients, especially those over 75 with multiple, complex, interacting physical and psychosocial problems. Then we need to build a new system of care with well-trained health personnel.

By the time today's young medical students reach the prime of their careers geriatrics will be in the forefront of the medical field. The elderly presently constitute a subgroup accounting for 40% of hospital care and physician contact, 30% of prescription drugs, and 50% of over-the-counter medications. Thus, they have an appropriate claim to decent, imaginative, and innovative health care.

Mount Sinai Department of Geriatrics and Adult Development

In the light of such impressive statistics, it is evident that no one should graduate from medical school without exposure to the realities of aging and its specific problems. I sought out, therefore, the challenge of creating the first department of geriatrics and adult development in an American medical school. We have fewer than a dozen senior academic geriatricians in the USA, so it would be nearly impossible to start a second department even if one wanted to. The British are clearly ahead here. In the Mount Sinai Department of Geriatrics and Adult Development, we pursue the three conventional academic goals of undergraduate, graduate, and post-graduate education, the provision of outstanding services that are the basis for the teaching of students, and the establishment of a research program. I will concentrate on features pertinent to care and rehabilitation.

The department is interdisciplinary in character. It is not a component or division of the department of medicine, for example, but free-standing, and cuts across all departments and services. We have moved towards joint appointments with the departments of neurology and medicine. The concept driving the department is not that the USA should create a new practice specialty, but rather an academic specialty, a cadre of leaders in teaching, research, and service innovation. All primary and specialty medicine should incorporate the growing body of knowledge of gerontology—biological, psychological, and sociological—and apply such knowledge to the enhancement of care and rehabilitation of older persons. The department is building a strong research program in basic neurobiology and molecular biology of aging, as well as clinical studies in osteoporosis, incontinence, and so on.

Clinical program

The department's clinical services are multisited—out-patient, in-patient, teaching nursing home, consultation, healthy elderly program—and rehabilitation is available at each site. Our students have required work in gerontology and geriatrics in all four years. During their mandatory one-month rotation in the fourth year, students are exposed to all the services, including 'special emphasis' clinics where common afflictions of the elderly—osteoporosis and metabolic bone disease, mobility problems, incontinence, and memory loss—are treated. Patients are seen in an interdisciplinary context. In the out-patient clinic, for example, a neurologist, a neuropsychologist, social workers and nurses are part of the geriatric team.

Another aspect of the program is the continuity of care provided to patients. Elsewhere, patients may see geriatricians only after they have been admitted to the hospital or an out-patient department assessment program. In contrast, we are able to provide consistent primary care and follow progress with the prospect of multiple entry points for our patients, including the in-patient unit, out-patient clinic, and special emphasis clinics. We now have a core group of 900 patients that we can follow longitudinally. As I understand it, the separation between the general practitioner and the hospital specialist in the British system does not allow for continuity of care or, perhaps more precisely, the opportunity for a single individual or team to follow the patient.

The healthy elderly program

An important feature of the program at Mount Sinai concerns the need to change the stereotype of the elderly as frail and helpless. Medical students traditionally see older persons only in a crisis, but do not have many opportunities to see healthy ones, yet only 5% of the over-65 group is institutionalized, and only 20% of those who survive past age 65 will ever have a nursing home experience. We therefore invented the healthy elderly program—the counterpart to the well-baby clinic—which brings medical students into contact with healthy older persons in health promotion and disease prevention efforts. If medical students only saw children with cerebral palsy, Down's syndrome and so on, they might not want to enter the field of pediatrics. Similarly, students who see only sick elderly people may feel pessimistic about geriatrics.

Teaching nursing homes

In the USA we are witnessing an increase in the number of what I have called 'teaching nursing homes' (7), and ours is an important site for geriatric education.

> The way to quality in the nursing home is through establishing an academic environment linked to health care. This is the mechanism to mutual excellence for both the nursing home and geriatrics. An academic environment brings to the long-term care institution an atmosphere of inquisitiveness, learning, and professional achievement; an attitude of openness and hope, a set of standards built into each professional discipline and more effective than those legislated by state and federal codes; a feeling of worth associated with working with the frail elderly; an involvement with the disciplines of gerontology and geriatric medicine; and, most of all, a respect for life, which is the key ingredient in all health care work (8).

The Jewish Home and Hospital for Aged (JHHA), with which the Department of Geriatrics is affiliated, has four teaching units and a rehabilitation program. Approximately 55% of the first group of patients who went through the JHHA program were able to return home. Ultimately, the JHHA program translates into a savings for society because the geriatric care it provides costs one-third of what hospital care costs (8).

Home care for the elderly

It is estimated that 20% of the hospitals in the USA will close in the next decade. Increasing out-patient care, including out-patient surgery such as cataract and hernia operations — a positive trend that constitutes an antidote to what Menninger called 'abuse of rest' (9), as well as nosocomial disabilities — will mean increasing home care for the elderly. Home health care expenditures were about $4 billion in 1982, and about twice that in 1985. Yet, as Dr Koren points out in a recent article in the *New England Journal of Medicine*, there is still a 'general isolation of the medical profession from home care' (10).

> Physicians,

she continues,

> appear to have little awareness of how home health agencies operate or how they are regulated. And since such knowledge is not considered germane to the practice of medicine, there has been no incentive to incorporate its teaching into medical education.

Physicians must, however, respond to the growth of home care by

> acquainting themselves with home care as a system of services to supplement the care they provide to patients in their offices and institutions (10).

But rehabilitation is broader than the above. Given the 20th century development of the mutability of the life course, rehabilitation has special meanings. Not only are people living longer, but they are living better, more active lives. We speak now of *active* life expectancy as well as *average* life expectancy. Preventive and therapeutic interventions, from exercising and taking calcium to reduce osteoporosis, to social and behavioral supports to relieve the pain of bereavement, are possible. To help

232   *R. N. Butler*

overcome the mobility, sensory, and communicative deficits that afflict some older persons (indeed some younger ones), there are special treads* in Tokyo train stations — and having one's own personal robot in the near future is no longer just a fantasy.

Collaborative care

From our experiences at Mount Sinai School of Medicine, I have come to a certain perspective that I call 'collaborative care'. This is certainly not entirely new, and I owe much to the contributions of Margery Warren and others to British geriatrics (11–13). In the USA, there is much talk, but less action, about 'case management' or 'managed care', which is part of the continuing political struggle between medicine and social services. (As I understand the situation in Great Britain, the interrelationship of medical and social services has not been worked out there either.)

There are those who despise these terms, and I am among them. When I grow old and frail, no less than when I am young, I do not want to be 'managed'. Such infantilizing and paternalizing are not acceptable. In contrast, older persons in Sun City, the retirement community in Arizona, speak of 'resource co-ordinators'. There is no doubt that we need gatekeeping, not as a negative, not simply as a triage, but as a rational assessment, and also outstanding integration of a variety of services and data.

I submit that we need joint or shared management, or collaborative care. We are beyond the days of the exacting authority, the mystery of the healer. The apostolic function of the doctor was perhaps allowable in the pre-scientific period, but hardly today when we have increasing numbers of patients who are educated consumers. Note, too, the self-help movement, with the proliferation of self-help books, in the USA. What is called for now is collaborative care, an egalitarian relationship between patient and physician team, and for shared knowledge, including full access to charts, fully informed consent regarding services, not just research, and some shared power. This becomes especially critical when it comes to older people because, for them, feeling autonomous can in itself be therapeutic. Docility and passivity of patients contribute to iatrogenicity.

Collaborative care involves not only the patient in a direct and powerful role, but also the family or family substitute. Therefore, there must be education of the family. Conversely, the family can educate the physician and health care team, for the family has accumulated daily experience with problems the physician does not and cannot know. Consider the support groups associated with the Alzheimer's Disease and Related Disorders Association of America. There we have seen ample illustration of the rich variety of responses that help make an incurable disease treatable in many ways. The family, then, is a teacher.

Responsibility for the control of hypochondriasis and greed rests on both sides. The patient has a responsibility for his or her own health by practicing rigorous health habits throughout life, including in old age. Too many contribute to the image of the older person as doddering, as characterized by the great octogenarian comedian, George Burns. The elderly patient must have a sense of autonomy and self-mastery. The physician also has responsibilities to avoid the bane of old age, iatrogenicity, by avoiding unnecessary procedures that are dangerous and unnecessary medications. Some of what is called failure in patient compliance turns out, upon examination,

*Flooring that is heavily ribbed and can be felt even through shoes. These treads actually direct passengers where they want to go.

to be prudence on the part of patients. Unnecessary hospitalization, nosocomial infections, mystery and authority, must give way to knowledge, truth, autonomy and egalitarianism. These form the basis of healing. Trust is the basis of healing.

This call for comprehensive care is not antithetical to specialized care. I personally favor strengthening primary and specialty medicine. Older persons frequently need acute high technology medicine. But the doctor must not over-doctor, and the work of Margaret Blenker has shown that social services must not be overdone either or dangers may follow (14). We must be conservative, *primum non nocere*, and the patient must practice what Myrna Lewis calls 'responsible dependency', not denying, or inappropriately or excessively demanding, but working with the healer or healing team and working hard at self-care and self-rehabilitation (15).

The interrelationship of health care professionals

So far, we have discussed the individual relationship between physician and patient, but the relationship between physician and other health care professionals also deserves attention. Physicians must alter their self-images and build a rapport with those who are usually called ancillary or allied health workers — nurses, social workers, physical therapists, clinical pharmacists and psychologists. This is a tall order. Physicians will fight to protect their territory and their pocket books. Eventually, however, the expectations and demands of patients will prevail. With a shift forward in time of morbidity and mortality and the rapid growth of the 80 + age group, the multiple, complex, interacting physical and psychosocial needs of patients will not be served alone by organ- and procedure-centered subspecialties, but by comprehensive care from a healing team. The old are the vanguard of the future and, as pioneer recipients of future health care, they will want, and will eventually receive more attention to assessment, restoration and maintenance of function, to homeostasis, and to rehabilitation and quality of life issues. These include concern with the meaning of life, the life they have led, dying, family relationships, social context, handling of stress, autonomy — territory of little professional interest to physicians today who do not usually wish to include socioeconomic factors in their work (16). Indeed, they defensively deny that such issues are any of their business, that they are not the business of medicine but of society. They must, however, come to appreciate the role of such issues in the genesis of pathology, and as obstacles to care and rehabilitation.

The concept of ageism

Physicians contribute, as does the culture as a whole, to ageism. This is exemplified in neglect of issues of sexuality when treating older patients, in the thoughtless prescription of medications that have adverse effects, deferred pelvic or rectal examinations in older women, or discontinued Papanicolaou smears in women over 65. Data show that physicians spend less time with patients over 40. It is as though conversation is also ignored, or the patient hears, 'what do you expect at your age?'. I am reminded of Morris Rocklin, a man who taught me a very great deal. He was a volunteer in our human aging study, and we followed him from 1955 to 1966 (17). I last saw him when he was 101. On that occasion he told me that he had a pain in his left knee for which he sought help from his doctor. The doctor asked him,

'Morris, what do you expect at your age?', at which point Morris, a feisty chap, got up out of his chair and said, 'now look here, my right knee is also 101. How come *it* doesn't hurt?'

I regret that there has been a continuing disinterest in medicine and psychiatry for older people. Before I arrived at the Mount Sinai Medical Center there was considerable discomfort that our program might take away patients from other departments. In fact, though, patients are constantly being referred to us by Mount Sinai Medical Center physicians as well as by other physicians in New York, which confirms my hypothesis that many doctors are only too glad to dispose of their older patients.

Geriatrics: the future

Geriatrics, as a field, is the future—not of medicine, but of comprehensive health and social services of which medicine will be only one component, albeit the most important one. There will be a new system that is more in accordance with the needs of the consumers rather than of the providers. In the USA, we need major new strategies that will help us sustain health and social service care for older people and, equally important, the economy necessary to support such services. The plan for reform must include a number of features.

A restructuring of Medicare

Medicare needs to be more in keeping with the realities that older patients face (18). It was set up originally as if older people were really only 40 years of age. It does not provide for out-patient medication, and covers only minimal out-patient mental health care and nursing home care. It was primarily a financing mechanism for acute illnesses in hospital. Now we must move from financing to reorganization, and that reorganization must reflect collaborative care. In addition, there should be funds from Medicare to support biomedical, social, behavioral and health service delivery research, as well as funds for education to mainstream knowledge of geriatrics through all primary and specialty medicine.

National health plan

A national health plan that incorporates a restructured Medicare must be established, providing universal entitlement and helping to eliminate intergenerational conflict. Taxation should be progressive or income-related.

I predict that the business community will soon support national health insurance in the USA. It already provides $91 billion for 130 million workers and their families, and $8 billion for retirees. American business is confronted with intense global competition. An American automobile, for example, may cost some $600 more because car companies have to cover workers' fringe benefits, health insurance, retirement, etc. A national program of supportive health care would therefore help free individual companies to be more competitive internationally.

I believe that physicians will also support national health insurance. They will soon prefer to negotiate with government or various consumer organizations than work for a commercial health industry.

A national health plan would result in a dramatic reduction in administrative costs. The for-profit effort is expected to lead to a 10% loss to the health care system. In my judgment, a rational reorganization of the health care system can be achieved with no significant increase in new dollars. Certainly, if 10% can go out of profits, 10% can be more sensibly used to expand coverage as necessary. Health is increasingly perceived as a necessary component of a vital and effective work force which, in turn, is important to national security.

Physician payment control

The US Congress has created a physicians' payment review commission under the Office of Technology Assessment that will address such problems as inadequate payment for time spent in assessment and care as compared with procedures, the so-called cognitive vs procedure argument.

Research strategy

The National Institute on Aging is devoted to understanding the role of aging which, with genetics and the environment, broadly defined, is one of the three great antecedents of disease. Should its efforts, together with those of other institutes, to find the cause and treatment for Alzheimer's disease succeed, our nursing home population would be halved. In a sense, then, Alzheimer's disease is the poliomyelitis of geriatrics, and the nursing home a halfway technology, the iron-lung of geriatrics.

Cost-containment strategy, control of avarice and excessive application of technology

Technology assessment has both quality-assuring and cost-containing aspects. Randomized clinical trials and consensus conferences are but two of the modalities of value.

Productivity of older people

There needs to be a movement towards the mobilization of the continuing productivity of older people (19,20). Productive aging refers to the fact that productive people are usually healthy. Our human aging studies in 1955–66 showed that people with goals and some organization to their daily lives outsurvived those who did not have goals (17). Health subserves productivity, and productivity subserves health. A lively, productive economy is necessary to sustain a society and its people, and the yeast in the dough that keeps the economic pie expanding consists of basic research, applied research and education.

It is essential not to stifle initiative, but this does not mean that there should not be active planning. Sweden has a ministry of the future; Japan, an economic planning agency, but in the USA we can barely move beyond bottom-line thinking—the next election for politicians, the quarterly earnings for business people.

Planning in the USA is likely to take the form of an increasingly effective alliance among government, business and labor. In addition to the development of an over-arching planning agency, we may soon see the development of a cabinet department of science and technology that would make decisions regarding a program of mapping the human genome, creating atom smashers, and so on, which other countries are beginning to do. We cannot afford to be anti-technology, nor can we be against the health care enterprise. It, too, helps create jobs and bolster the economy. The health care enterprise does not drain the economy *per se*, but is one of the main components of the economy—a fact that we must not forget.

References

(1) Butler RN, Lewis MI. *Longevity revolution*. New York: Harper & Row, 1987. [in progress].

(2) Shock NW, Greulich RC, Andres R, *et al. Normal human aging: the Baltimore longitudinal study on aging*. NIH publication no. 84–2450. Washington: US Government Printing Office, 1984.

(3) Reinhardt UE. Battle over medical costs isn't over. *Wall Street Journal* 1986 Oct 22: 32.

(4) Leontief W. Transcript from an evening with Nobel laureate Wassily Leontief: *Productive aging in the context of technological change*. The Forum on Aging, Health, and Productivity. Presented by the Center for Productive Aging, Gerald and May Ellen Ritter Department of Geriatrics, Mt Sinai School of Medicine (CUNY), New York City, May 5, 1985.

(5) Abel-Smith B. Economic commentary. In: Selby P, Schechter M, eds. *Aging 2000: a challenge for society*. Lancaster: MTP Press, 1982: 177–86.

(6) Simon J. *The ultimate resource*. Princeton NJ: Princeton University Press, 1984.

(7) Butler RN. The teaching nursing home. *J Am Med Assoc* 1981; **245**: 1435–7.

(8) Libow LS. Geriatric medicine and the nursing home: a mechanism for mutual excellence. *Gerontologist* 1982; **22** (2): 134–41.

(9) Menninger KA. *Man against himself*. New York: Harcourt, Brace, & World, 1938.

(10) Koren MJ. Home care—who cares? *N Engl J Med* 1986; **314**: 917–20.

(11) Warren MW. Care of chronic sick: a case for treating chronic sick in block in a general hospital. *Br Med J* 1943; **2**: 822–3.

(12) Sheldon JH. *The social medicine of old age*. London: Oxford University Press, 1948.

(13) Anderson WF. Geriatric medicine: an academic discipline. *Age and Ageing* 1976; **5**: 193–7.

(14) Blenker M, Bloom M, Wasser E, Neilsen M. Protective services for old people: findings from the Benjamin Rose Institute study. *Social Casework* 1971; **52**: 483–522.

(15) Butler RN, Lewis MI. *Aging and mental health*. St Louis: CV Mosby, 1982.

(16) Butler RN. *Why survive? Being old in America*. New York: Harper & Row, 1975.

(17) Birren JE, Butler RN, Greenhouse SW, Sokoloff L, Yarrow MR, eds. *Human aging I: a biological and behavioral study*: Public Health Service publication no. 986. Washington: US Government Printing Office, 1963. (Reprinted 1971 & 1974.)

(18) Butler RN. *The restructuring of Medicare*. Presented at conference on the societal impact of population aging in the United States and Japan, Tokyo. Submitted for the record to the Subcommittee on Health and Long-term Care of the Select Committee on Aging; hearing on catastrophic health care coverage (US Congress), Feb 19, 1986, and the House Select Committee on Aging; hearings on the plight of the black elderly: a major crisis in America (US Congress), Oct 3, 1986.

(19) Butler RN. The relation of extended life to extended employment since the passage of social security in 1935. *Milbank Mem Fund Q* 1983; **61** (3): 420–9.

(20) Butler RN, Gleason HP. *Productive aging: enhancing vitality in later life.* New York: Springer, 1985.

Discussion

Sir Martin Roth

There are three themes that I should like to take up.

First, Professor Grimley Evans' insistence on the equality of claim upon medical care of all individuals irrespective of age. Will it ever be possible for any society, politically, morally, ideologically or biologically, to allocate resources to, say, coronary bypass operations and dialysis in individuals aged 80+ equal to those allocated to ante-natal care, paediatrics and the treatment of suicide potentiality and depression in early life?

Secondly, should there be such a discipline, a specialty, as geriatrics? Does this not create a certain kind of ageism?

Thirdly, with regard to the two patterns outlined by Professor Grimley Evans, the integrated and the age-related, I think the point he is making is that in the latter we create an underprivileged status for those aged 65 and over in the UK. This is because we deny them access to specialist medical care in their acute illnesses, and convert the geriatrician into an all-knowing cornucopia of knowledge about every aspect of medicine, capable of dealing with all kinds of challenge.

These are all very difficult questions, and there are problems and advantages on both sides.

3. Specific problems: mental illness and handicap

Chairman:
SIR MARTIN ROTH
Cambridge, UK

A UK view:
needs and services for
people with mental disability

JOHN CORBETT

Professor of Mental Handicap, Department of Psychiatry,
University of Birmingham, Birmingham, UK

Introduction

There can be little disagreement that a major priority in the provision of health services lies in the need to plan better services for the mentally disabled. These include people with disability arising in the developmental period and leading in particular to severe mental retardation, those left disabled following mental illness later in life and, with increasing longevity, those with mental impairment arising in late middle and old age.

Although the paramount need is for prevention of mental retardation and treatment of acute psychiatric illness, advances in both have been relatively spectacular over the past 30 years and the main shortfall lies in our ability to apply this knowledge on a large scale. It is, however, in the field of chronic disability, with increased expectations, shortage of resources and competition with other areas of health care, that the apparently almost insatiable demands are most evident.

There are a number of common themes evident in the needs of these three care groups but, because of the compartmentalized nature of the services, it is uncommon to find a balanced discussion of the issues, and there are also differences in time scale and specific needs between the groups.

In the proceedings of a recent conference held between the main governmental agency responsible for the provision of services, the Department of Health and Social Security (DHSS), and the major professional organization involved, the Royal College of Psychiatrists, the editors conclude that:

> a number of critical issues still remain to be clarified and resolved. These concern: firstly, the identification of appropriate health and social services in each district, and the balance of their components; secondly, the co-ordination of these services and the identification of gaps between them; and finally, the evaluation of the provision and assessment of the financial consequences of changes in it, in a context of static or even diminishing resources (1).

Health Care Provision under Financial Constraint, edited by T. B. Binns and M. Firth, 1988: Royal Society of Medicine International Congress and Symposium Series No. 115, published by Royal Society of Medicine Services Ltd.

They quote Martin (2), who stated that

> We do not have a comprehensive national health service, nor in the fullest sense is
> there hope of achieving one. The task is rather one of creating systems which, while
> acknowledging existing divisions, provide a framework for joint planning and joint action.
> Without firm governmental commitment to the principle of active community based
> mental health services and a corresponding recognition of the practical implications of
> the principle, the national scene will not have changed by the end of the century; such
> advances as are achieved, through small scale local initiatives, will be counterbalanced
> by the growing problems of the elderly mentally infirm.

Priorities for community care

The governmental response to this pessimistic view by the Health Minister attending
the conference was to identify from evidence supplied to the Parliamentary Social
Services Select Committee (3) the key features required of services for the mentally
ill and mentally handicapped. They must be:

(1) local so they can help people where they are;
(2) flexible to meet people's real needs;
(3) comprehensive so that they do not leave gaps through which people may fall;
(4) integrated so that they do not leave the client to pull together loose ends;
(5) relevant—dictated by need not organization;
(6) multidisciplinary—pulling together and not apart;
(7) sensitive—responsive to changing needs;
(8) accessible—so that the consumer can get to them.

This list of priorities for community care seems disarmingly simple and is often
repeated. In order to understand the reasons why progress towards these ideals has
been so slow and incomplete, it is necessary to examine briefly some of the influences
which have led to the present situation.

Development of services for people with mental handicap

In the case of mental handicap services and (combined with other more complex
reasons) also of mental illness, it should be remembered that an important reason
for setting up institutions in the middle of the last century was a dissatisfaction with
care in the community, a realization of the unsatisfactory nature of care in workhouses
or the alternative of no care at all in the community. The numbers and size of
institutions increased. They were largely the responsibility of the local authorities
and, even before the last war, were called hospitals.

With the inception of the National Health Service (NHS) in 1948, these institutions
were taken over by the health service but there seems to have been little systematic
consideration of their role until the 1959 Mental Health Act drew attention to their
deficiencies and developed the concept of community care which had previously been
the subject of experimentation on only a limited basis.

Although there were exceptions, as in other countries these institutions were
characterized by:

(1) their large size;
(2) their relative inacessibility and isolation;
(3) their large catchment area, often serving populations of over one million
and thus, in many cases, several local authority districts;

(4) in the case of mental handicap, the fact that people admitted in childhood or adolescence tended to remain in them for long periods and often for life; in the case of the mentally ill, this was also mirrored by the accumulation of long-stay populations;

(5) their tendency to form the base for a multiplicity of functions including both acute treatment and long-stay asylum or custodial care;

(6) a recognition of the ill effects of institutional care, through the work of Goffman in the USA (4), and others in this country.

In 1969 the first of a number of critical reports on conditions in individual mental handicap hospitals was published, followed in 1971 by publication of the Government Command Document, *Better services for the mentally handicapped* (5), which laid out for the first time a plan for comprehensive district services for mental handicap based on a population of 1–200 000. This seminal work, like others before and since, laid emphasis on the residential component of care with services being provided jointly by health and social services, with small units in district general hospitals replacing the large institutions.

In fact, the outcome of this initiative has been very few district general hospital units for the mentally handicapped and a recognition that this is a relatively unsatisfactory environment for people with mental handicap to live in. What we have been left with is a legacy comprising the second half of the package of relatively large (12–20 place) local authority or, euphemistically called, locally based hospital units for both children and adults in the community. In some areas, although split up into smaller living units, these are still being built as part of the community care provision. In other areas this has been overtaken by a more normalized service utilizing much smaller group homes in ordinary housing in the community, much influenced by the principles of normalization laid down by Wolfensberger in the USA (6) on the Scandinavian model.

District services for the mentally ill

In the case of mental illness services, the elements that go to make up a comprehensive district service were set out in a further government white paper, *Better services for the mentally ill*, in 1975 (7). Although both this and the companion document for mental handicap were entitled Command Documents both were in the nature of exhortations, with less in the way of requirement or resources for local authorities, in particular, to provide community care.

Progress on both initiatives has recently been reviewed by the Social Services Select Committee of the House of Commons which examined a wide variety of evidence, travelling abroad and in this country to examine services (3).

In the case of mental illness the essential elements proposed were:

(1) A psychiatric department within a district general hospital providing facilities for in-patient, out-patient and day-patient assessment, treatment and rehabilitation, including support for those discharged after a shorter or longer stay in hospital.

(2) Accommodation within the hospital for the assessment and short-term treatment of elderly people with psychiatric disorders.

(3) Local accommodation, perhaps in smaller hospitals or new units, for the continuing care, relief and intermittent care of some elderly patients.

(4) In-patient accommodation for the 'old long-stay' patients which is at present concentrated in the 90 or so districts with traditional psychiatric hospitals.

It was anticipated that this number would decline quite rapidly from a combination of deaths and discharges, and in the past 25 years the number of in-patients has fallen from 145 000 to 69 000, of whom 56 000 are in the traditional hospitals. In spite of this, no large hospital has closed completely although there has been a reduction in average size and plans for closure in a number.

Even in specially funded projects such as that in Worcester involving the run down of the local mental hospital which was initiated in 1970, over 100 patients remain in the hospital. What has been shown, however, is that in spite of the fact that this is largely an elderly population, constructive alternatives have been devised and this process can be followed through without hardship.

Although there has been a decline in the total numbers in these traditional hospitals, the number of admissions rose slightly from 175 000 in 1972 to 183 000 in 1983. While this suggests an increasing throughput of patients, increasing concern has been expressed about the needs of the 'new long-stay' patients—people who, despite advances in treatment, cannot be supported in the community.

There is a realization of the difficulties caused when these people are expected to live indefinitely in an ordinary busy psychiatric in-patient setting. Proposals in the 1975 White Paper including the provision of hospital hostels but, generally speaking, only limited progress has been made to a solution of this problem.

The proposal for district general hospital departments of psychiatry has increasingly been followed, although not always in satisfactory accommodation and often having to compete for resources with acute specialties. While the proposal for mental handicap to be similarly sited was in the 1971 White Paper, people with mental handicap suffering from acute psychiatric illness have tended to be excluded from such services, and it is a matter for concern that in most areas a compartmentalized rather than an integrated service for the mentally disabled has developed.

In the case of the mentally ill, the district general hospital units have formed an effective base for the community services, particularly including community psychiatric nursing, although there has been an increasing tendency for these services to be based in primary care settings in health centres and the surgeries of family doctors, in a number of which psychological and psychiatric back-up is available.

Special services

In addition to general psychiatric services and those for the elderly with mental illness which are needed in every district, each regional health authority has been exhorted to provide a strategy for adolescent and children's services, for secure units, forensic services, and for alcohol, drug and solvent abuse. This has been mirrored by an awareness of the need to provide special services which, because of the small numbers or lack of expertise, may need to be organized on a supradistrict or regional basis. In the case of the mentally handicapped, this would involve those with mental impairment or severe mental impairment, as defined in the 1983 Mental Health Act, where intellectual impairment is complicated by severe behaviour disorder, and also those with profound sensory handicaps, and other special needs groups.

Here the need is to provide special services with access to appropriate assessment and treatment facilities rather than isolated special units which would only perpetuate a two-tier service.

Better services for the mentally handicapped (5) envisaged a gradual decline in the total number of NHS hospital beds allocated to mental handicap from around 60 000 in 1969 in England and Wales to a little over half that (in population adjusted terms) by the early 1990s. It anticipated an increase in community residential places of a similar order of magnitude (i.e. close to 30 000) together with a rise of nearly 50 000 in the number of adult training and day occupational places provided in the community.

This estimate is largely on target, and in some instances has been exceeded so that, for example, by 1985 there were only 1000 children under the age of 16 years in NHS hospitals and units against an anticipated requirement of 6000 places, and most health authorities have complied with the request of the DHSS to agree a date after which no more children will be admitted to hospital.

Thus, broadly speaking, the overall number of hospital and residential places has kept constant. Unlike the situation concerning the discharge from hospital of mentally ill patients with conditions such as schizophrenia, there is less evidence that progress towards community care has in practice led to previously institutionalized mentally handicapped adults being 'put out onto the streets' (8).

There is, however, evidence that these new community residential and day services have a lower tolerance to severe and profound disability than the more traditional hospitals.

In a study of community-based residential care in South London (9) it was found that only 5% of those in hostels were over 60 years of age, none was blind, fewer than 1% were deaf and only 8% suffered from epilepsy in the previous year, while 16% posed severe behavioural problems. Each of these was considerably less frequent than in a total population of adults in contact with mental handicap services, and on this basis less than half of those at present in hospital would be eligible for a place in community-based facilities as they existed in South London in the late 1970s.

This means that existing hospitals, although small, are having to cope with an increasing proportion of profoundly and multiply handicapped people, and that more people are remaining at home or being maintained in unsatisfactory residential accommodation in the community. There is, for example, concern about an increasing number of people excluded from day services in some areas—often young adults who have grown up in children's homes and reached the end of their schooling.

Future prospects

As with mental illness, few mental handicap hospitals have been closed. Rather, they have reduced in size while the total number has increased, which has limited the cost savings associated with the falling in-patient population.

On the positive side, joint planning of services for the mentally handicapped between health and social services has been encouraging, stimulated by regional funding policies which provide on-going revenue for individual patients relocated from hospital, based on the estimated cost of their hospital care. This has been supplemented by an increase in various personal allowances, including attendance, mobility and severe disablement allowances, and supplementary benefit, and also by the use of joint financing to enable new capital schemes to be initiated.

A pattern of community mental handicap teams has been established, often jointly staffed and, in some areas, incorporating voluntary agencies and housing associations. At their best, these encompass a number of services, including family support teams, specialist services, fostering schemes, toy libraries, clubs and other recreational facilities, baby-sitting, holiday schemes, linked families and other forms of respite care, etc.

It has become clear, in all this planning and revolutionary change in attitudes to the provision of community care for the mentally disabled, that the need for a range of services and for flexibility to enable services and planning targets to be modified in the light of changing circumstances has been underestimated in some of the simplistic and now seemingly rather stereotyped proposals of the 1970s. We are in the dilemma of needing to maintain existing services at considerable expense until satisfactory alternatives can be provided in the community and, even then, careful evaluation is required to ensure that these alternatives really do meet the needs of the people who are dependent upon them.

References

(1) Wilkinson G, Freeman H. *The provision of mental health services in Britain: the way ahead.* London: Gaskell, 1986.
(2) Martin FM. *Between the acts.* London: Nuffield Provincial Hospitals Trust, 1984.
(3) Social Services Committee of the House of Commons. 2nd report. *Community care with special reference to adult mentally ill and mentally handicapped people.* London: Her Majesty's Stationery Office, 1985.
(4) Goffman E. *Asylums. Essays on the social situation of mental patients.* New York: Anchor, 1961.
(5) *Better services for the mentally handicapped.* Cmnd 4683. London: Her Majesty's Stationery Office, 1971.
(6) Wolfensberger W. *Origins and nature of institutions.* Syracuse: Human Policy Press, Syracuse University, 1974.
(7) *Better services for the mentally ill.* Cmnd 6233. London: Her Majesty's Stationery Office, 1975.
(8) *Mental handicap—partnership in the community.* London: Office of Health Economics, 1986.
(9) Udall T, Corbett J. Non-hospital residential care for adults with mental retardation. In: Wing JK, Olsen R, eds. *Community care for the mentally disabled.* Oxford: Oxford University Press, 1979.

A US view:
issues in mental health services

HERBERT PARDES

Professor and Chairman, Department of Psychiatry,
College of Physicians and Surgeons, Columbia University;
Director, New York State Psychiatric Institute, New York NY, USA

It has been well documented by now that the problems of mental illness are widespread. Recent studies by the National Institute of Mental Health (NIMH), using the epidemiology catchment area program show that 19% of the population in the USA suffer from diagnosable psychiatric conditions in any 6-month period. This represents over 35 million people (1). Increasingly, however, mental illness is being recognized as constituting a broad set of disorders. These disorders have widely different consequences; the services necessary to deal with them are similarly varied.

The system for the care of people with anxiety disorders is quite different from that necessary to attend to people with schizophrenic conditions or, on the other hand, people with Alzheimer's disease. I emphasize this because many people outside the mental health field tend to think of mental illness as homogeneous. It would be as global and super-ficial a perspective to think of all surgical conditions as uniform in character.

To add to the complexity, secondary to the diversity of disorders there are also a host of settings in which mental health services are delivered. In the USA these range from clinicians' private offices through a full range of clinic type settings, hospitals as diverse as the Veterans Administration hospitals, large state hospitals usually for patients with chronic disease, psychiatric units in general hospitals, municipal hospitals and private hospitals. There is also a range of settings intermediate between out-patient clinic care and in-patient care including residential settings, day-care settings, and alternate 24-h living arrangements with some component of clinical psychiatric care among others. For the majority of individuals with mental disorders primary care settings provide their only treatment opportunity (2).

Mental health system changes in the last 30 years

The range of clinical settings is a reflection of considerable change in the mental health system in the past three decades. From 1954 to 1984 1000 new psychiatric units were founded in general hospitals. By contrast, there has been a profound reduction in the

Health Care Provision under Financial Constraint, edited by T. B. Binns and M. Firth, 1988: Royal Society of Medicine International Congress and Symposium Series No. 115, published by Royal Society of Medicine Services Ltd.

number of residents of state hospitals, which at one point reached almost 600 000 in the USA and is more recently in the neighborhood of 125 000. Average length of stay, which in 1954 in state hospitals was 9 months, had dropped to 3 weeks by 1984. This has been accompanied by a dramatic fourfold increase in out-patient care. In 1954 three-quarters of all encounters between mental health providers and patients took place in hospitals. In 1984 this had dropped to one-quarter (3).

These changes in the setting of care were in large part a result of de-institutionalization (4). A series of forces produced the de-institutionalization movement. These included the introduction of drugs which could control psychotic symptoms, sociological studies which emphasized the non-therapeutic character of some of the large chronic disease hospitals, legal changes in the balance between society's needs for committing patients and individuals' rights to avoid such committal, and economic incentives consisting of opportunities for federal government financing if patients were in nursing homes or were out-patients.

The de-institutionalization thrust went hand in hand in the USA with the NIMH plan to develop community mental health centers. National standards were established for the kinds of community mental health services that would be available in such centers, and a national granting program was instituted in the 1960s to cover the whole country with community mental health centers. Had that plan succeeded fully there would have been 1500 community mental health centers, but in fact only some 800 were ultimately built over a 15-year period.

Some saw these centers as settings in which to tend to the seriously mentally ill who are discharged from institutions. However, the centers were also encouraged to develop a capacity for early intervention in mental health problems of all sorts, and for prevention. For many practitioners the acute problem or the patient with the more treatable non-psychotic condition often seemed more rewarding to treat. Such patients tended to make more use of mental health centers than did the sicker chronically mentally ill. As a result, many de-institutionalized patients did not receive services from the community mental health centers. In fact, they became roaming citizens of the street, which led in the mid-1970s to a call for re-evaluation of the nation's system.

The Mental Health Systems Act

In 1977, when Jimmy Carter assumed the presidency, one of his first acts was to set up the Presidential Commission on Mental Health, with Rosalynn Carter as honorary chairperson. Over the next 3 years hearings, negotiations, multiple reports drafted and re-drafted led to what was called the Mental Health Systems Act that was signed in October 1980. In many ways the fate of this Act reveals a depressing awareness of the adverse consequences of the politicization of health programs.

The Mental Health Systems Act attempted to establish programs to fill the gaps perceived in the system. Special programs were to be created for the chronically mentally ill, minorities, children, elderly, and people in general health settings who had mental health problems. The complaint that state entities had been bypassed in the process of national granting to local mental health centers was to be addressed by involving the states more actively. A new prevention center was to be set up, and increased attention was to be given to the needs of minorities, the latter being assured by the creation of a major minority leadership position in the NIMH.

It is noteworthy that the Mental Health Systems Act was the only piece of health legislation of any consequence passed during the Carter administration.

In November 1980 Ronald Reagan was elected and new policy makers designed and then pressed Congress to an essential scuttling of the Mental Health Systems Act. The new administration took the position that directly funding treatment services was not the business of the federal government, but instead was the responsibility of local and state communities. Consequently, the same money that had gone for federally supported community mental health centers was to be sent in analogous amounts to the state in the form of a block grant. Congressional opponents, fearing that some states might not have any constraints on them to use the money for mental health programs insisted that this mental health money not be lumped into a more general state support grant from the federal government. Ultimately, the compromise was an alcohol, drug abuse and mental health block grant system which gave monies to the states exclusively for these three problem areas.

That 3 years of deliberation and work should be set aside in a matter of months and replaced by a federal policy of non-involvement graphically demonstrates the precarious nature of health policy too closely dependent on the occupant of the White House.

It is important to recognize that the Reagan administration was reflecting the mood of the country in calling for a more decentralized influence on many programs. The current administration has not been consistent, however. Some might argue that those in favour of less powerful government are remarkably interested in government involvement when it deals with problems in which they have interest, though ostensibly dedicated to a less powerful federal bureaucracy most of the time.

Discrimination against mental health funding

The elimination of the Mental Health Systems Act was demoralizing for those people concerned about mental health. Mental health programs and psychiatric illnesses suffer from a pervasive stigma as it is. This stigma is reflected in the tendency, for example, in health insurance reimbursement to limit or give less favorable coverage to mental health than to general health. In the USA this discriminatory treatment is so harsh that elderly people with little limitation on the amount of general health out-patient care they can receive (although they pay some modest co-payment) are restricted to the equivalent of about three visits to the mental health clinic if they have a psychiatric problem.

This means that an elderly person suffering from a depression, which potentially is easily treatable on an out-patient basis, might be hospitalized by a physician in response to the constraints of reimbursement (5). I was personally involved in the Reagan administration in attempts in 1983 to modify this during the work of the Secretary's Task Force on Alzheimer's Disease (6), but by that time the administration had become preoccupied with the deficit, and some policy makers dramatically overstated the financial risk of expanding medical coverage for out-patient mental health care. Consequently, the Task Force recommended improvement only for patients specifically with Alzheimer's disease. The very tight limitation on reimbursement for other psychiatric illnesses persists.

Those arguing for such tight reimbursement controls usually protest the propensity in the mental health system for huge expenditures if there are no restrictions. In fact, some 80% of the people who go for mental health care usually have their problem attended to within 20 out-patient visits (7). Experiences that create worry among reimbursement analysts include programs made more costly by adverse selection when they offer substantial benefits while other programs available to the client do not.

There have been other examples in which a pent-up need creates a short-term large increase in cost when a benefit is introduced or increased, and this frightens the carrier.

Aside from the vagaries of reimbursement however, it is a simple reality that mental health problems constitute a large part of the health pathology in the nation. Increasingly, private business has come to recognize that employees may become dysfunctional in large numbers due to alcohol, drug addiction and other mental health problems. The widespread nature of the problem makes it increasingly difficult to disregard.

The interruption of the momentum behind the Mental Health Systems Act and the blanket deferral to the states as being responsible for service delivery and policy have virtually left the country in a holding pattern regarding any national policy for a system of mental health services. The problems have been compounded by a decreasing tendency to use state hospitals, such that there is a large young chronic population which has not received any kind of intensive treatment. This group joins another population of de-institutionalized psychiatric patients and others who are not mentally ill but homeless because of the variety of social, economic, and political factors that make homes less available within parts of the country. Again, the federal government has shown a marked decrease in its attention to housing programs for the poor and the mentally ill.

Advances in psychiatry

Simultaneously, from another direction there has been cause for optimism, relating to the increasing excitement about the sciences related to psychiatry. In the words of Dr Lewis Thomas:

> The 1976–86 decade is already providing its own evidence that neurobiology is well under way as the most exciting of all fields in biological science. It seems safe to predict, from today's vantage point, that the events that lie in the decades just ahead will almost certainly revolutionize all our earlier notions about the brain, and about the mind that it operates (or that operates it) (8).

This perspective has been reflected in work using brain imaging technologies, and in increasing understanding of the elegant computer-like system of communication in the brain involving neurotransmitters and receptors. The potential of molecular genetics seems extraordinary. It may afford opportunities for unlocking the mysteries regarding the etiologies of the major psychiatric disorders. The recognition that the brain is a far more plastic organism, responsive to environmental factors and potentially treatable is most encouraging. Work delineating the biology underlying mental functions holds out the possibility that we might have a way of influencing functions such as memory and learning in the long run, thereby alleviating some of the symptoms and dysfunctions associated with Alzheimer's disease, learning disabilities and schizophrenia.

These exciting developments in research accompany a general tendency towards refinement and sharpening in clinical psychiatry. This is manifest in the new set of epidemiological techniques and surveys offering us the best data we have ever had about the incidence and prevalence of psychiatric disease. Simultaneously, there have been advances in diagnosis. In the DSM III*, observable phenomena are insisted upon as the criteria for diagnostic decisions. A multi-axial system has been devised to account for the array of factors contributing to a diagnostic assessment. These

*Diagnostic and Statistical Manual of Mental Disorders.

advances have led to far greater reliability of diagnosis and a greatly enhanced capacity to conduct collaborative research and share information in order to advance work generally.

Further, there is an increasing effort to delineate the specific treatments most appropriate for various specific disorders. This latter tendency fits well with the increased recognition of subtyping in psychiatric disorders. No longer are psychiatrists satisfied with the diagnosis of anxiety or depression, but instead bipolar affective disorders, social anxiety as opposed to panic attacks, the likelihood of multiple schizophrenias and other conditions are emerging from this steady process of refinement (9). This pattern resembles the growth of understanding of the many causes of mental retardation.

Contentious treatment issues

Thus, on the one hand, we have the service delivery system to some degree in chaos, while an increasingly refined clinical psychiatric capacity evolves, on the other. There are also themes about which there is contention regarding clinical delivery. These include:

(1) Arguments about continued de-institutionalization of patients, as opposed to some who would advocate re-institutionalization.

(2) Arguments between those who advocate the use of psychosocial methods versus those who advocate biological methods.

(3) Disputes between the various mental health disciplines regarding their roles in mental health delivery.

(4) Advocates of prevention *vis-à-vis* people who, focusing primarily on the major psychiatric disorders, see no sufficient understanding of etiology to allow for interventions.

(5) Tension between advocates of more legal rights for patients *vis-à-vis* advocates for protection of society's interests.

Recommendations for the system

The needs of people with chronic mental illness are many and complicated. They include needs for psychopharmacological treatments, for a sustained psycho-therapeutic relationship with a doctor, opportunities for work, and an ability to contribute to society. Also critical are interpersonal relationships, suitable housing, some financial support, and possibilities of rehabilitation.

Such patients require a different level and intensity of care depending upon the phase of their illness. They may require acute hospitalization or hospitalization of an intermediate or longer-term character, or emergency room attention with crisis intervention. They may require treatment in a residential, day-care or night-care setting, or they may need an out-patient department or placement in some rehabilitation setting, a sheltered workshop, etc. Unfortunately, there is a tendency among some people to decide that one intervention is all important and others may be disregarded. What then are some of the themes to which attention should be paid to ensure quality care?

(1) There must be a comprehensive plan in which all the various levels of service are available and of high quality. We must not focus on one service and let others deteriorate.

(2) The financial system must be such that the individual with mental illness can receive care. This means that the uninsured, the undomiciled, and the elderly person seeking out-patient care should all be covered.

(3) There must be an attention to the housing needs of people with long-term illness because often the absence of such housing is what creates unnecessarily prolonged hospital stays. The unnecessary hospital stays make the system more costly and divert resources from those who need appropriate hospital care.

(4) Some institutional flexibility and incentive should be given if institutions with responsibilities for longer-term care can develop ways to reduce costs without sacrificing quality, or can respond to the need of their patients more effectively. This might mean that a state hospital would create a day-care program or a program with less intense clinical care but in which people could live and have basic needs attended.

(5) The acute care system needs adequate reimbursement with peer review to ensure against abuse of services provided.

(6) We need a reversal of the tendency to dilute the capacity of the provider to give necessary care to an uncooperative patient. Legally, the USA is making it increasingly difficult for a psychiatrist to dispense psychopharmacological treatment.

(7) There should be more comprehensive attention to mental health liaison programs in in-patient and out-patient settings, in as much as they seem to lead to a more appropriate match of care to a patient's needs and also to reduction of services and costs in some instances (10).

(8) The system will have to recognize the increasing impact of the advances from research of the growing understanding of the intimate interactions of brain and behavior, and of improvements in therapeutics which will result in a greater need for skills in providers which blend biological and psychosocial expertise.

There are reasons why the mental health system may be more forcefully brought to the attention of society, certainly in the USA. These include the exciting advances in research which are catching attention. They also include a rising advocacy of citizen groups and also ex-patient groups. As the clinical psychiatric system becomes more refined, and as a corresponding diminishing of some of the stigma attached to mental illness is seen, it would seem that more and more families are joining movements to advocate for programs related to mental illness. This is not without its complications as many families emerge furious at the frustrations of the inadequate treatment capacity currently available. Also, ex-patients and their relatives have arguments which can become major policy differences between the respective groups. For example, the relatives are more in favor of involuntary hospitalization and the dispensing of drugs despite resistance on the part of the patients. Ex-patients tend to take the opposite position.

Conclusion

The mental health system is complicated by different kinds of patients, different needs, different kinds of caregiving settings and a large number of factions arguing various positions. To people outside the mental health care system this has often seemed like a confusing and even disagreeable morass. The problem has been further exacerbated by the tendency of political factors to intrude in the devising of the system.

The most significant changes, however, which may influence that system are:

(1) The research excitement.
(2) The refined and enhanced clinical psychiatric capacity.
(3) Increased advocacy from citizens, particularly families and ex-patients.
If we can quiet the single-minded advocate and emphasize the need for a range of systems of care, a variety—and often a combination—of therapies, and a need for the related social supports and financing which accompany these various programs, there is hope that the system can be put in better shape until the research brings us fuller explanations and even more effective therapies to improve what we can do for patients.

References

(1) Regier DA, Myers JK, Kramer M, *et al*. The NIH epidemiological catchment area (ECA) program: historical context, major objectives, and study population characteristics. *Arch Gen Psychiatry* 1984; **41**: 934–41.
(2) Reiger DA, Goldberg ID, Taube CA: The *de facto* US mental health services system: a public health perspective. *Arch Gen Psychiatry* 1978; **35**: 685–93.
(3) Taube CA, Barrett SA, eds. *Mental health, United States, 1985*. National Institute of Mental Health. Department of Health and Human Services publication no. (ADM) 85-1378. Washington: Superintendent of Documents, US Government Printing Office, 1985.
(4) Pardes H, Sirovatka P, Pincus H. Federal and state roles in mental health. In: Michels R, Cavenar J, Jr, eds. *Psychiatry 3*. Philadelphia: JB Lippincott, 1985: 1–18.
(5) Pardes H. The aging: mental health problems. *N Y State J Med* 1981; **81** (5): 798–801.
(6) The Task Force Report on Alzheimer's Disease. *Report of the Secretary's Task Force on Alzheimer's Disease*. Department of Health and Human Services publication no. (ADM) 84-1323. Washington: US Government Printing Office, 1984.
(7) *National Ambulatory Medical Care Survey; 1981 summary*. Department of Health and Human Services publication no. (PHS)83-1250. Washington: US Government Printing Office, 1983.
(8) Thomas L. *The Lasker awards. Four decades of scientific medical progress*. New York: Raven Press, 1986.
(9) Pardes H. Neuroscience and psychiatry: marriage or co-existence. *Am J Psychiatry* 1986; **143** (10): 1204–12.
(10) Mumford E, Schlesinger HJ, Glass GV, Patrick C, Cuerdon T. A new look: evidence about reduced cost of medical utilization following mental health treatment. *Am J Psychiatry* 1984; **141**: 1145–58.

General discussion

Sir Martin Roth

We have a mixture of good and bad news to consider in relation to mental health. The bad is: schizophrenics on the streets; institutionalization in the community; communities which do not care; the growth of drug dependence; alcoholism, which is unprovided for to a large extent;

the emergence of a new form of pre-senile dementia in the form of the acquired immune deficiency syndrome (AIDS), an organic syndrome which has recently become manifest in the form of dementia in relatively early life—a most menacing condition. On the other hand, there is the excitement and promise of neurobiology which, in the words of Professor Thomas, is 'the most exciting growing point of biological science' (1)—and, of course, of psychiatric science—and many other features which provide an element of hope.

A disparity is evident between the two countries. Bridges are being developed to cross the gulf and to learn from the comparisons and contrasts.

Dr Forsythe

Have the community mental health centres (CMHCs) in the USA achieved either of the two objectives to which Professor Pardes referred, namely, to prevent hospitalization and also to keep out of hospital those who are discharged?

I do not know whether there is in the USA the same sort of problem that I see in the mental health centres in the UK. I have five or six in my region, all of them quite different, with different operational policies, such as whether or not people can walk in and the sort of people involved.

My second reaction to some of the earlier discussions relates to whether or not we are heading towards the situation in the future where patients need to have a charter. I was a member of a European Economic Community committee concerned with health care. Many of the European delegates wanted to draw up a patients' charter. At the time, I thought that was not necessary as far as it applied in the National Health Service (NHS). However, I am now beginning to think that in fact it may well be necessary before too long. I would be interested to hear whether Professor Pardes has any comments about that.

Professor Pardes

The record of CMHCs in the USA varies across the country. Certainly the CMHC movement accompanied a decrease in the number of people in state hospitals, but I think it is questionable whether that decrease could necessarily be attributed to the existence of CMHCs. It would be difficult to disaggregate—I am not sure that anybody could answer that question.

What was of concern in the mid-1970s was the feeling that the CMHCs were not taking, as a substantial part of their mental health delivery, responsibility for the chronic care of people. Again, this varied around the country. Some centres were very active in that regard, others were not. This led to some additional programmes being developed, including one called the 'community support programme'. This developed a notion of an advocate for people with chronic mental illness who would help secure a range of services for those individuals—housing, some kind of financial assistance, and so on.

Studies on that community support system have shown a reduction in re-hospitalization. If we are going to have chronic mental patients out of hospital, one of the key issues is for them to have a variety of continuing services. The notion that the need will be met by some kind of acute care without continued follow-up is, for the most part, illusory.

It has also been demonstrated that people undergoing treatment with psychopharmacological agents have reduced hospitalization. While I cannot comment specifically on the CMHC system as such, both the use of psychopharmacological agents and the array of services assured by contact with somebody from the community support programme have reduced hospitalization and re-hospitalization of people with chronic mental illness.

Dr Forsythe

Does that mean there is no evidence one way or the other whether CMHCs have any effect in preventing hospital admission or in keeping people out of hospital, and does it suggest that a range of other factors help?

Professor Pardes

There are services and therapeutic ingredients which have reduced hospitalization. It is somewhat more questionable whether this can necessarily be attributed to the community mental health system . . .

Dr Forsythe

But a major financial investment has been made.

Professor Pardes

One of the things that the CMHC system did was finally to place within public view the phenomenon of mental health care. It made people who had often associated mental health care with a building on some remote site more aware.

I think that what the CMHCs have accomplished is not restricted simply to their effects on the chronically mentally ill. They began to make available to the poor population a set of acute and early intervention services which had not been available previously.

Dr Horder

There is quite a marked contrast in the predominant method of entry into the psychiatric services in our two countries. It seems to me that in America there is direct access for patients through the CMHC. In the UK, most people go through the primary medical care services which integrate mind and body in a certain sense which seems to be absent in America. I have the impression that entry through the primary general medical services in America is increasing, and through CMHCs is decreasing. Is that correct?

Professor Pardes

First, the preponderant setting for mental health service delivery in the USA is the general health sector. The largest number of people receiving mental health care receive it directly. I have not seen figures recently, but my recollection is that well over 55% were exclusively in the general health care sector.

Secondly, the wisdom of some integration between mental health and general health I think was recognized at the National Institute for Mental Health. In fact, part of the Mental Health Systems Act included programmes which would allow the placing of mental health clinicians within general health settings.

Perhaps Professor Corbett could comment on the degree of integration in the UK. I think that there has been much more recently, but there is probably still a long way to go.

As for the gatekeeper system, there is the gatekeeper in the UK, and in the USA we have direct access. It is different in that regard.

Professor Corbett

I think that is an important issue. A number of general practice studies have shown that 14% of general practice concerns the treatment of psychiatric disorders. However, as far as I know, the actual involvement of psychiatrists working together with general practitioners (GPs) has been relatively limited — although there is a number of outstanding experimental situations where that has happened.

Dr Horder

We now have a situation in which a considerable number of psychiatrists are working in the general practice setting — which is something new.

Dr Relman

To what extent does the planning process described so clearly by Dr Rue involve the general practice sector? How are GPs brought into the overall planning and distribution of resources?

Dr Rue

In the UK we are just undergoing a change in the arrangements for involving GPs in planning. The planning process is really aimed at getting good value for money, and accounting for it, from the cash limited part of the health sector — that is, the hospital and community health services. The community health and preventive services, as I referred to them, do not include the family practitioner services — that is, the direct primary health care services offered by doctors, dentists and others.

The GPs are the users of the specialist and the community support services. Through the medical advisory machinery they have always been involved in commenting on the priorities, levels and standards of the services for which planning is being undertaken. Of course, there are also GPs on the health authorities which have this public responsibility, and also on many of the planning and management teams by co-option and *ex officio*.

Recently, the family practitioner committees (FPCs) have been separated from the formerly integrated NHS. They have been asked to develop plans for primary health care. Until that time, I think primary health care planning as such was not done very comprehensively in the NHS. We certainly made a big effort at it in our region because it was seen as the key to the provision of all health services. Now, however, every part of the country is covered by an FPC with a planning responsibility. The arrangement is that there should be liaison (joint planning) between the hospital community health services, the FPCs and the local authorities. The difficulty, of course, is that the GPs are independent contractors. They and their services cannot be planned in the way that the other services are. It will be interesting to see what happens over the next few years in this regard.

Dr Relman

Would Mr Lewin please amplify and, by implication, defend his statement that although finances are not a problem with the American system we could not possibly afford a shift to a national health insurance system in the USA? I am thinking specifically of our neighbours to the north. Of course, it is a provincial and federal combined national health insurance system there, and the Canadians spend substantially less than the Americans. Indeed, for a number of years the percentage of gross national product hardly increased. Lately, it is beginning to rise, but they are still way behind ours.

I am beginning to think that perhaps something like the Canadian system would incorporate some of the best features of both the NHS and our totally disorganized arrangement, avoiding some of the pitfalls of both.

Mr Lewin

I will respond to Dr Relman's challenge by trying to make clear that I make a distinction between the acute in-patient and the out-patient. For the former, I believe that there are adequate resources in the system, although not always well distributed. Unless competition succeeds in eroding the resources for in-patient care, I believe that an adequate distribution of the burden is the issue there. While there are undoubtedly cases of people being deprived of in-patient services, or perhaps having to wait until their condition has become an emergency, by-and-large that system is not under-financed.

The primary and preventive care sector is under-financed — the sector that I believe to be particularly necessary for meeting the needs of special populations.

In that regard, I did not mean to imply that reliance on the medical model — or indeed its existence — is a problem. It is, indeed, a necessary part of the system. My point was that the medical model needs to be supplemented with social support services for some populations — mental health services in some cases, health education, etc.

How we can get more money into the primary care system, and whether or not it should be done through a national health insurance system remain highly debatable.

As a practical matter, it is unlikely that we will be able to adopt sweeping reform in the short-term. I realize that we are always at risk. There might be a change of administration or a radical change in tax policy.

A perfectly legitimate question is what would we do if those constraints were relaxed? I should not be allowed to hide behind fiscal constraints as a defence against national health insurance. But, if those fiscal constraints were to be relaxed, if we had available funding and could bring more funds into the system, would we, in fact, go to a Canadian type of system or continue to rely upon the patchwork, fragmentary system that we have now? I would like to see us move towards a system that is much more directed than the present system.

First, we need to resolve where we are as a matter of national policy on health. We also need to resolve this ambivalence about health care for low income people. I think this 'nags' at our inability to produce a sensible policy. Unless and until we resolve that issue, we are in trouble.

Secondly, we need to look at the delivery system, looking at the kinds of questions raised by Professor Butler, Professor Pardes, myself and others about whether the delivery system needs to be modified before we finance the one that is in place. Once financed, it is hard to change.

Finally, Professor Pardes made an important point about the danger of a too centralized system. I do not think that our Medicare system is a paragon that should be pursued as a model for financing. I am troubled about over-centralization because it tends to stifle a lot of innovation that can be produced. Innovation is a healthy aspect of the American system, for all its inefficiency and confusion.

Of course, too, I think that any system as highly centralized as the British and Canadian systems would, in the USA, which is given to wide swings in political parties and views, be in danger of being destabilized.

Even if the constraints were relaxed, I would not want to embrace fully the Canadian system, and the UK type of system is not consistent with the culture we have in America.

Dr Banta

An underlying focus or theme in this conference is an understanding of what we are providing through our services — as we have seen in almost all the presentations. I exemplify this by the fact that mental health services and services for the handicapped were included in our assessment studies at the Office of Technology Assessment. Outcome measures and cost-effectiveness studies cannot be applied to those kinds of services but, as Professor Corbett presented it, the problem of the mentally handicapped is basically a care problem — presumably, long-term, lifelong care. Is there a technology, or a knowledge, that can be more effectively applied, or is this not the only problem? It seems to me to raise very significant problems in resource allocation, defending what is done in that sector.

Professor Corbett

I concentrated on the care problem because it is the one that is consuming a large amount of money. I agree completely that more of that money needs to be devoted towards both improving the technology of prevention and also utilizing more effectively what knowledge we have about prevention. The problem is that much health service money is being devoted to hotel and residential care rather inefficiently. That is the point I was trying to make.

Dr Banta

Secondly, about the use of more medical technology in this area, I am curious to know whether what I hear said is true, namely, that care both for very small and for handicapped babies (perhaps the most rapidly growing area of medical technology) is leading to a growing population of mentally handicapped children.

Professor Corbett

Until 2 or 3 years ago there was anxiety that increased technology in peri-natal prevention was actually increasing handicap. However, there are some very encouraging signs that this is no longer the case, and that peri-natal intensive care has reached the stage at which it is no longer experimental. Undoubtedly, the peri-natal mortality rate has reached very low levels, and there is less evidence now that this is producing more handicapped children.

Mr Sieverts

I think that my question to Mr Lewin is more related to Dr Relman's question to him than may at first appear. Is there a political feasibility about, and perhaps some reason for hope in, the pressures to nationalize the Medicaid system?

I think that is a very important question because, if a typical, moderately well-informed American citizen were asked what is the status of public programmes in health care, he would probably answer that there is Medicaid that takes care of the older population, and Medicaid that takes care of the poor.

Mr Lewin's descriptions of the Medicaid programme may have sounded critical. I suggest that he was Panglossian about Medicaid, that in fact Medicaid is a disastrous failure. I do not think he mentioned that fully half the dollars in the Medicaid system go to support in nursing homes a very small number of older people with chronic disease, often at dismal levels of care. In fact, the very broad benefits that Medicaid programmes in the USA are supposed to provide are so broad that it is nearly impossible for any state with its financing to do anything approaching a decent job. I like to describe the Medicaid Law as setting out the house that is supposed to be painted, expecting the states to provide the paint. However, they do not have enough pigment to provide sufficient paint, so they simply add more and more paint thinner to what is being put on the house.

Therefore, not only are there the very low eligibility levels described by Mr Lewin, but also enormous bureaucratic hurdles to getting into the eligibility (which he mentioned). There are ridiculous payment levels in many states. For example, I believe that the State of Pennsylvania is still paying a maximum of $8 for a physician office visit, which is the same as it was in the 1950s.

It seems to me that there is a level of public support for fairly massive increases in the amount of health benefits provided to the poor, particularly if those health benefits could be much more clearly directed at socially useful outcomes.

Mr Lewin

I think that nationalization of the programme would help. It would probably have to be decoupled from welfare. That is probably a very good idea anyway—in fact, probably the first step. It is interesting that a group of southern governors have proposed it (for obvious reasons) because their welfare programmes are so poor. There is some political sympathy with that argument, and I believe that the more people understand it the better.

I want to stress that why I went through that process in such detail is because that programme is so poorly understood in America, even by state legislators. Mr Sieverts' point is absolutely right. It is probably both politically (if not fiscally) feasible and also a very good idea for the Medicaid programme.

Professor Butler

It is clear that in my presentation I failed to distinguish between my opposition to practising geriatrics as a specialty in contrast to the academic specialty of geriatrics. I do not wish to absolve any primary care or specialty physician from responding effectively to the needs of older persons. Therefore, I am dedicated to the mainstreaming of knowledge to all the primary and specialty medicine fields.

However, the importance of the development of academic geriatrics cannot be dismissed. We need to have the leaders in research, in innovation, in education. Fortunately, there have now been new movements within the American Board of Internal Medicine for the creation of a certificate of competence and, simultaneously within family practice boards, and under very active consideration, the notion of a special competence within psychiatry.

The department of geriatrics which I created has a mandated clerkship, so that all the undergraduate students must have direct exposure in multiple sites to older people, in order to break down those barriers between departments, attitudes and services, and to appreciate the interrelationship of mental, social, physical and other factors. Half their time is spent in a teaching nursing home. They get a direct opportunity to see the chronically impaired. They have a required human development course that gives them a vision from birth until death. Finally, incorporated within the classic courses in the pre-clinical years are the physiology of ageing, sexuality in ageing, nutrition and pharmacology.

Dr Mayer

On the subject of training, part of what Professor Pardes is proposing for the future involves members of the mental health disciplines working together. As I have got to know the mental health system, in North Carolina at least, over the last few years I am impressed that there are few places where I have seen people who work *less* well together. Psychiatrists do not like psychologists, who do not like social workers, who do not like psychiatrists. The circle goes on, and when the primary care physician and others are thrown into the mix it gets worse.

Does Professor Pardes know examples of where better team-work is being developed? Also, are there training programmes, in the USA at least, that are doing a particularly good job of leading their graduates in the direction of more effective interrelationships with other members of their team?

Professor Pardes

The mistake that is made when people say that there should be multidisciplinary clinical services is in thinking that it necessarily means all disciplines should be doing the same specialties. I do not think that is necessary. In those places where there is successful multidisciplinary work there is some joint discussion on the actual management of clinical care within either hospital or out-patient settings. There are many examples of successful multidisciplinary care.

The rivalry in the mental health system, to which Dr Mayer referred, will be seen increasingly in the general health system as there is direct competition for roles which many different disciplines can play. The problem comes in differentiating which discipline can play which role.

Dr Mayer

What is the UK doing with respect to the training of the people needed to manage the NHS, particularly at the regional level? How are people trained to do the kind of work done by Dr Rue and others?

Dr Rue

If I wanted to start training now to do in the future what I now do, I would get myself a good clinical background. I would then join the specialty of community medicine, and try to demonstrate my aptitude for management. I would try to get, through a competitive system of advertising and appointment, the job of regional general manager. I would be a *medical* regional general manager. In fact, I am the *only* medical manager. I grew up with the system. The other general managers have come from various disciplines. They came through the intake of administrators; some of them are financially qualified; there is a nurse; there are also some from outside industries who have been brought in with the recent management reorganization.

In the future it is intended that the NHS should grow its own general managers. There is a special health authority, an NHS training authority, which is using various agencies, such as the London Business School, etc. to pick out the high-flyers and to get them from whatever background, whether clinical doctors, community physicians or from non-medical disciplines;

to get them to a level of management training experience and ability through planned movement and education so that they can be managers.

Sir Martin Roth

Dr Rue is a unique phenomenon. We have to have more such people, and courses of training that bring us an adequate number of medical administrators. In the UK we have sinned in despising, or giving low status to, our medical administrators, and we are suffering for it.

Professor Wilson

I think we can learn a great deal from the Canadian experience. First, they nationalized the good and the bad that existed. They simply took the same people and put them in government departments very largely to do the same thing that they were doing previously for the insurance companies—except for Quebec. There was no reformation of the system. They have the largest hospital utilization in the world, but they are not closing their hospitals. Except in Quebec, I fear that the data show that the poor are getting less money spent on them than before the government became involved. To the extent that records are kept, it appears that the money is going to the upper classes.

The reason for that is unclear, but it looks very much like what the Black Report would say about the NHS in the UK, and also like the US pattern. There are cultural and other reasons why the poor in Canada are not getting the service. They have financial access—but what Mr Lewin's paper said to me is that just providing the money does not provide access. There are other great problems involved that require something different.

We can learn from Canada that perhaps our period of competition will be the purge of the US system, which we can then bring to some sort of federal regulation—but please do not nationalize what we now have, as the Canadians did.

At present, there is no Nobel prize equivalent for research into the delivery of health care. This would be an inexpensive way of bringing it to the attention of the young people from whom the ideas would flow.

Professor Reinhardt

We did research on health care distribution in Quebec—which as Professor Wilson said is the exception—and found a fairly egalitarian distribution. The data we had on utilization by income class showed that the poor in Quebec were definitely getting care, and that the effect of health insurance was to redistribute from the well-to-do to the poor.

I am not at all surprised by what Professor Wilson said. It generally happens when goods are made free, for example, as with education. Professor Lee Hansen has shown that the free Californian school system tended to redistribute income upwards. Are there any hard data about it?

Professor Wilson

There are very good data from Ontario, Saskatchewan and Alberta. I do not know the British Columbia data very well.

Professor Reinhardt

I think this is a very significant point, which comes up repeatedly. I believe that the barrier to health care is mainly in the heads of the poor. It might be possible to break through that barrier in some way, but it is probably where the problem lies.

Professor Marks

Part of the problem might be that we are devoting too few resources to disseminating what is already known. In the mental health field, for example, there have been significant advances in the delivery of care for the seriously mentally ill in Madison, WI, and in Sydney, Australia. For several years now there have been very good controlled studies showing how the status of the chronically mentally ill can be improved by means of the sort of support systems that Professor Pardes mentioned. However, dissemination of those programmes has been slow, and there is no training programme to disseminate that knowledge in any way.

Similarly, some of the advances made in behaviour therapy in the last few years for the treatment of anxiety disorders are still practised only in a very few areas.

I would like to contrast the slow dissemination of these psychosocial treatments with that of information about a drug recently introduced for anxiety disorders. About 1982 an advertising campaign was promulgated, and in 1985 I believe that sales of the drug in the USA totalled $150 million. This was before there had been a single controlled study demonstrating its value in the conditions for which it is prescribed.

Could we not take a leaf out of the pharmaceutical industry's book? After all, I believe that many companies spend up to one-sixth of their turnover on advertising and promotion. Both in Britain and in the USA we spend a risible amount on dissemination and training programmes of what is already known to work in certain conditions.

What kind of agencies can we set up better to disseminate those positive innovations that are already known to work? These need not be expensive. There have been many Nobel prizes awarded for all kinds of basic advances in medicine — but the very term 'basic' carries with it some kind of aura, as though any psychosocial innovation is *ipso facto* inferior. Could we not persuade bodies, and perhaps even pharmaceutical companies, to donate, say, $100 000 a year as a prize for the most useful advance in the delivery of care that has been taken and grafted into the system in a particular country or group of countries? The work of that person, group or consortium awarded the prize could then be published in one of the prestigious journals. People would take note, and strive to do the same.

Reference

(1) Thomas L. *The Lasker awards. Four decades of scientific medical progress.* New York: Raven Press, 1986.

DECISION-MAKING, CONTROL AND IMPLEMENTATION OF RESOURCE ALLOCATION

Chairman:
ARNOLD S. RELMAN
Boston MA, USA

A UK view

ROBERT MAXWELL

Secretary (Chief Executive Officer),
The King's Fund, London, UK

I shall give *a* UK view. There are a number of other views which would be considerably more authoritative and might well be different.

I will first examine what has happened in the UK, against the background of what I think has been happening internationally, then discuss the current situation in the UK, and finally look to the future. It is a rather different picture from the one to be given for the USA by Professor Reinhardt. We may be in the same business, but our economic context is different.

The historical background

The UK, of course, was early into the concept of a comprehensive, collective approach to health care provision although Scandinavia was probably first in the field. From the end of the second world war there was no doubt that was what the UK sought to do. Others have followed in one way or another.

The increases in expenditure within the National Health Service (NHS) were a concern from the early days after it was introduced. There was the idea in the Beveridge projections that once a backlog of neglect had been wiped out the service ought to become less rather than more expensive. That did not prove to be the case, and soon both politicians and economists asked why.

The first full survey was the Guillebaud Report in 1956 (1), which concluded—rather to everybody's surprise—that expenditures in the NHS up to that time had decreased relative to gross national product (GNP) rather than increased, from about $3\frac{3}{4}$% at the beginning to about $3\frac{1}{4}$% at that time.* This certainly did not look like an excessive expenditure on the NHS, even though money spending had increased.

*Economists who have analysed national health care expenditures differ in their choice of gross national product (GNP) or gross domestic product (GDP) as the denominator. The resulting differences are relatively small, principally relating to net overseas earnings. For the UK, health care spending as a percentage of GNP is slightly lower than of GDP. In the present paper both figures are used, depending upon the data source.

Health Care Provision under Financial Constraint, edited by T. B. Binns and M. Firth, 1988: Royal Society of Medicine International Congress and Symposium Series No. 115, published by Royal Society of Medicine Services Ltd.

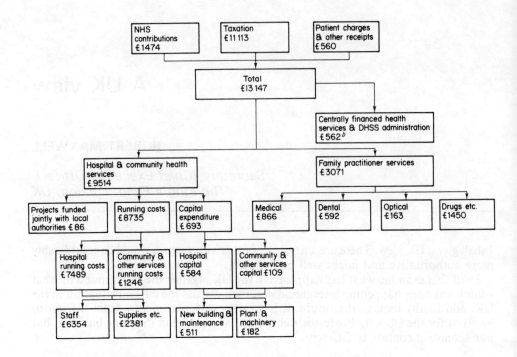

Figure 1. National Health Service funding and expenditure in England, 1983–84 (£ million)[a].

[a] Figures for health authorities and family practitioner committees are derived from their summarized accounts. They are before deduction of direct credits (e.g. receipts from staff for accommodation) and include certain other income and balances as well as funds made available by central government and through patients' charges.

[b] Includes:
A. Accommodation costs previously borne by the PSA (£23).
B. New provision for expenditure on central initiatives to promote development in high priority areas (£9).
C. Additional demand for welfare food (£13).
DHSS = Department of Health and Social Security.
PSA = Property Services Agency.

Table 1

Total expenditure on health care as a percentage of gross domestic product (GDP)

	1960	1965	1970	1975	1980	1983
USA	5·3	6·1	7·6	8·6	9·5	10·8
Sweden	4·7	5·6	7·2	8·0	9·5	9·6
France	4·3	5·3	6·1	7·6	8·5	9·3
Netherlands	3·9	4·4	6·0	7·7	8·3	8·8
West Germany	4·8	5·1	5·6	8·1	8·1	8·2
Canada	5·5	6·1	7·2	7·4	7·3	8·2[a]
Italy	3·9	4·6	5·5	6·7	6·8	7·4
UK	3·9	4·2	4·5	5·5	5·8	6·2

Source: Organization for Economic Co-operation and Development (3).
[a] 1982.

Table 2

Trend in total expenditure on health care as a percentage of gross domestic product (GDP)

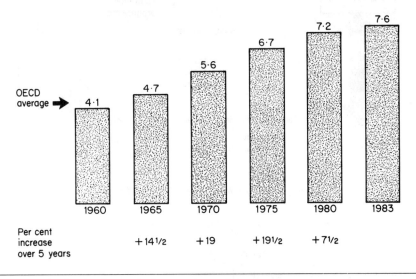

OECD = Organization for Economic Co-operation and Development.

Since then, British governments have been concerned in one way or another about the costs of this large service. The major era of expansion was in the 1960s and early 1970s — the days of the Hospital Plan (2). Major expansions in consultant manpower and the setting up of extensive specialist services in all the regions were planned. Every district was to have a district general hospital with a range of medical departments able to provide acute care in the main specialties. There was also a major — and successful — attempt in the mid-1960s to turn general practice into a service with a future, as opposed to a service with a past, through changes in the pay and contracts of general practitioners.

From 1960 onwards UK spending on health care, in gross domestic product (GDP) terms, grew from 3·9% to 6·2% in 1983. The current figure is somewhat higher, of the order of 6·5%. The Organization for Economic Co-operation and Development (OECD) figures shown in Table 1 attempt to include both public and private spending, for obvious reasons (3).

There has thus been a substantial increase in health care spending since 1960 in the UK. Throughout the same period some very substantial controls were exercised over expenditure increases.

The 1983–84 figures for NHS spending in England, presented by the Department of Health, (Fig. 1) show that of about £13 billion at that time, £9½ billion was going into hospital and community health services, with very tight budget controls, and £3 billion into family practitioner services on a different basis — more demand-led than constrained by global budgets. That does not mean to say that spending through the family practitioner committees is uncontrolled, but that it is controlled in a different way and very much less tightly than through a system of global budgets backed up by manpower and capital expenditure controls, which has always been the position in the NHS in the hospital and community health services.

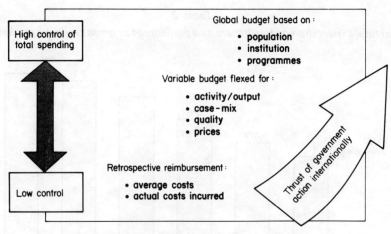

Figure 2. Controlling hospital expenditure.

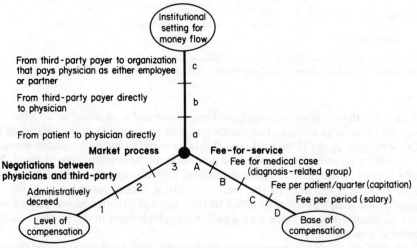

This three-dimensional graph illustrates the possible combinations of the three aspects of physician compensation: base, level, and institutional setting. Each cell is a distinct compensation system. Each country surveyed occupies several cells.

Figure 3. Basic facets of physician compensation system.
Source: Reinhardt (4).

International comparisons

As far as I can estimate, in 1984, in terms of dollars per head, health care spending in the UK was about $400, in the USA just under $1600, and about $1200 in Sweden. The percentage of GDP was 10% or more in the USA and Sweden, compared with 6·2% in the UK. The percentage of that money coming through public, as opposed to private, sources in the UK and Sweden was over 90%, and much less (41%) in the USA.

If we examine the trends in health care spending internationally, in the USA and in most other countries the increases have been bigger, in terms both of money and

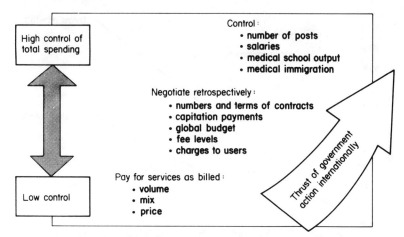

Figure 4. Controlling expenditure on physicians' services.

per cent of GNP/GDP than in the UK. But there has been a slowing down since 1975. Looking at the figures in terms of the average per cent for the OECD countries at roughly 5-year intervals, it is clear that the increases in the period between about 1960 and about 1975, not only in the UK but also elsewhere, were greater proportionately than since then. In other words, there was a long period of sustained growth in health spending in real terms in all western countries. From 1975 onwards the growth has slowed—not necessarily in all countries and not to the same degree, so that the international pattern has become more diverse.

In the earlier period there was a great increase in most countries in coverage of the population and also in the public share of health care spending.

Of course there were also great changes going on within medicine. People talk about the importance of demographic change when discussing impacts on expenditure, but in my view the major impact on expenditure in GNP/GDP terms in modern times has been the way in which medicine itself has changed. That transformation was taking place throughout this period.

Between 1975 and 1980 there has been a different economic and political scenario. Taking average figures for the OECD countries, the expenditure increases, stated as per cent of GDP, were about 20%, 20% and 7½% in the three 5-year periods, 1965–70, 1970–75 and 1975–80, respectively (Table 2).

Regarding hospitals, there have been attempts everywhere to move from a low to a high control situation, from one in which hospitals might be reimbursed in retrospect for all their expenditures on an item-for-service basis, to one that may be related to a prospective budget 'flexed' in certain ways, or to a fixed global budget, as in the UK—one that cannot be changed no matter what happens to workload or prices.

There has thus been a general trend by governments and other third-party payers to try to move from a low to a high control situation relative to hospital spending (Fig. 2).

The same is true of physicians' incomes. Figure 3, taken from a paper by Professor Reinhardt (4), shows that whether we look at the base of compensation for physicians, the level of their compensation, or the institutional setting, there is a variety of ways of handling physician reimbursement. There is a spectrum in terms of compensation from, for example, fee-for-service (a very low control situation) through to a fee-per-period, or a salary (a much higher control situation)—similarly with the way in which the negotiation is done and the setting in which care is delivered.

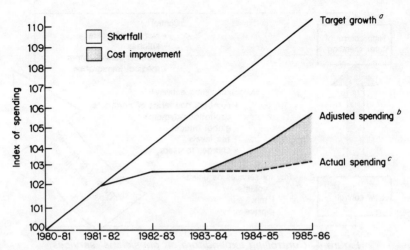

Figure 5. Hospital and community health services trends in current spending, targets and shortfall (£ million at 1985–86 prices).
[a] 2% compound increase over base spending.
[b] Actual spending plus cash-releasing cost improvements at 1985–86 input volume prices.
[c] Actual spending at 1985–86 input volume prices.
Source: Social Services Committee (5).

From 1975 onwards all third-party payers have tried to move outwards on the axes of Fig. 3 with more or less success and more or less impetus on one axis compared with another — but always trying to move from a situation in which physicians determine their own income to one in which somebody else determines it (Fig. 4).

The current situation

The current UK situation is one in which global budgets for hospital and community health services remain in place, subject also to strict cash limits. This is basically a check introduced by government to change from a system of budgeting in real resource terms to one of budgeting in money terms. In other words, the government is now saying for most public services, not only for hospital and community health services, that if the rate of inflation (including public sector wage settlements) is different from the projected rate, then it must come out of service provision and will not be made up by goverment.

Government recognizes in its rhetoric — or at least the Department of Health does — that approximately 2% a year increase is needed to fund demographic change and technological development. I view these figures with much scepticism. They are bargaining counters between the Department of Health and the Treasury. The impact of demographic change upon health expenditures can indeed be calculated, on the assumption that relative utilization by different age groups remains as it is now. We know how the population will change in age terms, and that can be translated through into health services demand and expenditure. Even though older people make much greater demands, the overall effect of demographic change is not actually very dramatic.

When it comes to funding technological development the arguments are entirely different. I do not think that it is possible to predict what technological development will be, what it will cost, or what should be chosen among a range of possibilities. All that can be said is that if we want a service that in some small way tries to creep forward with technological development, that will cost more money—and, almost certainly, whatever extra money we are prepared to put into health services, difficult choices will have to be made.

In recent years, however, this 2%, whether or not it is a good figure, has been more fantasy than fact as far as the UK is concerned. In other words, most health authorities have not received 2% increase in real terms.

Figure 5, taken from a recent report of the Social Services Committee (5), shows the target growth for the period 1980 onwards, based on 2% real growth. It also shows the actual level of spending. The difference between the two is largely explained by the difference between actual wage settlement levels and assumptions about inflation when the budget was formed. Wage settlements tend to run ahead of the estimated levels.

This is all, of course, a kind of confidence bargaining game. Even if it wanted to, government cannot safely predict the wage levels that it believes will actually prevail in the public sector. It can only predict the wage levels at which it is prepared to start the bargaining. Therefore, the final settlements will almost always be higher than the government's initial assumptions.

If government is budgeting on a cash limits basis, this will in itself always tend to erode what official rhetoric says is the money available for development. And that is certainly what has happened in the UK.

Part of the difference is bridged by efficiency savings—the difference between actual and adjusted spending in Fig. 5. The efficiency savings stem from a real attempt by government to introduce into the NHS (and other public services) greater management efficiency. There is no doubt that this initiative has had some impact. The attempts by regions and districts to achieve efficiency savings have resulted in some—but the order of magnitude of the savings actually achieved is much more debatable.

In effect, the government is saying *this* is your money. In arriving at this figure, allowance has been made for the achievements of efficiency savings at a particular level. Therefore, the amount of any growth in real terms depends on the level of the efficiency savings that each health authority is able to realize.

That is clear; it is part of the budget negotiation. What is not clear is what savings have actually been achieved and how they have been used—because there is no means at the moment that I know for identifying and reporting them with any precision.

The situation is also complicated by the differential effect of resource allocation within the NHS. Government policy is to attempt to redress regional differences by transferring money from the more highly endowed regions (which do not always recognize their relative privilege) to the less highly endowed (which certainly feel that they *are* less highly endowed).

That has been happening to some extent. The national policy to try to adjust allocations has had some real effect, and the regions are less dispersed than they were in terms of their distance from national average funding.

This does complicate the situation. The funding from efficiency savings, to which I have referred already, has partly been used for regional redistribution. This means that the pressure to make savings has been softened in 'gaining' regions, and sharpened in the regions that are losing resources. The regions have had to find different levels of efficiency savings from their cost improvement programmes.

There have also been, and continue to be, attempts to improve priority services for the mentally handicapped and the mentally ill, and some shift of services from hospitals to community. All that complicates the funding pattern.

In government policies there is a heavy emphasis on improving efficiency, making management more effective and encouragement of the private sector. There has been a substantial expansion of the private sector, albeit from a very small base, in the acute field.

Table 3
Comparative availability of selected technologies

Renal treatment (patients treated per million)		Heart surgery (operations per million)		CT scanning (inhabitants per scanner) (1000)		Megavolt therapy (inhabitants per radiation unit) (1000)	
Belgium	263	Netherlands	397	Belgium	268	France	136
France	260	Belgium	202	West Germany (N. Rhine)	293	Denmark	182
West Germany (N. Rhine)	250	West Germany (N. Rhine)	190	Netherlands	353	Belgium	220
Italy	239	Denmark	160	Italy	487	Britain	273
Netherlands	212	Italy	154	Greece	812	Netherlands	288
Greece	156	Britain	89	France	1019	Greece	325
Britain	152	Greece	72	Britain	1400	West Germany (N. Rhine)	567

Source: EEC Report (6).

Family practitioner services have remained outside the budget envelope, as defined by cash limits, and remain to some extent demand-led — athough government has tried some measures, such as the limited list of drugs available for prescription, to reduce or control family practitioner service spending.

Recently (the cynics would say in the run up to the last general election), the government has become generous, and announced an increase for next year of 2½% in real terms, and something less than that for the succeeding 2 years. So far as one can see, therefore, the next year or two in the NHS should be easier than the past few years have been.

Issues for the future

The indications, not only in the UK, are of a series of quite substantial future problems.

Lack of investment

The first of these is lack of investment. Anyone walking round our hospitals would be struck by the poor state of their fabric, maintenance and general upkeep, and by the difficulty of getting new equipment. At the moment, we are spending something like 5% of the budget on capital. The figure that used to be assumed in the relatively prosperous days of the 1960s and early 1970s was nearer 10%. I suspect, in capital investment terms, that the UK is at the moment the least well funded of any major health care system.

This not only affects fabric, but also the level of provision in expensive technologies and the (slow) rate at which in the UK they tend to be introduced (Table 3) (6).

Comparing running costs is another matter, but there is no doubt in my mind that we are investing absolutely minimal amounts in capital development of any kind.

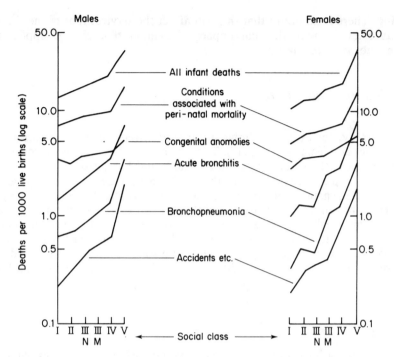

Figure 6. Inequities in health: infant mortality by sex, occupational class and cause of death.
N = non-manual.
M = manual.
Source: Office of Population, Censuses and Surveys (7).

Inertia and constipation

The consequence of lack of investment is what I call 'inertia and constipation'. When there is no growth in spending, the tendency is to stop any kind of development. Everything seizes up.

In logic, what ought to happen is that we should consider what as a nation we can afford to spend on the NHS and how best to use that sum. How we would spend our money now ought to be different from 5 years ago because the nature of medicine has changed during that time.

If there is very low growth, it becomes difficult in management terms to make radical redistributions of resources. What tends to happen is that people take the relatively easy way out of changing as little as possible. Anybody with a new idea or with a new appointment takes years to fight through a system in which all the resources are already committed, and where there are few incentives to disturb the *status quo*.

The elderly

There is also the issue of the ageing population. Whereas the number of over-65s is already stabilizing in the UK, the numbers of over-75s and over-85s are still increasing. There is no doubt that this will affect the services that we need and the expenditure levels required. That impact of demographic change applies to all countries, not only to the UK.

Inequities in health care

Infant mortality, for example, shows substantial differences by occupational class for both males and females (Fig. 6) (7). These kinds of differences across social classes are echoed across the whole spectrum of health and handicap.

Sometimes people try to make a case that the NHS has failed because there are these differences and inequities. I do not accept that. Differences by class are really very small in the NHS in health services demand, but the differences in outcome still remain and represent a major challenge if we are interested in trying to optimize health and minimize handicap. The occupational and social class differences, quite apart from interests of equity, have a marked impact on national health statistics. Improving standards of health for the least fortunate could have a dramatic impact on the national figures.

Choices

There is also increasing disquiet about the difficulties of making choices. At a recent conference I found substantial differences between countries from this standpoint. The West Germans are still saying, from a health insurance point of view, that if they are convinced that any treatment is needed and is effective, it will be funded. That is their national responsibility. In the UK we are saying that, on the contrary, tragic choices are inevitable.

The NHS and the future

As we look ahead, the position for the UK is something like the following. The NHS was set up to achieve certain objectives: comprehensive care of good quality for all, based on need, or (to put it another way) *not* based on money or social class.

The particular model of pursuing these objectives through the NHS served us very well up to the late 1970s — a period of relatively high economic growth generally in the world, and of sustained investment in health care. The NHS enabled us to make people aware that health services have to be provided within economic limits, that choices have to be made, and the whole exercise has to be constrained.

We have now entered a very different era, when constraining excessive growth may be the problem in the USA but is not the problem in Britain. The problem in Britain is how to sustain a public service that has reached beyond the limits of what government is willing to put into it, how to look after its fabric, maintain its quality, and prevent it gradually disintegrating and winding down.

In these circumstances, I am not sure that the strengths of the NHS stand us in the sort of stead for the future that they have offered in the past. It is inevitable that we will be continually in a situation in which governments of any political hue are not prepared to put enough into the NHS to do what is required within it. That means that hard choices have to be made. Among these decisions has to be (implicitly or explicitly) a strategic choice about the principles on which the NHS is based. If everything for everybody is not to be done (which is what the NHS has always said it would do), what are we trying to do and why?

We are bound to take a selective view of the services we are trying to deliver because we simply cannot afford to do everything. The selection will be in terms of (for example) types of technology and quantities of service. I am less sure about selectiveness in terms of income. We have to be extremely careful not to get into a situation where the NHS is simply a poor service, a safety net for those who can afford nothing better, while those who can afford a good service get it elsewhere.

Whatever we decide to do within the NHS we should try to do to a high quality. It is not good enough to settle for a low quality because that is all that can be afforded. If we can do fewer things as a result of settling for high quality, perhaps that is what should be done. The emphasis should be towards the primary care end of the spectrum, with considerable limitations at the high technology end—except in an experimental way.

We have to learn to live with the private sector and make more use of it than has been the case in the past—view it not as an enemy, which is how it is so often viewed within the NHS, but as a way in which services that will not be available within the NHS can be provided.

There have been some real gains from the tightening of efficiency by Mrs Thatcher's administration in the last 5 years. Let me not mislead anybody about that. My belief is that there have been some real gains: management is better than it was, and the administrative system is tighter. *But* we have to build on that in order to go into the future. Among other things, this requires a new vision of what we are trying to do in public services.

References

(1) *Report of the Committee of Enquiry into the Cost of the National Health Service.* (Guillebaud CW, chairman). Cmnd 9663. London: Her Majesty's Stationery Office, 1956 (Jan).

(2) *A hospital plan for England and Wales.* Cmnd 1604. London: Her Majesty's Stationery Office, 1962 (Jan).

(3) Organization for Economic Co-operation and Development. *Measuring health care 1960–83.* OECD Social Policy Studies no. 2. Paris: OECD, 1985.

(4) Reinhardt UE. The compensation of physicians: approaches used in foreign countries. *Quality Rev Bull* 1985; **11**: 368.

(5) Social Services Committee of the House of Commons. 4th report, Session 1985–6. *Public expenditure on the social services*; Vol. 1. Cmnd 387–1. London: Her Majesty's Stationery Office, 1986 July 2: xvii (Fig. 1).

(6) Commission of the European Communities. *Advanced and expensive medical technology in the member states of the European Community: legislation, policy and costs.* Internal EEC working document, V/943/82-EN, 1982 Dec 13.

(7) Office of Population, Censuses and Surveys. *Occupational mortality 1970–1972, England and Wales.* Decennial supplement. Series DS no. 1. London: Her Majesty's Stationery Office, 1978: 158.

A US view:
the resource transfer from patients to providers of health services

UWE E. REINHARDT

*James Madison Professor of Political Economy,
Princeton University, Princeton NJ, USA*

Introduction

Decisions regarding the allocation of resources in health care can be viewed through very different disciplinary prisms, each with its own instructive refraction.

For example, the process may be styled simply as an exchange of favors among members of society—in this case, between the providers of health services and the rest of society. So viewed, decisions on the allocation of health care resources boil down to bargaining over the distribution of economic privilege among members of society. Economists find themselves particularly comfortable with that view. It will serve as an analytic framework for this paper.

People not reared in the economist's culture may look with dismay upon this narrow and philistine perspective. Granted, it does eclipse the rich complexity of the human interactions by which resources are actually allocated to and within the health care sector. The purpose of taking the narrower view here, however, is not to deny these many other dimensions of the process, nor even to denigrate their importance. It is merely to move the spotlight from relatively well-lit ground to terrain obscured amidst the more benign imagery typically conjured up in discussions on resource allocation in health care. Specifically to be explored in this paper is the question of what resource transfer society must make to the providers of health care in return for the latters' ministrations.

Health care as an exchange of favors

If the process of health care is styled as an exchange of favors, it can be described by two distinct transfers of resources, namely:

    (1) Transfer of real health care resources (physician time, drugs, band aids, and so on) from the providers of health care to patients.

Health Care Provision under Financial Constraint, edited by T. B. Binns and M. Firth, 1988: Royal Society of Medicine International Congress and Symposium Series No. 115, published by Royal Society of Medicine Services Ltd.

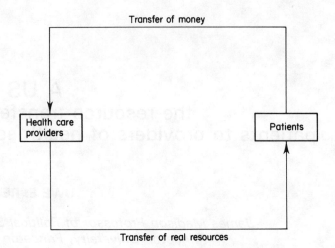

Figure 1. The bilateral transfer of resources in health care.

(2) Reverse transfer of money, that is, generalized claims to real resources (houses, automobiles, vacations, and so on) from patients to providers.

Figure 1 illustrates these resource flows graphically. The first is intended to enhance the patient's health status. It is the transfer we usually have in mind when we discuss the topic of 'resource allocation in health care'. Under this rubric we may ponder weighty issues such as the allocation of resources to preventive and curative care, to different age groups and to terminally ill people. We also tend to think of this transfer when we discuss the somber topic of 'rationing' in health care.

The second resource transfer shown in Fig. 1 is intended to enhance the providers' economic status. Because professionals find it embarrassing to dwell upon that transfer, and laymen are loath to embarrass professionals, this transfer is usually relegated to obscurity at conferences on resource allocation in health care. It is a pity, because that transfer is fascinating in its own right.

In the aggregate, the money transfer from society to providers represents their written entitlement to carve from that proverbial pie known as the gross national product (GNP)—that collection of all good things produced by an economy in a given year—a piece of a certain size. In the USA, for example, the slice of the GNP handed over to American providers of health care collectively is now close to 11%. In France and Canada, it is between 8% and 9%, and in Japan and the UK only about 6%.

What is the relationship between these two resource transfers? Are they so tightly linked that, in discussions on health care policy, one resource flow can be viewed as a proxy for the other?

The providers of health care certainly seem either to think, or at least to pretend to think, that is possible. Hence, any proposal to constrain the money flow from patients to providers (upper loop, Fig. 1) is immediately decried as a proposal to limit the flow of real health care resources from providers to patients (lower loop). It is branded as an attempt to 'ration' health care.

Conversely, it is usually pretended by the providers of health care that any increase in the money flow to them—for example, supplementation of the British National Health Service (NHS) through private health insurance or increases in the American Medicare budget—would lead *ipso facto* to a proportionate increase in the real health

Table 1

Comparison of 1984 medical fees, USA and Canada

Procedure	Prevailing charges under Medicare, California ($)	Median fees, USA ($)	Fees, Ontario ($ Canadian)
ECG (professional charges only)	40	35	7
Pacemaker insertion	1815	1200	334
Appendectomy	734	600	259
Lens extraction	1341	—	368
Hysterectomy	1393	901	503
Coronary artery bypass	5200	—	1300

Source: Reinhardt (2) (Table 2).

care resources made available to patients.* But ought we to posit such a tight linkage between the two resource transfers?

Suppose, for example, that a nation had budgeted somehow for a finite transfer of money to the providers of health care during a given year. Exactly what resources this budget would make available to patients obviously would depend upon the money transfer per unit of real health care resource that providers insisted upon extracting from society. More crudely put, it depends upon the lifestyle that providers seek to carve out for themselves from the health care process. If the providers can insist somehow upon driving Cadillacs or Rolls Royces, the allocated money budget will make available to patients fewer real health care resources than if providers could be induced to be content with Hondas or Chevrolets. The relationship between the upper and the lower loops in Fig. 1 is as simple—and as complex—as that.

In the context of the British health system, for example, supplementation of NHS funds through private insurance may serve, in the first instance, merely to enhance the lifestyles of British health care providers and to redistribute a given set of real health care resources from poorer to better off British patients. In the longer run, the monetary supplementation may or may not bring added real resources to patients. It would depend upon the money transfer per unit of real resource that providers could extract from it.

That the preceding observations are also germane to the North American scene can be illustrated with Table 1, which shows the fees charged by physicians in the USA and in Canada for a variety of standard surgical interventions.

A budget allocation of $1 million obviously buys far more operations of a given type in Canada than in the USA, and far fewer such operations in California than in most other regions of the country. In 1984, for example, the federal Medicare program for the aged paid surgeons in Mississippi a maximum fee of $2200 for a coronary bypass, while surgeons in California were paid $5000 for the procedure, and those in New York, $6000. In general, surgical fees in New York City tend to be twice those charged in Philadelphia (2). For some surgical and non-surgical procedures, fees across the USA may vary by a factor as high as 10.

Even more remarkable is the variation in the hourly remuneration earned by American physicians in different specialties. For certain surgical specialties—e.g. ophthalmology and thoracic surgery—prevailing fees imply an hourly remuneration at least 10-fold that paid to primary care physicians for non-procedural care.

*In their perceptive essay on the public/private mix in health care, McLachlan and Maynard also wonder openly just what objectives such supplementation would serve in the end (1).

Differences in practice costs or even in the general cost of living cannot fully explain the observed variations in fees and hourly remuneration. These variations remain a perplexing mystery among both researchers and policy makers, and even among physicians themselves, and naturally lead to questions of the following sort. Let us suppose the Medicare program could somehow reduce its monetary allocation for coronary bypass surgery in California below previous levels, so that the annual rate of such operations in California could be maintained only if Californian surgeons were content with a money transfer per operation equal to, say, the US median fee. Would that budgetary move necessarily *have* to lead to 'rationing' of coronary bypasses in California—and, if it did, who would be to blame for that rationing?

This line of questioning is sharpened if we contemplate the data presented in Table 2, which represent charges for diagnostic tests ordered by a physician during one visit for a patient employed by the Caterpillar Tractor Company (CTCO)—a company which funds and administers its own health insurance program for employees. Table 2 shows, first, the amounts that the physician billed the company for that patient and, secondly, the amounts he was charged by the laboratory that processed the tests. Depending upon whether or not the physician enjoys a volume discount, his mark-up over costs was either $298 on costs of $190 (156% of costs) or $374 on costs of $114 (328% of costs). If now the CTCO sought to reduce this mark-up to, say, a mere 100% over costs, could the firm's cost-containment program be fairly accused of rationing health care?

These questions can be further broadened to the entire American health care scene. Throughout the 1980s the providers of health care in the USA have loudly lamented sundry meek attempts at cost-containment by government and business. There have been dark hints that such policies will inevitably push the US health sector down to the level of rationing practiced by the much loathed British NHS (see 3).

Table 2

Charges to insurer and costs to the physician for a series of diagnostic tests ordered for one patient during one office visit

Test	Billed by physician to CTCO ($)	Charge to physician by laboratory ($)
Chem 23	30	10
High-density lipoprotein (HDL)	60	included in Chem 23
Electrolytes	40	included in Chem 23
RA factor	18	8
Sedimentation rate	20	7
Thyroid panel	60	14
Thyroid-stimulating hormone (TSH)	60	37
Estrogen	90	53
Progesterone	80	49
Complete blood count	20	6·50
Urine analysis	10	5·50
Total	488	190
Net mark-up (profit)	298	

Note: The mail order laboratory's common practice is to discount charges by 40% to physicians with any volume. If this is the case here, then the (60% × $190 = $114) charge on $488, billed to insurance as − $114, equals net mark-up of $374 on *one* patient.
Source: In-house data supplied by the Caterpillar Tractor Company.
CTCO = Caterpillar Tractor Company.

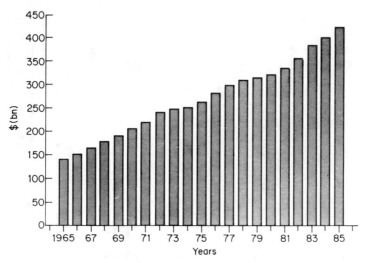

Figure 2. National health expenditures (in constant 1985 dollars).
Sources: Data on national health expenditures from the Health Care Financing Administration of the US Department of Health and Human Services (6).
Data on the consumer price index, which was used to convert the expenditure series into constant dollars, from the Economic Report of the President (7).

There has, in fact, been a marked reduction in hospital admissions and in average length of stay per admission in the USA since 1980. Between 1980 and 1985 the number of hospital days per capita in the USA has fallen by about 25%. There has also been a reduction in the number of physician visits per capita. There have appeared in newspapers throughout the country disturbing anecdotes of outright denial of critically needed health care for want of the patient's ability to pay for that care. The following vignettes, taken from the prestigious *The Wall Street Journal* (4), a newspaper not given to either Yankee bashing or Fabianism, are illustrative of such rationing:

A 32-year old accident victim lies unconscious in a Florida hospital that has no neurosurgeon available. But two larger hospitals with neurosurgeons refuse to accept him upon learning that there is no guarantee that his bill will be paid.

A pediatrician in a Rock Hill, SC, hospital wants to transfer a comatose 3-year old girl to a better equipped urban medical center. But her family has no health insurance and two hospitals refuse to take her in. A hospital 100 miles away finally accepts her.

Such vignettes take on poignancy when it is recalled that American health care providers also lament an ever-growing physician surplus and a veritable glut of hospital beds. The nation is literally rationing resources of which it has too many.*

The headline by which *The Wall Street Journal* introduced these sad stories read, 'Hospitals in cost squeeze "dump" more patients who can't pay bills'. It conveys the impression that American society has drastically reduced the money flow to its health care providers, forcing the latter to reduce commensurately the flow of real resources to patients (with much regret, one would assume).

*Just how representative such anecdotes are of American health care in general is anybody's guess. Curiously, the issue is somewhat under-researched, perhaps because it is so embarrassing. It *is* known that between 30 and 35 million Americans have no health insurance at some time during the year. Although some of these persons might be able to afford adequate health insurance, and most of them do not fall ill in a given year, a nationwide survey undertaken in 1982 by the Robert Wood Johnson Foundation suggested that as many as 1 million Americans may have been denied needed health care in that year for want of ability to pay (5).

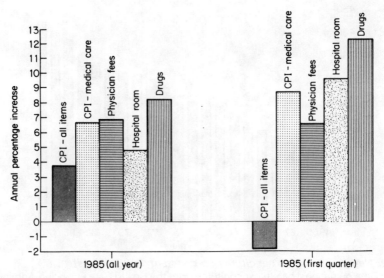

Figure 3. Inflation: consumer price index (CPI) (total) vs consumer price index (medical care) (1985 and first quarter 1986).
Source: US Bureau of Labor Statistics.
CPI = Consumer Price Index.

In fact, there has been no such reduction in the aggregate money flow. On the contrary, that flow has increased apace since 1980, whether it is measured in current dollars, in constant purchasing-power dollars, or by the percentage of GNP devoted to health care (Fig. 2). It is very probable that this percentage will come close to or even exceed 11% in 1986, having risen from 9·1% in 1980.

The driving force behind this increase in national health expenditures appears to have been rapid increases in the prices (i.e. in the money transfer per unit of health resource) that providers of health care have been able to extract from patients or third-party payers (Fig. 3). During the 1970s, these prices tended to increase roughly in step with general price inflation. Since 1980, they have increased at between two and three times the rate of the general price level. These price increases have been sufficient to more than offset whatever reduction there has been in the number of health services delivered to patients. Who should be blamed for such rationing of real health care resources as unquestionably now takes place in America is an intriguing question.

As noted earlier, Canada now devotes somewhere between 8% and 9% of its GNP to health care. In return for that transfer, *all* Canadians are assured access to needed health services on equal terms. Although there may be some queuing for elective surgery, it is inconceivable that critically ill patients in Canada would ever be denied access to available health services, most assuredly not within sight of empty beds and underemployed doctors.*

In view of the Canadian data, there is the temptation to pose American health care providers the following indelicate questions. In return for the much higher allocation of financial resources from American society as a whole to American providers collectively, do the latter return to society a commensurately superior flow of real health care resources? If so, precisely what are the extras, and why is it that

*For an excellent survey of the Canadian health system see Iglehart (8).

so many Americans are still denied dignified access to a health system that regularly flatters itself on being 'the best in the world'?*

Resolution of conflict over resource allocation in health care

A further question emerges from the preceding observations, namely, does there exist an objectively determinable 'proper' relationship between the two resource transfers in Fig. 1 and, if so, what mechanism best assures its establishment? Table 3, for example, suggests that the generosity of nations towards their physicians varies considerably. The table raises the question whether British physicians are underpaid or American physicians overpaid, or whether both might be the case. Analogous questions could be raised regarding the incomes earned by other direct or indirect providers of health care—for example, the rates of return to assets and to equity earned in the manufacture of drugs, appliances and equipment, the lifestyles that health care bestows upon the executives of such manufacturers, or the incomes earned by the non-physician health workers.

Table 3

Net pre-tax practice income of general practitioners (GPs) as a multiple of average employee compensation and gross domestic product (GDP) per capita (ca. 1978)

| Country | Ratio of physician net income to: | |
	Average employee compensation	GDP per capita
West Germany (GPs)	4·7	7·4
USA (all doctors)	4·5[a]	6·5
(GPs)	3·9	5·6
Japan (all doctors)	3·8[b]	6·2
France (GPs)	2·8	4·5
Great Britain (GPs)	2·1	4·3
Italy (GPs)	1·8	3·8

[a] Relatively few American physicians are GPs, and these earn relatively low incomes. For all American physicians the ratio was 4·5 and 4·6 in 1975 and 1983, respectively.
[b] For Japan, the numbers represent the 1975 income of all physicians.
Source: Data for Japan from Nishimura (9) (Table A-4).
Data for all other countries from BASYS (10) (Table D.10).

The standards set by freely competitive markets

Economists are probably the only professionals who would even pretend to be able to answer these questions objectively. Those economists bold enough to make that pretense draw their insights from a hypothetical world populated by well-informed,

---

*'Dignified' in this context means that patients are not forced to approach doctors and hospitals as uninsured health care beggars hoping for unpredictable professional *noblesse oblige*, but as patients whose bill will be paid and will not devastate their household budget.

rational adults who use their initial endowments with productive resources (or with generalized purchasing power) in the production of widgets, gidgets, gadges and gloobs that are traded freely among these well-informed, rational adults in a multitude of mutually beneficial exchanges. Widgets, gidgets, gadges and gloobs are imaginary goods or services that share the one common characteristic that their potential purchasers can always accurately assess *ex ante* what effect their acquisition would have on their own welfare. Furthermore, they are simple enough that potential purchasers can consistently rank alternative bundles of them in terms of preference. If the effect cannot be precisely predicted, at least it can be accurately assessed actuarially.

If, in this hypothetical world, both the offerers of these commodities and their potential purchasers can freely enter the giant auction markets in which the commodities are exchanged, and public authorities make sure that individuals can freely choose to trade with whomever they please in a civilized manner, it can be assumed that each such trade will be mutually beneficial and, as such, have passed an appropriate benefit-cost test by both traders. Furthermore, it can be shown that the ultimate distribution of commodities among members of society will be efficient in the sense that no person can be made better off by further redistribution without making someone else worse off.

Finally, on the crucial (although much overlooked) assumption that the initial distribution of endowments with productive resources (or generalized purchasing power) among members of society before the onset of the auction has been *just,** the ultimate distribution of widgets, gidgets, gadges and gloobs among members of society after the auction might be judged not only *efficient*, but also *optimal* in the sense that it is just.

In this hypothetical world, the imagined giant auction would, of course, automatically determine the proper absolute sizes of the two resource transfers that would be the analogs of the two pipes in Fig. 1. If the absolute sizes of the transfers are proper, so must be their relative size, that is, the reward the providers of a particular commodity have obtained in exchange for that commodity. If, during a given period, gloobs had been in vogue, those individuals who had chosen to specialize in the production of gloobs would obviously have been able to extract relatively large resource transfers of widgets, gidgets or gadges per gloob surrendered in trade. In the end, these individuals would be relatively better off than might be offerers of, say, gidgets, which might have been out of favour at the time of the auction. Such inequality in economic status in the final, optimal state would clearly not be unjust under the postulated assumptions, and might be judged objectively as 'appropriate'.

Arbitration in the real world

Can this hypothetical world instruct us on the proper relationship between the two transfer pipes in Fig. 1? In other words, is the commodity 'health care' sufficiently similar to the imaginary widgets, gidgets, gadges or gloobs to let a freely competitive market arbitrate the inevitable conflict over resource allocation inherent in the process of health care?

---

*It is assumed that, if the distribution was not just to begin with, appropriate lump sum transfers of initial resource endowments will have been made to make the distribution just before production and exchange take place.

Some economists — for example, the British Lees (11), the American Friedman (12) and sundry of their libertarian disciples — clearly think so. On occasion, many physicians on both sides of the Atlantic also profess to think so although, typically, they change their mind very quickly when it is proposed that non-physician health professionals be allowed to compete freely with them for patients — that is, that professional licensure be abolished, as Friedman, for one, has openly advocated (13).*

The world at large, alas, does not seem to share the libertarian's vision for health care. At this time, no country seems prepared to surrender its health care system completely to arbitration by unfettered market forces, not even the self-professed market devotees in the Thatcher or Reagan governments. Could it be, then, that a handful of libertarian economists have it right nevertheless, and the remaining billions of people on earth simply have it wrong — or might the obverse be more nearly the case?

To a thoughtful person, the catalog of reasons for the worldwide aversion to unfettered market arbitration in health care will be apparent in the very description of the hypothetical world from which libertarian thinkers draw their insights.† First and foremost is the realization that, with the income distributions typical of modern societies, a free market in health care would lead to an ethically offensive distribution of health services among members of society. Although, in principle, that problem could be avoided with appropriate redistributions of generalized purchasing power, in fact no society appears to be willing to tolerate the implied large transfers of income, some of which might be diverted by the recipients into directions not desired by the donors. To be sure, vouchers valid only in exchange for health care could preclude such diversions, but the fact that, in a free market, well-to-do households could top off vouchers with money and thus outbid lower-income households appears to have made vouchers suspect as well. In any event, no society has so far seriously entertained the voucher-cum-free-market approach either. (That is not to say, of course, that vouchers have no place in a more generally regulated health care market.)

Eventually, even libertarians must mature to the realization that certain ethical and political constraints border on states of nature. It appears that, for better or for worse, the two resource transfers in health care will always be determined in 'quasi-markets' in which bargaining over their absolute and relative magnitude is delegated substantially from individuals to larger collectives who do their bidding within a set of both market and political constraints. To be negotiated in these quasi-markets is not only the size of the monetary transfer per unit of real health care resource transferred to patients but also, of course, the quantity of real resources that providers may transfer to patients.

Decisions on resource allocation in *quasi-markets*

The real-resource transfer from providers to patients

Although physicians and hospitals quite understandably resent second-guessing of their clinical decisions, no country now seems content to entrust the allocation of resources from providers to patients solely to the privacy of the doctor-patient relationship. Even the ostensibly market-oriented health policy of President Reagan,

---

*In this connection, illumination and amusement may be found in the present author's 'Table manners at the health care feast' (14).

†For an elegant and devastating critique of the pure market approach, see Culyer (15).

for example, calls for strict external monitoring of that transfer through so-called peer review organizations which perform that regulatory function under government contract. The American business community, too, has come to embrace these regulatory interventions in its own dealing with doctors and hospitals. In the face of pervasive excess capacity in the American health system—a phenomenon perceived by government and business as an excess demand for health care incomes—American physicians and hospitals appear to have lost society's erstwhile trust in them.

In Great Britain the transfer of resources from providers to patients is also regulated, but primarily by politically determined limits on the overall capacity of the health system. One suspects that, because of this externally imposed limit on capacity, there is much less need in Great Britain for the rather direct and often grating regulatory interventions now *de rigeur* in American health care.

Herein lies an irony that ought not to escape either American or British physicians, that the less tightly society regulates the overall capacity of a health system and the providers' economic freedom* to price their services as they see fit, the more direct appears to be the private or public payer's regulatory intrusion into the treatment of individual patients. Thus, in fighting as tenaciously as they have for the principle of free enterprise in medicine, American physicians seem unwittingly to have surrendered much of their clinical freedom. Perhaps the trade-off was worth it.

With abiding loyalty to both ideology and preferred analytic structure, some economists may well argue that the lower loop in Fig. 1 could safely be left to individual patients and providers if only society permitted patients to bear an appreciable share of the cost of their treatments at point of service. These economists, and their allies in the medical profession, could base their case on multiple regression analyses that have demonstrated rather convincingly that the price borne by patients at point of service does tend to influence the choice whether or not to contact the medical system. (However, that price does not appear to induce patients to shop for low-cost providers once the decision to seek medical help has been made, nor does it seem to influence the resource intensity of hospital treatment once the decision to seek admission to a hospital has been made (see 16,17).)

These multiple regressions, however, represent small victories at the fringes of a much greater challenge, namely, to explain, with appeal to consumer-choice theory, the remarkably large variations in health care utilization per capita identified by the American physician and epidemiologist, John Wennberg (18). Wennberg's analyses have shown that age-sex adjusted utilization rates for a host of common surgical procedures—e.g. tonsillectomy, hysterectomy or open-heart surgery—vary by factors of up to six among regions in the USA, with no discernible link to health status before or after. So far, the only widely accepted explanation of the phenomenon has been that it reflects physicians' 'preferred practice style'. In the face of these data, and of their explanation so far, neither public nor private insurers are confident any longer that mere cost-sharing by patients will ever create sufficient countervailing power among patients to entrust to them and their physicians the lower pipe in Fig. 1. (There is the added problem that close to 75% of total national health expenditures in any given year is accounted for by only about 10% of the population. The degree of cost-sharing that can be loaded on to these relatively few, sick individuals is limited.) American physicians must expect that resource flow to be ever more closely monitored and regulated by outsiders as, directly or indirectly, it is almost everywhere else in the world.

---

*By 'economic' freedom, in contrast to 'clinical' freedom, is meant the power to set the money transfer per unit of service.

The money transfer per unit of real health care resource

Bargaining in quasi-markets over the monetary transfer per unit of real health care resources (e.g. the remuneration per physician hour) permits a wide range of alternative transfers and associated lifestyles, none of which can be judged either optimal or clearly wrong.

The relative generosity of the transfer will be strongly influenced by the structure of the quasi-market in which bargaining takes place. Other things being equal, that structure depends upon the relative number of actors on each side of the bargaining table. If the structure is *monopsonistic* (one or a few organized buyers/payers pitted against numerous independently competing providers), the transfers to providers are likely to be lean. If the structure is *monopolistic* (one or a few organized sellers pitted against numerous independently competing buyers/payers), the transfer is likely to be lush. In between are bilateral monopolies, in which one or a few organized buyers/payers are pitted against one or a few organized providers. Moral judgments on the relative size of the money transfers to providers thus implicitly involve us in moral judgments on these alternative market structures.

Under the British system, for example, the predominant weight of bargaining power appears to have been amassed by society's representative, the government's NHS. If that assessment is valid, the health care incomes earned in Great Britain are likely to have been pushed fairly far down towards the minimum dictated by market forces. That minimum is a transfer just large enough to attract the (politically) desired quantity of real resources into the health system. Whether this asymmetric market structure is fair to the providers of health care resources is arguable, but the algorithm appears feasible within prevailing market constraints — which is what matters in the end.

Under the American system, by contrast, the predominant bargaining power has hitherto rested with the providers of health services. Until very recently, these providers had the luxury of transacting with patients who were largely insulated by insurance from the providers' prices, and with a myriad of independent private insurers none of whom had sufficient market power over any one provider to bargain effectively over prices. Furthermore, the political process in the USA is such that public sector programs (e.g. the Medicare program for the aged and the Medicaid program for the poor) have had to adapt their terms of trade to the terms worked out in the provider-dominated private sector. Consequently, the money transfers per unit of real health care resource in the USA have been high by international standards — so high, in fact, that they have sucked into the American health care sector a troublesome surplus of human and non-human resources eager to do well by doing good.

These handsome money transfers, however, now seem to be approaching the upper limit tolerated by private market forces and political constraints. Their very size, and the surplus capacity they have begotten, have led private and public insurers to search vigorously for increased market power over these resource transfers through monopsonistic procurement practices.* If such efforts are successful, American providers of health care may yet have to switch from their proverbial Cadillacs to Chevrolets although, as noted, they have so far been able to resist that onslaught on their incomes.

Somewhere in between the British and the traditional American arbitration systems lie the Canadian, West German and French systems. Under these systems, large

---

*Manifestations of these efforts are the so-called health maintenance organizations and preferred provider organizations, both of which are designed to reduce both the transfer of real health care resources to patients and the money transfer per unit of real resource.

aggregates of purchasers (provincial governments in Canada, and sickness funds in France and West Germany) bargain collectively and in more or less good faith with large aggregates of providers (regional and national associations of physicians and hospitals), subject once again to outer boundaries set by free market forces and by political constraints.

It will be recalled that the slice of their GNP that Canada and France surrender to their providers of health care ranges between 8% and 9% of the total pie; that is, somewhere between the 6% or so in Great Britain and the close to 11% in the USA. On the quite unscientific but comforting thought that the 'proper' remuneration of providers may lie somewhere between the British and American extremes, perhaps the quasi-markets operated by these other systems deserve a closer look in the years ahead.

Summary and conclusion

My objective has been to highlight a much neglected facet of resource allocation in health care: how society decides what lifestyle the providers of health care may extract, directly or indirectly, from their patients' pocket books. For any given slice of GNP that society pays for health care, the quantity of real health care resources made available to patients obviously varies inversely with the lifestyles among providers which that GNP slice must support.

These reflections are triggered by a vexing paradox. Conference after conference in the USA is devoted to the agonizing choices forced upon American health care by the contraction of resources. Remarkably, few speakers ask precisely what resource flow is being contracted. The meetings proceed largely in a data-free environment.

As seen in Fig. 2, the flow of funds to American providers of health care increased rapidly after 1980, just when they began in earnest to complain of contracting resources and to turn away those hapless people too poor to pay. So far, the incomes of American health care providers have hardly been impaired. On average, the profit margins earned by hospitals have attained historic highs. Physicians still earn about 4·5 times more than the average employee. In July/August 1986, the trade journal *IN VIVO* reported that the revenues of the nation's 50 largest health-related companies increased at an annual compound rate of 11% between 1982 and 1985 (when nominal GNP grew at only 8% per year) (19).

What has been contracting is thus not society's allocation of generalized purchasing power to the providers of health care, but its ability to extract from them in return an equitable distribution of real health care resources among the nation's sick. What is needed to solve that problem—if solve it we wish—is not yet more funds flowing from society to providers, but a system capable of redirecting real health care resources from those who now receive too many to persons who receive perilously too few. What may also be desirable, though not necessarily as crucial, is further discussion on the lifestyles that the health care process needs to support. (We would probably object less to a certain opulence among providers if the health system as a whole were ethically acceptable.)

In an ideal libertarian world, the resolution of these issues could safely be entrusted to the free market, if only society would redistribute adequate amounts of general purchasing power (money) among its members. However, no modern society is willing to adopt that form of arbitration over resource allocation in health care. We therefore must accept that conflict over the distribution of economic privilege in health care will always be arbitrated in quasi-markets, in which administrative decree and political judgment substitute in good part for the proverbial 'invisible hand'. These will never be seen as *fair* by all concerned, but neither is the 'invisible hand', as America's physicians and patients may soon discover, much to their chagrin.

What is needed in health care, then, is an elegant algorithm for muddling through, and the realization by all concerned that muddling through elegantly would be the best of all possible worlds in that sphere. The suggestion was made that, in our search for such an algorithm, we look beyond Great Britain and the USA to Canada or Europe. We might even contemplate the development of an honest two-tier health care system, with one socialized tier for the poor and one libertarian tier for those who want and can afford it. The author has recently recommended such a system to the US Congress (see 20).

References

(1) McLachlan G, Maynard A. The public/private mix in health care. In: McLachlan G, Maynard A, eds. *The public/private mix for health*. London: The Nuffield Provincial Hospitals Trust, 1982: 515–58.
(2) Reinhardt UE. The compensation of physicians: approaches used in foreign countries. *Quality Rev Bull* 1985; **11**: 366–77.
(3) Aaron HJ, Schwartz WB. *The painful prescription: rationing hospital care*. Washington: The Brookings Institution, 1984.
(4) *The Wall Street Journal* 1985 March 8.
(5) The Robert Wood Johnson Foundation. *Updated report on access to health care for the American people*. Princeton NJ: The Robert Wood Johnson Foundation, 1983.
(6) Waldo DR, Levit KR, Lazenby H. National health care expenditures, 1985. *Health Care Financing Rev* 1986; **8** (1): 13 (Table 1).
(7) *Economic Report of the President*. Washington: US Government Printing Office, 1986.
(8) Iglehart JK. Canada's health care system (1). *N Engl J Med* 1986; **315**: 202–8.
(9) Nishimura S. Physician manpower allocation and the rising cost of health care. *Kyoto University Economic Rev* 1981; **51**: 36–51.
(10) BASYS. Die Wirkungen von Verguetungssystemen auf die Einkommen der Aerzte, die Preise und auf die Struktur aertzlicher Leistungen im internationalen Vergleich. Mimeographed draft. Augsburg: BASYS GmbH, 1986 (May).
(11) Lees DS. Health through choice. In: Harris R, ed. *Freedom or free-for-all?* London: Institute of Economic Affairs, 1968.
(12) Friedman M. *Capitalism and freedom*. Chicago IL: The University of Chicago Press, 1962.
(13) Friedman M. *Capitalism and freedom*. Chicago IL: The University of Chicago Press, 1962: 158.
(14) Reinhardt UE. Table manners at the health care feast. In: Yaggy D, Anlyan WG, eds. *Financing health care: competition versus regulation*. Cambridge MA: Ballinger Publishing Co, 1982: 13–34.
(15) Culyer A. The NHS and the market: images and reality. In: McLachlan G, Maynard A. *The public/private mix for health*. London: The Nuffield Provincial Hospitals Trust, 1982: 23–56.
(16) Marquis SM. *Cost-sharing and the patient's choice of provider*. Santa Monica CA: The Rand Corporation, 1984.
(17) Newhouse JP, Manning WG, Morris CN, *et al*. Some interim results from a controlled trial of cost sharing in health insurance. *N Engl J Med* 1981; **305**: 1501–7.
(18) Wennberg J, Gittelsohn A. Variations in medical care among small areas. *Sci Am* 1982; **246**: 100–11.
(19) The *IN VIVO* 50: new faces, restructuring revealed in health care's top 50 companies. *IN VIVO* 1986; **17**: 31–6.

(20) Reinhardt UE. *Rationing the nation's health-care surplus: a paradox? Or as American as apple pie?* Testimony before the House Select Committee on Aging, US Congress; hearing on the catastrophe of America's uninsured and underinsured: in search for a US health plan. Mimeographed. Washington: US Government Printing Office, 1986 Sept 12.

Discussion

Professor Butler

Given the original aim of the National Health Service (NHS) not to have money or social status play a role, would it not be inevitable that, if there were a selection of only certain goals to be done very well, those who were better off would simply turn to the private sector to realize those priorities in their lives which were not being fulfilled by the NHS?

Mr Maxwell

What I am presenting is a conundrum. If there are people here who can answer it — particularly economists, because they know the answers to conundrums — I shall be delighted.

Professor Butler is right. There is a basic problem in that, if what seems to be sensible is done, i.e. the NHS provides services for those who are in greatest need, targeting them in that way, it very quickly becomes a separate service for the poor. I was groping for something rather different. For example, the situation genuinely is that for any kind of emergency in the UK we are better served by the NHS than by anything else. If someone has an accident in the street and has to go into hospital for treatment to a head injury, there is absolutely no advantage in the UK in buying private treatment. Indeed, the advantage is in staying public.

I would view that as part of the core concept of a national health service. If we have to restrict treatment, the problem is what to cut off at the edge.

I say with hesitation that I have many questions about several aspects of general practice, but I am not sure whether most people can afford to pay the relatively small amounts that might be involved.

Dr Relman

Mr Maxwell said that he thought the NHS is doing a good job with respect to emergency services — the management of acute services. In my opinion, based on what I have seen of how acute services are handled in the UK, and on what I know about how we in America handle them, on average I would much prefer to take my chance with a random acute illness or injury in the UK than in the USA. I say this even though I am a great admirer of the best in the USA, which is as good as anywhere in the world. We have failed to deal with this problem in America. Acute care there is very variable, unpredictable and not always even available to those who need it.

Professor Butler

The problem, though, is that in the future so much of it will be chronic care and not emergencies and acute care. It is that increasingly expanding margin to which Mr Maxwell refers that troubles me.

Dr Relman

I feel that we are on the verge of solving the conundrum — if we could only start another conference where this one will end. We are groping for something that will combine all the lessons, deal with all the obvious inadequacies of both our systems, supplement the strengths, combine the wisdom and produce something better.

Professor Alwyn Smith

May I suggest that, if Dr Relman is contemplating having an acute medical emergency while he is in the UK, he stays in London or in another large city. The rosy picture which has been painted certainly does not apply to poor districts in the poor regions of the UK.

The problem, of course, is that if there is a large private sector then the basic resource, physicians, tends to be concentrated in those areas where private practice is most available and most lucrative. Consultant posts can be advertised in the poorer districts of the poorer northern regions and attract no candidates.

Dr Relman

Within sight of the Massachusetts General Hospital in the USA — a very good hospital — some of the worst medical care that could possibly be imagined is delivered routinely. I still insist that with the law of averages I am more likely to survive my diabetic coma or my street accident in the UK than in America — although if I had the choice I would like to be taken to the Massachusetts General Hospital.

Dr Ford

I have been in the business of medical manpower planning for years. When there is an increase in money invested in the health care system in America is there also an increase in numbers or does it just go into the incomes of the medical staffs?

Professor Reinhardt

We are fair about it. It goes into both. There is a rapidly growing supply of physicians which I think is now, on average, about 220 per 100 000. It used to be 150 per 100 000 in 1970. It is projected to go as high as 250 per 100 000 patients. There are regions, such as San Francisco and Washington, DC, where the ratio is much higher, being over 600 physicians per 100 000 in San Francisco, each of them still making quite a good living. The elasticity of the system to absorb them seems rather high.

There is not really any national control on numbers. The American Medical Association (AMA) recently submitted a report in which this was gingerly raised as an issue.* However, it did not have the courage to come up with any remedial action, but just suggested that others could legitimately talk about such limits and that the AMA would not object. There is no real policy about it.

Professor Rabkin

It is only fair to say that those numbers are strongly influenced by government policy. It was the government that decided a few years ago that more doctors were needed. The pipeline, having been built, is only now being slowly turned off. In 40 or 50 years' time when it is realized that there are not enough doctors, the cycle will repeat itself.

Professor Reinhardt

We should never forget the baby boom, and the parents with dreams for their son or daughter, the doctor. If the government turns off the pipeline, they will go to the Caribbean and import education. If the government had never meddled in this business, we would still have roughly the same numbers of doctors, I think.

*An internal, unpublished memorandum that received some press coverage.

REFLECTIONS ON THE PROCEEDINGS

Co-chairmen:
ALAN MAYNARD
York, UK
STUART BONDURANT
Chapel Hill NC, USA

A UK view

ALAN MAYNARD

*Director, Centre for Health Economics,
University of York, York, UK*

I will be perhaps slightly controversial and abrasive in my short overview of this
meeting. If I was a delegate from Mars attending this meeting, I would be confused
about the National Health Service (NHS). Consequently, my purpose here is to increase
that confusion because, from the pedagogical point of view, I think that confusion
may generate thought and the quest for a few solid facts about what is going on in
the UK health care system and the nature of the problems that confront us.

I do this with some trepidation. A couple of years ago I was at a World Heath
Organization meeting, and was put in the role of a rapporteur for a session. It was
an extremely boring session and seemed to have little content. I reported back what
I thought *should* have been said. Afterwards, a Russian said that now he knew what
was meant by 'the freedom of the press'!

My response was to offer him the following quotation:

> If we have a correct theory but merely prate about it, pigeonhole it and do not put it
> into practice, then that theory, however good, is of no significance. (1)

That is clearly the rule on which the Americans operate. Occasionally the British have
followed it, particularly during the last 10 years in the NHS.

Thomas Carlyle in an essay in 1849 (2) described political economy as not 'a gay
science but a dismal science'. That is certainly true, and is certainly the role played
by the economist today in the NHS.

We are trying to emphasize that the productivity of valuable alternatives has to
be foregone, that we have to ration, and that scarcity is unavoidable in our system.
We do not want a debate about scarcity, but a debate about the principles or criteria
for rationing health care. We are not going to use price and ability to pay, so we
have to decide who will die and who will live in what degree of pain and discomfort
using some sort of alternative criteria.

The criteria that have evolved are really to maximize benefits. The argument is
currently about how to identify the benefits of competing therapies, and how to
channel resources into those procedures which give the greatest benefit. Therefore,
we want somehow to measure improvement in health status, and to allocate health
care on the basis of benefit to the patient regardless of ability to pay. To pursue those
sorts of objectives we need information about costs, additional life years and about
the quality of life.

*Health Care Provision under Financial Constraint, edited by T. B. Binns and M. Firth, 1988: Royal
Society of Medicine International Congress and Symposium Series No. 115, published by Royal
Society of Medicine Services Ltd.*

Table 1

The equitable (RAWP) allocation of the UK hospital
(HCHS) budget: changes as a percentage of actual
revenue allocation

	Changes in allocation	
Country	1984–5	1985–6
England	+2·27	+4·11
Wales	+7·56	+0·32
Scotland	−14·94	−19·32
Northern Ireland	−13·65	−26·94

Sources: Maynard and Ludbrook (3); Birch and Maynard (4).
RAWP = Resource Allocation Working Party.
HCHS = Hospital and community health services.

There has been some discussion about quality-adjusted life years (QALYs). I think QALYs are very useful because they concentrate the minds of decision-makers wonderfully. They also concentrate the minds of medical scientists and managers because they have to obtain that sort of cost and outcome data.

It can lead to discussions about whether a year of life at age 44 is equal to or more valuable than a year at age 75 (which Professor Grimley Evans discussed earlier). I think that is a valid point, and an empirical one on which we have done some research at York, showing that people value a year of life in different ways at different stages of their life.

What we are really interested in—and should concentrate on more in our debate on the NHS—is in obtaining information so that we can get cost-QALY data. Many people oppose this sort of approach, and even economists realize that it is less than complete. Indeed, some of us have argued that we should try to analyse quality-adjusted life *months*, because then we could talk about QALMs!

Problems faced by the NHS

Equality

The first problem which I must discuss briefly is equality. Here there is a great deal of difficulty in defining terms and measuring what is going on in our system. From a cynical point of view, many liberal economists argue that health care is relatively ineffective at the margins, and that the poor should have more of it.

The conflict in those two statements is not readily apparent to many people arguing from that point of view. We have a discussion which goes on about inputs and processes, and we have very poor data about what is going on in our system. That data stock, if anything, has become worse during the last 5 or 10 years.

We can see that there are enormous inequalities in our health care system, whether we look at processes, at financing or at outcomes. With regard to financing, we just try to redistribute the hospital budget, but 20–25% of our NHS budget is primary care and no attempt has been made to redistribute the primary care budget.

Furthermore, as I indicated earlier, the NHS is not a *national* health service in the sense that there are four different countries in the UK.

Table 1 indicates what would happen if we began to redistribute the budget. If we look at the combined UK budget of the four constituent parts of the UK and apply the Resource Allocation Working Party (RAWP) formula to the hospital budget, there would be significant losses in Scotland and Northern Ireland, slight gains in Wales (depending upon which year is considered) and also England would gain something (3,4).

When similar data were published in 1981 a surgeon in Glasgow wrote to us saying that he had been a socialist all his life, but this was just too much!

There are thus significant inequalities in the UK health care system, which is a problem about which we still worry.

Compartmentalization

The second problem area is the division of the NHS, which has not been emphasized at this meeting as strongly as perhaps it should have been. There has been a tendency to *discuss* the hospital budget but only *mention* the primary care budget. There has been little discussion about local authority social services or about the informal caring sector, and also how public service activity interacts with it.

There is a hospital budget, a primary care budget, and a local authority budget, all of which to varying degrees are cash-limited and RAWPed, but they tend to operate on independent rules with very little virement between them. There is very little 'bargaining at the margins', as the economists would say. In fact, there is a set of perverse incentives at the margins which enables decision-makers in the two main parts of the NHS budget to shift costs and patients on to one another.

Dr Horder talked about referral rates. General practitioners (GPs) can refer their patients to hospital. For a leisure-maximizing GP, that is a very good way of getting a patient out of the surgery.

Not much is known about those referral rates, but they are known to vary 25-fold between practitioners. Some GPs refer one in four patients to hospital, but little is known about the efficiency of that referral rate and the shifting of costs on to the hospital system from the primary care system.

Costs can also be moved in reverse because perverse incentives operate in that direction too.

I want to emphasize this division of our system and the lack of bargaining strategy between the different sectors. Dr Relman asked why cannot UK hospital consultants get into primary care. Apart from domiciliary visits, there is very little in the way of exchange mechanisms, very little virement between the sectors.

Inefficiency and ignorance

The question of inefficiency and ignorance has been discussed extensively at this meeting. We are in the situation, which was summarized nicely by Victor Fuchs in the *New England Journal of Medicine* (5). He said that 10% of health care probably reduces health status, 10% has no effect, and 80% probably improves it. The problem is that we do not know which therapies lie in each category.

We certainly work with great ignorance, a problem which brings us back to the question of whether we can begin to generate better data, even if still crude, which make our choices more explicit, and which confront doctors, managers and researchers with data which they will probably regard as of dubious scientific value, but which is a challenge to them to improve upon.

Table 2
Cost-QALY data (UK) (£ 1983-4)

Procedure	Cost per QALY
Pacemaker implantation for atrioventricular heart block	700
Hip replacement	750
Valve replacement for aortic stenosis	900
CABG for severe angina with LMD	1040
severe angina with 3VD	1270
moderate angina with LMD	1330
severe angina with 2VD	2280
moderate angina with 3VD	2400
mild angina with LMD	2520
GP advice to stop smoking	167
control of hypertension	1700
control of total serum cholesterol	1700
Kidney transplant	3200
Heart transplant	5000
Hospital haemodialysis	14 000

Source: Williams (6,7).
QALY = quality-adjusted life year.
CABG = coronary artery bypass graft.
LMD = left main coronary artery disease.
VD = vessel disease.
GP = general practitioner.

Table 3
Cost-QALY[a] estimates (North America) ($ 1983)

Procedure	Cost per QALY
CABG for LMD	4200
Neonatal intensive care (1000-1499 g)	4500
T4 (thyroid screening)	6300
Treatment for severe hypertension in males aged $\geqslant$ 40 years (diastolic > 105 mmHg)	19 100
Treatment for mild hypertension (94-105 mmHg)	19 100
Estrogen therapy for post-menopausal symptoms in women without prior hysterectomy	27 000
Neonatal intensive care (500-999 g)	31 800
CABG for 1VD, moderately severe	36 300
School tuberculin testing program	43 700
Continuous ambulatory peritoneal dialysis	47 100
Hospital dialysis	54 000

[a]See Table 2 for key to abbreviations.
Source: Torrance (8).

Cost-QALY measurements

I think that the cost-QALY type of measurements offer crude ways of generating league tables about the costs and benefits of alternative ways of spending scarce health care money.

There has been much reference to some of the data that have been produced. Alan Williams' results for the UK are shown in Table 2 (6,7). Hospital dialysis is extremely expensive, hip replacement is much cheaper. Many routine GP procedures, such as advice to stop smoking, control of hypertension and of serum cholesterol, seem to generate one year of life at very low cost, with no disability or distress, by whatever way quality is measured — i.e. using a very crude measure of quality of life.

There are similar sorts of league tables in other publications. Shown in Table 3 are some North American data collected by Torrance from McMaster (8). This league table shows that neonatal intensive care for very low birth weight, for instance, is a very expensive way of generating QALYs.

A mountain of data is beginning to appear. These data are of course fraught with some difficulties. We have just to accept the difficulties — perhaps what we should be doing is arguing about their resolution.

Problems with QALYs

Evaluation of new therapies

Are new therapies to be allowed on to the market freely? Should they be given a product licence? Are people to be allowed to undertake these large- and small-scale activities without going through some procedure, and funding the research and development? Are there economies of scale? Not very much is known about that.

Validity and consistency

There are arguments about both the validity of, and the consistency between, different quality of life measures. Much work needs to be done there.

Future research

We need to extend the application of existing measures, which is going ahead here. Also, a review and extension of existing quality of life measures to given populations should be undertaken.

The future of the NHS

The great debate that I think will develop in the NHS is whether we are going to use these sorts of criteria and, if not, whether we will continue to allocate resources crudely on the basis of 'shroud waving' and hysteria about children and cancer, and other special groups that advocates want to defend.

What are the implications of trying to improve the efficiency of resource allocation? We will obtain a flow of information about evaluation. This needs to be increased because most decision-making in the NHS is based on fiction rather than fact. We need to use the results of evaluation as a guide for action.

This will clearly generate conflict — conflict about the individual ethic of the doctors and the collective ethic of the economists' view of society. It will generate some interesting problems with regard to the inflexibility of the NHS. Our health service is in no way *national*. There are 192 health authorities in England, let alone the rest of the UK. They are very different from one another; they are not very well regulated. Indeed, in many ways, there is much discretion at the local level.

Considerable inflexibilities confront policy makers, and they will be raised as 'problems'. Dr Forsythe, for instance, discussed nursing 'shortages'. What will have to happen there is clearly a much more flexible use of prices or wages to adjust markets, and much more discussion of substitution possibilities — which, again, have been exploited in the NHS but have not been systematically evaluated.

Specific areas of concern

I would like briefly to comment on some areas where I think we have not been as completely open about the NHS as we need to be.

Primary care

Primary care is a subject about which I have very strong views. I am not sure that GPs are the only people providing primary care. Indeed, the Cumberledge Report, recently published, says that perhaps primary care should be based on a system of the nurse being the first point of contact in the NHS, the nurses being organized on patch (or neighbourhood) systems (9).

My general comment about primary care in the UK is that I would reject totally the assertion of the GPs, collectively and individually, that our primary care system is cost-effective. There are no data to prove that. It is a black box; we have little knowledge of our primary care system, and there has been no systematic evaluation of its costs and processes, let alone outcomes.

Community care

I listened with interest to the discussion about community care, but here again we have been very poor about evaluating the costs and benefits of these particular 'technologies' which are very expensive.

This process which was begun in the mid-1970s by a Labour government has been continued by the present government. It is based on a humane argument that patients should be returned to the community, and on the belief (often implicit) that it is cheaper. There was very great reluctance on the part of the research councils and the Department of Health and Social Security to fund research to evaluate this policy. However, it is quite clear from the available evidence that the costs of community care are very much higher than the costs of institutional care. If we are cynical, we might argue that institutions institutionalize neglect, but that we cannot neglect people when they are living next door in the community.

Mentally handicapped people, for example children, are being discharged from our large hospitals, where their average annual cost of care is about £12 000, and are being deposited in communities, in small units with high quality care in terms of environment, where the cost of that care is £16 000–20 000 per patient per year. The NHS budget cannot meet these costs of 'Rolls Royce' care. This problem has to be confronted, and it is a major problem for the NHS in the next 5 years.

The elderly

Similar sorts of problems exist with regard to the elderly. We have failed to control the social security budget. This has led to a boom in private nursing homes and residential homes. The result is that there are many patients in both those types of home who should not be there. In these cases, it might be much more cost-effective to look after these people in their own homes. They have gone into high-cost care because of the incentives in our system.

Funding

With regard to the funding of the NHS, we have heard various arguments about whether there is enough or too little, and what sort of level it should be. It is about 6% of gross national product (GNP) in the UK—and our GNP is far smaller than in the USA. Per capita, on 1982 exchange rates, the Americans are spending about 2·7 times more than we are.

My reaction to the advocacy of increased funding of the NHS is that I would be happier to hold it at the present level, and squeeze very hard. Dr Rue indicated in her presentation that if the present level of funding is held and we squeeze very hard, we produce increased activity rates. There is much resource wastage in the system. If the budget is constrained very tightly, it concentrates the mind of resource allocators wonderfully. It persuades them that in order to bid for marginal resources they have to evaluate their practices because their claims increasingly have to be based on scientific knowledge and explicit good research rather than on vehement advocacy of their cases.

Conclusions

We need to be rather more scientific. So often during this meeting I have felt that the debate has become value-laden and uninhibited by our ignorance. We have tended to see examples of extrapolation on the basis of a few observations and lots of prejudices. Policy making can—and should—be based more on careful evaluative research. We need cost, quality of life and survival facts. This should be a basis for future action: a joint and urgent venture for doctors and economists alike.

However, I think we have to be realistic. Both in the USA and in the UK we are continually 're-disorganizing' our health care systems. In Britain, we re-disorganized in 1974 and again in 1982. Recently, we have had the Griffiths management changes. Increased activity must not be confused with the production of better outcomes.

This, however, is not a new problem. I will end with a quotation which is on the walls of many NHS managers' offices, and which some of our North American colleagues may not have seen and may find amusing:

We trained very hard, but it seemed that every time we were beginning to form up into teams we would be reorganized. I was to learn later in life that we tend to meet any new situation by reorganizing, and a wonderful method it can be for creating the illusion of progress while producing confusion, inefficiency and demoralization.

The man who wrote that was an administrator (Caius Petronius) for the Emperor Nero, in AD 66. All I can say is *'plus ça change . . .'*.

References

(1) Mao Tse-Tung. *Quotations of Chairman Mao*. Peking: Government Press, 1966.
(2) Carlyle T. Respectable Professors of the Dismal Science [Political Economy]. Latter Day Pamphlets, 1, *The Present Time*, 1849.
(3) Maynard A, Ludbrook A. Applying the resource allocation formulae to the constituent parts of the UK. *Lancet* 1981; **i**: 85–7.
(4) Birch S, Maynard A. *The RAWP review: RAWPing the UK*. Discussion Paper 19. York: Centre for Health Economics, University of York, 1986.
(5) Fuchs VR. The 'rationing' of medical care. *N Engl J Med* 1984; **311**: 1572–3.
(6) Williams A. The economics of coronary artery bypass grafting. *Br Med J* 1985; **291**: 326–9.
(7) Williams A. Screening for risk of CHD: is it a waste of resources? In: Oliver M, Ashley-Miller M, Wood D, eds. *Strategy for screening for risk of coronary heart disease*. Chichester: Wiley, 1987.
(8) Torrance GW. Measurement of health state utilities for economic appraisal: a review. *J Health Econ* 1986; **5**: 1–30.
(9) Department of Health and Social Security. *Neighbourhood nursing: a focus for care*. (The Cumberledge Report). London: Her Majesty's Stationery Office, 1986.

A US view

STUART BONDURANT

Dean, School of Medicine,
The University of North Carolina at Chapel Hill
Chapel Hill NC, USA

I want to begin by reflecting on the very serious matters presented by Professor Reinhardt with respect to the role of the medical profession and the problems of the personal rewards that are built into the system in the USA. It was presented with good humour and great force in an impressive way.

I shall not whine on that at all. I think he is absolutely right. It is a serious problem in the USA — in fact, so serious that a colleague of mine, who was dean of another medical school in the USA, has resigned. He is unwilling to continue to manage the education of students who will go into practice in those circumstances, because of his own feeling about the unethical behavior of some of our physicians.

I doubt whether this is an entirely new phenomenon. There have been those who have perhaps aggrandized their incomes in the system for a very long time. I am persuaded, however, that the industrialization of health care delivery, addressed so eloquently by Dr Relman, has been a very important force in making such behavior more prevalent in the USA. The adoption of the model of a commodity, and the purposeful insertion of competition into the system by the government itself, have relieved physicians of the sense both of responsibility and of delivering a service, and have stimulated behavior which I agree is unconscionable. I am deeply concerned that some of the most precious things in the system are at risk as a result. Dr Relman has also spoken on that in the past.

I am supposed to be addressing the governance, control and implementation of the system. I wish I could see the levers to pull with which to correct the situation — and which are likely to be pulled. I am anticipating slightly by saying that my own judgment is closer to that of Mr Lewin than perhaps to that of Dr Relman and Professor Butler. I think it is unlikely that there will be substantial political changes in the short term which will result in any improvement.

This leads me back to a comment made earlier by Dr Cooper. He gave emphasis to the cultural determinants of our health care systems. It is accurate, I think, to say that, in the limit, it is cultural values — imperfectly expressed and understood — which determine the system. We grapple clumsily with the problems of health care as we do with other great issues of our society. This is because we lack not only a database but also an acceptable and accepted construct and context for reconciling social values, and for adapting real decisions to the social values.

Health Care Provision under Financial Constraint, edited by T. B. Binns and M. Firth, 1988: Royal Society of Medicine International Congress and Symposium Series No. 115, published by Royal Society of Medicine Services Ltd.

304 S. Bondurant

It seems, to me at least, that the problem is greater in the USA. I can think of no more dramatic demonstration of this than Professor Stevens' list of the true goals of the US health care delivery system. It was only at about the seventh position that the list contained anything to do with *health*. The first six of the goals of the delivery system, as cited by her, were quite independent of health. That is a telling and powerful statement of the culture in which we live.

It suggests, too, that some of the organizational, behavioral, technical and resource allocation characteristics of the system are in fact cultural characteristics that transcend the health care system. In order to manipulate those characteristics reflected in the health care system, broad pervasive cultural problems will have to be addressed by our society—which I believe to be unlikely in the short run.

Discouraging though this may be, it seems worthwhile to reflect that the US health care system, with all its deficiencies—and now I am about to whine—is arguably among the more effective social agencies. I think it beats our systems of jurisprudence, agriculture, education, equity ownership, management of the economy and foreign policy—to name just a few others.

I do not make that statement to advocate acceptance of the *status quo*, but only to emphasize that I think we grapple with a problem that may be more serious and more pervasive, more deeply rooted in our culture, than we have acknowledged in our discussions so far. It is also perhaps not so amenable to some of the micro or situational interventions that seem so attractive to us at the moment. I am reminded of another one-liner attributed to H. L. Mencken, to the effect that for every human problem there is a solution which is obvious, simple and wrong!

Let me say a brief word about governance from the US perspective. The matter has been covered very well. Mr Lewin said earlier that planning in the USA is in a shambles. Dr Relman referred to our 'totally disorganized system'. I wish I could say that our system was analogous to the marvellous characteristic that was attributed to Voltaire—that this man was a chaos of clear ideas. Our system is a chaos, but not a chaos of clear components. It is made up of components, each of which is fuzzy in important ways.

Let me say a few words about some of the individual actors as background, perhaps, for future discussion.

In the USA the individual citizen is a powerful force in determining the direction of health care resources. The power of that voice is increasing. Considerations of malpractice and of informed consent are pulling the individual patient into a key role in resource allocation decisions, in my view more than in the past.

Providers of all kinds are obviously important governing agents. They are all now playing a game to maximize some function of value to themselves. Each of the providers has a different agenda of value systems, some of which are noble and some of which, as we have heard, are not so noble. These are in conflict, and there is no central place, to my knowledge, in which these different value systems are in any way reconciled.

There are the so-called 'third parties'—government, corporations, even churches, industry (medical and other kinds)—all pursuing their own values in a quasi-independent manner.

The research enterprise is not trivial. Not only does it drive the economy, but it profoundly influences the medical education of the country because our medical schools are financially and operationally coupled in considerable measure to the research enterprise. This has a powerful effect on the dispersal—perhaps certainly on the premature dispersal—of technologies.

One of the consequences of this is that medical education in the USA, in effect, is a technology advocacy system. Those of us who have worked on curricula are familiar with the difficulties in modifying them to adjust for that.

Then there is the malpractice climate in the USA. The plaintiff's bar, to be specific, is not a trivial actor in the shaping and governance of the health care delivery system.

It will be observed that I have not even mentioned government *qua* government. I mentioned government earlier as a third party, but not government *qua* government.

I cite this list simply to show the number of actors who interact in determining the health care system, without even a single forum in which they communicate, and without coherent behaviour. Those who are responsible for hospitals and other parts of the system live with these difficulties daily.

General discussion

Professor Stevens

A question that has been raised several times at this conference concerns information. In America we have one massive system — massive in terms of resources. Ideally, one would suppose that the competition would give rise to all sorts of information systems, evaluations and so on, both for provider and for consumer needs. In the UK there is a regionalized system, with an overall framework which should also give rise to information and evaluations, particularly in an era of overall cost limits and cost constraints. Yet we keep being very frustrated, not only because we do not have cross-national comparisons (which are also needed) but because we do not have some basic information and evaluation about either system.

The only answer to this which I can devise is that there is indeed a systematic need *not* to know — a systematic bias against information one way or another — that exists somehow within the health care system. Perhaps we do not want to find out so that we do not have to deal with problems — 'we' being in global, health system terms. Perhaps there is a fear of negative findings — that we find out that physicians in hospitals are not doing a very good job. Perhaps nearer home, in terms of academia and those of us in health services research, we prefer to be fashionable and reply to apparent questions of the moment rather than dealing with longer-term issues which are not trendy in this sense.

One useful result from this conference is a real demand for health services research in unfashionable fields which do not necessarily have current relevance, and in areas where there may be points of comparison between our two countries and other countries — as well as in the more obvious areas as discussed by Professor Maynard.

Dr Rue

We have a very large amount of information in the National Health Service (NHS). Its value largely is that it is population based, a very important difference from the kind of information that comes from the USA which is usually based on special studies and surveys.

The information is a mixture of process information, both clinical and management. We have broad costs, but not the sort of item by item costings which there is in the mixture of systems in America.

We have taken a collective decision to try to achieve a common minimum database on a comparable basis for management information by spring 1987. I regret that one of the problems in complying with the deadline is the shortage of capital funds to invest in the necessary technology to effect this. I agree with Professor Maynard that we are now seeing real signs of being under-resourced in terms of capital investment. This is one area in which we do not have the necessary information technology.

Outcome information is much more difficult. Many people are thinking about that. I very much agree with Professor Stevens that health services research is *urgently* required. It has been a casualty. It was classified as an administrative cost for many years, and therefore was a candidate for being reduced. I saw many a health services research group disappear under that particular drive for efficiency. I fully expected that one of the first things that the new management arrangements in the health service would bring about would be some identification of the correct proportion to be spent on health services research. There has been a great silence about it in the last 2 years which I much regret.

Professor Shapiro

Both Professor Maynard and Professor Stevens pointed to an extremely important deficit. I want to stress that it is not all that dismal. There is a considerable body of information in the USA, although much more is needed. Very heavy investment is about to be undertaken, for example, by the National Center for Health Services Research (NCHSR), in conducting what is called the national medical expenditure survey.

The problem that researchers have faced in the USA is that questions posed to them call for a rapid, immediate response, and very often the information has not been available.

Many of us are hoping that here we can talk about a two-tiered system of research: first, research that is very highly targeted with a very rapid turn round, which lays the foundation for the second type, very long-term research on issues that researchers, in collaboration with others, identify as having enduring importance.

For example, I have recently been chairman of a panel, the National Research Council on Statistical Requirements for Health Policy in an Aging Society. Many of the points discussed by Professor Butler are embedded in the report of that committee, which is accompanied by specific sets of recommendations to various agencies and government to engage in both the short- and long-term types of research.

Professor Maynard also referred to a third type of research, which calls for controlled trials. In the health services field we are not faced with a barren situation there either. There have been heavily funded research programmes, for example, to find alternative methods for delivering care to the infirm aged. In terms of the underlying hypothesis, they have produced negative results. However, it is a move in the right direction. Whether it continues depends upon the nature of the pressures that the constituents of health services research can bring to bear.

Mr Lewin

I agree with Professor Stevens. There is no question that the kind of breakthrough research that has taken place by the NCHSR in other areas, and which is so desperately needed in the area of quality, has essentially been systematically resisted by the present administration, for exactly the reasons outlined by Professor Stevens.

It is sometimes said that competition is a process that brings out the best in products and the worst in people. Another point to add to this data question may be unique to the USA where an enormous amount of data is available. With the growing degree of competition, particularly among hospitals and health maintenance organizations (HMOs) these data are becoming increasingly viewed as being proprietary in nature in order not to give up presumed competitive advantages.

That is bad enough in the arena of health services. It is also of concern to me—and perhaps of more acute and immediate concern to others at this conference—that as academic, particularly biomedical, researchers become more involved with the commercialization of their work, the traditional sharing of technical knowledge in that field will also fall prey to proprietary considerations.

To the extent that we lose that sense of community, and of being involved in the same process where we are trying to help people and need to build on each other's experience, we are heading for some serious trouble. To me at least, that is the most frightening and upsetting aspect of this information problem.

Mr Buxton

I would reinforce that further. It is true that the information for which we here are generally calling is threatening. Many people do not want to be threatened. There are two groups of such people. First, individuals, not just clinicians but people with a vested interest in maintaining the *status quo*. Secondly, it is also threatening at a political level because it takes away some of the ability to respond in a politically convenient way, rather than actually relating to a set of data.

Those are two of the reasons why we have been so slow in collecting effectiveness information, and both must be recognized.

The explanation about competition is true also in the health service. There is competition for a slice of a fixed 'cake' of resources, not for patients but for allocation of resources. I think that in the health service the only way to get the competition to produce the information is to say that the resources will not be given unless the information is produced.

A step was taken towards that position with the requirement that bids for the supraregional advisory services, for instance, had to be supported with benefit and cost information. I have not seen those bids, but some of them must have very flimsy supporting information.

Dr Bondurant

Those of us from the USA would support those two attributions: the vested interest and the political perspective also being threatened.

Professor Wilson

At the risk of being thought to be against having more information, I wonder how well we have used what we have had all these years. We have known for quite a long time in the USA that we have too many hospital beds, but we cannot really discuss it. We frequently make decisions in health care in the way it is done in the North Carolina General Assembly: when they have a difficult question, they find someone who knows nothing about the subject and ask his advice, because he will be neutral.

Dr Relman

I do not share Professor Shapiro's sanguine view of all that we know. I would not contest his superior knowledge of what kind of health services information we may have, but the kind of health services research that I am talking about has to do with outcome and the relationship between what doctors do and what happens to patients. That is where the action is, it seems to me.

As a physician, and as a teacher of physicians, I am utterly convinced that the area of ignorance is enormous, and that of confident information relatively small. In order to illuminate the huge dark areas in the practice of medicine we will have to invest a lot of money — money that has to be obtained somehow from the total resources that are being put into the health care system. We ought not to pretend that we know what we do not know.

What concerns me about competition is exactly what Mr Lewin said. Perhaps it produces good products (although I am not convinced about that), but it brings out the worst in people. It certainly brings out the worst in doctors. That is not a good way to start trying to answer the questions which have to be answered if we want a more civilized, rational, effective system. The doctors have to be relatively more neutral than they are in any kind of a competitive system. That is why I have felt so strongly for so long that doctors should not have an entrepreneurial interest in the competition.

Professor Shapiro

I certainly agree with Dr Relman's description of the extreme importance of developing outcome information. In fact, most of my professional life has been devoted to precisely that. I wanted to point out that there are information resources for a variety of issues that we have been addressing, in part available but not used, in part in the process of being developed now. The investment in outcome measurements has to be viewed as a long-term proposition, and it requires the kind of resources described by Dr Relman, from both a developmental and an experimental standpoint.

Dr Bondurant

It should be remembered that the first and most eloquent plea for more information of this kind came, I believe, from Professor Jennett earlier in this conference. It included a plea for ennobling this kind of work within the clinical academic departments.

Professor Jennett

Dr Relman and I seem to be reinforcing each other, ignorance being the flag we fly. This is very serious. The National Institutes of Health (NIH) and the Medical Research Council have to see this as serious and respectable research. It may be easier for them to do that at the outcome end, which is more clearly oriented to biomedical procedures, if you like, than the process end of money and managerial figures.

Of course, the assessment of information on outcomes is itself a call on resources. However, we have done it with maternity and with peri-natal services. I think we now need to get into these rather more threatening and 'harder' issues, such as surgery.

Dr Bondurant

In 1966 I directed a programme at the National Heart Institute, in which $7 million was allocated for a controlled study of coronary bypass surgery. That was not enough money to purchase the participation of the surgeons in the USA.

Professor Marks

Certainly, we have vast areas of ignorance but, even where we have the information, the problem is the use to which it is put.

I understand that 12 years ago there was an investigation of the drilling and filling outcomes of dental hygienists versus those of dentists in Massachusetts (1). The dental hygienists won hands down in this inquiry by blind assessors. The net outcome was the closure of the training programme for dental hygienists.

There is another interesting controlled study, by Sackett and colleagues, in Burlington, Ontario, of nurse practitioners (2). (See also Spitzer *et al.* (3) and Marks (4).) The study found that the health status of the population looked after by nurse practitioners was at least as good as a comparable population looked after by family practitioners. Despite these results, the system was unable to respond by arranging appropriate reimbursement for the doctors who were actually losing out by employing the nurse practitioners, and the nurse practitioner programme closed down.

That brings us to the whole question of manpower planning. Do we have the right structure of incentives to decide who, in fact, is doing the care delivery, how many medical students we have, how many nurses, rehabilitation counsellors, etc.? Perhaps there are huge amounts of savings to be made if incentives can be restructured there.

It was earlier stated that community care is necessarily more expensive than hospital care. In fact, there are now at least 11 controlled studies of serious mental illness in Canada, the USA and Australia. The results in all of them showed that community care either cost about the same or effected savings up to 26%. Whether or not community care is more expensive depends very much upon the condition being treated and the kinds of treatments employed.

Professor Reinhardt

That information about the dental hygienists is really interesting. I did not know about the Massachusetts data, but such a body of data exists in Saskatchewan on drilling and filling in schools (5). Some of the classes had been treated by dentists, the others by dental hygienists. Some years later three dental professors checked the quality of the work, and the dental hygienists won hands down.

I was on an Institute of Medicine (IOM) panel in 1981 when President Reagan had just been elected. The IOM is *the* most august scientific body in the USA. We discovered that the poor in America have terrible dental health because dental treatment is not insured and it is rationed strictly by ability to pay. It was a major policy issue. What did we do? We whined. We said that we needed a federal programme with more money. I suggested at the time that we have a chapter in the panel's report on alternative methods of task delegation and on employing such personnel as dental hygienists. The dental professionals on the panel took me aside and said that this was an issue too complicated for me to understand! I wrote a 30-page minority report, of which a few pages reached the final report.

When we know something, not only do we not act upon it, but those of us who carry the mantle of scientists do not even release what we know when it is too dangerous to act because action might hurt the funding or stature of our bodies.

Professor Pardes

The question of health services research and the degree of its support depends very much upon whether those who will give the support care about hearing the answers. When the community health system was block granted, we were virtually expressly forbidden to do any assessments sponsored by the NIH to find out the outcome of the block grant implementation.

A few years later, one of my last arguments with the Office of Management and Budget (OMB) was to try to defend implementing a manpower survey to see what practising psychiatrists did in their offices. The OMB, which was supposed to keep out of policy determinations, said it was not interested.

On a different issue, Professor Reinhardt's figures showing that the amount of money put into the system is increasing are impressive. Without having the opportunity to examine them carefully, I will just accept them. On the other hand, Professor Rabkin said that it does not appear from his perspective to be so good. I might add that at the Presbyterian Hospital, New York, it does not seem too good from our perspective either. It does not feel to those within the system trying to launch virtually anything new that the money is in the system at all. In fact, if I compare the situation today with about 15 years ago, things seem both extremely tight and extremely over-regulated.

I believe that the tendency for global correction misses the fact that there are entirely different actors and institutions within the scene. Often we find ourselves blaming the wrong people when others may be creating the problem. The correction has in some way to be tailored to that considerable differentiation within the system.

Professor Reinhardt

It is often said that if one man is put on dry ice and another on a hot stove, on average they are comfortable! The same could be said about any such averages that I gave. I mentioned (perhaps too quickly) that some hospitals are being hurt in America—rural hospitals or any hospital in an area with a lot of uninsured poor. Professor Pardes' hospitals are situated in such areas. Yet there are others which are doing rather well. I mentioned the Catholic hospital (in Orange County), also many medical schools, for example, Stanford. It is a valid point which should be noted.

On this question of data, the clinical researchers may have their own problems, but we health services researchers put on a rather saintly front when asking for research money and we think that we are a pure science. In fact, I was struck by Professor Grimley Evans' remark earlier that ethics is an exercise of extracting logical principles from an over-arching ideology. That is the finest definition of ethics that I have ever heard.

However, there is also such a thing in social science. As we are seen to practise it, it may sometimes be concluded that social science is just playing politics by other means. Very often our ideological preconceptions are packaged in the questions we ask, the sample picked and the data excluded. For instance, we have a hypothesis and run a regression. This comes out negative whereas we had expected it to be positive. The first thing we then do is to get the research assistant to re-run that regression. Had it come out positive, we would have said it was a solid result.

One reason why we are not well funded is because we are not very reliable. We differ from accountants in that their work can be audited by others. There are rules of auditing, and access to the raw data can be obtained. Rare is the health services researcher who would share his or her raw data with someone else. Some of the grossest things are in fact published, when it would not be possible to replicate the results from the original data.

Mr Lewin

I do not think that is characteristic of the main body of health services researchers.

Professor Reinhardt

Certainly in health economics I would say that the entire debate on whether or not competition works and whether or not physicians can create demand is driven by an ideology. Mr Lewin's type of research may be of a quite different sort, but there is a strong strain of ideology that runs right through health economics. I invite Mr Lewin to read the debate on physician-induced demand—a powerfully important policy issue—and look what we have made of it.

Mr Lewin

But the issue is not whether or not there are biases, but whether the biases are made explicit. An honest researcher will make his or her biases explicit so that they may be audited. That is the difference.

Dr Relman

On Professor Rabkin and Professor Pardes' comment that we may be doing much better but they do not feel it, it is clear that some kinds of hospitals in the USA are doing much worse. They are the public hospitals, particularly the large public hospitals that are being asked to carry a very much heavier burden of unreimbursed patients.

Reverting to one of my favourite themes, I raise the question of whether the progressive change in ownership of facilities in the American health care system may not be in part responsible for this phenomenon too. That is, over the last 20 years in which Professor Reinhardt has shown this great increase in the amount of money and resources being put into health care—excluding now the non-patient care aspects, the pharmaceutical industry, the manufacturers and so on—we have gone from virtually no private-for-profit investor ownership to nobody knows how much because we have no good data. My guess is that it now accounts for perhaps one-third of the system. That may mean that the remaining two-thirds is beginning to feel effects that would otherwise have been spread out over the whole system.

Professor Ibrahim

I would like to follow up the spirit of this discussion by saying that I agree completely with the need for research and more data. May I, however, challenge the group by asking whether on the basis of the data and information presented during this meeting the following conclusions could be made:

(1) That we consider diverting resources from the big-ticket items which benefit relatively few people at high cost, to more conventional procedures that benefit a large number of people at low unit cost.

(2) That we consider diverting resources from the curative medicine activities to prevention and health promotion procedures.

(3) That health care for the vulnerable groups is not entirely satisfactory, and some rethinking may be in order to make it more sensitive and responsive to the needs of these particular groups.

(4) Finally, in allocating resources we may want to distinguish between those resources going to the provider and those going to the patient.

Dr Bondurant

Is Professor Ibrahim asking whether we have an adequate database to subscribe to the conclusions he has just stated?

Professor Ibrahim

We have spent 3 days talking about these issues, and I would say that we have enough data at least to make those conclusions — if we are willing to do so. That is the challenge I am making.

Professor Teeling Smith

In response to that challenge, there is a great deal of truth in what Professor Ibrahim says. I absolutely support the argument for better data. On the whole, we are less prejudiced in Britain than in the USA in our collection of data. I think that we do it rather better.

That, hopefully, is fairly non-controversial. What is more controversial is to say that it is my fundamental belief, based on 35 years' experience of the NHS, that it is virtually impossible to get change by taking things away from people who have them. Change comes by putting new resources in the right place.

However much Dr Relman, Professor Reinhardt and others may argue that there is overprovision to the current doctors in the USA, we cannot imagine that the problem will be solved by taking resources away from them and giving them to the more needy. Extra resources have to be invested, and we have just to live with the fact that many doctors are overpaid at the moment.

Professor Maynard

My response to Professor Ibrahim's four proposed conclusions is the following:
(1) We should probably change from a few at high cost to a lot at low cost.
(2) I am less sure about health promotion because I do not think that we have convincing cost outcome data. Indeed, some data show that promotion may be very expensive.
(3) We certainly need to do something about vulnerable groups.
(4) I would probably agree with a distinction being made between resources going to providers and patients.
With regard to Professor Teeling Smith's points about data biases, health economics has taken very different routes in the USA and the UK. The North American debate has been much more about the effects of incentive mechanisms using econometric techniques. The UK health economists, on the other hand, have tended to get their hands grubby working with clinicians doing evaluations, trying to analyse costs and (crudely) outcomes. I would be reluctant to generalize about the data biases because in both sets of data I think we can see things that worry Professor Reinhardt about North America. I think there are things in Europe too which are rather worrying.

Professor Teeling Smith makes the point that we cannot effect change by taking away. I would like to seek change by refusing to give anyone incremental resources unless he can provide good, clear evaluative data about costs and outcomes. Let me provoke him even further by saying that I would like to see this applied to the pharmaceutical industry, to all technology and to all types of health care. In fact, I would like to see the 1968 Medicines Act and the Food and Drug Administration legislation based not just on safety and efficacy, whatever that means, but also on whether there are desirable outcomes for patients and whether those outcomes are achieved at a lesser cost in comparison with competing therapies.

Professor Teeling Smith

Professor Maynard and I are not in disagreement. He has just phrased it slightly differently.

Dr Relman

Some of us in America are not daring to suggest that doctors get *less*, but that the pie be distributed in different ways. The disparity between the highest and the lowest physicians' incomes in the USA must be vastly greater than in the UK, and even than in Canada. What would happen if we could somehow tell the doctors collectively that they were going to get the same pie—in fact, that it might expand a little, slowly—but we wanted them to agree among themselves that a somewhat different distribution would be in the common interest? Is that possible?

Mr Lewin

That is exactly what several of the Canadian provinces tried to do. I visited Ontario and British Columbia when they were trying to do it. My understanding is that they were unsuccessful. A commission in the USA is now trying to do it there, but I think there will be a great deal of difficulty.

Professor Reinhardt

But it has been done in Canada. That is why the Ontario doctors struck. They became angry for a while, shouted, and said that the sky was falling—but, when the sky did not fall, they quietened down. The fact is that the procedurally oriented doctors in Canada have not had the extraordinary increase in their incomes, and the so-called 'cognitive' doctors do relatively better. If we in America could arrive at the position where the Canadians are now, I think we would begin to see a very different health care system.

Mr Lewin

We are seeing some of it within HMOs. Some HMOs and preferred provider organizations are effecting those changes. It is not the doctors who are doing it, but the managers of those systems.

Professor Wilson

We started by talking about data and the need for better health services research data. I will defer to the other, better trained, economists present, but I am unaware that anyone is suggesting any significant growth in the output of either the USA or the UK in the short- or mid-term. If we cannot do new things with old money, it seems very clear from the data that there will not be *new* money for us to do them with. I believe that we do not need any more data to understand that there will not be large new sums of money to pay for health care in either country. I will stand corrected if someone thinks that the economy will grow very rapidly and suddenly produce a lot of new money for health care.

Dr Bondurant

A couple of years ago I heard Professor Reinhardt make the projection that the percentage of gross national product (GNP) consumed by health could grow to 20% in the US economy while still allowing more rather than less money to be spent on other resources.

Professor Reinhardt

That is correct. I think I had assumed inflation at 6%, and health care and GNP growing at 15% and 9% per year, respectively. In the year 2000 one-fifth of every health care dollar would actually go to health care. When I presented that to the American Medical Association, I received a standing ovation. When we take the non-health GNP left over after that, taking out inflation, per capita it was still considerably higher in real terms than it had been in 1980. Whether it bankrupts the nation is not an issue. I said at the time, and I still feel, that the issue is not a cost crisis, but a benefit-cost crisis.

The one type of research that I believe we need much more of is exactly the kind, whether quality-adjusted life months, years, or whatever, that gives some idea at least about eliminating things that do not really work, or that reasonable people would agree are not meritorious.

Dr Lister

This is a splendid debate, and we seem to have set the Americans amongst themselves in deciding what is wrong and how to put it right. We have not heard so much about the NHS recently.

We were asked to discuss the 'free enterprise' medical system versus a national health service system. From the discussion so far, it does not seem that we are doing too badly in the NHS at the moment, even though many of us are quite discontented with what we have, and slightly cynical as to how far any extra spending can be achieved by increasing efficiency.

Can economists say whether or not we are measuring the same thing when we say that we spend 6% of GNP in the UK and in the USA they spend 10·5%? This is an enormous difference. The indices do not seem to be very different: the peri-natal mortality and expectation of life are about the same. If we are measuring the same thing, perhaps we should accept the difference for the sake of all the extra money that we save.

Do economists and others think that we are perhaps sacrificing something else? Are we paying the price with a loss of freedom? Freedom and equality are apparently mutually exclusive in the end. When the doctors in the UK entered the health service they were assured that their clinical freedom would be preserved and that the patients would have freedom of choice of doctor.

With regard to clinical freedom, Hampton, from Nottingham, wrote a paper in 1983 in which he said that it is dead — and a good thing too (6). Clinical freedom is clearly compromised by all the constraints that we have.

Freedom of choice of doctor is a bit of a myth. It is very difficult in primary care. In hospital care, the patient sees the man on duty — he might be a senior registrar — but there is not freedom of choice, although we say it is there.

How can we explain this enormous difference in the proportion of GNP, comparing it with the apparent outcome? Secondly, are we actually paying a price of some loss of freedom as a hidden cost?

Professor Butler

It seems that the difference is in the capital investment.

Professor Maynard

The data presented by Mr Maxwell and Professor Teeling Smith, and virtually all the data on international comparisons, come from the Organization for Economic Co-operation and Development (OECD), Jean-Pierre Poulier being the man responsible there. They attempt, as best they can, to adjust for different definitions, but it is very approximate. There is also the major problem of translating it into purchasing power and purchasing power exchange rates, particularly if per capita comparisons are being made.

The best data available are probably those OECD data. They tell us that we spend about 6% of a much smaller GNP, and the Americans spend about 10·5%. The usual explanation is that it is a problem of the disgusting affluence of the Americans. As they become rich, so they spend more on health care. That is also the basis of Professor Reinhardt's type of approach, that as people become more affluent they choose to spend more on health care.

I have little to say on the question of freedom. There is certainly little choice of doctors in the UK system. This is partly because consumers do not have information to make choices. Aaron and Schwartz described it as our class system which is preventing us from making those sorts of choices (7). Perhaps this will change as better information becomes available.

Professor Reinhardt

Returning to the point I tried to make earlier when asked what patients *get*, anyone really interested might look at how many physician-hours, how many nurses, and how many beds per capita are made available a year. We should look at real health care resources, not at money and percentage of GNP. I think that the difference there between the USA and the UK may be much less than it is by looking at the percentage of GNP.

I believe that we have better paid providers in the USA. Table 3 of my paper shows that the physician in the USA now earns — and has earned since the 1970s — 4·5 times the average compensation, where 'average employee' includes executives and their bonuses. In the UK that figure is bound to be below three times. Our health personnel live better. That is part of it.

Secondly, I would imagine that Americans who are insured have much more freedom of choice — although I do not know whether that is good or bad. There are no queues. It is rare for anyone insured who wants to be hospitalized to have to queue for anything. Anyone not insured is in a much worse position than in the UK, however.

Finally, I would think that the bulk of US hospitals have more pleasant facilities than those in the UK. Perhaps New York would not qualify for that. Elsewhere, hospitals have atriums, gourmet shops — much more pleasant facilities.

I re-emphasize that the percentage of GNP is not what patients get. It is the piece of the cake that the providers get. What that triggers is what we really want to measure — but no one has ever done that.

Dr Relman

Another great difference which is not shown in the percentage of GNP is the kinds of medical services provided in the USA. We provide much more elective, consumer-oriented options, for example cold surgery, cosmetic surgery — all sorts of things that many doctors would say are not really necessary, but which are profitable and attractive to patients, are consumer-oriented, and once again are a part of our industrialized, competitive, consumer-oriented health care system — a system which is growing. One-third of our health care system is run by people who think about what they are doing as a product to be sold to patients. That includes silicon mammoplasties, face-lifting, eyelash tattooing etc.

Dr Bondurant

Dr Relman is describing our cultural value systems. That is part of the problem.

References

(1) Lobene RR. *A study of new duties for dental hygienists.* Report to the Robert Wood Johnson Foundation. Boston: Forsyth Dental Center, 1975.
(2) Sackett DL, Spitzer WO, Gent M, *et al.* The Burlington randomized trial of the nurse practitioner: health outcomes of patients. *Ann Intern Med* 1974; **80**: 137–42.
(3) Spitzer WO, Roberts RS, Delmore T. Nurse practitioners in primary care. VI. Assessment of their deployment with the utilization and financial index. *Can Med Assoc J* 1976; **114**: 1103–8.
(4) Marks IM. *Cure and care of neuroses.* New York: Wiley, 1981: 260 (Chapter 9).
(5) Saskatchewan Dental Plan. *A quality evaluation of specific dental services provided by the Saskatchewan Dental Plan.* Final report. February 1976.
(6) Hampton JR. The end of clinical freedom. *Br Med J* 1983; **287**: 1237–8.
(7) Aaron HJ, Schwartz WB. *The painful prescription: rationing hospital care.* Washington: The Brookings Institution, 1984.

Summary and conclusions

ARTHUR J. MAHON

*President, The Royal Society of Medicine Foundation Inc.,
New York NY, USA*

It is a privilege to have this opportunity to make summary comments and to draw this meeting to a close. As President of the Royal Society of Medicine (RSM) Foundation, I am pleased to have been part of such a gathering, and to see our work in helping to organize it pay off so handsomely.

This conference is the latest in a series of Anglo-American conferences organized by the RSM and the Foundation since 1971. It is the third occasion when we have been associated with the University of North Carolina at Chapel Hill. It has been a productive and happy association, and I want to add my thanks to Chancellor Fordham, Dr Stuart Bondurant, and Dr Eugene Mayer, all of whom have been good supporters and friends of the Foundation.

Over the past 3 days we have listened to a series of outstanding presentations and some fascinating discussions. It is not possible for me to summarize the subject matter in a way that would do justice to the speakers or to the conference. However, I thought it might be of interest to present, by way of a summary, some observations and questions that are a purely personal response to the presentations.

(1) Four years ago we met at the University of North Carolina for a conference, 'Responsibilities in shaping health policy in the UK and the USA'. The world was a different place then than it is now, but it seems to me that it is not dramatically different. The media on a rather regular basis provide us with details of political episodes and developments, both national and international, that are expected to threaten our lives and security. I think the issues that we have talked about here have far greater implications for the well-being and security, certainly in the long term, of our society than many of the things that we read about regularly regarding, for example, military actions.

I raise the question whether changes over the next 4 years will come to grips with the challenges presented to us here. Will the USA bring the resources to bear to protect the 35 million Americans who today are outside the current health care system? If so, how will it be done? Will the situation worsen? Is it not likely that industry in the USA, by itself or with the federal government, will have to assume greater responsibility both for its terminated employees who are without medical coverage and for its retired employees who are ever growing in number? And is it not likely to force into place a system that covers everyone in the USA?

Health Care Provision under Financial Constraint, edited by T. B. Binns and M. Firth, 1988: Royal Society of Medicine International Congress and Symposium Series No. 115, published by Royal Society of Medicine Services Ltd.

(2) By and large, speakers expressing the UK point of view, and detailing conditions existing in the delivery of UK health care, were less critical of the National Health Service (NHS) system, as complemented by private practice, than were the US speakers regarding gaps which exist there in the delivery of health care. There seems to be an optimism, however, on the part of all speakers that the problems which exist with regard to their system (or, if you will, the non-system in the case of the USA) are curable, and that substantial advances will be made. My guess is that few, if any, people at this meeting would trade their system for that of their colleagues on the other side of the Atlantic. This seems to me to confirm a sense of optimism in tackling the shortcomings of one's own system.

(3) Both sides (and I use this expression in a complementary not adversarial sense) called for more efficient use of resources and appropriate use of new technology, while recognizing that the overall cost of medical care is expected to increase and to consume an increasing proportion of gross national product (GNP). No one seems to expect the demand for better and better medical care by our citizens to decrease. The answer to our initial question, 'How high a priority will society accord health care in financial terms?', was a consistent *very high priority*, certainly a priority that is no less than what we have seen through the 1960s, 1970s and the early 1980s.

(4) I was impressed by the extent to which the problems raised as priorities for the future agenda are in many ways the unintended consequences of success in achieving earlier goals and priorities. The increased capability of the medical profession to treat illnesses and injuries means that more patients are being maintained in the system for a longer period. Changing living patterns are leading to increased life expectancy, thus expanding the demands and expectations for high quality health care.

(5) It has been said here that a number of the concerns expressed about interfering with medical autonomy are perhaps not as dire in their consequences as might be imagined. Some intervention in market forces and reimbursement formulae may not hold back innovation, impede incentive, or slow down the development of new technology. It is probably true to say that the jury is still out on this one, and that it involves a series of issues which definitely require further research, monitoring, and evaluation. We heard on occasions that, at least in some areas of the NHS, incentives are lacking to adopt new technology. Despite this, the system does sustain innovation. It seems that where such incentives are lacking in the *system* they are more than compensated for by the dedication, curiosity, and integrity of the *medical professionals*.

(6) There was a prediction at this conference that both our nations will be spending an even larger part of GNP in the future for delivery of health care. On the other hand, some speakers pointed to a growing need for cost-containment and a willingness to accept that there are limits in providing care. But is the ever larger aging population willing to accept these limits? Several said no. And what about acquired immune deficiency syndrome (AIDS)? Unless eliminated or dramatically contained in the near future (neither of which seems likely), will this not test the resolve of our medical delivery systems? Can the systems, organized as they are at present, bear the cost of providing dignity in dying for large segments of our society?

If we meet the challenge posed by AIDS, is it possible that we will fashion for the future new approaches and alternative sites for the care of the elderly, the mentally ill, and the terminally ill?

(7) We have heard that the American system of delivering health care is inherently unequal, and yet we were told of more dramatic advances over a recent period of some 18 years in the health of blacks, particularly black women, than in the health of whites. Does this argue at all against a suggestion that we have a formal two-tiered system with the lowest 25% of our economically disadvantaged group in one system and the other 75% in another?

(8) Speakers from both sides of the Atlantic recognize room for considerable improvement, particularly in the development of information necessary for informed decision-making. The US speakers, on the whole, seemed to be dissatisfied with the delivery system. They suggested the need for a major overhaul to reach all people, but were satisfied generally with the financial resources currently available and the willingness of Americans to commit even greater resources in the future—so long as questions of equity, greed, and waste can be dealt with.

The UK speakers, on the other hand, seem dissatisfied with the commitment of financial resources and were pessimistic about probable future financial commitments of national resources. They were generally satisfied, however, with the delivery system as developed through the NHS. By and large, the NHS is seen as meeting the health needs of the people as had been intended.

It seemed to me that the American speakers were almost instantly critical of their system for delivering health care, whereas the UK speakers 'warmed up' to being critical as the meeting progressed. Towards the end of the conference we heard more about some problems within the structure of the NHS, and concern about issues of cost-effectiveness in the delivery of primary health care. I was impressed by the agreement about the need for greater concentration in establishing the information base that is critical to informed decision-making. This perhaps may serve as a wonderful follow-up conference.

(9) The structure of this conference again shows the value of Anglo-American dialogue in relation to medical health matters. It confirms the value of purpose of the RSM Foundation to promote the exchange of medical/scientific information between the USA and the UK. It was assumed in 1967 when the Foundation was formed, and confirmed as late as this conference, that we are prepared, and indeed want, to learn from each other.

(10) Finally, the quality of the papers delivered and of the discussions was of the highest quality. All the contributions tended to show that, while differences exist in our systems, there is a special bond between us within the medical and health care systems and, indeed, in a much broader sense, between us as people who want to achieve for both our great nations an ever better quality of life.

In bringing this conference to a close, let me pay tribute to everybody who played a vital part in making it a reality. First, Sir John Walton, immediate Past President of the RSM, who was involved in the initial planning, Bob Thomson, Executive Director, Drs Bondurant and Mayer, Sir Gordon Robson, and all who presided so graciously at events during the last 3 days.

Our special thanks to Dr Graham Bennette and his staff, in particular Ms Barbara Komoniewska, for paying attention to the details so necessary to the success of a meeting. Also, to William G. O'Reilly, Executive Director of the RSM Foundation in New York, who handled the details in planning and made sure, as he always does, that arrangements worked smoothly on that side of the Atlantic.

Our thanks are also due to Dr Terry Binns and Dr Mary Firth for editorial work in preparing the proceedings for publication.

Last, but not least, our thanks to the sponsors and contributors, without whose financial support this meeting would not have taken place. Many of them have been friends and sponsors for many years.

NEVIL**SHUTE**
Trustee from the Toolroom

HOUSE OF
STRATUS

This edition published in 2000 by House of Stratus, an imprint of House of Stratus Ltd, Thirsk Industrial Park, York Road, Thirsk, North Yorkshire, YO7 3BX, UK.

www.houseofstratus.com

Typeset by House of Stratus, printed and bound by Short Run Press Ltd.

A catalogue record for this book is available from the British Library and the Library of Congress.

ISBN 1-84232-301-6

Cover design: Marc Burville-Riley
Cover image: Telegraph Colour Library

An engineer is a man who can do for five bob
what any bloody fool can do for a quid.

– Definition: origin unknown

CHAPTER ONE

WEST EALING IS a suburb to the west of London, and Keith Stewart lives there in the lower part of No. 56 Somerset Road. No. 56 is an unusual house and a peculiarly ugly one, a detached house standing in a row but in a fairly spacious garden, four storeys high if you include the basement, a tall, thin slip of a house. It was built in the spacious days of 1880 when West Ealing stood on the edge of the country farmlands and was a place to which Indian Civilians retired after their years of service, but it was built of a particularly ugly yellow brick, now toned to a drab grey, at a period when English suburban architecture was going through a bad patch. The years have not dealt kindly with West Ealing; the farms are now far away. Most of the big old houses have been split up into two or three flats, as Keith Stewart had converted No. 56.

He had bought it when he married Katie in the middle of the Second World War. That was soon after he moved down from Glasgow to the London area to work as a toolroom fitter with Stone and Collinson Ltd, who made subcontract parts for aeroplanes at Perivale. It was, of course, the first house that Katie or Keith had ever owned, and they were very proud of it. They contemplated quite a family, so that they would need quite a house, the upper rooms for nurseries and children's rooms and playrooms while the garden would be a nice place for the pram. When, after a few years, it became evident that that was not to be, they

1

had separated the two top floors from the remainder of the house and let them off as what the agents called a maisonette, retaining the ground floor and the basement for themselves. On the ground floor they had a bedroom in the front, the living-room and kitchen at the rear overlooking the garden, and a bathroom at the side. In the basement they had adapted what had once been the scullery as a small spare bedroom; the whole of the rest had been taken by Keith as his own domain.

Here he made models, and here he wrote about them weekly for the *Miniature Mechanic*, a magazine with a considerable circulation in the lower ranks of industry and with a growing popularity amongst eccentric doctors, stockbrokers, and bank managers who just liked engineering but didn't know much about it. All his life he had made models, little steam engines, little petrol engines, little speedboats, little locomotives, little diesels. He was a considerable horologist; in his time he had made many clocks with motions of antiquarian interest and had written full directions for constructing them, always in the *Miniature Mechanic*. He had made little beam engines which would have delighted James Watt and still delighted those who are fascinated by such things; he had made little jet engines which would have delighted Frank Whittle. He had made pumps and boilers and *carillons* that played a tune, all in the miniature scale. He was a quick worker and a ready writer upon technical matters and he delighted in making little things that worked. He had now so ordered his life that he need do nothing else.

All through the war he had written about his hobby after the long hours of overtime in the toolroom. The coming of peace had given him more leisure for his models and his articles about them, and two years later he had taken the great plunge of giving up his job in favour of his avocation. It had not benefited him financially. He would have made more money in the toolroom progressing up from charge-hand to foreman; he would have made more money as an instructor in a technical college. He would not have made more happiness than he had now attained.

He was a very serious and well-informed student of engineering matters, though he would have been amazed to hear himself described in such terms. He read about techniques for pleasure. One morning each week he would spend in the Ealing Public Library browsing through the technical magazines, slightly oppressed by a sense of guilt that he was not working. On Fridays he always went to London to deliver his weekly 'copy' to the editor of the *Miniature Mechanic* and arrange about the blocks, and being in London, he would take time off and sneak away for three or four hours to the library of the Patent Office for a period of interest and pleasure before going home to catch up with his work. He worked normally till eleven or twelve each night.

He called the front basement room his clean workshop, and this was his machine shop. Here he had a six-inch Herbert lathe for heavy work, a three-and-a-half-inch Myford, and a Boley watchmaker's lathe. He had a Senior milling machine and a Boxford shaper, a large and a small drill press, and a vast array of tools ready to hand. A long bench ran across the window, a tubular light system ran across the ceiling, and a small camera and flashgun stood ready for use in a cupboard, for it was his habit to take photographs of interesting processes to illustrate his articles.

The other room, which once had been the kitchen of the house, was considerably larger. He called this his dirty workshop, but it was in this room that he had his desk and the drawing board, for it was usually free of oil. Here he did what small amount of carpentry and woodworking might be necessary for his models. Here he welded and brazed, here he tempered and hardened steel, here he did steam trials of his steam engines, so that it had been necessary for him to fit an extractor fan into the window. It was in this room that he stood talking to his brother-in-law, Commander Dermott, the red leather jewel case in his hands.

The copper box that he had made stood on the bench before them, the rectangular sheet of copper that was to be the lid loose beside it. 'I've left room for packing this asbestos card all round it,' Keith said. 'I'll braze it up with a small oxy-acetylene flame, but I'm afraid it's going to get a bit hot inside. I'm afraid it may scorch the leather, even with the asbestos.'

'I don't think that matters,' said the naval officer. 'It won't set it on fire?'

Keith shook his head. 'The top is a good fit, and I'll clamp it down all round while I'm brazing. There won't be enough oxygen inside to support combustion. I'm just worried about the look of it when you take it out. It could be a bit brown.'

'That doesn't matter.'

Keith shook the case; it was fairly heavy, but nothing rattled. He glanced at his brother-in-law. 'What's it got in it?'

'All Jo's jewels,' John Dermott told him. 'You're only allowed to take so much out of the country.'

'This is going somewhere in the yacht?'

The other nodded. 'Somewhere where nobody's going to find it.'

Keith said no more but took off his jacket and hung it on a hook at the back of the door. He put on a leather apron that covered his body from the neck down, and turned on the gas at the cylinders, picked up the torch, and went to work. He never questioned anything that his brother-in-law said or did; they came from different worlds. John had been a regular naval officer, and Keith was a modest little man.

4

His sister had done a good job for herself, he reflected as he brazed the seam, when she married John Dermott; it had turned out well in spite of the social disparity. Jo had been a pretty child with good Scots sense; she had been fond of dancing and at the age of twelve she had become one of the Tiller Girls. Her first part was one of nine Elves in the Magic Wood, in pantomime. She had stayed with the organisation and had played in theatres and music halls all over the British Isles, with occasional runs in London. It had been partly upon her account that Keith had left Glasgow and come down to work in the south, to see more of his only sister. It had gone on till at the age of nineteen she had been in the Christmas pantomime at Portsmouth. She was playing a small speaking part that time as the Widow Twankey's maid, more noticeable than in the chorus. She had gone with a party of show girls and young naval officers to the Queen's Hotel after the performance; she told Lieutenant Dermott that she was going to see the *Victory* next day. He took her there in pouring rain, which neither of them noticed. He followed her to London. Six weeks later, in the Palm House at Kew Gardens, he asked her to marry him, and she accepted. It wasn't till nearly a month afterwards that she learned that she was marrying the nephew of Lord Dungannon.

Inevitably she had drifted somewhat apart from her brother Keith, the toolroom fitter in the factory at Perivale. She had the makings of a good actress in her; she was observant and could project herself into a part. It was no effort to her to take up the part of a young naval officer's wife, abandoning her Renfrew antecedents; with the Tiller Girls she had learned to abandon or assume her Scots accent at will. She married Lieutenant Dermott in 1939 and almost immediately the war came, taking him away from her for the best part of five years. In those years she saw him only for brief spells of leave. They did not start a family during

5

the war. She lived in a small flat over a shop at Cosham and worked as a woodworker with many other girls in a small dispersal aircraft factory at Havant. In the evenings she attempted to catch up on education to be on equal terms with other naval wives. She attended classes at the Polytechnic in French and History and Geography and English Literature; the latter she found infinitely tedious, but struggled on with it.

John Dermott came back to her in 1946, a lieutenant commander with greying hair and a face lined on the Murmansk convoy route; in 1947 their only child, Janice, was born. They bought a little house in Southsea and lived modestly, as naval officers do. They could have lived better, for John Dermott had a private income of about a thousand a year, but already the shadow of an early retirement from the Navy lay upon him. He was a general duties officer, a salt horse, impatient with the rush of new techniques that were invading his service. Early retirement lay ahead of him as he passed out of the promotion zone. They saved their money but for the extravagance of two years in Hong Kong for Joanna and the baby Janice when he was drafted to the China Station, and for the mild extravagance of duty-free gin in increasing quantities as John Dermott passed out of the Zone. Early in 1957 the axe fell and John Dermott was retired from the service to which he had given his life; he was then forty-five, the same age as his brother-in-law, Keith.

Joanna sat talking to Katie while the two men worked in the basement room below. 'It's terribly kind of you to offer to look after Janice,' she said. 'I do want you to know how we feel about that.' She paused. 'I wouldn't feel very comfortable about leaving her for all that time with the Dungannons.'

Katie said anxiously, 'I do hope she'll be happy, though. Ealing isn't very exciting, not after what she's been used to.

6

Do you think she will? I mean, never having had any myself, one doesn't know ...'

She was a plump little woman in her early forties; she worked in the Household Linen department of Buckley's drapery shop, in Ealing Broadway. She had been in Household Linen as a girl, but in the war she had been directed to running an automatic lathe at Stone and Collinson, at Perivale. Here she had met Keith Stewart in 1941; they had married in 1942 and she had gone back to her automatic lathe after a week's honeymoon. They had no children. The purchase and conversion of the house had taken all their savings and left them with a heavy mortgage. She had tried it for a year after the war as a lady of leisure and had tired of it; when Keith gave up his job and took up freelance writing and construction for the *Miniature Mechanic* Katie went back gladly to the Household Linen, a red-faced, dumpy little woman, well liked by the customers.

Joanna said, 'I think she'll be very happy with you, very happy indeed. I wouldn't leave her if I thought she wouldn't. I think you'll spoil her, though.'

'She's such a dear little thing,' said Katie. 'I was saying to Keith, perhaps we ought to have a kitten.'

'You'll be landed with a cat for the rest of your lives,' Joanna said practically. 'She'll only be with you for about six months. I don't think it will be longer. Then you'll just have to take her to London Airport and put her on the aeroplane to us in Vancouver.'

'Would that be somewhere in America?'

'In Canada,' Jo said. 'It's on the other side, on the Pacific coast. Everybody says it's a lovely place to live in, and John thinks he can get a job there. It's got quite a mild climate, but it rains a lot.'

'My ...' The thought of the aeroplane was troubling to Katie. 'I don't like the thought of her going all that way, all alone. Would she have to change, like at a station?'

Jo shook her head. 'She goes right through in the same aeroplane, over the North Pole.'

'Fancy ...' Katie said. 'Is that the way you're going, in the yacht? All in among the ice?'

Jo shook her head. 'You couldn't go that way in a boat.' Katie was a dear and she was going to look after Janice for them while they travelled, but she had lived in Ealing all her life. 'We're going to go southwards into the warm seas,' she explained. 'When we leave Hamble on Thursday week we go to Falmouth to clear Customs and to pick up anything that we've forgotten. Then John wants to make a passage straight for Las Palmas in the Canary Islands. From there to Barbados, and then to the Panama Canal. When we get into the Pacific, first of all we go to the Galapagos Islands, and then to Tahiti. We do want to see that, and it's not much out of the way. Then we go up to Honolulu and from there to Vancouver. It ought to take about five months. A bit less, if we're lucky with the winds.'

The string of foreign names perplexed Katie; she did not know where any of them were, except the Panama Canal. The whole venture was entirely alien to her experience; she struggled to make sense of it. 'Will there be anyone to help you with the boat?' she asked. 'With the sails, and that?'

Jo shook her head. 'We don't need anybody,' she said. 'John and I can sail her by ourselves.'

Katie was perplexed. 'But what happens at night, when you want to go to bed? I mean, do you anchor or something?' A sudden doubt assailed her. 'You have *got* beds, haven't you?'

'We've got very good beds,' said Jo. 'I sleep marvellously on board. No, we couldn't anchor. It's too deep. Sometimes we can let her sail herself while we both sleep.' She tried to make the matter simple, but it was rather difficult. 'She'll do that with the wind forward of the beam, or running under the twin spinnakers. Otherwise we keep watch and watch –

one up in the cockpit steering and the other one down below sleeping.' She smiled. 'It's quite all right. We're very used to it.'

'You wouldn't be sailing all the way, though, would you?' Katie asked. 'Keith was saying you could go some of the way with the motor.'

Joanna shook her head. 'We shall sail all the way,' she replied, 'except perhaps just getting in and out of harbour. We have got a small motor, but we don't use it at sea. It's only a little one, and it's dirty, and it makes a smell.' She paused, and then she said, 'John's such a *seaman*.'

Presently Katie reverted to her own problems. 'It's just the holidays,' she said thoughtfully. 'School time – well, I'm back in the house by a quarter to six, always. School finishes at four so she'd be back here by a quarter past, but Keith is almost always here then, unless it's a Friday. It's really just the holidays.'

'The Christmas holidays,' Jo said. 'We don't sail till the first of August. I'm going to take her up to the Dungannons in Tyrone next week. I think school starts – Miss Pearson's school, here – I think she said term starts on September the 15th. That means she'd be corning to you about the 13th, I suppose. I think you'll have to meet her at Euston, but I'll make sure that the Dungannons let you know.'

Katie nodded. 'Keith would meet the train and bring her down here. He'd like doing that.'

'I think we'll be sending for her about February,' said Jo. 'We should be there by then, and if we haven't got a house she can live on the boat with us. But anyway, I'll be writing to you from each place. It's just the Christmas holidays.'

Katie said, 'Of course, Keith is in the house most of the time, down in the workshop. They're not very long, the Christmas holidays.'

'I don't want her to be a burden on you and Keith.'

9

'She won't be that – honestly she won't.' Katie paused. 'I think it would be nice to have children's parties, and crackers, and presents, and all that.'

Joanna eyed her uncertainly, wondering how far she meant it. 'I'm sure Margaret would have her.'

'Do whatever you think would be best for her,' said Katie. 'But don't do it for us. Keith's always wanted to have kids about the place. I mean, with a great big garden, like we've got ...'

In the room below Keith turned off the gas at the two cylinders, hung the torch up on its hook, took the copper box to a sink in one corner of the room, and scrubbed the brazing with water and a wire brush. He dried it on a dirty towel, and examined the seam carefully, inch by inch. Then he handed it to his brother-in-law. 'She's tight now,' he said briefly.

John Dermott took it from him. 'No chance of sea water getting into it? Corrosion?'

'Not in a hundred years.' He paused. 'When you want to open it, just cut the top off with a hacksaw – round here.'

The naval officer hesitated. 'I'm going to set it in concrete,' he said diffidently. Keith stared at him, surprised; he had thought the box was to go into the yacht. 'Do you know how to mix it?'

'I know how to mix concrete,' the mechanic said. 'You mix it different proportions, depending on what it's for – what it's got to hang on to. How much would you want?'

The naval officer hesitated, and then indicated the box upon the bench before them. 'About as much as that, or a bit more.'

Keith frowned; this was getting difficult. 'I should grease it before setting it in concrete,' he suggested, trying to be helpful without knowing the job. 'Come out easier when you want it out.'

'I see.' The naval officer hesitated, irresolute; he had never had to do this sort of work before and he wanted a good job made of it. 'You wouldn't like to come down to the boat and do it for me?'

'Down to Hamble?' John Dermott nodded. 'When?'

'We're going down tomorrow, in the car. Would it take long?'

'If it's a straight job it might take about an hour,' Keith said. 'Then you ought to leave it for a while to set – two or three days. I could come tomorrow, but I'd have to be back tomorrow night.' His eyes strayed to a corner. 'I've got half a bag of cement there, but I'd have to slip up to the builder for some sand. Got some aggregate down there?'

'What's that?'

'Little clean stones – just a few pounds. Not salty – washed in fresh water.'

'There's plenty on the beach. We could wash them under the hose, couldn't we?'

Keith nodded. 'Doesn't matter if they're wet.'

They left it so, and turned to go upstairs. The naval officer paused by the littered desk with the drawing board beside it. 'This where you do your stuff?'

Keith nodded. 'I used to do it up in the parlour, but it's better down here. You'd be surprised at the number of letters that there are – all over the auction. I save the foreign stamps and give them to the boy next door – Jamesie Morris, he collects them. Six or seven in a day, some days. You'd be surprised.'

John Dermott opened his eyes. 'How many letters do you have to write – say, in a week?'

'Twenty or twenty-five,' the mechanic said. 'It's letters all the time, and then there's the articles each week. I spend more time writing than I do working.' He paused, and added a little resentfully, 'It's fifteen bob a week for stamps

11

– more, sometimes. Of course, one has to do it. Some of them send international reply coupons, though.'

'Do a lot of them come from foreign countries, then?'

'About a third.'

John Dermott went back to the bench and picked up the copper box. 'I'll take this along with me,' he said. He hesitated. 'You'll keep this under your hat?' he enquired diffidently. 'I mean, it's quite all right. They're just Jo's rings and bracelets and things – they're all her own property. But the regulations are so stupid about taking things like that out of England, and she'd be miserable without them. I mean, a woman sort of values her little bits and pieces when she's away in a strange country. And we may be away for years.'

Keith said, 'Oh, that's all right. I shan't talk about it.' He paused, and then he asked, 'You're going to live out there?'

'I think so – if we like it. Jo says she wants to live in Tahiti, but I don't go much on that, myself. It's French, and it's a very little place, you know. Still, she wants to see it. I think we'll probably end up in British Columbia – it's a grand country, that. I'd like to buy a house in Victoria, on Vancouver Island.'

Keith nodded. He had only the vaguest idea where Vancouver Island was, but it was the sort of place that people like his brother-in-law who sailed about the world in little yachts would want to go to. 'Suppose I tell Katie that I'm going down to rig up an electric light over the compass, so you can see it at night?' he suggested.

John Dermott smiled. 'That's just the thing.'

They went up the narrow wooden basement stairs to the main floor and Keith went to wash the grime off his hands. When he rejoined them in the parlour his sister and her husband were standing, ready to leave, having pleaded a somewhat formalised dinner engagement to Katie. He did not press them to stay for tea, because he had learned long ago that they pursued different meal habits. Katie and Keith had their main meal in the middle of the day. Their evening meal was high tea at six o'clock when Katie got back from work, a meal of perhaps a kipper, bread and jam, and a piece of plum cake, washed down with tea. They knew that Jo and John ate differently at eight o'clock, favouring perhaps potted shrimps followed by soup, a grilled steak, and mushrooms on toast, the meal preceded by a couple of gins and followed by coffee. The couples got on well together, but they had long ago accepted differences springing from their ways of life.

Jo and John Dermott called for Keith at about nine o'clock next morning, driving their vintage sports Bentley open four-seater, nearly thirty years old and with many prosecutions for noise and speeding to its credit. They loved it very dearly. Katie had already left for work, so she did not see the two small sacks that Keith put into the back compartment beside him, or she might have wondered why a small electric light required cement and sand. It was a warm summer morning in late July, and Keith enjoyed the drive through southern England. They got to Hamble on the creek that runs into the east side of Southampton Water, parked the car near the entrance to Luke's Yard, and carried the sacks out on to the long wooden walkways above the tidal mud, the yachts moored bows-on in tiers. Presently they came to the Dermotts' ship, *Shearwater IV*.

Shearwater was a healthy-looking, modern Bermudian cutter about twenty-eight feet on the waterline and nine feet beam. On deck she was practical and well equipped for deep sea cruising, the dinghy stowed upside down over the cabin skylight between the mast and the aft hatch, the twin spinnaker booms in chocks beside it. She had roller reefing to the mainsail and a very short bowsprit no more than four feet long for the jibstay. Aft, she had a self-draining cockpit well protected by the vertical extensions of the cabin top, and a sail locker in her canoe stern. Below, she was conventional in her arrangement. A roomy forecastle served mainly as a sail store. Aft of that there was a washroom and toilet to starboard, a galley and pantry to port. Aft again came the saloon with the settees on each side and a table in the middle; a small chart table was arranged against the forward bulkhead. Aft again there were two quarter berths, the companion ladder leading up on deck, and a small petrol motor underneath this ladder, rather inaccessible. *Shearwater* was such a yacht as is to be found by the hundred cruising the south coast of England, though rather better equipped than most.

John Dermott led Keith down below. The linoleum on the deck of the galley and the washroom had been taken up, and the floorboards lifted. What was exposed to view was a smooth level floor of concrete into which the frames disappeared and in which the mast was stepped. About two feet behind the mast step was a fairly deep, rectangular recess in the concrete, large enough to hold the copper box that Dermott carried, and about two inches deeper.

'That's the place,' he said. 'That's where I want to put it.'

Keith wrinkled his brows. 'What's all this concrete doing here?'

'Internal ballast,' said the naval officer. 'They often do it like this. Pour it in when she's building, and bury pig iron or any old scrap iron in it. She'd be too lively with all the ballast on the keel. She's got about three tons of lead outside, as well.'

'I never knew that,' said the mechanic. 'What's this hole been left here for, then?'

'I don't really know. She's got another like it at the stern, but that's used for a sump; the bilge pump suction goes down into it. Perhaps they thought she'd want another sump up here. I don't know. She never makes any water, anyway.'

Keith knelt down and fingered the concrete hole. 'It's a bit oily,' he remarked. 'I think I'll chip it a bit first – clean it up and make a sort of rebate, so it'll hold.' He fetched his tool bag, and set to work with hammer and cold chisel.

Half an hour later he was mixing a little concrete of cement, fine stones and sand. He made a bed of it at the bottom of the hole, greased the copper box, and set it carefully in the middle. Then he filled in the spaces round it with the wet mixture, working it carefully into the corners and the newly cut recesses. 'Look your last on it,' he said, and covered it over with a smooth layer of the mix, patting it, working it with a little builder's trowel, taking up the surplus, till it was smooth and level with the original concrete floor, only the darker wetness of the new material showing the difference. He gathered his tools and the remainder of the mix in newspaper, cleaned up the mess, and got up from his knees a little stiffly. 'I'd leave the floorboards up for a day or so, till it's set hard,' he said. 'It'll take a week to harden properly, but you can put the boards back.'

His sister asked, 'What do we do when we want to get it out, Keith?'

'Just cut around the edge with a cold chisel and a hammer, like this,' he said. 'You'll probably be able to see where the concrete's a bit different, but even if you can't, it'll sound hollow when you tap it with a hammer. The top layer of concrete'll come off easy enough, because it's only an inch or so thick. Then when you can see the box you'll have to cut around with the chisel till you can get it out. You won't have any trouble.'

He stayed for a cold lunch with them on board, and while the meal was in preparation he examined the ship, a short, white-faced, plump little man completely out of his element. He knew nothing of yachts and the sea. She seemed to him to be cosy enough downstairs, though a bit

15

cramped; upstairs he was confused by the complexity of her and by the unfamiliar materials, the sisal, nylon, flax, cotton, hemp, and teak. He was unfamiliar with the sea and did not like it much; it was a place that made you cold and wet and sick. His brother-in-law was a sensible man in most ways though not in matters technical, and he liked the sea, so there must be something in it for some people, though not for him. They had asked him once or twice to go down with Katie for a weekend on the yacht in the Solent, but he had always made excuses, and they had not pressed the point. The Stewarts had their way of life, and the Dermotts had theirs.

After lunch John Dermott drove Keith into Southampton and put him down at the West station to catch a train to London. They would meet again before the Dermotts started off across the world in *Shearwater*; they parted cordially, the naval officer grateful to his dissimilar brother-in-law for his help. He drove back from Southampton to Hamble; they would live on the yacht now till they sailed but for one last trip to London. There was still much to be done.

He parked the car and went on board. Jo met him in the cockpit. 'Catch his train all right?'

He nodded. 'Ten minutes to spare.'

'Oh, good. I've just put on the kettle for a cup of tea.'

They had their cups of tea sitting in the cockpit in the sun. The naval officer glanced down into the forward end of the ship, to the rolled-back linoleum and the floorboards piled beside it. The dark wetness of the concrete patch was already drying, turning a lighter grey at the edges that would match the original surface. 'Well, that's the most important job done,' he said with satisfaction. 'I was worried about that, but it's all right now.'

Joanna nodded. 'Keith's awfully good at that sort of thing,' she said quickly. 'When he's got somebody to tell him exactly what to do.'

She seldom talked openly to him about her brother; now in their shared satisfaction and relief that remark had slipped out. He glanced at her. 'I know,' he said. 'Not much initiative.'

She sat silent for a minute. 'Poor old Keith,' she said at last. 'I always feel he's missed the boat, somehow. That I've had everything, and he's had nothing.'

'Everything?' he asked. He was morbidly conscious of his truncated career, of the failure inherent in his early retirement, of the forty years of idleness that might lie ahead of him unless he could reorganise his life.

She knew what he was thinking, and he mustn't think it. She turned to him. 'Oh yes,' she said. 'I've had Janice, and money, and the Navy, and this boat. And I've been to China, and to Italy, and Malta. And now we're going off across the world, and we'll see the coral islands, and Hawaii, and Canada, and the States. I've had everything. But poor old Keith, he goes on in that ghastly half-a-house in Ealing and just makes his models and gets practically nothing for them, and Katie has to work in the shop. And he's so good at what he does. It isn't fair.'

He tried to comfort her. 'I don't think he's unhappy.'

'No,' she agreed, 'he's not. Nor Katie, either. They're neither of them a bit jealous of the things we've got. I think it's going to do Janice a lot of good to be with them for a bit. But he's so much better than I am, he ought to have so very much more.'

He smiled. 'Wants somebody to put a squib up his behind.'

'He always has to be told what to do,' she agreed.

'Apart from making models,' he remarked. 'He seems to be original enough in that.'

'Yes,' she agreed. 'But that doesn't get him anywhere.'

Keith Stewart got to Waterloo at about half past four, and travelled out to Ealing Broadway on the Underground. From there he took a tram to West Ealing and walked up to his house. He got in about ten minutes before Katie and put the macaroni cheese into the oven as she had told him to, and took the mail from the letter box in the front door and shuffled it through; there was one letter for her and eleven for him, three from the United States. He sighed a little. You could produce an induced current on the surface of a metal sphere that would act as a gyroscope, and from this you could devise a tiny automatic pilot for ship or aircraft models that would weigh only a few ounces. He was aching to get on with the experimental work on that, but first he had to write the last instalment of his serial upon the Congreve clock. After that this heavy mail must be dealt with, and he would be too tired then, and it would be too late, to start off on experimental work. He was already inclined to be sleepy from his unaccustomed day in the open air.

He sat with Katie at the kitchen table over the macaroni cheese and the cups of strong tea. 'Get the light fixed up for them all right?' she asked.

'The light?' And then he recollected. 'Oh, the compass light. Yes, I fixed that for them.'

'What's it like in the boat?' she asked. 'How do they cook anything?'

'It's like a caravan,' he told her. 'They cook on Primus stoves.'

'Oh. With everything rocking about?'

'I suppose so.'

'It must be ever so uncomfortable.'

'I think it is,' he agreed. 'It looks all right when she's tied up in calm water, like she is now, but even then she goes up

18

and down a bit. I don't know what it's like when she gets out to sea, where it's rough. Wouldn't suit me.'

'Would the water come in, say in a storm?'

'I think it would. Of course, she's all decked in. I don't suppose that much would get inside.'

'It sounds awful. I mean, Jo was saying that one of them must be on top to steer. Why do they want to go like that, K? I mean, they've got plenty of money. Why don't they take a cabin on a proper ship, or else fly?'

'I dunno,' he said. 'I think they just like doing it.'

They sat in silence; they would never understand the Dermotts and there were times when they abandoned the attempt. At last Katie said, 'They won't get shipwrecked, will they?'

Keith shook his head. 'That's one thing they won't do. John's a naval officer and he knows all about it. They've got two sextants to take sights with to tell them where they are, and all the rest of it. They'll be safe enough. But if you ask me, they'll be darned uncomfortable.'

Katie gathered the plates together and put them on the draining board. 'I'm glad it's not me going with them.'

'So am I,' he said. 'I can't imagine anything much worse.'

CHAPTER TWO

SHEARWATER ROLLED LAZILY upon the ocean swell as she forged ahead under her twin spinnakers, making about three knots and towing the log line behind her. It was early in the morning and John Dermott was taking a sight upon the sun on their port quarter, dressed only in a pair of faded shorts. Jo sat at the tiller in blue jeans and shirt, watch in hand and pad and pencil at her side, taking the time for him.

They were three and a half months out from England, and now it was the middle of November. They had crossed the Atlantic to Barbados without incident though more slowly than they had anticipated; they had been delayed a little in the West Indies for a broken gooseneck to the boom, and they had been delayed for a long time at Panama after passing through the Canal waiting for a permit from the Ecuadorean Government to call for water at the Galapagos Islands. In the end they had sailed without a permit, had watered at Floreana without trouble, and proceeded on their way. They were thirty-four days out from Floreana, and all was well.

They had not hurried on their way. Thirty-six hours previously they had lain hove-to all night rather than approach the island of Reao in the darkness, their first landfall in the Tuamotu group of islands. With the coming of the dawn they had seen cloud forming above it and had sailed close enough to see the tops of the trees; then they had borne up and resumed their course towards the south and west, leaving the island ten miles to the north. They would not set foot on land until they reached the island of Tahiti, more than eight hundred miles ahead. They did not particularly want to do so; they had settled into the rhythm of their life at sea, the rain squalls, the warm easy days, the unending maintenance of sails and gear, the cooking and the housework down below. They had grown accustomed to this routine and liked it. For John Dermott it meant full occupation in the way of life that he preferred; shore life to him was now a matter of frustration and unwanted idleness. For Jo, this way of life meant a happy John.

She jotted down the altitudes as he called them out and the exact time from the watch in her hand, and gave the pad to him. He disappeared below to work the sight and plot it on the chart. He came on deck again after ten minutes. 'It *was* Reao?' she asked.

'It was Reao all right,' he replied. 'I think we're getting set just a bit to the north, though. You're still steering two four zero?'

She nodded.

'Make it two three five,' he said. 'Pinaki should be showing up upon the starboard bow before long. I want to pass about ten miles south of it.'

'There's a bit of cloud there now,' she said.

He stood looking at the little white patch on the horizon with her. 'Could be.' He went below, entered the change of course in the log, and came up again with the hand bearing compass and squatted on the cabin top with it, sighting upon the cloud. 'That's probably Pinaki.'

They sailed on all the morning over a long swell before a moderate south-east breeze, under a hot sun shrouded by occasional clouds. In good conditions such as these it was their habit to take their main meal in the middle of the day; Jo cooked a corned beef stew and an apple crumble from dried apples, and they had it in the cockpit. Then she went down to sleep. In the middle of the afternoon the sky clouded over, the wind got up suddenly, and a vicious rain squall swept down on them. They were accustomed to these short-lived tropical squalls and before it started John at the helm could see clear weather behind it. He carried on, the ship scudding before the strong breeze with everything taut and straining, but a seam in the port spinnaker suddenly let go, the sail ripped across, and there was nothing but a flapping shambles of loose sail and wildly flailing boom across the foredeck forward of the mast. John shouted but Jo was already awake and coming out on deck to take the helm; such incidents were part of their daily life and she was well accustomed to them. By the time John had got the sail down and the boom under control the sudden wind had dropped down to a gentle breeze, and they could see the squall driving away to leeward. They set the mainsail and the second jib, took in both spinnakers, and went on. Jo went down to finish her sleep before taking the first watch, and John spread out the damaged sail to dry in the cockpit with him while he measured and cut new sailcloth on his knees for the repair, sailing the ship as he did so.

They sailed on easily all night. Under twin spinnakers they could perhaps have slept at the same time, but running under the mainsail they had to steer the ship. Jo took the first watch until midnight, sailing easily under a bright crescent moon with little to do but to keep awake. She roused John as he had instructed her and he put on the Primus and made cocoa; they had it together in the cockpit before she handed over to him and went down to sleep.

At dawn they were still sailing easily. She relieved him at the helm, and presently when the sun was high enough he took another sight and went down to work out the position line. When she saw him plotting it upon the chart down in the cabin she called out, 'How do we go?'

'Not bad.' He brought the chart to the companion, and standing on the cabin ladder he showed it to her in the cockpit. 'We must be about *here*.' He made a little cross upon the chart. 'We might be a little south of the course now. I'll take a noon sight today, I think, and see if it makes sense.' He did not trust a sight with the sun practically overhead.

'How far before we change course, John?'

He took the chart back to the chart table and measured with dividers, and came back to the companion. 'About forty miles. Sometime this evening, if everything goes well.'

They had been sailing substantially the same course since leaving the Galapagos Islands thirty-five days before. 'What will the new course be?'

'Two hundred and seventy. An easy one.'

'That's for Tahiti?'

He nodded.

'I don't suppose the compass will work,' she said. 'It's probably got rusty and stuck up, we've been on this one for so long.'

He smiled. 'Like me to get breakfast?'

'No, you come and take her. I'll get breakfast. After that we'll have to mend that spinnaker.'

He nodded. 'We'll be bringing the wind more aft when we change course.'

All morning they worked on the spinnaker together in the cockpit. It was finished before the noon sight had to be taken but they did not set it, for the wind was still well on the quarter. The noon sight confirmed their position, for what that was worth, but when they went to check it with the reading of the log they found the line trailing idly; the rotator had been taken by a fish. They had left England with a dozen spare rotators and were now reduced to three; they fitted one of these last ones and started to get dinner.

They slept in turns all afternoon in overcast, rainy weather without much wind; in the hot humidity they paid little attention to getting wet at the helm save to wear a hat to keep the rain out of their eyes. The overcast prevented an evening sight. John stood for a while at the chart table weighing the doubtful evidence of the noon sight and of the log, the more certain evidence of the morning sight, which did not give much indication of the latitude, the landfall that they had made the day before at Pinaki. Eight o'clock, he thought, would be a convenient time for the change of course when Jo took over for the first watch; if the wind held as it was they would take in the main and the jib then and set the spinnakers. They should be far enough by that time to make the turn, but he was very conscious of the massed coral islands of the Tuamotus over the horizon to the north. He didn't want to get mixed up with that lot.

They followed on this plan, and started to change sails at half past seven, the wind still moderate from the east-south-east. By eight o'clock they had her settled under the twin spinnakers on the new course. 'I think this deserves a drink,' he said. At sea they drank little alcohol.

She smiled. 'Whisky and lime juice for me. The compass seems to be working, anyway.'

They had the sheets of the spinnakers rigged to the tiller and the ship would steer herself before the wind without attention. They watched her for a few minutes, and then went down into the cabin and sat with their drinks in the light of the oil lamp. 'What are the hazards, John?' she asked.

He pulled the chart over and showed it to her. 'Ahunui,' he said. He showed her the island. 'Should be about twenty miles to the north, and abeam about three in the morning. We probably shan't see it. After that there's nothing much until Tahiti.'

They finished their drinks and put their heads out on deck at the companion; the ship was sailing easily on course in a gentle breeze and a long swell, the tiller moving now and then to the pull of the sheets. In those waters there was little chance of meeting any other ship and they sailed without lights as one chore less to do. They went below together and slept intermittently, one or other being up on deck every hour or so.

All next day they sailed on placidly under the twin spinnakers, and the next night. The massed chain of islands constituting the Tuamotus now lay a hundred miles to the north of them; there was nothing in their path before Tahiti and they were making good about ninety sea miles each day. Rain squalls came occasionally without much strength in them. The barometer, which John watched unobtrusively but closely, pursued its regular diurnal variation according to the book. They began to make plans for cleaning the ship up, including themselves, before entering the harbour of Papeete.

Jo had been reading the sailing directions for entering the port. 'We can lie alongside there, at the Quai du Commerce,' she said. 'It's going to be good for getting the stores in, but we'll have to get everything all tiddley.'

John said, 'Going to be bad for little boys spitting on the deck. I think we'll lie off if we stay for any length of time.'

On the second morning after they changed course the barometer displeased him. It was two millibars lower than it should have been according to the book; he tapped it gently, mindful of the delicacy of the mechanism, but it showed no difference. Jo was on deck at the helm when he made this discovery, for the wind had got up a bit and was veering towards the south, and *Shearwater* was now careering along with the spinnakers at a cock-eyed angle fore and aft, and needed someone at the helm. He bit his lip, and looked again at the barometer, but there was no sense in trying to argue with the evidence. They were late at Tahiti, and the hurricane season was now on.

He sat down on his berth and turned to the sailing directions. He knew the part about tropical revolving storms pretty well by heart, for he was a careful seaman and had briefed himself before entering these waters. He read the page again. It fitted with his observations of the barometric pressure and the wind. Now it was up to him.

The wind had already veered a little, so the centre of the storm, if storm it was, must lie away to the northeast, two or three hundred miles away from them. It would probably move west-south-west towards them at about ten knots, far faster than they could sail to escape it. At some time it would turn towards the south. The wind direction showed them to be south of its path now. The course of safety was to run north and west before the increasing wind ... and north of them lay the coral islands of the Tuamotus. If they escaped the eye of the storm the wind would go on veering to the south and then to the south-west, blowing them dead on a lee shore.

They must make towards the west, every mile they could, to gain sea room.

He put the book back in the bookcase, and went on deck. He looked around; the spinnakers were straining. It would be unwise to carry them much longer, anyway. He said to Jo, 'I think we'll put the trysail on her, and take these in.'

The trysail was their storm mainsail. 'The trysail?' she asked.

'Barometer's dropping a bit,' he said.

'Oh.' She knew the situation almost as well as he did. 'Want any help?'

'Not yet.' He went below and bundled the heavy canvas up on deck through the forehatch, brought it aft of the mast and began to reeve the lacing, the halliard, and the sheets. It was work that he was well accustomed to and liked; while you were doing something physical like that you couldn't worry about falling glass and veering winds. He hoisted the sail in the calm air before the spinnaker and made the halliard fast, and pulled the sheet out to the cockpit, putting weight into the sail. Then he got down the lee spinnaker, and then the weather, stowing them both below. Finally he set the storm jib. Under the reduced canvas the yacht went more easily, with little reduction in her speed.

He came aft to the cockpit. Jo asked, 'Is anything bad coming?'

'I don't know,' he said. 'She's going all right like this, anyway.'

It was an hour since he had looked at the barometer. He went below and found that it had dropped another point; it was now three millibars below normal. He went back to his wife at the helm. 'I don't much like the look of it,' he said. 'We may be in for something.'

She smiled at him. 'Too bad.' She remembered that you steered in certain directions to avoid the path of a tropical storm, but it was different in the northern and the southern hemispheres, and all a bit complicated. 'Ought we to change course?'

He shook his head. 'I think we'll keep on as we're going for a bit. See what the wind does. Like me to take her?'

She relinquished the helm to him. 'I think I'll go below and make some sandwiches and put some coffee in the thermoses, if we're in for something.' She knew storms.

All morning the wind rose steadily, veering a little as it rose. The sun grew weaker, covered over with a thin layer of cloud. Before it disappeared for good John took a sight and came to the conclusion that they were in about latitude 19° 30' south, longitude 142° 35' west. The wind was now south of south-east blowing about Force 5 or rather more. By noon the barometer was five millibars lower than the normal reading.

There was now no doubt of the position in his mind, and he braced himself for what was coming. The wind would continue veering to the south and would increase in strength, driving them to the north on to the Tuamotus. A hundred and forty miles ahead of them and a little to the south of west lay an isolated atoll called Hereheretue; there was no harbour there, no entrance to the lagoon, and no safe landing in this weather. Yet if he could reach it he might shelter behind it from the fury of the storm, using it as a breakwater; in any event a more southerly course would take him further from the Tuamotus. He altered course to 245°, and his ship went racing along with a beam wind, making about six knots. At that rate they would reach the shelter of the atoll in about twenty-four hours, but from the first he doubted if they would make it.

They put on their waterproof storm clothing with bright orange lifejackets and waist lifelines that they could clip on to the rigging. They locked the forehatch down, and fitted the weatherboards over the glasses of the cabin skylight under the dinghy.

All day the wind increased and veered towards the south. They could take in one reef in the trysail with a lacing round the boom, and they took that in with difficulty towards evening. With the reduced canvas they made much more leeway, and now John Dermott gave up the attempt to reach Hereheretue. With the last of the light he backed the foresail a little and hove his vessel to on the port tack in the increasing wind; she lay fairly quietly, making about two knots to leeward in the direction of the Tuamotus. At any rate, he thought, they had made some useful offing.

They sat together in the cabin, dimly lit by the swaying oil lamp turned down low because it smoked with the motion, listening to the crash of the seas against the bow as the vessel rode the waves. Jo asked, 'Where do you think we are, John?'

He showed her on the chart.

'It's a bad one, this, isn't it?' she asked. He nodded.

28

'The worst we've ever had?'

'It might be,' he admitted. 'I'll tell you when it's over.'

'I suppose it's because we're late in getting here,' she said. She had known in theory that hurricanes were apt to happen in those waters from November onwards. Now that theoretical knowledge was being translated into fact.

'We're not so late as all that,' he said a little resentfully. 'This is an early one.'

She knew that he had first proposed that they should leave England in June. 'We had to see Janice settled for the summer holidays.'

He nodded. 'We couldn't have started any earlier.'

Presently they lay down on their berths to get what rest they could. From time to time Dermott got up and put his head out of the hatch; the wind seemed stronger every time he looked, and the sea higher. Each time the ship's head pointed, on the wildly veering average, a little more towards the west and north.

At about three in the morning there was a great crack, the ship's motion changed, and a wild beating of heavy canvas was heard above them. They tumbled out on deck, and saw in the light of a flashlight through the flying scud that the jib had gone; only the bolt ropes remained with tattered streamers of canvas flying from them. Without the jib the ship had come up to the wind, and the heavy blocks of the trysail sheets were flailing the cockpit, threatening death to anybody in their way.

Without the jib he could not lie the vessel to in such a wind. He shouted to Jo to get a warp from the forecastle and went forward carefully himself on deck, clipping his lifeline on to something fresh at every two or three steps. At the mast he slacked off the main halliard and let the trysail down and quietened it; with the warp that Jo had brought up to him from below they furled the trysail on the main boom, wrapping it round with the rope.

29

Without any sail at all the yacht now lay rolling wildly in the trough of the waves, safe enough for the time being, but blowing to the north. John Dermott sent his wife below to get some rest, and stayed in the cockpit himself to watch his vessel and assess the situation. The wind was now only about a point to the east of south and this was good so far as it went, for it indicated that the centre of the storm might pass southwards of them. The sea, however, was rising very high; in the grey of the dawn it seemed to be breaking everywhere around him. He judged that his ship was drifting to the north at the rate of three to four knots.

The line of the Tuamotus to the north of him ran about north-west to south-east. The more he could get towards the west, the more sea room he would have to the north. He took the helm and set himself to sail his vessel under bare poles as much towards the west as he could manage. He found that he could steer about north-west upon his compass parallelling the line of islands, and at that he seemed to make about five knots with the wind on his quarter. But now, running in that way, the seas behind were menacing and occasionally the top of one came on board, lukewarm, flooding the cockpit and drenching the helmsman. From below, Jo put the fashionboards in the companion.

'How are we doing?' she asked.

'All right,' he said. 'If we can keep going like this I think we'll be all right. It's doing what they tell you in the book, anyway.' Deep in his heart he knew that they could not maintain that course much longer.

At seven o'clock in the increasing wind and sea he could no longer run towards the west, taking the seas upon his quarter, without fear of broaching to and being overwhelmed by the rising sea. Each time a big sea came, and they now came very often, he had to run off before it taking it dead stern-on, so that now he was making about five knots towards the Tuamotus in the north.

This could not go on. He had a sea anchor in the forecastle, a conical canvas drogue stiffened by a hoop of iron, and he called Jo up from below to come and take the helm while he rigged this thing. *Shearwater* was a cutter with a shape below the waterline that was cut away at the bow and deep at the rudder, making her easy to tack and manoeuvre in the narrow seas and waterways of the Solent, for which she had been primarily designed. Running before the wind she was very stable by reason of the windage of the mast, but held up to the wind by a sea anchor from the bow she would not be good, unlikely to lie closer than forty-five degrees to wind and sea. She had a canoe stern, however, fairly well tucked up. He decided to put out his sea anchor from the stern, battening the companion down and retiring below, using the forehatch for getting out on deck.

He bent his heaviest warp on to the sea anchor, made the other end fast around both pairs of stern mooring bitts, and put the drogue overboard, taking a turn of the warp round one of the bitts as he paid out to ease the strain. The warp strained like a bowstring as the drogue sank in and took hold of the water; then the ship slowed, the strain eased, and he paid out the remainder slowly.

He sent Jo below and stood himself on the companion steps for a while behind the fashionboards, his head out of the hatch, watching the seas. The ship was riding well to her sea anchor, her buoyant stern lifting to the seas so that little came on board. The wind had steadily increased, however, and he judged that now it was blowing at about Force 8. It was so strong that it seemed to be blowing the tops off the seas in the form of flying scud beneath the heavily overcast sky flattening the very seas; the warp stretched taut behind the vessel to the submerged drogue, hard as a bar. With this increasing wind the speed of the ship through the water did not seem to be very much reduced; she still seemed to be making about three knots towards the north. Visibility was now only a few hundred yards.

He went below and secured the companion hatch behind him. In the cabin it was dark and stuffy, lit only by one small glass port, tight shut, at the galley, and another at the companion. He went forward and lifted the forehatch a little, letting some air into the ship, and then came back and sat upon his berth, opposite Jo. He pulled the chart over to him from the chart table and sat studying it.

Jo leaned across in the dim light. 'Where do you think we are?'

He did not know with any certainty. 'I should say we're about here.' He laid his finger on the chart. Actually he was further to the north and not so far to the west, but he did not know that.

'What happens next?' she asked.

'We'll just have to lie like this now till it moderates,' he said. 'I think the centre will pass south of us.'

'How long before it moderates?' she asked.

'Two days, I should think,' he said. 'Two days. Maybe, three.'

'Have we got that much room?' she asked.

He shook his head. 'No,' he said. 'No, I don't think we have.'

'Too bad.' She smiled a little, and then said, 'Tell me, do you think we're going to pile her up?'

He glanced up at her. 'I hope not,' he replied. He ran his fingers down the line of the Tuamotus. 'The line of islands isn't very thick, and there's deep water all between them. We can steer her a bit downwind, running, if there's any visibility we should be able to run through them.' He paused, and then said a little bitterly, 'Like a drunk crossing the traffic in the Strand.'

'We aren't drunk,' she said gently. 'A bit out of luck, perhaps, but not drunk.'

He glanced at her. 'I'm sorry about this, Jo.'

'We'll be all right,' she said. 'Lie down and get some sleep.'

They lay down and rested, if not slept. The motion of the ship was too violent for any cooking, but in the course of the afternoon Jo managed to light a Primus and to brew some strong, sweet chocolate, and this revived them a little. She still had a few sandwiches left, but neither of them could eat. The bilge water was slopping over the cabin floor; inevitably a wooden ship will leak a little under such strains, and in the last two days a good deal of water had found its way below.

In the middle of the afternoon John Dermott decided to pump the ship out. He pulled up the floorboards near the engine and left Jo to keep the suction clear of any debris in the bilge, and went out on deck himself by the forehatch. He was startled and concerned at the strength of the wind now, and the steepness of the seas behind them. As the yacht's stern rose upon the forward slope of each great wave the warp to the sea anchor stretched out taut behind her, the water pattering off it with the strain; then the crest passed, the surf filling the cockpit, and the rope relaxed.

He crept aft on hands and knees on deck against the wind and the loose surf of each wave crest that slapped at him. With each step he refastened his lifeline, for the danger of being swept overboard was now a real one. He gained the cockpit, but he did not immediately begin to pump the ship. The sea anchor warp was more urgent, and he turned his attention to that.

He had wrapped three teacloths around the rope at the stern fairhead, tying them to the warp with marline, to take the chafe. They were just about worn through; he cut the marline, working mostly under water, and remade the packing. The rope below the cloths did not seem to be damaged. He crouched waist-deep in water in the flooded cockpit, watching it for a time. Everything seemed to be holding, but the strain was immense. If the sea anchor went – or when it went – there would then be nothing to be done but to come to the helm and steer the ship, running under bare poles before the storm towards the islands.

He turned and started work upon the pump. There was a little opening glass porthole in the aft side of the cabin top by the companion, and from time to time Jo opened this to tell him how the water level was before shutting it again. It took him about an hour to clear the ship of water, sitting mostly in lukewarm water up to the waist in the force of the gale. By the time he had finished and the pump had sucked he was exhausted, but he did not immediately go forward to the hatch.

He made another inspection of the sea anchor warp; it looked all right. He sat for a time looking round the horizon. An early dusk was creeping down upon the scene. He could see nothing but blown spray and breaking, towering seas; he did not think he could see further than about two hundred yards. There was nothing to indicate the presence of land, but then he knew there wouldn't be until they saw and heard the breakers.

He glanced around at his ship. She seemed to be in perfect condition, but for the tatters of the sail upon the jibstay. The helm swung quietly and loose. The ends of halliards and sheets were streaming overboard; they did not matter. Seeing the strength and order of his ship, he felt suddenly tired, As usual, he thought, the ship was stronger than the people in her.

He took a final glance at the compass; the wind had gone round further, and was now west of south, blowing harder than ever. The eye of the storm would pass to the south of them now, though pretty close; before the wind eased it would haul round into the west. Before then, he knew, they would be in among the Tuamotus. He left the cockpit and crawled forward to the forehatch, waited his chance, then opened it and slipped below, pulling it down behind him.

He was shivering a little, more from fatigue and shock than from cold. They heated up the remainder of the cocoa and drank that, and then lay down, fully clothed with lifebelts on, in their sodden clothes upon their sodden berths. There was nothing further to be done on deck; it was more important now to conserve their strength.

Darkness came swiftly, but they did not attempt to light the lamp. They had electric torches, and there were still dry spare batteries in sealed tins. They lay trying to rest, listening to the struggle of the ship, the wash of waves along the deck over their heads, and the insensate screaming of the wind. Presently they may have slept a little.

At about ten o'clock John Dermott went out on deck again to adjust the wrappings round the warp. Conditions were similar but it was dark as pitch and raining hard, or so it seemed to him for it was only possible to distinguish rain from the blown spume by taste. He worked largely by feel, renewed the wrappings, and returned down below.

'We'll have to stand a watch as soon as it gets light,' he said. 'We may be getting pretty close to something by tomorrow.'

'Would you like me to go up now?'

He shook his head. 'We're all right for tonight. You can't see anything up there, anyway. Hardly the ship's length.'

'What's the wind doing?'

'Seems to be a bit more over in the west.'

They lay down on their berths again, but not for the whole night. Soon after midnight the yacht surged forward on the forward slope of a wave, a motion they were well accustomed to, and did not check her run. Instead she went surging forward wildly and then round in a crazy turn to port, throwing John out on to the cabin floor. Then she was thrown on her beam ends and buried in the seas; everything fell down on to the starboard side within the cabin, John on top of Jo in a mass of tins, books, tools, bedding, sextants, and cooking gear. The ship lay on her side for what seemed an age till gradually she rose again as they struggled free and to their feet in a foot of water over the cabin deck.

They knew what had happened; the vessel had broached to. In fact, the sea anchor warp had chafed and parted at the drogue end, and now the yacht was lying broadside on and at the mercy of the waves. They ripped the companion hatch back and struggled into the cockpit, and as they did so she went over again in a breaking sea.

She came up again more slowly, sluggishly, and they were both still there in the cockpit. The companion hatch had been half open, and she had taken much water in through it; she now lay heavily and sluggishly at least a foot deeper in the water, in the trough of the waves. But Dermott had the helm now and was steering her round down wind, and Jo had slammed the hatch shut and bolted it. When the next wave came they took it stern-on and she rose to it with far less than her normal buoyancy, but rise she did; the top of the crest swept green across them but they did not broach again. There was now a little faint light on the scene, probably due to the moon above the clouds.

John said quietly, 'Start pumping, Jo. We'll take it in turns.'

She bent to the pump and began the endless, backbreaking motion on the handle. Presently he gave her the helm and took the pump himself; so they continued alternately pumping and steering for the rest of the night, while the wind screamed around them and the surf beat on them. From time to time the suction blocked with debris in the bilge; then John had to wait his chance to open the companion hatch for a moment to get down into the flooded cabin, shut the hatch above him, and, working with his hands and arms deep in the water in pitch darkness, clear the pump. The night passed like this, but when the grey cold light begun to make things visible the ship was buoyant again, almost clear of water.

In the cockpit as they rested, Jo asked, 'Did you think we'd had it that time, John?'

'I don't know that I had time to think of anything except getting her straight and running,' he replied. 'When we got her running I knew that we were going to make it all right.'

She said, 'I've been thinking so much about Janice.'

'Don't,' he said gently. 'We'll have her with us in a month or two.'

'If we get out of this.'

'We'll get out of it, all right,' he said. 'But if anything should happen, if we buy it, she couldn't be with anybody better than Katie and Keith.'

'They'll look after her,' she said. 'But she's only ten. And, John, they haven't any money.'

'She'll have money,' he replied. 'It's all left in trust to Keith for her, until she's twenty-five. She'll get as good an education as anyone can get, and after that she'll have a good lump sum. Don't you remember how we made our wills?'

'But, John, she won't have anything! We've got it all here!'

He stared at her in the half light. 'I never thought of that.' This was another disaster that had come upon him, and one that hit him far harder than any that had come so far. The approach of the storm, the parting of the jib, the chafing of the sea anchor warp, the broaching to, the nearness of the Tuamotus – these were challenges to his seamanship. When you went to sea and crossed the world in a small yacht you wagered your courage and your skill against the elements with your life as the stake, and if you were good you usually won. It was what you went to sea for in this game; if you didn't like the game you needn't play it. He had wanted to play it because the sea was his whole life, and Jo had wanted to play it with him because she loved him. Now, suddenly and without warning, his small child's future had been added to the stake.

Inevitably, perhaps, he held strongly right-wing views: he was a conservative in politics. He held that if a man worked hard and well and saved money he had a right to pass some of it on to his children, especially if they were girls, who usually got a raw deal anyway. He approved of moderate death duties because he did not hold that grandchildren should live in idleness because grandfather had worked; all people ought to work, as he had worked for the Navy himself. He held, however, that it was the duty and the right of every decent man to give his children as good a start in life as he had had himself. He had been blessed with money from the start and he had tried to use it wisely and to save it for his child so that she should grow up in the way of life he was accustomed to. That she should go to the council school and be fed and clothed by charity was quite unthinkable.

Joanna did not follow him in all of this. For twenty years she had lived as a naval officer's wife and she had absorbed a good deal of it, but she had come from a labourer's home and had gone to the council school herself in Renfrew. She had raised herself when she went on to the stage with a serious, well-managed troupe of girls; she had raised herself again when she had married John Dermott. In many ways she was now more conservative than he. The slum streets and the council school were not terrifying novelties to her for she had come from them, but she had long been determined that Janice was going to have no part of them. She had borne Janice into a different world, a world of naval officers and impoverished noblemen in Northern Ireland, and she was going to stay there.

As the full daylight came they could see the binnacle, and see that the wind was now about west-south-west by their compass. At the same time, it had risen higher than ever, and was now screaming in their ears, deafening them, so that John judged it to be Force 10 or more. The sky cleared with the morning so that they could see much further than before, and away to the south there seemed to be a line of blue sky just above the sea. John pointed it out to Jo, and put his lips to her cold ear. 'That'll be the eye of the storm,' he shouted.

'Passing south of us?'

He nodded. There were no great waves now, just a smoking, hissing sea flattened by the insensate torrent of the wind. To talk was an effort and a strain; it was better to conserve their strength. They sat in silence, each busy with their thoughts turning over slowly in their stunned minds.

John Dermott was thinking always of the ship. She was still sound and practically undamaged. The mainsail and the trysail were still lashed firm upon the boom, ready for use. No sails could stand a minute in such wind; it was no good thinking about them. There was one resource still left to them, however. They still had a little engine.

He had scant faith in it, but it was there. In dead calm weather it would give the ship a speed of about four knots for going in and out of harbour or up windless estuaries, but the wind was now blowing sixty knots or more. This puny little engine, if he could make it work, could not affect the major issues of their course, yet if he could get it going it might serve to pull them out of trouble somehow. It was the last resource still left unused.

He gave the helm to Jo and went below, shutting the companion after him. In the light of his torch he saw that the battery had been thrown from its crate when the ship broached to and was lying on its side; everything was streaming with sea water. He stood the battery upright, checked the leads, and tried a light switch. There was the faintest of red glimmers from the filament, which faded as he watched.

There was no help in the starter. He wiped the magneto and the plug leads with a wet handkerchief, having searched in vain for a dry cloth, and tried her on the handle. For a quarter of an hour he laboured over her, and never got a kick. Finally he gave up the effort and went back on deck. There was no help in the engine.

While he was below, Jo sat at the helm in dull despair. The huge efforts needed to pull the tiller continuously one way or the other to keep the ship stern-on to the seas were draining the last of her strength; she could still make them mechanically but she was now near collapse. There was no ending to this storm and would not be for days and days and days; the ship might see it through if she had fresh hands at the helm, but they would not. She was near failure now, she knew; half an hour longer, or perhaps an hour, and she would be no longer able to swing the tiller. Then the ship would broach to and lie swept by every sea; they would be drowned. *Shearwater* would fill and sink, and Janice's future would sink with her. She was too tired now to care about themselves, but Janice was a sharp pain. Keith would look after her and bring her up, and he would do it well. But he would have to bring her up into his own way of life, not theirs; at sixteen she would have to start work in a shop.

John Dermott came back to the cockpit and took the helm from her. 'No good,' he shouted in her ear.

She shouted back, 'Won't it go?' He shook his head, and she settled down beside him, listless.

About the middle of the morning something in the water ahead drew John's attention. He gave the helm to Jo and stood up against the companion, the wind tearing at his clothing, lashed by the spray. Visibility was between one and two miles. There was something different half a mile or so ahead of him; the backs of the seas looked different in some way. Then, over to the left a little, in a quick, passing glimpse, he saw what looked like the tops of palm trees above the waves.

He turned with a heavy heart, and went back to his wife. 'There seems to be an island dead ahead,' he shouted. 'I think we're driving down on to a reef.'

She nodded. She was now past caring.

He took her hand. 'I'm sorry about this, Jo.'

She smiled at him. 'It doesn't matter.'

'Can you take her a bit longer?' he asked. 'I want to see if we can dodge it.'

She nodded, and he stood up again by the companion. It was clearer now, for they were closer. What he had seen was the backs of great combers breaking on a coral reef; the line of different surf extended both on port and starboard hands as far as he could see. He searched desperately for a break in the surf, something to indicate a passage through the reef into the sheltered lagoon that might lie beyond. If there were any break he would try and steer her off and run in through it, even though they might be overwhelmed in the process. He could see no break at all; it all looked just the same on either hand as far as he could see. There was no escape for them now. *Shearwater* was driving straight on to a coral reef in the Tuamotus somewhere and would leave her bones upon the coral as many a tall ship had done before. He had not the remotest idea where they were.

He came back to her and took the helm. In bad moments in the last forty-eight hours he had imagined this situation, and had thought it out. Better to take the coral straight, head-on, than to be thrown on to it on their beam ends, to have the hull crushed like an eggshell by the fury of the waves. Better to take it head-on, taking the shock on the lead keel and trying to keep stern-on to the seas. Reefs were seldom uniform in height; if they had the luck to strike a fissure, a patch where in calm water the coral was a couple of feet or more below the surface, they might possibly be driven over it into the lagoon, and still float, and live. He bent to explain this to his wife.

'I want you to go below,' he shouted. 'When we strike, stay in the hull. She'll probably get full of water, but stay in the hull. Just keep your head above the water, but stay inside.'

She shouted, 'What are you going to do?'

'I'm going to stay up here and steer her on. I'll join you down below as soon as she strikes. It's our best chance. I don't think she'll break up.'

'If she breaks up, she'll stay on the reef, won't she?'

He knew what was in her mind. 'The keel will, and probably the frames.' He paused, and then leaned across and kissed her. 'Now go below. I'm sorry to have got you into this.'

She kissed him in return. 'It's not your fault.' She stood up, waited her chance, opened the hatch and slipped down below, leaving it open for him to follow her.

She sat down on one of the settees, the first-aid box in her hands. There were now only a few minutes to go. She thought she ought to say a prayer, but it seemed mean to have neglected God and her religion for so long and then to pray when death was imminent; the words would not come. She could only think of Janice, Janice whose future happiness lay buried in the concrete beneath her feet. The concrete would survive upon the coral reef, but nobody would ever know of it but Keith, Keith who had never made much of his life, Keith who had never been anywhere or done anything, Keith to whose keeping she had trusted Janice.

From the cockpit John Dermott shouted above the screaming of the wind, 'Next one, Jo!'

In those last moments the power of prayer came to her, and she muttered in the accents of her childhood, 'Lord, gie Keith a bit o' guid sense.'

Then they struck.

CHAPTER THREE

AT ABOUT ELEVEN in the morning the telephone bell rang upstairs. Keith Stewart stopped his lathe, wiped his hands, and went up the narrow wooden stairs to answer it. The girl said, 'Mr Stewart? This is Gordon and Carpenter. Just one moment – Mr Carpenter is calling.'

In a moment the solicitor came on the line. Keith had met him once before, a heavy, methodical man whose office was in Bedford Square. He said, 'Mr Stewart, have you had any news of your brother-in-law and your sister? Do you know if they have reached Tahiti yet?'

'I haven't heard anything. Not since they left Panama.'

'Nor have I. I would have thought that they'd have cabled their arrival by this time.'

It seemed an unnecessary extravagance to Keith. 'An air letter would do. That's what they've been sending all along.'

'Yes, I know. The airmail to Tahiti is very infrequent, though. All mail seems to be infrequent to Tahiti. They're building an aerodrome there now, but it's not working yet. I would have expected a cable to say they had arrived. But you haven't heard anything?'

'No, I haven't. They should be there by this time, though, shouldn't they?'

'The last letter I had was from Panama posted on September 29th. Commander Dermott says in that they expect to arrive in Papeete on November the 20th. Well, here we are, and it's December the 1st. We should have heard something by now.'

They discussed the possibilities of delay in arrival and delay in mails for a minute or two. Finally Mr Carpenter said, 'There's no British Consul in Papeete. I think I'll send the Governor a short cable asking if there's any news of their arrival.'

Keith went back to his lathe, vaguely disquieted. He had a great respect for John's solicitor. In his lifetime he had never had much to do with the Law. He had met solicitors from time to time; some that he had met in pubs were clearly not so good. Others had been better; one had come to see him once because he was making the little Burrell traction engine and was in trouble with the governor, and because of that he had handled the purchase of the Ealing house for Keith. Mr Carpenter, John's solicitor, was different again, part of the wider world, John's world, infinitely competent and infinitely courteous. Keith would have hesitated to suggest that Mr Carpenter should take his work.

When Katie came in she gave Janice and Keith their tea, and then he read an Enid Blyton book to Janice for half an hour till it was time for her to have her bath and go to bed. Katie looked after that, and he went down to his desk in the basement to write an article about fusible plugs. He sat for a long time fingering the four little screwed pieces that had been loaded with the different solders, the paper ready to his hand, but the words would not come. It was incredible that anything could have happened.

When Janice was safely in bed in the room beside his workshop, he went upstairs and told Katie all about it in the parlour. 'I don't think anything could have happened,' he said uneasily. 'It's just that they haven't got there yet.'

Katie said, 'They wouldn't have got jammed among all that ice, would they?'

He knew that she had it in her mind that John and Jo had taken a course somewhere over the North Pole, but how she had got hold of that idea he did not know. He pulled out the school atlas that they had. 'They didn't go that way,' he explained. 'It's hot the way they went.' He turned to the map of the Pacific. 'Down here.' He traced the route from Panama to Tahiti with his finger.

'Oh, I remember. It looks an awful long way, Keith. All that blue would mean it's sea, wouldn't it?'

'That's right,' he said. 'It *is* a long way.' He studied the longitudes with an eye well accustomed to calculations. 'It's – it's seventy-five degrees. That's more than a fifth of the way round the world.' He checked the figures in wonder.

She stared at him. 'All in one trip? I mean, not landing anywhere in all that way?'

'I don't think so.'

'Well, they might take any time. I mean, the wind might be against them.'

'I suppose so,' he said doubtfully. 'I think it's quite all right. Still, we'd better not say anything in front of Janice.'

'There couldn't be anything wrong, though, could there?'

'I dunno. I don't like that Mr Carpenter sending cables all about the world. Don't look as though *he's* any too happy.'

For the next two days he was restless and ill at ease, mainly because he felt himself to be quite incapable of assessing the situation. He knew nothing about yachts or the sea; the oceans to him were something painted blue upon the pages of the atlas and no more. He had never been out of England. He had sailed once on an afternoon's excursion in an old paddle steamer from Weymouth to Lulworth Cove, a distance of six miles; he had liked the look of the cliffs from the water but had been appalled at the machinery and interested in its antiquity till the smells of the engine room coupled with the slight motion of the vessel made him sick. He knew that this experience was no guidance for assessing any hazards that might lie around his sister on her voyage, and his ignorance distressed and worried him.

Mr Carpenter rang him up again on the morning of the 3rd. 'Mr Stewart,' he said, 'I wonder if you could come up and see me? I've got an answer to that cable, and there's a good deal that I think we should discuss.'

'Have they got to Tahiti?'

'Not yet,' said the solicitor. 'I'm having further enquiries made out there. But in the meantime, I would like to see you if you could look in.'

'I can come up now, if you like,' said Keith. 'I don't punch a clock.'

They fixed a time; Keith took off his apron and washed his hands, put on his dark suit, and started off towards the bus. It was raining with a cold December drizzle; he wore a greasy old raincoat and an equally greasy old soft hat; he had a shabby muffler round his throat. He was pale with lack of sun and exercise, and running a bit to fat. He looked, as he sat in the trolley bus taking him to Ealing Broadway, like any one of thousands of men to be seen in buses in any industrial district, and he was.

He got to the solicitor's office at about half past eleven, and he was shown straight in. Mr Carpenter got up from his desk to meet him. 'I told you that I had an answer to that cable, Mr Stewart,' he said directly. 'I'm afraid it isn't very satisfactory.'

He passed the flimsy to Keith, who could not read it without the steel-rimmed spectacles he always had to use for close work. He undid his shabby coat, fumbled for his spectacle case, and put them on. The cable was in English, and it read:

NATIVES FROM KAUTAIVA ISLAND REPORT SMALL VESSEL WRECKED IN HURRICANE NOVEMBER 19TH ON REEF OFF

MAROKOTA ISLAND BODIES ONE MAN ONE WOMAN BURIED
MAROKOTA STOP SHEARWATER NOW MUCH OVERDUE
MAKING FURTHER ENQUIRIES.

ADMINISTRATION PAPEETE.

The solicitor, watching closely, saw the fat, pallid lips quiver
a little. The shabby little man stood motionless, staring at
the cable. 'Sit down, Mr Stewart,' he said gently. 'I'm afraid
this isn't very good news.' He went on talking, as was his
habit upon these occasions. 'There's nothing very definite
in that,' he said. 'As you see, it seems to be just a rumour
brought to Tahiti by natives from another island. We can't
come to any conclusion till we get more news.'

Keith sat down heavily, loosening his muffler. 'It's
terrible,' he muttered. 'I never thought anything like this
could happen.'

'We must hope that it isn't true,' the solicitor said. 'I
thought it was sufficiently serious to ask you to come up,
though. I didn't want to read this out to you upon the
telephone.'

Keith said, 'Thank you, sir.'

He raised his eyes. 'I've got their daughter staying with us
in the flat,' he said. 'I'll have to tell her, won't I?'

'How old is she? Twelve, is it?'

'Ten. Only ten.'

The solicitor tightened his lips. 'If it's true, she'll have to
be told some time, Mr Stewart,' he said. 'I should talk it over
with your wife. When you've had time to think this over for
a little you may decide it's better to wait until the news is
definite.'

Keith asked, 'You think it's definite now, don't you? I
mean, you think they've been drowned?'

'I think the Governor thinks it's definite,' Mr Carpenter
said carefully. 'I don't think that he would have cabled quite
in those terms unless he was fairly sure.'

47

Keith laid the cable down upon the desk. 'It's got to happen to us all, some day,' he said. 'It's when it happens suddenly, to your own people, it comes as a bit of a blow.'

'I know.'

The solicitor picked up a sheaf of papers from his desk. 'I don't know if you want to talk about the future just now, Mr Stewart, or if you would rather come up again when we know more. If, unhappily, your sister and her husband should be dead, a new set of circumstances comes into being, as you probably know.'

'I know they wanted us to take care of Janice if anything happened,' Keith said. 'It might be better if we talk about that now.'

'You know the contents of their wills?'

'I think so. They wanted me to be trustee or something. I said I would.'

'Yes. That was at our previous meeting, in this office. It was after that meeting that I drew up these wills.' He handled them upon the desk before him. 'They are very simple wills, Mr Stewart. I don't think I should show them to you till the deaths are established, but as you are already acquainted with the most important features I think we can discuss what may arise from them.' He paused. 'Both wills are in identical terms, as perhaps you know. That seems to make it immaterial which spouse died first. Each will leaves the entire estate to the surviving spouse. If the spouse should be already dead, then the entire estate passes to the daughter Janice, to be held in trust for her until she attains the age of twenty-five. You are appointed the sole trustee, and you and I are appointed joint executors to the wills. In consideration of your trusteeship, you are to receive the sum of one thousand pounds from the estate.' He paused. 'If the daughter should decease before the expiration of the trust, or if she should be already dead, you receive the same legacy of one thousand pounds, but the balance of the estate passes back to the Dungannon family.'

'That means, I'd have to sort of look after the money for her and give it her when she gets to be twenty-five, does it?'

'That is correct, Mr Stewart. Both wills name you as the guardian of the child Janice and both wills appoint you as the sole trustee. You would have to invest the money for her in certain selected securities that we call Trustee Stocks, and you would devote the interest to her education and general benefit during the period of the trust. In case of necessity you have power to realise some of the capital for her benefit.'

'I've never had to do anything like that before,' Keith said doubtfully.

The solicitor nodded. 'You may need a little help. I realise that. If you have confidence in your own solicitor he would be the best person to assist you. Otherwise, I should be glad to.'

Mr Cannon had made a nice little model of the Burrell traction engine, but privately Keith did not think that he had handled the purchase of the house at Ealing any too well. It had taken a long time and there had been trouble with the Council over the alterations, which might not have been his fault. 'I'd be grateful, if it's not putting you out.' He meant, if the scale of the business was worth the time of a man like Mr Carpenter. 'Do you know how much money there might be?'

The solicitor turned over the papers on his desk. 'I hold a power of attorney both for your sister and for her husband,' he said. 'I know of three bank accounts. Your sister has an account at Southsea, your brother-in-law has one at Alverstoke, and he has another at the head office of the bank here in London, in Throgmorton St. When I began to get troubled about their non-arrival at Tahiti I wrote to all three banks for a statement of account and a list of securities that they might be holding on behalf of my clients, using the power of attorney.'

He paused. 'The Throgmorton St office report a credit balance of fifty-six pounds eighteen shillings and fourpence,' he said. 'Your brother-in-law's account at Alverstoke is three pounds four shillings and tenpence in credit. Your sister's account in Southsea shows a debit balance – that is to say, an overdraft – of four pounds sixteen shillings and fivepence. Adding those up, there seems to be a total credit balance of fifty-five pounds six shillings and ninepence. All three banks state that they are holding no securities.'

Keith stared at him. 'But that's daft. I mean, they've got more than fifty-five pounds!'

'I have always imagined so, myself,' said Mr Carpenter. 'I must say, at the moment I am perplexed. Do you know of any other bank accounts that they might have had, or where they might have deposited their securities?'

Keith shook his head. 'They never talked of things like that. Not to me, anyway.'

'Oh. I had hoped that you might have the answer.' The solicitor paused in thought. 'I have a number of Commander Dermott's papers in my keeping,' he remarked. 'When he gave up his flat he left a suitcase full of receipts and correspondence with me, with instructions to send it to him later on in Canada, or wherever he decided to settle. Probably I shall find the answer in that.' He thought for a moment. 'He certainly told me that the contents were receipts and correspondence. But probably the share certificates themselves are there. I shall have to look and see.'

'That's where they'll be,' said Keith. 'Do you know how much money they might have left? I mean, if they *are* dead?'

'Commander Dermott gave me to understand that the estate would be between twenty and twenty-five thousand pounds.'

'That's about what I thought,' said Keith.

They left it that they would meet again when Mr Carpenter had received further news from the Administration in Papeete, by which time he hoped to have found the missing securities. Keith lunched absent-mindedly in a Lyons cafeteria, and went back all the way to Ealing down Oxford Street, through Notting Hill Gate and Shepherd's Bush, on top of a bus, deeply troubled in his mind. He had loved his sister though in recent years he had seen little of her, and he had felt honoured when John Dermott had suggested that he should be their trustee and guardian of their daughter, rather than one of their naval friends or one of their relations in Northern Ireland. They had chosen him, he knew, because of his stable life, because he was always there, in the same place, with the same wife, doing the same things; the Dungannons fell in and out of marriage with the greatest alacrity and *savoir faire*; their naval friends were apt to uproot and go to Kenya or Hong Kong. They knew that through wars and rumours of war, whatever happened in the greater world, Keith Stewart would go on living at No. 56 Somerset Road, Ealing, because his workshop was there, built up and established over the years. To uproot all his machine tools and remove the whole of his equipment to another house would mean a dislocation to his work that was unthinkable. He was anchored firmly in the same place by his workshop, and by his own inclinations.

He got back to his house an hour before Janice was due back from school, his mind full of his little niece. If her parents were indeed dead, they would have to tell her, but he could not imagine how they were going to do it. Katie might have some ideas; Katie was good with children. His mind ranged on beyond the bad half-hour to the part that he could play. Janice would have to have something to play with, to take her mind off death. A doll's house? She already had one, and was getting a bit old for it. A bicycle? Not old enough, and children didn't seem to have them nowadays, perhaps because of the traffic. A scooter? Somerset Road was a quiet bye-street that carried no through traffic; she could use a scooter there and be in no danger, and it would take her out of doors, and keep her warm. His mind ranged over the job. He had a couple of eight-inch, rubber-tyred wheels left over from a little traction engine passenger truck, and he could bore them out to take a ball race each side. Inch-and-a-quarter steel tube for the steering head, parallel five-eighths tubes for the frame; he could braze that up in no time. Make the handlebars first, because they would have to be chrome-plated. He had some red paint for the rest of it, which would make it look gay. He went down to the workshop directly he got home and took the little bronze sphere of the automatic pilot from the bench and packed it carefully away in rags in an old cigar box with its tiny transistor rectifier and the delicate relays, clearing the decks for a more mundane job, and started work upon the handlebars. Better to work at something than to sit thinking of Joanna and their childhood together in the Renfrew streets.

When Janice came in he suggested that she should draw a farm with all the animals for him, and he took her down with him to the workshop and settled her down at his desk with a large sheet of paper, clearing away letters from Cornwall and Colchester and California to make a space for her. He went on working at the handlebars, which were too immature as yet to draw her notice, and as he worked he measured her furtively with his eye for the height of the steering head. Thirty-two inches from the ground ... From time to time he stopped work to admire her picture.

That evening, after Janice was in bed, he told Katie all about it. 'This chap in this place Papeete – the Governor – he thinks they're dead,' he said heavily. 'There's no doubt of that.'

'It might have been some other boat,' she suggested.

'They buried two people,' he replied, 'a man and a woman. On this other island, Maro ... something or other.'

They looked for it on the atlas unavailingly. 'Ought we to tell her?' he asked.

She shook her head. 'Not now. Wait till we know for sure. She's not old enough for things not being certain.'

'I started to make her a scooter,' he said. 'I'll keep it under cover, all in bits, until we know.'

'That'll be nice for her,' she said. 'She can use it up and down the pavement, not in the road.'

He told her about the missing securities. 'He'll find them, all right,' he said. 'I mean, they must be there somewhere.'

'They couldn't have taken them with them, in the boat?'

'That's possible,' he remarked. 'They might have done that. But then, that wouldn't matter, because they'd still be the owner of the shares in companies in England, or where have you. It just means that the lawyers would have to get copies. Be a bit more expense. The money would be there just the same.'

She did not fully understand this, but let it pass. 'Until it's all squared up, though, there's just fifty-five pounds?'

He nodded. 'Not much to bring her up on, not in the way they'd want. But it'll be all right. The money must be somewhere.'

'It's enough,' she said. 'She'd live with us till she's grown up, like as if she was our own kid. I don't want any money with her.'

'Be a bit tight,' he said.

She smiled. 'We'll manage.'

He was content with that; if Katie said that they could manage, it was so. He himself had never cared much about money, or wanted it, or taken any interest in it except so far as it controlled the equipment of his workshop. That was very largely over now; the tools he had would last his lifetime and only minor additions would be necessary from time to time. He was content to take what income he could derive from the work he loved and live on that without complaint; the management of the *Miniature Mechanic* knew all about him and gave him just enough to keep him in a very modest way of life, the finances of their magazine allowing no more. He kept no car, drank very little, and hardly smoked at all. Each year they took a fortnight's summer holiday in Cornwall and went for motor-coach rides, but that was only possible because Katie worked. She managed all of their finances and saved about a hundred pounds a year for the gradual repayment of the mortgage.

It was a week before Mr Carpenter rang again, again at about ten o'clock in the morning. He said, 'I have a further cable from the Governor in Papeete, Mr Stewart. Could you come up and see me again, do you think?'

Keith said, 'I'll come up right away. Can you tell me what's in the cable?'

'Not very good news, I am afraid.'

'Oh. They're dead, are they?'

'I am afraid so. The vessel that went on the reef at Marokota Island was undoubtedly *Shearwater*. They have some of the clothing from the bodies.'

Keith said dully, 'I'll come up right away, sir.'

He was sitting with the solicitor in Bedford Square an hour and a half later, reading the cable. 'There doesn't seem to be any doubt about it now,' he said. 'This full report he says he's sending – we haven't had that yet, I suppose?'

Mr Carpenter shook his head. 'This only came in during the night.'

'Well, that's the end of it.' He sat in silence for a minute. 'We'll have to tell Janice now.'

'I am afraid so.' The solicitor paused, and then said, 'If I may speak from my experience, don't be too much influenced by the child's first reaction, Mr Stewart. It will be very painful, because there will be floods of tears. They will go on for a day, and then they will dry up. A child's wounds heal very quickly – or appear to, anyway. The thing is patience, and enduring kindness.'

The engineer glanced at him gratefully. 'I know. I've been making her a scooter.'

'A scooter?'

'You know – what kids have, to push about on with one foot. I've got it painted red. She hasn't seen it yet.'

'A very good idea, Mr Stewart. You say you made it yourself?'

Keith nodded. 'I can do that sort of thing?'

'How fortunate you are ...' The solicitor turned back to the papers on his desk. 'I have been going into my client's financial affairs since I saw you last,' he said. 'I am afraid they are rather unsatisfactory.'

'You haven't been able to find the securities?'

'The securities that John Dermott held were all sold, Mr Stewart, between February and April of this year. The proceeds were paid into the Throgmorton St branch of his bank. They totalled –' he glanced at a paper '– twenty-six thousand eight hundred and forty-four pounds, eleven shillings and tenpence.'

'What's happened to that money, then?'

'Between March and the end of May,' said the solicitor, 'cheques were drawn in favour of a firm called Rosenblaum and Franck totalling twenty-seven thousand nine hundred and thirty-eight pounds, sixteen and twopence.' He raised his eyes and looked at Keith. 'Rosenblaum and Franck are dealers in precious stones, Mr Stewart – principally diamonds, I think. They are quite a reputable firm.'

Keith stared at him. 'What on earth did they want with those?'

Mr Carpenter said, 'I know no more than you do, Mr Stewart. But I have talked to a partner in the firm, Mr Franck.'

'What did he say?'

The solicitor leaned back in his chair. 'Mr Franck is still a youngish man, under forty, I would say. He told me that he knew Commander Dermott well. He served under him in the recent war, when he would have been between twenty and twenty-five years old. He has a very high opinion of your brother-in-law. I am telling you this in order that you may understand the background of this business.'

He paused. 'I would say that Elias Franck is a Jew, and a very good one. He inherited the family business from his father. He told me that Commander Dermott came to him last spring and wanted to buy diamonds that would be readily saleable in any part of the world. Mr Franck told me that they sometimes get enquiries of that sort, and in such cases they avoid asking questions. It is no business of theirs what the purchaser wishes to do with the gems. Their business is to sell precious stones in London.'

Keith nodded. 'I see. They don't want to get mixed up in anything.'

'Exactly.' The solicitor went on, 'Commander Dermott bought diamonds to the value I have stated, twenty-seven thousand pounds odd, and took them away with him.'

'Just like that?'

Mr Carpenter inclined his head. 'Mr Franck tells me that he was very careful in his selection of the gems for Commander Dermott on account of the sincere regard that he feels towards him. He thinks that your brother-in-law might well make money on the resale, and if the diamonds should come again upon the market he would like to have the first refusal of the business.' He paused. 'There is just one other thing. Commander Dermott asked him for the name of a reputable broker on the west coast of America. Mr Franck gave him an introduction to a firm in which he has confidence, in Los Angeles.'

He paused. 'I have been wondering if Commander Dermott took those diamonds with him in the yacht.'

Keith stared at him. 'I suppose he might have done. But why should he want to do a thing like that?'

Mr Carpenter sat in thought for a minute. 'I can only surmise, Mr Stewart,' he said. 'But, as I understand the matter, it was the intention of your brother-in-law to settle permanently in the dollar area, perhaps in British Columbia. There are restrictions on the transfer of capital from England to the dollar area, as perhaps you know. Under the present regulations your brother-in-law could only have transferred a very small part of his capital into dollars each year. It might have taken ten years, or more, to transfer the whole of it.'

'You think he bought diamonds and took them with him in the yacht, to sell them in America and get his capital that way?'

'I think it possible.'

'Did he ever tell you he was going to do that?'

The solicitor placed both hands on the desk in front of him. 'Mr Stewart,' he said, 'if Commander Dermott did that, it was an illegal act. It was very highly illegal, and would have resulted in a considerable prison sentence if he had been detected. A solicitor must not allow a client to tell him that he intends to commit a felony. If the client should do so, the solicitor must refuse to advise him or to handle his case; in certain circumstances his duty would be to inform the proper authorities. Commander Dermott never told me or gave me any indication that he intended to do such a thing.'

Keith said, 'I'm sorry, sir. I didn't know.'

'That's all right, Mr Stewart.' He smiled. 'If your brother-in-law had such a thing in mind, he knew enough not to come and tell me about it.'

'I don't understand why it should have been so illegal,' the engineer said. 'It was his own money.'

'That is the law of the land,' the solicitor replied. 'Dollars are short in this country. I am not allowed to spend more than a hundred pounds in America if I wish to go there for a holiday. In the same way, your brother-in-law was not allowed to take twenty-six or twenty-seven thousand pounds to spend in the United States or Canada.'

'I see.' Keith glanced at the solicitor. 'He did tell me once that he wanted to buy a house when he got to a place called Victoria, on Vancouver Island.'

'He told you that?'

Keith nodded.

'I doubt if he could have done that very easily by any legal transfer of capital. Not unless the payments could have been deferred over an excessive period of time.'

'He didn't say anything about that. He just said that he was going to buy a house there.'

'I see.' They discussed this for a time, but Keith could remember nothing more. Presently the solicitor said, 'If in fact these diamonds were with them in the yacht, I am afraid that the prospects of recovering them do not seem very rosy.'

'We don't know yet how badly the yacht was wrecked,' Keith said. 'Things might have been saved off her – luggage, or things like that.'

'From a yacht, a wooden yacht, wrecked on a coral reef some distance from the land, in a tropical hurricane? I think she must have broken up, Mr Stewart, otherwise the bodies of the crew would hardly have been washed ashore. In that case all her contents would have been scattered over the sea floor. But we shall know more of the condition of the vessel when we get that report. I do not personally feel very hopeful.'

Keith glanced at him. 'It's fifty-five quid, then?'

'I am afraid it looks rather like it. Do you think that you can manage with the daughter, without any appreciable money, Mr Stewart? In the circumstances I should have no hesitation in approaching the Dungannon family on her behalf.'

'Katie says that we can manage.' said the engineer. 'Katie – that's my wife. After all, it's no more than if we had a kid of our own.'

'There would be no difficulty in approaching the Dungannons. I could write to Lord Dungannon personally.'

'If they paid for her schooling and that,' said Keith shrewdly, 'they'd want to have her, wouldn't they? I mean, they wouldn't want for her to go on living with Katie and me, and going to Miss Pearson's school down the road, and Ealing High School after that? Holidays, they'd want her to be with them in Northern Ireland?'

'They might,' the solicitor agreed.

The engineer shook his head. 'That's not what Jo wanted for her,' he said. 'Nor did John. When they left her with us, they did it of a purpose. They could have left her in Northern Ireland with the big house and people with titles and ponies to ride and all of that. But they didn't do that. They didn't even like her going there last summer much, but they kind of had to. What they wanted to do was for her to stay with us.'

'Do you know why they took that line?' asked Mr Carpenter. 'I know that that was their intention, but do you know why?'

'They had ideas,' Keith said awkwardly. 'I mean people getting divorced two or three times, and mess and muddle over the children. They didn't want Janice to grow up thinking that was the usual way people did. They thought she'd be better off with Katie and me in Ealing, seeing it was just for a short time.'

'It's going to be for a long time now,' said the solicitor.

'I know. But Katie says we can manage.' He paused. 'I'd like to find out all we can about things that might have been washed up from the yacht.'

'It's just possible that the diamonds might have been recovered,' said Mr Carpenter. 'If so, they would be in the hands of the French authorities.' He sat in silence for a minute, and then said, 'I will find out everything I can, Mr Stewart. But I shall have to word any enquiry rather carefully. If the diamonds were taken out of the United Kingdom it was a most illegal act.'

Keith sat with his brows wrinkled. 'How do the French come into this?' he asked.

'Tahiti and the Tuamotu Islands are a part of French Oceania,' the solicitor told him. 'Just as if they were French colonies.'

'I didn't know that,' the engineer said humbly. 'I thought that they were Japanese or something.'

He left the solicitor's office a few minutes later with the thought dominant in his mind that now either he or Katie would have to tell Janice that her father and mother were dead. He had the red scooter finished and painted, hanging up in what had once been the coal cellar of the house and now was used as a box-room. He had made it with pleasure for her, but now that the moment had come to use it as an anodyne it did not seem to be quite the right thing after all. He walked down to Holborn and then eastwards looking in the shop windows till he came to Gamage's. He went into the big store, mingling with the crowd of Christmas shoppers till he found the toy department and browsed around there, a pale-faced, rather fat little man in a greasy raincoat. He was already conscious of the need for economy, and finally he bought a yellow and blue plastic duck that would float in the bath. He knew as he bought it that it was much too young a present for a child of ten, but he bought it feeling that somehow it might be the right thing in the circumstances.

He got back to the flat in Ealing early in the afternoon, carrying the duck in a paper bag. He had thought of stopping at the store in Ealing Broadway and discussing the position across the counter with Katie in the Household Linen, but he had abandoned that idea. Katie would want to come home early in order to be at home when Janice got back from school, and it did not seem quite fair to him to throw all the dirty work on Katie. He felt that he would rather tell Janice himself and get the back of the job broken before Katie got home; enough would fall upon her later, anyway.

He was sitting in his chair before the fire in the parlour when Janice came back from school, a slim, dark-haired child in a thick blue overcoat and a blue hat with the school ribbon on it. He called, 'That you, Jan? Take off your coat and come in here. I've got something I want to tell you.'

She came in, and he sat up in his chair. 'What do you want to tell me?' she asked.

'Come over here,' he said. She came close, and he put his arm around the slender little waist in the gym tunic. He could only take this straight. 'Look, Jan,' he said. 'I've got something serious I've got to tell you. You know about boats and yachts, and how they get wrecked sometimes, running on shore, on rocks?'

She nodded.

'Sometimes,' he said, 'the people in the boats get drowned when that happens.'

She stared at him, and he knew that the realisation was already with her. She asked, 'Drowned dead?'

'That does happen sometimes, in a shipwreck,' he said gently.

'Has that happened to my Mummy and Daddy?'

'I'm afraid it has, Jan,' he said steadily. 'They got into a terrible storm, a long, long way from here. And they were wrecked.'

'Are they drowned dead, Uncle Keith?'

'I'm afraid they are, both drowned,' he replied. 'Come and sit up on my knee.'

He had thought that she would burst into tears, but that did not happen. She came up on his knee and he held her close, and so they sat in silence for ten minutes. At last she asked, 'Do you think my Mummy and Daddy were very frightened when the ship got wrecked?'

The adult quality of the question amazed him; children were so much older than you thought they were. 'No,' he said. 'No, I don't think that they'd ever have been frightened. They weren't that sort of people. And you won't be frightened of things either, I don't think.'

She shook her head. He reached down beside his chair and brought up the paper bag. 'I bought you a duck,' he said. 'I'm not sure if it's a very good present, but I wanted to bring you something and this was all that I could think of.'

She pulled it out of the paper bag upon his knee. 'It's a lovely duck,' she said. 'Can I have it in the bath?'

'Of course,' he said.

She wriggled round upon his knee and kissed him. 'It's a lovely present,' she said. 'Thank you ever so much for it.'

He held her for a moment, and then said, 'What about a cup of tea?'

She got down from his knee. There were still no tears. 'Can I come and watch you make a bit in the workshop?'

'Why, yes,' he said. 'I'll make a bit specially for you. What sort of a bit shall we make?'

Her eye fell on the duck, clutched close in her arms. 'Can you make an egg for the duck to lay?'

His mind ran quickly over techniques and materials to hand. 'I can make you all sorts of eggs,' he said, 'but none of them would be quite the right colour. A duck's egg ought to be a sort of bluey-green.' He thought rapidly. 'We could do a silvery egg in steel, or a yellow egg if we heated a steel egg a bit, or a blue egg if we heated a steel egg quite a lot, or a grey egg if we case-hardened it. Or we could make a coppery-coloured egg if we made it out of copper. But I can't just see how we could make a proper-coloured duck's egg, unless we painted it.'

She smiled at him. 'It isn't a proper-coloured duck, so it wouldn't have proper-coloured eggs, would it? But it's a lovely duck.' She stroked its plastic hide. 'Can I have one egg of each sort, so that we can make a nest for her to sit on?'

'I can't make them all before your bedtime,' he said. 'We can make one now, and then I'll make the rest after you're in bed, and then I'll put them on the table by your bed and you can have them in the morning.' He paused. 'Which one would you like me to make now?'

'The blue one,' she said.

He got up from his chair. 'All right, we'll go down and make a blue egg.'

He took her by the hand and they went together down the steep wooden stairs into the front basement room that was his clean workshop. He pulled out the high stool that he sometimes sat upon before the bench and sat her up upon it so that she could see everything that he was doing at the three-and-a-half-inch lathe, and began a running commentary on his operations. He picked a three-inch end of inch-diameter steel rod out of the scrap box, put it in the three-jaw chuck, started the lathe, and chamfered the end to forty-five degrees. A lifetime of such work had made him very quick; in a minute he was working with a hand-scraper on a rest turning the end of the steel to form the large end of the egg, talking to the little girl all the time. Three emery sticks of successive fineness followed the scraper, and the large end was finished. He brought forward the parting tool and parted off the piece one and a half inches long down to a diameter of about a quarter of an inch, and chamfered the small end shape roughly by the careful manipulation of a knife tool in the four-tool post. Then came careful work again with the hand-scraper, then the final parting off. He gave the warm, nearly finished egg to the little girl to hold while he found a one-inch-bore copper collar and put it in the chuck. Then he put the egg in it, small end outwards, and pinched it up, using the tailstock centre to set it roughly true, started the lathe again, and went to work very gently with the hand-scraper and the emery sticks till he had it finished to his satisfaction. Then he took it from the lathe, gave it a final burnish on a rouge polishing mop at the tool grinder, and gave it to her to hold, a new, silvery, shiny egg. It had taken him less than twenty minutes to make.

'There'll be another one like that in the morning,' he said, 'and a grey one and a yellow one and a copper one. But now we'll make this one blue.'

He helped her down from the stool, still clutching the plastic duck and the new, shiny egg, and led her into his dirty workshop. He lit a bunsen burner and arranged a tin filled with about an inch of sand above the burner on a little metal stand and began to heat the sand. Presently he took the egg from her and dropped it on the sand and began to stir the sand expertly with a small pair of tongs, always keeping the egg on top of a good layer of the hot sand, turning it over and over. As the heat increased it took a yellow tint, which grew darker as they watched and began to turn to blue. He made the little girl stand back, turned out the bunsen, put on a thick leather glove ready on the bench beside him, picked the hot egg from the sand quickly and dropped it in a tin of oil upon the bench. It made a sizzling splash and a little spurt of hot oil; he waited a moment, took off the glove, and fished it out of the oil, and wiped it carefully on a clean rag. Then he gave it to Janice, a deep, brilliantly blue egg.

'It's a *lovely* egg,' she said. 'It's such a pretty colour, just like Diana's frock. Thank you ever so much, Uncle Keith.'

There was the sound of the front door upstairs, and Katie's step in the hall. 'Lord!' he exclaimed. 'There's Katie, and we haven't done anything about the tea!'

She scurried to the stairs, the duck held firmly in her arms, the egg clenched tight in one hand. 'I'll go and put the kettle on.'

He followed her more slowly, and arrived in the hall in time to hear her greet Katie. 'Uncle Keith has bought me a duck and I can have it in the bath and he made me a blue egg for it to lay and he's going to make me more eggs tonight, a silver one and a yellow one and a grey one and a copper one so she'll have five eggs to sit on in a nest.'

He heard Katie say, a little dazed, 'What a beautiful duck and what a lovely egg. Keith spoils you.'

Janice said, 'He made the egg in the lathe and I watched and we forgot all about the tea. But I'll run and put the kettle on now.'

She scurried off into the kitchenette, duck and egg held close. In the hall Keith said in a low tone, 'It's true enough, old girl. I went up and saw Carpenter again this morning. They were both drowned, and buried on the island.' He paused. 'I've told her.'

'You've told Janice?'

He nodded.

'How did she take it?'

'She didn't cry,' he said. 'She just sat quiet on my knee for a bit, and then we went down and made the egg.'

'She didn't cry at all?'

He shook his head.

'Oh, that's bad,' she said in a low tone. 'You're sure she understood?'

'She understood all right,' he replied.

She stood in silence. 'Well, I dunno,' she said at last. 'We'll talk about it tonight after she's in bed. In the meantime, don't let's say anything unless she brings the subject up. Let her take it her own way.' She paused. 'I think I'll give her one of those phenobarbitone tablets tonight.'

She went into the kitchenette to run up a dish of scrambled eggs, and Keith went down into his clean workshop to sweep away the steel shavings from the lathe and to start work on another egg. He had it nearly finished by the time the meal was on the table, and was halfway through a third one by the time the meal was washed up and he was called upstairs to see the duck swimming with Janice in the bath. He went downstairs and worked till he had finished the fifth, and brought them up to the parlour. He found Katie sitting and darning a hole in one of Janice's stockings.

He put the eggs down on the table by his chair. 'Did she say anything?'

Katie shook her head. 'Only about the duck and the eggs. It's as if she's kind of closed her mind to the other thing.' She sat in silence for a moment, and then said, 'I think I'll put my coat on and run round and have a talk with Miss Pearson, so that if anything happens at the school tomorrow you could go round and fetch her home. You wouldn't mind doing that, K, if she rang?'

'Of course not. These eggs all ought to have a coat of lacquer before they get scratched. I might do that tomorrow, while she's at school. You think it's all right for her to go to school, Katie?'

'I'm sure it is, the way she's taking it. It's just in case anything comes out in the newspapers, and the other

66

children start asking her that might set her off crying or something.'

'You'd think there'd be a fair chance that the newspapers won't get hold of it,' he said. 'It's all in a French colony on the other side of the world.' He paused, and then he said, 'I've got that scooter I made for her. When do you think she ought to have that?'

'Tomorrow's Friday,' she said. 'Give it to her Saturday morning and she can play with it all morning if it's fine. And then in the afternoon she can have Diana Soskice round to play. I'll see Mrs Soskice, or else ring her up.'

'There isn't any money, Katie,' he said. 'If there was, they had it in the yacht with them.'

She darned on placidly. 'Mr Carpenter couldn't find the securities?'

'They sold them,' he told her. 'Seems like they turned everything they had into cash, and then bought diamonds, and took them in the yacht. Kind of illegal it was, so he says. Seems like they meant to sell the diamonds in America or somewhere and buy a house.'

'That doesn't sound illegal to me,' she said, her eyes fixed on the darn.

'Well, it is,' he told her. 'It's about the worst thing you can do, apart from murdering somebody.'

'And now the diamonds are lost, so she'll have nothing?'

'That's about the long and the short of it,' he said. 'He asked if he should ask the Dungannons to help with educating her and that, but I said, no.'

She shook her head. 'I wouldn't want that, and we can manage.' She dropped her busy hands down to her lap, and they were still. 'I know we can't give her all that John and Jo would have wanted her to have,' she said quietly. 'I'm sort of sorry about that, in a way. But it does make it more as if she was our own child now, and maybe that's for the best, things being like they are.'

He stirred uneasily in his chair. 'Those diamonds are her diamonds now, and they must be somewhere,' he said uneasily. 'I mean, I'm the trustee.'

She picked up her darning again. 'You can't be a trustee for what's at the bottom of the sea,' she said.

'The ship's not at the bottom of the sea,' he said stubbornly. 'She got wrecked on a coral reef near an island.'

'Same thing,' she said, and went on darning.

She went out presently to see Miss Pearson, and he went down into the basement. He looked into the little bedroom off his dirty workshop and saw Janice sleeping deeply, the plastic duck clutched in her arms. He laid the other four eggs down beside the blue one on the table by her side, and pulled the bedclothes gently up around her shoulders, for the night was cold and the window open. He closed the door, and sat down at his desk. There was the morning mail, seven letters still unopened. Amongst them was one from the United States in an ornate airmail envelope, the back of which announced to him in neat print that it was from Solomon P Hirzhorn, Box 6507, Tacoma, Washington. He sighed a little. Mr Hirzhorn was an enthusiast who was building the Congreve clock from Keith's serial in the *Miniature Mechanic*, and Mr Hirzhorn couldn't read a drawing very well, and Mr Hirzhorn evidently had a secretary with an electric typewriter to whom he could dictate, because each letter was about fifteen hundred words long; this was the third that Keith had answered patiently, though not at such length. He settled down to work, and worked till midnight.

The succeeding days passed anxiously, in a state of inarticulate tension. Janice never cried, so far as they could see, and she never once spoke of her father and mother, but she lost appetite and got very pale. Katie went to see Dr Simmonds about her, and he came round and stethoscoped her chest and put her on cod liver oil and malt, which she liked, and approved the phenobarbitone at night for the next week or so. Nothing happened at school because no parent of a child at Miss Pearson's school happened to read *The Times*, the only paper which picked up and printed a short account of the yacht wreck in the Tuamotus. Janice played with her scooter in Somerset Road on Saturdays, and achieved some distinction amongst the other children in the road because her uncle had made every bit of it himself, instead of buying it in a shop. But she continued pale and peaky in appearance.

Katie said, 'She'll pick up as the spring comes on.' But she took her down each Saturday morning to Mr Evans, the chemist, to weigh her on the machine in the shop, and kept a careful record of her weight.

The Christmas holidays came. It seemed better to Katie and to Keith to cancel the arrangements that had been made for Janice to go and stay with her Aunt Margaret at Tunbridge Wells and to keep her with them in Ealing, to the extent of disrupting their own routines a little for the period of the holidays. Mr Buckley agreed to let Katie go on half time, working mornings only till school started again, and Keith suffered an influx of children into his workshops at all hours, sometimes working on till one o'clock in the morning to keep abreast of his current jobs. They did their work in a welter of children's parties, parties in their own flat, fetching Janice from parties in other people's homes loaded with little presents, with paper caps and unpulled crackers.

In the middle of all this a letter arrived from Mr Carpenter enclosing the report from the Governor in Papeete, and suggesting that Keith might like to come up for another discussion when he had digested the contents.

It was a fairly long, typewritten report. It said that the vessel in question was undoubtedly the yacht *Shearwater*, and the two bodies were those of Commander and Mrs

Dermott. The yacht had struck on a reef about two miles to the south-west of the island of Marokota, which was only intermittently inhabited by natives from Kautaiva Island according to the demands of the copra harvest. The yacht had struck at the height of the hurricane and at that time there were about ten natives on Marokota who had seen the vessel as she struck the reef, but could do nothing to help. She had apparently broken up in a few hours; all that now remained was the keel and some of the frames wedged firmly on the reef, from which most of the planking had been washed off. There was no question of salvaging the yacht. The engine had remained attached to its bearers and had been removed by the natives three days later and placed under cover on the island. Much of the remaining heavy articles which were within the hull had been recovered by the natives by diving, including the two Primus stoves and the binnacle, and had been taken for their own use. The same applied to lighter articles that had been washed ashore, such as bedding, spars, planking, sails, etc. The Governor did not consider it practicable to recover these things from the natives. He would, however, appreciate instructions whether any attempt should be made to salvage the engine or whether it should be disposed of at his own discretion. He also asked for instructions regarding the marking and the upkeep of the grave.

Keith showed this letter to Katie one evening when the turmoil of the current party was over. She read it carefully, and then said, 'I should think the best thing would be to let him sell the engine for what he can get for it, and put the money towards the cost of the headstone for the grave. There's nothing much else that we can do.'

Keith said, 'There's no hurry. It all wants a bit of thinking about.' To his mind, it certainly did.

She said no more. To her the matter was perfectly clear and straightforward; put the money for the engine to the cost of the headstone and everything would be cleaned up, neat and tidy and done with. But Keith was handling all this with Mr Carpenter, and she knew her husband to be slow and vacillating in matters of business. Let the men settle it in their own way. It didn't matter.

On New Year's Eve, Keith went up to see Mr Carpenter. In the solicitor's office they went through the report together. Finally Mr Carpenter said, as Katie had, 'I think we should instruct the Governor to set the cost of the headstone against what he can get for the engine, and accept the balance either way. Would you like me to write to him in those terms?'

Keith sat in silence. Finally he said, 'I think I'd rather leave it be, and think things over a bit longer.'

The solicitor glanced at him curiously. 'There is no immediate hurry, of course.'

The engineer looked up. 'That's right,' he said. 'John and Jo, they're buried and all decent, far as I can see. Suppose they had a headstone, well, there's no one there to read it.' He paused. 'I'm not against a headstone,' he said. 'Don't think that. But there's a lot of things in this that want some thinking over.'

The solicitor sat in silence. 'I'm here to help you, Mr Stewart,' he said at last. 'I know that you are keeping something from me, and you may have very good reasons for doing so. I'd just like you to remember that your brother-in-law was not only my client, but a friend. Just bear that in mind.'

Keith smiled, and said shrewdly, 'Unless it came to telling you I might be going to do something illegal.'

'There are degrees …' said Mr Carpenter. And then he smiled, and said, 'Are you trying to tell me that you see some chance of getting back those diamonds?'

'I don't know where they are,' Keith said defensively. 'I don't know anything. I'd like to leave the whole thing rest

a while until I think it out, what's best to be done.' He got
to his feet.

The solicitor rose with him. 'As you like. Just remember
that I'm here to help.' He picked up the report from his
desk. 'Would you care to take this with you?'

Keith took the report and thrust it deep into the pocket of
his greasy raincoat. 'I don't want you to think I don't
appreciate everything you've done, sir,' he said. 'But there's
just one thing sticking out like a sore thumb, and that's that
I'm the trustee. I don't want to do things in a hurry. Like
selling anything.'

He left the office and walked down to Holborn. He stood
at the Kingsway corner waiting for his bus, and from habit
he bought a copy of the *Evening Standard*, but he did not
read it. He stood in a doorway in the milling crowd deep in
thought, trying to resolve his problem. Twelve thousand
miles away there was a coral reef in French territory, washed
by the sea, not far from a coral island. Wedged upon that
reef there was a three-ton lump of lead surmounted by
another lump of concrete. Deep buried in the concrete
probably would still be the copper box that he had brazed
up for John Dermott. In the copper box was Jo's jewel case,
red leather, and he was now certain in his mind that in her
jewel case were twenty-six thousand pounds worth of
diamonds that belonged to Janice, who had made a little
basketwork nest at school to hold the coloured eggs for the
plastic duck to sit on.

And he was the trustee.

CHAPTER FOUR

PETER JAMES SANDERSON was a navigator with the British Overseas Airways Corporation. He lived in South Ealing, convenient to London Airport, and at that time he was working the London-Karachi sector of the Eastern route, flying in Britannias. This gave him about a fortnight of each month at home with his young wife and baby, and plenty of time for his hobby, which was model engineering. He was a devoted reader of the *Miniature Mechanic* every week. He had fitted up a workshop in a garden shed, and in it he had built a Stuart Turner steam engine and two of Keith Stewart's designs, the 5 cc Hornet single-cylinder compression ignition engine with its built-in reduction gear, and the more ambitious 20 cc Gannet four-cylinder horizontally opposed four-stroke engine. He had exhibited the latter at the annual exhibition of the Ealing and District Model Engineering Society which had been judged by no less an authority than Keith Stewart, and he had received a bronze medal from the hands of the great man himself. He treasured this medal and valued it more highly than any of his professional certificates.

It was therefore with surprise and pleasure that he received a telephone call from Keith Stewart asking if he could come round and have a word with him. 'Of course,' he said. 'Any time you like, Mr Stewart. Now? That's fine. As a matter fact, I was just reading about your Congreve clock, but I'd rather talk to you yourself.'

He hung up and went to tell his wife of the honour that was to befall them, and she was duly impressed, and hurried to make some hot scones for tea.

Over the scones and tea Keith Stewart unburdened himself partially. 'I'm in a kind of an awkward position, and I don't know what to do for the best,' he said, and he proceeded to tell Mr and Mrs Sanderson about John and Jo and *Shearwater*. The navigator said softly, 'I remember reading about this ...'

'Marokota was the name of the island they got wrecked on,' Keith told him. 'It's not marked on our atlas, but seems like it's somewhere near a place called Tahiti or Papeete or something. Sometimes they say one, and sometimes the other.'

'Tahiti is an island,' said the navigator. 'Quite a big French island. In the Pacific. Papeete is the town on it. Wait a minute, I think I've got a chart here that would show it.'

Maps and charts were his speciality, the tools of his trade, and he had acquired a considerable private store. He pulled out a blue volume, the *Pacific Islands Pilot*, and consulted it. 'Nine nine two,' he said. 'I haven't got it. But seven eight three – I know I've got that somewhere.' He pulled out the bottom drawer of a long chest, rummaged, and pulled out a chart and laid it on the top of the chest. 'Well, there's Tahiti,' he said. 'Now, Marokota.' He turned again to the *Pilot* and extracted the latitude and longitude of the island. He laid these off upon the chart with pencil and parallel ruler, and marked the position with a little pencil cross. 'There's your Marokota,' he said. 'About three hundred sea miles more or less due east of Tahiti.'

Keith Stewart studied the chart. He had never seen one before, but he had heard about them, and he was a technician. 'All these little bits of figures,' he said. 'They mean depths?'

'Depths in fathoms,' said Mr Sanderson. 'A fathom is six feet.'

Keith nodded, and stood looking at the chart. He pulled out a packet of Players and offered one to his host. 'How would a chap set about getting out there?' he asked. 'I mean, there's things to be done – the grave, and that. I don't kind of like to let all that go, if you understand me. If it was just over the way, in France – well, of course one would go there and see everything done right. What would it cost to get to a place like that?'

The navigator stood in thought. 'By air, tourist, it might cost about three hundred pounds. You might be able to do it for a little less by sea. Perhaps two hundred.'

'That's just for the one way?'

Mr Sanderson nodded. 'The return fare would be double.'

Keith Stewart said, 'I was afraid that that might be the size of it. The *Miniature Mechanic* doesn't pay that sort of wage packet.'

'You feel it's very important that you should go there to tidy things up?'

The engineer nodded. 'Yes, I do. But there's things you just can't do, and that's all about it.'

They talked for a little while. Finally the navigator said, 'Take that chart, if it's any good to you. Let me have it back when you've done with it.'

Keith Stewart said goodbye and walked off down the street in the grey dusk, the chart under his arm. Mr Sanderson watched him go from the front door, and went back into his sitting-room, where his wife was clearing away the tea. 'What did you think of him?' he asked her.

'I liked him,' she said. 'He's a very genuine little man.'

'That's what I thought,' he replied.

'He didn't mind a bit telling you straight out that he hadn't got the money to go out to the Pacific.'

'I know,' he said. He leaned against the mantelpiece in thought. 'Of course,' he said, 'there *are* ways.'

'Ways to get to Tahiti without any money?'

'Of course there are,' he said smiling. 'People get all over the world without any money.'

'How, Peter?'

'In aircraft, when the load factor's a bit down,' he said. 'It's just a question of working the right racket.'

Two nights later he rang up Keith Stewart. 'I don't know if this is any good to you,' he said. 'Do you remember a chap called Oliver Thorn, who had a model of the Petrolea locomotive in the Ealing and District exhibition?'

'I remember him,' said Keith. 'Fair-haired chap, shortish, with glasses. Works at Blackbushe airport or somewhere.'

'That's the chap,' said Mr Sanderson. 'He's chief storekeeper to Albatross Airways. I used to work for Albatross before I got into the Corporation. He thinks a lot of you.'

'Nice of you to say that,' muttered Keith.

'Well,' said the navigator, 'the point is this. Albatross have a job coming up to fly a generator rotor to a ship that's stuck at Honolulu, the *Cathay Princess*, fifteen thousand tons. She's a tanker, I believe. She can't move till she gets this rotor, and she's costing the owners God knows how much a day. They've got to make a new one up in Lancashire, and Albatross are flying it to Honolulu one day next week. They're sending it in one of their DC6b freighters, but it won't be a full load. It struck me that it might be possible to wangle you a ride.'

Keith was startled. 'To Honolulu?'

'Yes.' Distances meant nothing to the navigator; one day he would be in Singapore and the next in Sydney. The world to him was a succession of indifferent hotels united by long, dreary stretches of cloud.

'How far would that be from Tahiti?'

'About two thousand five hundred sea miles. It's not very close, but it's a good deal closer than you are now.'

'Can one get from Honolulu to Tahiti?'

'Ah, now,' said the navigator, 'that may be the snag. I can tell you this much – there's no airline. You'd think there must be some sort of shipping line, but, honestly, I just don't know. It could be that you'd have to find out that in Honolulu. Mr Thorn told me that the aircraft would go straight through by way of Frobisher and Vancouver, and that it would load the generator rotor at Speke. Well, Speke to Honolulu must be close on thirty hours, so the crew would want at least forty-eight hours' rest before starting home. There should be plenty of time in Honolulu for you to find out about sea passages to Tahiti. If there aren't any, then you could come home again with Albatross. The machine's got to come back empty, as I understand it.'

'You don't think they'd want any money?' asked Keith, still a little dazed.

'You'd have to talk to Oliver Thorn,' said Mr Sanderson. 'There may be some accountant in Albatross who'd cut up rough, but I don't see why there should be. After all, if a journalist wanted to go and write up the trip and Albatross Airways, they'd take him fast enough. You're a journalist, aren't you?'

'I suppose so,' said Keith uncertainly.

'Well, there you are!' They talked a little more, and Mr Sanderson gave Keith the address and telephone number of Mr Thorn, and rang off.

Keith Stewart hung up, and went down to his workshop to sit down at his desk. He had Janice's school atlas there, and he traced the route so far as he was able. Speke – he did not know where that was, nor had he heard of it before; it would be somewhere in the North because the generator rotor was being made in Lancashire. Somewhat to his surprise he found Frobisher Bay without difficulty, but it was in Baffin Land, up further north than Hudson Bay. Then to Vancouver; he knew where that was. And then to Honolulu, girls in grass skirts and not much else. He knew about Great Circle courses, and though he had not got a globe he could visualise this as the shortest route. Besides, when Jo had been speaking to Katie about Janice's journey, she had mentioned that the aeroplane went near to the North Pole.

He had never been out of England. It was incredible that he should even be contemplating such a journey, with all its expense, all its uncertainties. He would have to have a passport, and he had no notion how to set about getting such a thing. Still, he knew that the bank manager would tell him. He would have to have money, quite a lot of money, for if he succeeded in getting to Tahiti from Honolulu that would cost a lot. Then he would have to pay his own fare back to England. That might perhaps be possible if he were to find the diamonds. But if he didn't, then he would be stranded out there, in this outlandish place, Papeete.

He thought perhaps that he could raise about a hundred pounds without increasing the mortgage on the house. But Katie would have to know.

If he took a hundred pounds from their bank account it would drain it to the very bottom, to the utmost limit of overdraft that the bank manager would allow. There was a little money owing to him from the *Miniature Mechanic*, perhaps about fifteen pounds. Katie, in theory at any rate, could carry on for a month or two upon her salary to meet the living expenses of Janice and herself; they had just paid the school fees for the coming term. Without his earnings they could not pay off the debt upon the house, or maintain anything; they could not paint the windows or replace sheets or blankets or pillowcases or clothes. If he were to take a hundred pounds and go off on a trip like this, Katie would be down to the barest of bare bedrock.

He got up and walked about the workshop, uncertain in his mind. Presently it occurred to him that by his movements he might be waking Janice, who slept in the little room off the workshop that once had been the scullery. He opened the door gently, and looked in. Janice was sleeping deeply, the plastic duck on the table by her side perched hazardously on its basketwork nest stabilised by the weight of the metal eggs. She had thrown the bedclothes off from her shoulders and one arm was out. The room was cold; he went over to the bed and gently put the arm inside and tucked the bedclothes up around her shoulders. She did not wake, and he went back into the workshop, closing the door softly behind him.

The diamonds *must* be in the jewel case, safely buried in the lump of concrete that had once been *Shearwater*. It was the only place where they could be. It was just a matter of someone going there and getting them, without attracting too much attention.

And he was the trustee.

He sat down at his desk again, irresolute. Suppose he didn't go. With the help of Mr Sanderson and Mr Thorn and Albatross Airways he might have enough money to get there – just – but he certainly hadn't got enough money to get back. He would be leaving Katie with little or no money for an indefinite time, with Janice to look after. John Dermott and his sister Jo wouldn't have wanted him to do that …

If he didn't recover her little fortune, well, Janice would be all right. Katie had said that they could manage, and Katie knew. She'd have to work like any other girl as soon as she could leave school; probably Mr Buckley would give her a job in the shop. It would be just as if she was their own daughter. She'd never be a fine lady, but who wanted to be a fine lady these days, anyway?

He sat there in mental torment, knowing that he couldn't take it that way. Unless he made a real effort to get back what belonged to her, he'd never be able to look at her without feeling ashamed of himself. He'd never be able to think of John and Jo without feeling ashamed of himself. They had made him the trustee.

But, dear Lord, what was Katie going to say about it all?

He went upstairs presently, conscious of a bad half hour ahead of him. Katie was still up, sitting by the fire knitting something for Janice and looking at the television. He sat down opposite her, and said, 'I've got something I want to talk about.'

'I know what that is,' she remarked, turning off the set.

'What's that,' he asked, startled.

She said complacently, 'You want to go out to this place Tahiti. I heard you talking about it on the telephone. I think it's silly.'

'Better wait to say that till you know all about it,' he replied, a little nettled.

'What don't I know?'

'Everything,' he said. 'You remember that time when I went down to the yacht with them to fix up an electric light over the compass?' She nodded. 'Well, it wasn't an electric light at all. It was something quite different.'

'I guessed that much,' she said. 'What was it?'

'Jo's jewel case,' he said. 'Sort of building it into the boat.' He started in and told her the whole thing; it took about a quarter of an hour. 'Course, I believed what John told me,' he said. 'He told me it was just Jo's rings and things like that. But now we know that they took twenty-six thousand pounds of diamonds along with them, I bet that they were in that jewel case, too.'

Katie got up from her chair. 'Make a pot of tea,' she said. She went and busied herself in her little kitchenette while she thought it over. She came back presently with two cups of tea. 'Suppose you went out there,' she said, 'what's it all going to cost?'

'Everything we've got and probably a bit more,' he replied. 'That's just to get there. Getting back would cost as much again.'

She stared at him helplessly. 'But that's crazy!'

He rubbed his hand across his eyes. 'I know. The other way is to do nothing and just leave it be.'

She sat in silence for a minute. 'That don't seem right,' she said at last. 'I can't say I like that much better.'

He looked up at her gratefully; Katie was coming round to the unthinkable course he had proposed. 'I like it a bloody sight worse,' he said. 'I'd never be able to think of John and Jo again if we just sat tight on our fannies and did nothing.'

'That's enough of that shop language,' she said. 'Drink your tea while it's hot.' He obeyed her. 'This Governor in this place Papeete,' she said. 'Suppose you were to write to him and tell him all about it, couldn't he go there and get the box out of the keel?'

Keith nodded. 'I thought of that. Tell you the truth, I don't just know what a Governor does. Would he be the top man? An asylum's got a Board of Governors, but they aren't top of anything.'

'I think he's the top man,' said Katie. 'I read about a Governor in a book once.'

'That's what I thought,' said Keith. 'If that's right he'd be paid by the Government – the French Government, I suppose, in Paris. Well, when John and Jo took those diamonds out of England they could have gone to prison for it – that's what Mr Carpenter said. Maybe the diamonds would have been confiscated if they'd been found out.' She nodded. 'Well now, who's to say that if this Governor got his hands on them they wouldn't be confiscated again? I just don't know, and, what's more, I don't know who to ask, safely. I mean, twenty-six thousand pounds is worthwhile anybody going after, if they know it's there. I don't feel like telling anyone about it, least of all this Governor.'

She nodded slowly. Twenty-six thousand pounds was an incredible sum of money to her, but if it existed at all it belonged to Janice, and no one else was going to lay a finger on it. She knew from her Sunday newspaper that many a bank manager had fallen from grace for much less than that, and who was to say that a French Governor would be any better? She was reluctant to admit it and to face the infinite difficulties that would ensue, but Keith had the right idea. Better to say nothing to anybody and go after this himself. She asked him, 'What were you going to do in this place, Papeete, if the island's three hundred miles away?'

'I don't honestly know,' he said. 'But look at it like this. Suppose we had lots of money, enough to do whatever we wanted without thinking about it.' She nodded. 'Well, I'd go out there and get a headstone for the grave made in this place Papeete, and then I'd hire a ship with a crew that knew the way around, and I'd go to this island and get the headstone set up on the grave and everything done proper. And I'd take a lot of photographs for Janice to see when she's older. Well, while I was there I'd go out to the wreck upon this reef in a small boat, and I'd know soon as I laid eyes on it if the box was still there in the concrete. Just behind the mast it was, towards the rudder end. I'd be a poor sort of a fish if I couldn't lay my hands upon it then, and get it away.'

'Well, we haven't got lots of money,' she said. 'Not for hiring ships and that. I suppose you'd say that if you can get a free ride out to this place Honolulu you can do the rest of it free, too.'

'I could try,' he said simply. 'Maybe I could do some work out there or something, if I get into a jam. How much money do you think I could take with me? I was thinking I could take a hundred pounds.'

She laid her teacup down. 'I'll get the bank book.'

They discussed finances for a time, upon the basis that he would be away for three or four months. 'You forgot about the rest of the top flat,' she said. She figured with a stub of pencil on the back of the cheque book. 'I think it would be all right if you took a hundred and ten pounds,' she said. 'But we'd have to have money coming in by the middle of April or we wouldn't be able to pay school fees for the summer term for Janice at Miss Pearson's.'

'She'd have to go to the Council school.'

'I know. But Jo was against that.'

He nodded. 'That gives me a deadline, anyway.'

She sat deep in thought. At last she said, 'It'll be hot out in those parts, Keith. You'll have to take your cricket shirts and your blazer.' On that note they went to bed.

He knew shop hours, and he knew that half-past six on a pitch dark January morning was no time to ring a busy man hurrying to catch the transport out to work at Blackbushe, forty miles from London. He waited until eight o'clock and rang Mrs Thorn, and got from her the telephone number of Albatross Airways, and the extension number. He enquired a little delicately if it was all right to ring Mr Thorn at his work, and got a somewhat affronted reply. 'Of course it's all right,' she said. 'Mr Thorn has a secretary.' He apologised and hung up, well pleased. Mr Oliver Thorn apparently was somebody at Albatross Airways Ltd.

Ten minutes later he was speaking to the man himself. He got a courteous reception, somewhat to his own surprise. 'Nice to hear your voice, Mr Stewart. We met last at the Ealing and District exhibition.'

'That's right,' said Keith. 'I liked your Petrolea – liked it very much. If I'd been judging the locos I'd have given it a bronze.'

'It wasn't worth it, Mr Stewart, not really. I should have fluted the connecting rods, and it's got cheesehead screws all over where they should be hex. I'll do better next time. But it goes all right.'

'Well, that's the main thing,' said Keith. 'Tell me, Mr Thorn, did you hear anything from Mr Sanderson about me?'

'Sure. He said you wanted to know if there was any chance of a ride with us to Honolulu.'

'That's right.'

'Well now, there is and there isn't, Mr Stewart. What I mean is, we don't carry passengers; we aren't allowed to. We run a freight service. We do sometimes stretch a point, but then it's for someone special like yourself, and we sign them on as crew – second engineer under instruction, or something like that. It's all at the discretion of the Chief Pilot, Captain Fielding. He'll be taking this Honolulu flight, and he's the one you'd have to get round.'

'You have got a machine going to Honolulu?'

'Oh, yes. Thursday or Friday of next week, as soon as the component is finished. We load at Liverpool, at Speke.' He paused. 'Are you doing anything today, Mr Stewart?'

'Nothing urgent.'

'Think you could come out here to Blackbushe and meet the boys? Captain Fielding, he's taking off for Ankara about three o'clock with four jet engines and spare parts and that, and then on the way back he picks up a load of cut flowers at Nice. He'll be gone three or four days. Then his next trip is the Honolulu one. He'll be here at dinner time, and you could have a talk with him.'

'What's the best way for me to get out to you at Blackbushe?'

There was a pause, and Keith heard, 'Daisy, what time is that truck leaving Belgrave Road with the manifolds? ... Why not? ... Okay.' He came back on the line. 'We've got a truck leaving Belgrave Road, that's by Victoria, about ten-thirty, Mr Stewart. One of our red trucks with Albatross all over it. If you wait for him on the Great West Road at the corner of South Ealing Road, say – say about ten-fifty, I'll ring him and tell him to pick you up there then.'

'I'll be there waiting for him.'

'That's fine, Mr Stewart. There's four or five of the boys in the maintenance shop would like to meet you. I'll have a word with Captain Fielding, tell him what it's all about.'

There was plenty of time before he had to meet the truck. Janice went off to school, and Katie to the shop, and he went down into his workshop to find something that would entertain the fitters at Blackbushe. A couple of years before he had been doing some research upon miniature electric generators in connection with the Showman's version of his traction engine. He had evolved a little six-volt generator no more than an inch and a half in diameter running at three thousand revs. For research purposes he had adapted the basic castings of his Hornet engine to make a new four-stroke 7 c c engine running on petrol with a little carburettor, and in place of the reduction gear he had fitted a governor; ignition was by a tiny magneto of his own design and a miniature sparking plug. The whole lot mounted on a little baseplate was about four inches long, two inches wide, and two and a half inches high. It was an easy starter. He could flick it into life by swinging the flywheel at one end with his thumbnail, and as it speeded up to the governed revolutions a pea bulb at the other end glowed with the electricity it generated. It had always been a great success in workshops, and he put it in a little box and slipped it into his pocket.

By half-past eleven he was sitting in the office with Mr Thorn, drinking a cup of tea. Albatross Airways Ltd was an independent company operating three ten-year old Vikings and a couple of DC6bs, one of which was permanently on a trooping contract. Their offices in an old wartime hutment were not luxurious, but their shops were clean and adequately equipped.

Mr Thorn said, 'Glad to see you again, Mr Stewart. Look, before we start, would you mind telling me what this is all about? Do you just want to go to Honolulu, or was it your idea to go there and come back with the aircraft?'

'I don't really know.' Keith Stewart pulled the newspaper cutting from his wallet and showed it to the chief storekeeper, and told his story. 'I've got to try and get to this place Tahiti and fix up about the grave and the salvage and all that,' he said. 'I haven't got the money to get there in the normal way – it's too expensive. But I did think if I could get a lift to Honolulu it would be a help.'

'Sure.' Mr Thorn handed back the cutting to him. 'You want to show that to Captain Fielding,' he said. 'I won't say we've never done this before, Mr Stewart, because we have. But I can tell you now, we'd have to have it both ways if Captain Fielding agrees to take you. We'd have to sign you on as second engineer under instruction at a salary you wouldn't get, and at the same time you'd have to sign our legal form of indemnity to say that there'd be no claim against us if you get killed or injured on the flight.'

Keith nodded. 'Fair enough.'

'You haven't got any Ground Engineer's tickets, I suppose?'

Keith shook his head. 'I'm afraid not. You know what I do.'

'I do indeed. I don't know if Captain Fielding does, though. We'd better get along down to the hangar and see if we can find him. He's down there somewhere.'

Keith pulled the box a little shyly from his pocket. 'I brought a bit along with me I thought the boys might like to see.'

Mr Thorn took the tiny generator set and examined it with interest. 'My ...' he breathed. 'That really is something! Does it go?'

'Of course it goes.' Keith took it from him, primed the tiny carburettor by turning the model upside down, and flipped the little engine into life with his thumbnail. It buzzed like an infuriated wasp as he made delicate adjustments to the jet and settled to an even note as the pea bulb lit up. Mr Thorn gazed at it entranced. 'Have you ever shown it?'

Keith shook his head. 'I only made it up for research, when I was working on the generator.' He paused. 'The commutator is the tricky part. The rest of it's quite simple.'

He stopped the little engine by shorting the plug with his propelling pencil.

'Bring that down into the shop,' Mr Thorn said. 'The boys will like to see it.'

Ten minutes later the little generator set was running on a workbench in an annexe to the hangar, surrounded by a crowd of mechanics attracted by the noise and by the rumour that Keith Stewart of the *Miniature Mechanic* was actually there in person. He faced the barrage of questions that he was accustomed to at exhibitions, dealing with them one by one, a little shyly. In the middle of all this a man in uniform, dark-haired with a small dark moustache, pushed his way through the crowd. 'What's all this going on?'

Mr Thorn said, 'This is Captain Fielding, Mr Stewart.'

Keith stopped the engine with his pencil, and turned to the newcomer. 'Glad to meet you, sir.'

The pilot nodded, smiled, and fixed his eyes on the little model on the bench. 'Don't you know we aren't supposed to run engines in the hangar? Start it up again – if you can.'

'She usually starts all right,' Keith said diffidently. He flipped it into life again with his thumbnail; the note steadied, the pea bulb lit up, and it went on running evenly. The pilot bent to examine it. 'I wish our engines started as easily as that.'

'She's warm,' Keith said apologetically.

'Ours are worse when they're warm.' The pilot moved Keith's hand and studied the tendency of the running model to move about the bench. 'Not badly balanced. What revs is she doing?'

'About three thousand.'

'Where did you get the dynamo from?'

'I made it.' Someone in the crowd said, 'And designed it. He wrote an article about it in the *Miniature Mechanic*. Two years ago, was it?'

'About that,' Keith said.

The pilot grunted. 'What about the magneto?' Somebody said, 'He designed that, too.'

The pilot looked at Keith. 'What *didn't* you design and make in it?'

Keith said, 'The sparking plug.' He added diffidently, 'Working in ceramics is a bit specialised, and you can buy them so easily.' He stopped the little motor again with his pencil, and the pea bulb glowed red and went out.

Captain Fielding took it in his hand and examined it closely. Then he passed it to somebody else, and it went from hand to hand. He said to Keith, 'Just a minute, Mr Stewart.' He turned and they walked together out into the main hangar under the wing of the DC6b. 'Mr Thorn was saying something about you wanted a ride with us to Honolulu.'

Keith started in to tell his story again, and showed the pilot the cutting from *The Times*. 'I don't know anything about the services from Honolulu to Tahiti,' the pilot said at last. 'Do you?'

'No. I was thinking I'd find out in Honolulu, and if it wasn't any good or expensive, then perhaps you'd let me come back with you.'

Captain Fielding stood in thought. 'That's possible.'

'How long will you be there?'

'Two days at least. Probably three – or four. It's over thirty hours from Speke to Honolulu, and there's such a thing as crew fatigue. I've told the directors it'll be a week's job altogether.' He paused. 'The officers of the *Cathay Princess* might know about services to Tahiti – or they could find out.' He turned to Keith. 'All right, Mr Stewart – you're in. Mr Thorn told you the conditions?'

'Yes, sir,' said the new second engineer under instruction.

'Okay. You'll need a passport and an American visa and a vaccination certificate. Got any of them?'

'No.'

'Well, you'll have to hop around. I can't take you in the aircraft without them. Keep in touch with Mr Thorn. We'll probably be leaving here for Speke on Thursday morning.'

Keith made a good start on his formalities before he left Blackbushe. The provision of passports at that aerodrome was a matter of routine; the Ministry of Civil Aviation had a supply of application forms and a tame justice of the Peace to witness signatures. He presented this at the Passport Office in Westminster next day, got himself vaccinated, and was well on the way through the formalities by the weekend.

He saw Mr McNeil, the managing editor of the *Miniature Mechanic*, and told him that there would be a gap of several weeks in his articles. Mr McNeil was disgruntled, but less so when Keith had told his story and had shown him the cutting from *The Times*. 'Well, if you've got to go, I suppose you've got to,' he said reluctantly. 'I think I'll put a para in the book to say you're on holiday. Or – wait now. Think you could do a piece upon the flight to Honolulu and mail it when you land? Flying to Honolulu ... right from the flight deck, over the North Pole ... The readers might like that as a change.'

'I think I could do that,' said Keith. 'I'd have to get the permission of Albatross, of course. The trip's a bit irregular, you see, because they aren't allowed to carry passengers. I'll ask them.'

'When do you think you'll be back?'

'April, I hope,' said Keith. 'It's got to be early April, somehow or other, because of the school holidays. My wife works, you see.'

The editor opened his eyes. 'I never knew you had any children.'

'I haven't,' said the engineer. 'This is my sister Jo's little girl, Jo who got drowned.' He indicated the cutting from the paper. 'She left her with us to look after till they got to Vancouver,' he explained. 'She's ours for keeps, now.'

The editor's eyes softened a little; it was just what a silly unbusinesslike mutt like Keith Stewart would let himself in for. But a fine engineer in his own line ...

'Going to make things difficult?' he asked.

Keith shook his head. 'Katie says we can manage.'

Mr McNeil sat for a moment in thought. 'You know what it's like with the book,' he said. 'We just scrape along. We have to use such a hell of a lot of blocks. Still, we *do* scrape along. If while you're away you want a bit of an advance on stories that you'll do when you come back, let me know. If there's any cash in the kitty, I'll do my best.'

Keith thanked him, and went back to Ealing. Janice was now one of their main problems because school ended at four and Katie did not get home much before six; moreover there were Saturday mornings to be considered, when Katie worked and there was no school. What to do for Janice in those periods perplexed them very much indeed; always before, Keith had been at home. It worried Keith far more than the problem of how he was to get from Honolulu to Tahiti.

'I might ask Mr Buckley if she could come to the shop just for the hour before closing,' Katie said doubtfully.

'John and Jo wouldn't have liked that,' said Keith uneasily.

'I know. I'll find out about that dancing class from Miss Pearson. Some of the children do go to that, I know. Miss Grayson, or Gleeson, or some name like that.'

The dancing class filled one evening and the Saturday morning, and Mrs Soskice, mother of Diana, filled the rest; Janice could go to Mrs Soskice and play with Diana till Katie called for her. With that problem cleared away, it then remained to tell Janice that Keith was going to the island. They decided that they had to tell her where he was going to rather than to fob her off with some indefinite journey. She was too intelligent, and would probably find out where he had gone to, and lose confidence in them.

They told her together. 'Going to the place where my Daddy and Mummy was drowned?' she asked. It was the first time, so far as either of them knew, that she had spoken of her parents. She had been putting on a little weight, however, and was no longer quite so peaky.

'That's right,' said Keith. 'We've got to see about selling the engine and the bits and pieces from the wreck and that.'

'Can I go too?'

Katie shook her head. 'No, darling. It's too far, and it costs too much.'

'Mummy and Daddy took me to China when I was little.'

'That's right,' said Katie. 'But you were very little then, just a baby, and you know a baby doesn't have to pay a fare on the bus or the Underground or anything. But you're a big girl now, and you'd have to pay.'

Janice nodded thoughtfully. 'I have to have a half ticket. Diana's much bigger than me, but she has a half ticket just the same.'

'We couldn't afford even a half ticket,' Katie said. 'It's going to clean us right out if Uncle Keith goes there. But we think it's necessary.'

Janice nodded again. Already she had become accustomed to the straitened finances of the Stewart household; the free spending ways of her father and mother were already fading from her memory. She turned to Keith. 'Are you going to see that my Daddy and Mummy are buried right?' she asked.

'That's one of the things I was going to do,' he replied.

She wriggled on his knee, and prompted by some obscure chain of thought she asked, 'Would you like to take one of my eggs with you?'

'Why, yes,' he said. 'That would be a lovely thing to take.'

'Which one would you like to take?'

'Which one can you spare most?'

'No,' she said. 'You choose.'

The case-hardened one would take the friction of a long journey in his pocket best. 'I'd like the grey one,' he said.

She clapped her hands, laughing. 'I was so afraid you'd say the blue one because I like the blue one best because it's the prettiest and because I saw you make it right from the start.' She slithered down from his knee. 'I'll go and fetch the grey one now.' So that moment passed.

In the last day or two problems of health in the tropics obsessed Katie's mind. 'Pith helmets,' she said. 'That's what people out there wear in the sun. You must buy one of those as soon as you get there, Keith. You don't want to go getting sunstroke. And mosquito nets to sleep under at night, else you get malaria. Perhaps you ought to take one of those along with you.'

'There's some kind of a pill you can take for that,' he said. 'I'll ask at Evans's in the morning.'

92

They decided that he should travel in his best blue suit and the heavy woollen overcoat that he had bought after the war and kept for best, and wear the imitation Panama hat that he reserved for his annual August holiday in Cornwall. He packed a suitcase with his cricket shirts, blazer, and grey flannel trousers, two suits of heavy woollen underwear, and a clean grey workshop coat. He got from his bank a hundred pounds' worth of dollar travellers' cheques, and took with him a few pounds in notes. He put the small petrol-electric generator set into his pocket in its box. Then he was ready to go.

CHAPTER FIVE

THE JOURNEY TO Honolulu in the DC6b was an unmitigated, sheer delight to Keith Stewart. He had never been out of England and though he had flown once or twice as a passenger he had little practical knowledge of aircraft. He had, however, an almost encyclopaedic knowledge of things electrical and mechanical, and to be given the free run of the big Douglas was to open a glittering storehouse of technical interest to him. He caught a transport down to Blackbushe very early on the Thursday morning, and entered his Wonderland.

The aircraft had been stripped of all passenger seats and upholstery. Behind the flight deck was a crew restroom; on the port side two pairs of seats faced across a table, on the starboard side there were two bunks. Behind again there was a toilet to port and a small galley to starboard, and aft of that the cabin was an empty shell right to the aft bulkhead.

Keith spent an hour in the office with Mr Thorn and Captain Fielding, putting his signature on various documents. In the course of the formalities he learned the names of the other crew members, and was a little surprised at their number. There were six apart from the captain and himself: three co-pilots of varying experience and standing, a navigator, a radio operator, and an engineer, Dick King, who knew all about Keith Stewart. The formalities over, he carried his suitcase down to the aircraft with Mr King, who showed him where to put it, and changed, putting on his grey workshop coat.

Presently, soon after eleven o'clock, the crew came aboard, led by the captain, who told Keith to sit in one of the unoccupied rest seats and strap himself in. The doors were slammed shut, the steps withdrawn, and two of the younger pilots came and joined him in the other seats. On the flight deck the crew commenced the preflight checks, the engines whined and started one by one, the captain spoke to the tower and got clearance to taxi. Engines were run up at the threshold of the runway, and presently the aircraft moved forward, lined up, and took off.

She got off very quickly with no load on board, and only half fuel. As the flaps came up the two young pilots undid their belts, indicating to Keith that he should do the same. They all moved forward to the flight deck, Keith keeping behind out of the way.

There was nothing to be seen out of the windows or through the pilot's windscreen but the grey January cloud. Everybody on the flight deck seemed to be busy; though they sat relaxed and motionless he could sense the nervous tension. The grey wisps of cloud whipped past, and once they emerged into clear air between two layers of cloud and entered cloud again, so that he knew that they were climbing. From time to time the captain spoke to Dick King, who made adjustments to the throttles and the prop controls; from time to time the navigator or the radio officer left his seat and spoke to the captain, who nodded, sometimes glancing at the clock on the instrument panel.

Keith had never before been on the flight deck of a large aircraft, or been in any aircraft at all while it was flying blind. He was impressed and somewhat amazed by the things he did not know. These men were working as a team, doing things together quickly and accurately, things that he could only guess at. He knew that on their teamwork the safety of the aircraft depended. All his own skill and ingenuity could not assist them by one iota; the most that he could do to help them in their work was to keep right out of their way.

He went aft again into the rest quarters and examined the galley. That was understandable, at any rate; there were tins of coffee and tins of tea, and tinned milk, and tinned meats and vegetables, and bread and butter and cheese and jams. This was within his competence. He could not assist these people in their work, mechanical though it was, and that was humiliating, but he could keep them well supplied with coffee and biscuits. He set himself to discover where everything was stowed.

Presently he sat down again; there was nothing to be seen at all but the grey fog. One of the young co-pilots came and sat beside him. 'Half an hour to go,' he said. 'He'll be starting the let-down in a few minutes.'

'How high are we?'

'Fifteen thousand. We're going to do a GCA approach.'

Keith asked timidly, 'What's that?'

'Ground control. They get us on the radar screen and talk us down on to the runway. It's quite interesting. You can hear it all on the loudspeaker if you come forward. But don't get in anybody's way.'

The note of the engines changed as the let-down began, but nothing else seemed to alter. When the young man beside him got up and went forward Keith followed him. A trickle of remarks was coming from the loudspeaker over the windscreen between the pilots, half heard by Keith at the rear, one quarter understood. 'Delta November, you are cleared down to six thousand feet, six zero zero zero feet, QFE nine nine eight, nine nine eight, course three two zero.' And then, 'Delta November, Roger.'

He could not understand any of it. The co-pilot seemed to be flying the machine; Captain Fielding sat relaxed, watching the instruments and fingering a black hand microphone, occasionally raising it for a short remark. Everyone was standing or sitting very quiet. Nobody was peering from the windows, for there was nothing to see. Once Captain Fielding, turning to say something to the navigator, noticed Keith Stewart at the back of the standing officers, and smiled slightly at him. Then he turned and faced the instruments again.

The stream of half-heard, quiet orders from the loudspeaker brought them lower, lower, upon changing courses. 'Delta November, you are cleared to descend to two thousand feet. Check your QFE, nine nine eight.' Keith saw the captain raise the microphone, and heard, 'Delta November, Roger.' They sat in motionless tension. Then, 'Delta November, turn now, right, on to heading zero four zero.' And presently, 'Delta November, you are now on final and eleven miles from touchdown. Commence your descent at six hundred feet per minute. Check your wheels and flaps for landing.'

There was activity in the cockpit; the wheels went down with a thump, the flaps crept halfway out, the note of the engines rose higher as the pitch decreased. There was still absolutely nothing to be seen but the grey fog outside. There was dead silence on the flight deck. 'Delta November, you are four miles from touchdown, closing with the centre line. Turn left now five degrees on to heading zero three five.' The captain said laconically, 'Roger'.

'Two miles from touchdown now, and on the centre line.'

Suddenly the fog was ripped apart, and streaks of it flew past the windscreen and the windows. The quiet voice said, 'Turn right two degrees on to zero three seven; you are one and a half miles from touchdown. Can you land visually?'

The runway, broad and long and comforting, lay immediately in front of them. The captain lifted the microphone and said, 'Delta November is visual. Thank you.' He hung the microphone upon a little hook and placed his hands and feet on the controls, nodding to the co-pilot. One of the juniors turned to Keith and said, 'Captain likes everyone strapped in for landing.' They went back to the seats, and as they settled down in them the wheels touched the runway.

The engines roared suddenly in reverse pitch and died again, the brakes squealed a little, and the aircraft slowed, turned from the runway, and taxied to a remote part of the tarmac where the batsman waited. One of the lads by Keith grumbled, 'They're putting us the hell of a way from anywhere. I got an aunt in Allerton. I told Ma that I'd try and get to see her.'

The other said, 'They're putting us over here so the truck can get to us to load, and be out of the way.'

The machine came to rest, and the engines stopped. On the flight deck the crew entered up their various log books and forms; one by one they came down the cabin to the door, now open. The captain stopped by Keith. 'Saw you watching the talk-down,' he said. 'Did you understand it?'

Keith smiled. 'Some of it. Not very much.'

'Everyone to his trade,' the officer said. 'As soon as we get clear of this foggy muck you can come and sit up front.'

He passed on, and Keith left the machine with Dick King. 'How did you enjoy the flight?'

Keith smiled. 'Like being on the Underground.'

'It was a bit. Not much to look at, is there? The Met says we'll be out of this by the time we're over Ireland.'

'What time do we take off?'

'Depends what time we finish loading. I don't see any sign of the truck yet. We'd better get some dinner while the going's good.'

They made for the restaurant. 'That's one thing I wanted to ask you,' Keith said. 'Who cooks and dishes out the food while you're in flight?'

'I do,' said the flight engineer.

'All the way? You've got to sleep some time.'

'Oh well, one of the others does it if I've got my head down, or they go without.'

'I could help with that,' Keith said. 'I can serve coffee and biscuits or heat up a can of stew. I don't know that I can help in any other way.'

'Well, that might be a help. I'll show you what we do.'

The loudspeaker broadcast a call to the telephone for Mr King while they were having lunch. He came back to the table. 'Bloody truck's arrived,' he said, and gulped down his cup of tea. 'See you later.'

He made off back to the machine. Keith finished his lunch quickly and followed him, anxious to miss no moment of the play. The semi-trailer stood by the aircraft with the sausage-like component on the tray swathed in hessian, twelve feet long and weighing about five tons. Beside the truck Dick lounged with one of the co-pilots, idle. 'Needn't have hurried over dinner,' he said to Keith. 'Waiting for the bloody crane now. Captain, he knew better.'

Presently the mobile crane arrived, and a Land Rover loaded with baulks of heavy timber, and the slow, delicate business of loading the rotor into the cabin through the door began, and positioning it in the right part of the cabin when it was in, and straining it down to holding lugs with steel ropes and turnbuckles. Keith could do nothing technical to help these men who knew their job so well, but he worked all afternoon as a labourer for them, moving heavy timbers under their direction and passing wires. It took three hours to get the load in place and secured. Then the tank wagon came to refuel the aircraft. It was half-past five before everything was finished.

'We'll have a meal before we go,' said Captain Fielding. 'Take off at seven o'clock.'

A foreman electrician from the works was to accompany them and install the rotor in the *Cathay Princess*, a man called Adams. Dick introduced Keith as they walked towards the restaurant again. 'This is Mr Keith Stewart,' he said. 'Writes for the *Miniature Mechanic*.'

Mr Adams stopped dead in his tracks. 'Not *the* Keith Stewart?' he enquired.

'That's right.'

Mr Adams put out his hand. 'Well, did you ever! Wait till I tell the lads in the shop I met Keith Stewart!'

The words comforted Keith, assuaging something of the inferiority complex that had begun to descend upon him; there was so much here that was technical that he did not know. Here, in Dick King and in Mr Adams, were two who recognised what he could do in the little technical field that he had made his own. He went on to the restaurant with them with restored confidence in himself. Technical fields, he reflected, of necessity were small; if you were expert in one subject you could not be expert also in all the others, for no man's mind was big enough. The man who designed the radar presentation that the controller had used to talk them down that morning would not himself have been able to bring them into a safe landing, for he would not have known sufficient about aeroplanes.

They ate together at a long table in the deserted restaurant, all nine of them. The navigator sat next to Keith. In reply to a question, he said, 'Be about midnight, local time, when we refuel at Frobisher. Nine hours flight. Be just the same if it was daytime, because they don't see the sun there much this time of year. Say it's an hour to refuel. Another nine hours to Vancouver gets us there around dawn. After that it's daylight down to Honolulu.'

In the cold, windy January darkness they walked back to the aircraft at about half-past six, and climbed on board, and made their way forward through the cabin, climbing over the many securing wires of the rotor. Lights were switched on, the steps were withdrawn from the door and the door itself was slammed shut and secured by one of the young pilots. Mr Adams and Keith settled in a couple of the seats and strapped themselves in, and the routine of pre-flight checks began on the flight deck.

'You done this often before?' asked Mr Adams.

Keith shook his head. 'I've never been out of England.'

'You don't want to, either,' said Mr Adams decidedly. 'Last year the missus and the daughter kept on at me. Would I take them to the South of France? They'd read about it in the books, and Grace Kelly and all that. Well, I did. God love us, what it didn't cost, flying to Nice and flying back again! And when we got there, not half so much fun as we'd have had at Blackpool. But they liked it ... Gave them something to talk about in Salford.'

'That where you live?'

'Aye. Ever been there?'

Keith shook his head.

'The Salford and Eccles Model Engineers would like it fine if you could come up to judge one of their exhibitions, Mr Stewart. They had the last one in the Town Hall – October was it, or November? A lot of your designs were there ...' They went on talking model engineering while the starters whined, the motors caught and ran, and the Douglas turned and taxied slowly to the runway, framed in amber lights.

They took off down the runway, and were airborne. For a moment or two Keith saw the lights of Liverpool away over on the left; then they were blotted out by cloud and only the bright glow of the exhaust manifolds could be seen, and the rhythmic pulsations of the red wing-tip light reflected from the mist. 'Looks like we're in cloud again,' said Keith. 'It was like this all the way from Blackbushe.'

Mr Adams stirred from a post-prandial doze. 'Wonderful the way they find their way about,' he said comfortably, and dozed again.

Keith was too technically interested to follow his example. He got up and stood in the dim alley leading to the flight deck, watching what was going on. Nothing much seemed to be happening; the pilots sat relaxed and he judged that the machine was on the automatic pilot, for neither of them seemed to be flying it. The pilot's microphone hung idle on its hook, but now and again the radio operator seemed to speak to someone from his desk. Dick King sat upon a folding seat between and behind the pilots, but he did not seem to be doing anything.

As he watched, the darkness ahead through the windscreen seemed to lighten for a moment, darken again, and lighten. Suddenly a wisp of white cloud ripped by the windscreen and they were momentarily in moonlight. More cloud rose up ahead and enveloped them, and that in turn was ripped away. Then they were flying in full moonlight over a white, moonlit floor of cloud and climbing away from it. It seemed to Keith the most wonderful sight that he had ever seen, for it was new to him.

He could not repress his technical interest. He moved forward and spoke to Dick quietly: 'How high are we?'

The engineer said, 'Thirteen thousand five hundred. Have a cup of coffee presently, when we level off to cruise.'

The captain heard the question, and the answer. 'We're going up to twenty-one thousand,' he said. 'I'll let you know when we've settled down at cruising altitude, and you can come and sit up front here, if you like.'

Keith went back to his seat, and sat looking out on the moonlit clouds below, at the serene, untroubled security of the wing. Presently the note of the engines altered, the nose of the machine dipped slightly, and she seemed to take a new, stable, and rather quieter flight. He judged that this was the change to the cruising condition, and this was confirmed when Dick came aft to the galley. Keith got up to help him with the coffee and biscuits.

'Captain says we'll have a meal for anybody who's awake and wants it at twenty-three zulu – at eleven o'clock English time. Then another sometime after we leave Frobisher. Breakfast on the ground at Vancouver. Coffee and biscuits every couple of hours or so.'

'When are you going to sleep?'

The engineer smiled. 'Pretty soon, mate. Take off, landing, and refuelling … those are my busy times. I'll take one of the inside chairs soon as we've cleared this coffee.'

'Show me what you do about the meal. I can look after that if you're asleep.'

When coffee was over and the cups rinsed, Keith went forward. The captain got out of his seat and stretched, and at his invitation Keith got into it and sat relaxed, watching the wide, dim panorama of deep blue sky and moonlit cloud far below. He studied the instruments massed on the panels in front of him, examining them one by one. Most of them were familiar to him in theory; some of the others were explained by the legend on the dial. When prolonged cogitation failed to yield the function of a lever or a dial he asked the first officer beside him, who explained it to him. He passed over the radio equipment without questions, knowing that the explanations would be quite beyond his understanding.

His day had been a long one, and at the conclusion of an hour he found that he was growing sleepy. He got out of the captain's seat, and one of the young pilots took his place. The navigator smiled as he brushed past him, and Keith paused to look at the chart. 'We'll be about *here* now,' the officer said, putting his pencil on the thin pencil line that led across the North Atlantic to Greenland.

Keith studied the line. 'Do we go over Greenland?' It seemed incredible that he, Keith Stewart, should be doing this.

'That's right. We might be over the ice cap about one in the morning, Greenwich time.'

'Shall we see it?' Eskimos and explorers, and the dogs with tails curled up over their backs that they called huskies.

'I doubt it. There's usually a lot of cloud cover. We might. Like me to call you if there's anything to see?'

'I would.' Keith hesitated. 'Are you going to be up for the next hour or two?'

'Captain's having a ziz now,' said the navigator. 'Supper's at eleven o'clock, Greenwich. He's getting up for that. After that I'll have mine.'

'Don't wake Dick King to get the supper if he's asleep,' Keith said. 'Give me a nudge. He showed me what to do.'

'Okay.'

He passed aft to the rest quarters. The captain and the radio operator were sleeping in their clothes in the two bunks. Keith settled down in a vacant chair and pushed it back to the reclining angle. So many technical interests that he could not absorb because of the need for sleep. Janice and Katie in the flat at Ealing all seemed very far away; his many years of work for the *Miniature Mechanic* were something that had happened in a previous existence, quite unreal. The even murmur of the engines, the motionless flight, wrapped him round, and presently he slept.

He was roused by Dick climbing over him from the inside seat to start getting the supper. He got up and lent a hand. The whole crew seemed to come to life with the smell of the meal heating on the stove. Captain Fielding and the radio operator got down from the bunks, shook themselves, and put on their shoes. Keith realised for the first time that the aircrew were divided virtually into two watches, that the pilots could do the routine navigation and the routine radio checks. The meal, served in two sittings, signified a change of watch.

He rinsed the dishes when Mr King went forward, and put everything away. Mr Adams slumbered again, uninterested in the flight, and Keith went forward to the flight deck again. He sat at the navigator's desk for some time, but presently he grew sleepy and went back to his seat.

He was roused by the changed note of the engines as they began the let-down an hour out from Frobisher. He knew what was happening from the slight pressure difference in his ears, and from the time. He went and washed his face to clear his mind, and then went forward again to the flight deck. The navigator was back at his desk. 'Clear for landing,' he said. 'Cloud two tenths at three thousand. Temperature on the ground minus ten Fahrenheit. Good and cold – forty-two degrees of frost. I should stay in the machine, if I were you.'

Keith was startled. 'What's the outside temperature here, now?'

'I don't know.' The officer leaned back and glanced at the panel. 'About minus thirty.'

'I'd like to do anything I can to help – if there's anything that I can do.'

The navigator shook his head. 'It's just the refuelling, then we'll be off again. Get your bloody nose frostbitten if you go outside.'

They landed presently upon a white, snow-covered runway lit with amber lights, using the brakes very little and the engines in reverse pitch a great deal. They followed a blue-lit taxiway to the few buildings constituting the base and came to a standstill in front of the control tower. Steps were wheeled up and the door opened; the captain and the flight engineer and the two youngest pilots put on heavy coats and leather gloves, and went down on to the snow. Keith followed them to the door and stopped in the entrance, checked by the bitterness of the cold.

The moon was bright upon the snow plain of the airfield and the snow-covered buildings, the lights brilliant. He saw the captain and the navigator hurrying to the control tower. He saw a refuelling truck drive up and stop by the port wing, he saw a ladder erected and Dick get up on to the wing with one of the refuelling crew and commence to sound the tanks. Then he could bear the cold no longer, and retreated forward into the machine across the web of cables lashing down the rotor.

In the rest quarters warmth still lingered, though cold air was seeping forward from the rear. Refuelling took three-quarters of an hour. The crew made a quick external inspection of the aircraft and came hurrying into the fuselage again. The door was slammed shut, the steps removed, the motors started again, and the machine moved out on to the runway and took off with a slow, careful acceleration on the icy surface till she was airborne on the long flight over the northern wastes of Canada to Vancouver.

Presently Keith went forward and spoke to Dick King seated between the pilots at the console. 'What time for the next meal?' he asked in a low tone.

'Nine or nine-thirty, Greenwich,' the engineer replied. He pointed to the clock above the navigator's table. 'That time, there.' It showed about five-thirty when Keith looked. 'We'll have coffee and biscuits soon as we level off.'

'I'll start getting that ready. What are you having for the main meal?'

'There's some pre-cooked steaks in a carton on the left-hand side, up at the top.' They went on to discuss the detail of the meal. 'I'll probably be up for it,' the engineer said. 'Get my head down for a bit presently, but I'll be up.'

'You don't have to be,' said Keith. 'I can do all that.'

In spite of his bold assertion, he was growing tired. The flight from Frobisher to Vancouver was a repeat of the flight to Frobisher, a night flight without incident, with nothing to be seen. The four pilots, the radio officer, and the navigator took their turns in the bunks; the flight engineer slept in one of the seats. These men were all younger than Keith Stewart, physically more fit and accustomed to long hours of flight and irregular sleep. They seemed to stand it well, but for the first time Keith realised the meaning of crew fatigue. By the time they reached Honolulu, he knew, he would desire nothing so much as sleep in a bed. He could well understand the necessity for two or three days' rest before the crew flew home again to Blackbushe.

He slept most of the way to Vancouver, only rousing himself to help to serve the meal. Few of the aircrew ate much during that stage of the flight, but the demand for coffee and biscuits was brisk. They landed in from over sea on the long Vancouver runway in the darkness at about six in the morning of local time, refuelled and inspected the machine in misty rain, and walked wearily to the airport restaurant.

'You won't get bacon and eggs, English fashion, here,' the engineer told Keith. 'Hot cakes and syrup with a side order of bacon. I'll show you.'

Where everything was strange this seemed no stranger than the rest; he accepted the North American food and enjoyed the novelty, though Mr Adams grumbled at the little tea bag hanging in the cup of hot water. They ate altogether sitting up in a long row at a stainless steel counter, while outside the grey dawn showed in the rain. 'Might as well be in England,' Mr Adams said.

The navigator heard him, and smiled faintly. 'You'll be gasping for breath tonight in Honolulu.'

In the grey morning light they walked through the rain to the machine, and settled in their places. The clock over the navigator's desk showed either 4 or 16; both seemed quite inapplicable to Keith and which it was he had no means of knowing. They took off to the west down the long runway and climbed away over water till they entered cloud. 'Eleven more hours,' the navigator told him. 'Then we'll be through.'

Half an hour later they broke out into sunshine over a cloud floor; the pilots reached for their sunglasses and put them on. Presently, while the first cups of coffee were being consumed, the cloud beneath them thinned into holes through which they could see the sea, corrugated with waves. By the time the empty cups had been collected, rinsed, and placed in their racks to dry, the cloud had practically disappeared, and they flew on under a cloudless sky, over a blue sea. Later they met cloud again.

The day passed in boredom and fatigue for Keith. He had long exhausted those technical interests of the aircraft that were within his comprehension, and he was growing very tired indeed. He dozed wearily much of the day with his shoes off, for his feet and legs were swelling with the continued sitting and lack of exercise. He ate little of the midday meal. As the hands of his watch moved gradually past twelve and on to one he began to come to life again, for three was the hour of landing, English time, when this slow purgatory would be over. Since they were nearly half-way round the world and they were to land in the late afternoon, he guessed that his watch still cherished the opinion that it was the middle of the night.

Soon after two activity began on the flight deck, and the let-down began. He went forward, and the captain pointed out a very small cloud dead ahead of them and very far away. 'That could be over Oahu,' he said. 'It's either that or Maui. But I think it's Oahu. We're on the range now.'

Keith nodded and went back to the navigator's desk to look at the chart. Honolulu, it appeared, was the name of a town and not an island, as he had supposed. It was on an island called Oahu, by no means the largest of the group. He went back to his seat and sat down, wondering for the first time if he was not absolutely crazy to be here at all. Ealing was his place, and writing articles for the *Miniature Mechanic* was his job. These wastes of sunlit sea, these islands with strange names like Oahu, were no part of his life. He owed it to Janice to try to get back her inheritance ... but still ... Ealing was his place. He could stay with the aircraft, of course, and presently the crew would take him back to Blackbushe, only forty miles from Ealing; a truck or a coach would take him up the Great West Road, a red bus up the South Ealing Road, and he would be home again, home in his workshop, in his own routine.

Abruptly he realised that he was afraid, afraid of the unknown that lay before him. He must do better than that for Janice before he could have licence to go home. The island grew ahead of them, and there was more activity upon the flight deck. Dick King was in the folding seat between the pilots and the captain was talking into the small microphone. They dropped off height as they approached the island and approached it from a little to the south of east. A considerable town with docks and shipping lay upon the southern shore, and to the west of this there was an enormous airport, apparently about five miles long. They made a wide circuit of this and approached from the south-west, and touched down upon a runway halfway up the length of the field. They taxied to the Customs entry building near the garlanded civil airport building, and stopped the motors.

Keith asked the flight engineer, 'What time is it here?'

'Ten minutes to five – in the afternoon.'

Steps were wheeled up to the aircraft, the door opened, and they made their way out on to the tarmac, carrying their luggage. The humid heat hit Keith like a blow. He was wearing a blue serge suit with a waistcoat, a woollen shirt, and thick woollen underwear, clothes that had been reasonable enough in England thirty-six hours before but which were intolerable in the tropics, where everybody seemed to be wearing a light shirt and trousers and little else. Moreover, he was carrying his suitcase and his raincoat. He stood with the crew in a small group while a small Oriental man in charge of a brawny Customs officer came up and greeted Captain Fielding.

'Very good afternoon, Captain,' he said. He spoke with a slight American accent. 'I am Harold Yamasuki, of the Yamasuki Trading Company, Incorporated. We are agents for the tanker ship, the *Cathay Princess*. You have had a good flight? You arrived exactly on time.'

Captain Fielding put out his hand. 'Nice to meet you, Mr Yamasuki,' he said. 'Yes, we had a good flight – no troubles.' He turned around. 'This is Mr Adams, who is to superintend the installation of the rotor. You had a cable about him?'

Mr Yamasuki stopped shaking hands with the captain and shook hands with Mr Adams. 'Very glad to know you,' he said. 'Yes, we had the radiogram about Mr Adams. He will be great help. Now, everybody must go to the entry formalities with passports and vaccination certificates ready, please, and after that the Customs. You give bags to the boy here and he will meet you with them in the examination room. There are nine? Yes, nine. I will now call the Beachcomber Hotel and arrange accommodation. You will not mind if two must share a room, a room with two beds? I will meet you as you come from Customs, and we go to the hotel. Then we can talk more. Now you go with officer to passport examination.'

The captain said, 'They'll want us to shift the aircraft away from here before we go to the hotel. Are you unloading tonight?'

'It is too late now,' said Mr Yamasuki. 'Tomorrow, I think, at seven o'clock we will begin to unload. By the time we could begin tonight it will be dark, and there would be the possibility of accident and damage to the rotor. I think it will be better in the day.'

Mr Adams said, 'I'm with you there, mate, all the way.'

They went from the brilliant sunshine into the cool shade of the air-conditioned examination room. Keith passed through with the crew without difficulty and emerged into the Customs shed with them. Nobody had anything to declare and only a cursory examination was made. The bags were loaded into an elongated motor car, the captain spoke to the control tower and to Shell upon the telephone, and the crew went back to the machine to move it to the park. Keith Stewart went with them, leaving his coat, jacket, and waistcoat in the car. Even so, he sweated profusely as he walked out to the aircraft in his braces and blue trousers.

There were palm trees by the foreshore, and the sea was glittering and blue. It was incredible that he, Keith Stewart, should be in a place like this.

Moving the aircraft nearly a mile away and refuelling it took an hour. The sun had set and the quick darkness was covering the airport when the last man got down from the aircraft, slammed the door, and locked it. In the fading light the aircraft movements seemed to be continuous; they took off and landed with their winking navigation lights in the soft, velvety dusk, in what appeared to be an endless stream. Keith stood watching them, fascinated. 'Busy place, this,' remarked Mr King.

The long car appeared with Mr Yamasuki and took them to the hotel. The agent consulted with the desk clerk about the rooms, and then turned to the captain. 'I will now leave you to rest,' he said. 'Tomorrow, at half-past six in the morning, I will come back with a car, and the truck will be beside the airplane at seven.'

They talked about the mobile crane. 'I will arrange,' said Mr Yamasuki. 'One thing. I have called the ship, the *Cathay Princess* to say you have arrived. I think some of the officers may come here tonight to meet you, and to talk about the electrical work with Mr Adams.'

As he was going down the steps to the car Keith Stewart stopped him. 'You can tell me, Mr Yamasuki. Is it possible to get from here to Tahiti?'

'To Tahiti? There is no regular service. The Matson ships, they go Tahiti to Honolulu but not from here to Tahiti. There are rumours that they will change, but I do not know. There are Norwegian cargo steamers which call sometimes from Vancouver to Tahiti. They carry a few passengers.'

'Will one of those be going soon?'

Mr Yamasuki shook his head. 'I do not think so. One was here last week. Perhaps in two months' time. I will find out. Sometimes there is an island trading schooner going to Tahiti. They take passengers, not very comfortable. Sometimes, to sleep on deck.'

'Would one of those be going soon?'

'I do not know. I will ask tonight, and tell you in the morning. You wish to go from Honolulu to Tahiti, yourself?'

'That's right.'

'I do not think it will be easy. But I will ask.'

Keith Stewart was depressed, and tired, and very, very hot in his unsuitable clothes. He went back to the group at the desk and signed his name in the register, and found that he had been allocated to share a room with Dick King. They went up in the elevator to the fifth floor.

The Beachcomber was a fairly modern hotel on the unfashionable, dockside side of the city, much used by aircrews and ships' officers on account of its nearness to the airfield and to the docks. It had no swimming pool, but it commanded a pleasant view out over the ocean in the front and the mountains at the back. Keith and Dick King found themselves in a back room with a shower, two beds converted in to lounges for the day, and a wide, deep verandah furnished with wicker chairs and table. The door of the room was louvred for the full height, permitting the cool trade wind to blow through the room continuously.

'I'm for a shower,' said Dick King, throwing off his clothes and making for it.

Keith Stewart had never had a shower in the whole of his life. He had seen them in shop windows and had read about them, but one had never come his way. As a boy and a young man in Renfrew he had had a bath once a week, and though he had graduated from that to having a bath whenever he felt like it, it would have seemed to him a senseless extravagance to have one every day. He certainly felt like one now. While Dick was in the shower he stripped off his heavy woollen underwear with a sigh of relief, and stood in the cool breeze with a towel round his waist. Presently he opened his suitcase and stood looking at his clothing ruefully. His woollen cricket shirts and grey flannel trousers were the best he could do; they might be tolerable after dark but he knew now that they would be very hot in the daytime. Still, they were all he had.

Presently Dick King came out and he went in and tried the shower experimentally. He found it strange but not unpleasant and he stayed under it for a long time, gradually reducing the temperature of the water and washing away his fatigue with the sweat. When he came out he was cool and refreshed.

He would have to have some money in his pocket, and they used dollars here, it seemed. He had never cashed a travellers' cheque before and consulted Dick, who showed him where to sign it and told him they would cash it at the desk. He followed this advice when they went downstairs. Then they went to the verandah bar.

'Beer's the cheapest,' said Dick. 'Not like the English beer – a kind of fizzy lager. But it's what we mostly drink here, on account of the dollar allowance.'

In the bar most of the rest of the aircrew were already gathered, with Captain Davies of the *Cathay Princess*, the chief engineer, and the third engineer, a lad called Alec Bourne. Captain Fielding turned to Dick and Keith to introduce them. 'This is Mr King, flight engineer,' he said. He smiled. 'This is Mr Keith Stewart. We call him flight engineer under instruction, which means he's come along with us for the ride. He writes for a model paper in London. We're hoping that he'll give us a good spin when he gets back.'

The third engineer's jaw dropped, and they all shook hands. The Third said, 'It wouldn't be Keith Stewart of the *Miniature Mechanic*, by any chance?'

Dick King said, 'The very same. You read the *Miniature Mechanic*?'

'I've read it every week, ever since I was a little nipper,' said the lad. 'I've got every copy since 1948 at home, and a lot on board. Ma sends it to me every week. Fancy meeting you, sir. I never thought I'd do that, except maybe to see you opening an exhibition.' He hesitated, and added, 'Would you like a beer, sir?'

A beer was just exactly what Keith Stewart needed, and while it was coming he talked models to the third engineer. 'I made a Hornet about two years ago,' the young man told him. 'I'm working on a Gannet now.'

'Did the Hornet go all right?'

'It went fine. I had a bit of difficulty getting it started at the first go off, but then I got a bottle of American fuel, and she goes fine. I got a little airscrew on her for the load.'

Keith nodded. 'They generally put more ether in the American fuels. If you're using that, I think I should wash out the cylinder with a light oil after each run. I've heard that the American fuels are more corrosive than ours. Put in a drop or two of Three-in-One, or something like that.'

The young man nodded gratefully. 'Thanks for the tip, Mr Stewart.'

'Where do you work?'

'Oh, in the engine-room workshop,' the Third said. 'We've got a six-inch lathe there, and a shaper. It's quite well equipped, really.' He paused, and added a little shyly, 'if you've got the time to come on board and have a look round, Mr Stewart, there's one or two of the lads would like to meet you.'

'I'd like to do that very much,' said Keith. 'I'd like to see your workshop.' Twelve beers arrived upon a tray carried by a very pretty Asiatic girl in a cheongsam of figured silk. These were distributed around, and the talk became general. Alec Bourne turned to his captain. 'I've just asked Mr Stewart if he'd like to come on board and see the engines and the workshop, sir.'

'Of course.' Captain Davies turned to Keith. 'There's more model engineering done in that workshop than was ever done on bits for the ship. You should see the commotion when Alec here was trying to get his little engine started up. They had to use the main engines as a starter motor for it, so the Chief was telling me.'

The Third flushed uneasily. 'Mr Stewart designed it, sir. It was the fuel that was wrong.'

There was general laughter. 'Come on board any time you like, Mr Stewart,' said the captain.

'That's very good of you, sir,' said Keith. 'I thought perhaps I'd stick with the rotor and lend a hand unloading that tomorrow morning, and perhaps come down with it to the dock.'

'Fine. What are your movements, Mr Stewart? Are you staying here a bit, or going back to England with the aircraft?'

Keith said, 'Well, that's just the point. I really want to get to Tahiti, but I asked Mr Yamasuki and he said he didn't know of any service from Honolulu to Tahiti. He was going to find out this evening and let me know.' He hesitated. 'I suppose you don't know of any service, sir?'

Captain Davies shook his head. 'I never heard of one. There must be an odd tramp or two, of course. It's got to be

Tahiti, has it? You've got some business there, or something?'

'That's right.' These merchant service officers would probably be understanding and sympathetic about events following on a wreck. He pulled out his wallet and took the cutting from *The Times* from it. 'My sister and my brother-in-law were sailing out here in a yacht,' he said. 'They got wrecked on an island in the Tuamotus. I've got to get down there and see about things – the grave, and salvage, and anything that might need to be done.' He gave the cutting to the captain.

The officers were very interested, and asked a number of questions about the yacht, and about John Dermott. Captain Davies had been an officer of the Royal Naval Reserve in the last war. 'I'm almost sure I remember him,' he said thoughtfully. 'At Invergordon ... or was it Scapa? An RN two-and-a-half, in one of the Tribal class. Wait now. The man I'm thinking of had a broken nose, boxing or something.'

'That's right,' said Keith. 'He had a broken nose.'

The captain dropped his eyes again to the cutting. 'He was a good seaman,' he said. 'Better than most RN. It's curious it should have to end like this.'

The three merchant officers turned their minds to Keith Stewart's problem, and discussed it carefully. 'There's a fortnightly air service from Fiji through Samoa to Tahiti,' said the captain. 'You can probably fly from here to Samoa, but it's the hell of a long way round.'

'How far would that be?' Keith asked.

'I'd only be guessing. Might be four thousand miles. I'll work it out for you tomorrow when you come on board.'

'Sounds like it might be a bit expensive for me,' said Keith, a little ruefully. 'I was hoping there'd be something more direct – and cheap. Something like a cargo steamer taking a few passengers.'

Captain Davies shook his head. 'I don't know of anything. But I'll find out for you, Mr Stewart.' He handed back the cutting, and Keith put it back into his wallet.

They all turned to the beer. In the buzz of conversation the chief engineer said to his captain, 'There's always Jack Donelly.'

'Nonsense,' Captain Davies said shortly. 'The man's mad.'

It seemed to be an unwelcome subject and Keith did not pursue it, but he noted the name. They set to work upon the beer and to a consideration of the unloading and the handling of the rotor from the aircraft to the ship, the air officers being principally concerned to avoid damage to the aircraft by the crane reaching into the fuselage through the door, and the marine officers being principally concerned to get the rotor undamaged into its field magnets and bearings in the engine room. Keith stood a round of beers and was concerned at the inroad that it made into his small store of dollars, and presently they all went to dinner in the hotel dining-room.

All who had flown from England went to bed early that night. In the bedroom that Keith shared with Dick the moon was bright upon the mountains, the palm trees rustled continuously, and a warm wind hardly cooler than in daytime blew steadily through the room. Keith unpacked his thick woollen pyjamas and eyed them with distaste. 'You'll boil in those, in this place,' said Dick King. 'I don't sleep in anything, these tropical places. Look, put the sheet over your middle and tuck it in, like this, so you don't catch cold. Then you've got your shoulders, arms, and legs out in the cool.' Keith followed his example, fell asleep at once to the murmur of the palm trees, and slept like a log all night.

Next morning he was up with the aircrew and out on the aerodrome with them at seven o'clock. Mr Yamasuki said, 'I have asked about the ships or airplanes to Tahiti. 'There are no ships on regular service, no airplanes. The next Norwegian freighter is due here on March 3rd.'

That was seven weeks ahead. 'Nothing before that?'

'I am so sorry. It is possible to go to Tahiti by air through Samoa, or else perhaps by Los Angeles. I think either way would be expensive. Pan American can tell you what the fare is, and the services, at the passenger terminal.'

Keith nodded. 'I'll go and ask them presently.' He knew quite well that the answer would be far beyond his means. 'You didn't hear of any irregular service – a trading schooner, or anything like that?'

Mr Yamasuki said, 'I have no news of one. Sometimes with a trading schooner there would not be any advance news. She would arrive one day, and stay perhaps three or four days, and let it be known that she was calling at Papeete and other places. One might come today, or perhaps not for six months.'

Keith thanked him, and went on working with the aircrew to get the rotor out of the aeroplane without damaging either. It took about two hours to get it on the truck. Most of the aircrew then went back to the hotel to rest and swim and shop on their small dollar allowance for the next two days before beginning the long flight back to England. Mr Adams and Dick and Keith rode on the truck through the streets of Honolulu to Kapalama Basin, where the tanker was berthed.

There was nothing he could do to help the dockyard engineers get the rotor into the ship, and he went on board with Dick King. The third engineer met them and invited them below to see the main engine room and the workshop and, more particularly, the Gannet engine of Keith Stewart's design, which was half finished, a little box of carefully machined unassembled bits. 'Half the engine room have had a hand in this,' the lad from Dartford said proudly. 'Whenever somebody gets tired of reading Peter Cheyney he comes and asks if he can machine one of the pistons. I sometimes think that I'm just managing the job, not making it.'

He was in trouble over the crankshaft machining jig. 'You said to make it of high tensile steel in the serial, Mr Stewart, but I can't seem to lay my hands on just a little bit anywhere in Honolulu. The smallest I can find is four-inch bar. Would it be all right to use mild steel instead?'

Keith had had this one before in letters from Andover to Auckland. He picked up the *Miniature Mechanic* from the bench and turned to the jig drawing that he had made in the basement room in Somerset Road, Ealing, with Janice sleeping in the room next door, eight thousand miles away. 'I've got a mod for that,' he said. 'You've got to retain this eighth-inch thickness, here, because of the tool clearance. If you're going to make it in mild steel, make it an L section, like this.' He added swift pencil lines to the printed drawing. 'It's just a little bit more complicated. You'd have to get out this bit with an end mill – about three-sixteenths. Have you got a mill like that on board?'

The Third nodded. 'That's easy, Mr Stewart. I could do that in the drilling machine best, I think. Thanks a lot.'

Presently Keith pulled a small box from the pocket of his blazer. 'I've got a little thing here that might amuse you.' He unwrapped the little Hornet-engined generating set from the rag that wrapped it round, and put it on the bench. 'Gee,' said the Third reverently, 'that really is something!' He studied it carefully. 'What's the engine, Mr Stewart? It looks a bit like a Hornet.'

'It's a Hornet with a different cylinder and piston, cam gear and valves, to run on petrol, and a governor in place of the reduction gear,' he said. He picked it up, shook it to check that there was still petrol in the little tank, turned it upside down to prime the carburettor, and flipped it into life with his thumb. The little engine caught with a crackling roar, speeded up, steadied as the pea bulb glowed with light. The noise attracted other engineers from the engine room, and soon the workshop was crowded. Somebody said, laughing, 'Has Bill Adams seen this?'

'No – I don't think he has,' said Keith.

'Cor! – that'll give him something to think about. Anyone can build a big generator set that you can get your hands around inside. Fetch him along, Bert, and ask him how he'd like to service this one!'

Mr Adams was fetched and stood in reverent awe till the little motor ran out of petrol and stopped, and almost at the same time the dockyard hooter sounded for twelve o'clock, knocking-off time for dinner. Keith wrapped his generator set up again and put it in the box in his pocket; later he filled the tank with an eggcup of petrol provided for use in the ship's launch, strained carefully through a piece of chamois leather. The officers escorted Mr Adams and Dick and Keith up into the wardroom for lunch.

After lunch, as they were sitting smoking at the table over cups of tea and coffee, Captain Davies said, 'I've been making some enquiries about your journey to Tahiti, Mr Stewart. Not very satisfactory, I'm afraid. I can't find out anything about a cargo boat in the near future, and there's no regular service.'

Keith nodded slowly. 'Mr Yamasuki said this morning that a trading schooner might come in at any time. No one would know beforehand she was coming.'

'It's a possibility,' the captain agreed. 'We've been here for four and a half weeks now. There was one just after we came, but she was going to Palmyra. I don't know where she was going after that.'

'Where do they tie up, in case one did come in?' asked Keith.

'This one berthed just inside the harbour, just the other side of the Merchant Officers' Training School,' the captain said. 'I think they like to sail in and out if there's a fair wind, save the cost of a tug.'

'You don't think there's one there now?'

'Not that I know of. But that's where you'd get news of them, if anywhere. It might be worth a walk along and talking to the longshoremen. They might know more than the harbourmaster.'

The first officer smiled. 'He doesn't bother much about the small fry.'

'The trouble is, I've got so little time,' Keith said. 'If there's nothing turns up that's within my means I'll have to go back with the aircraft the day after tomorrow.'

'More like Tuesday,' said Dick King. 'Captain Fielding said this morning we'd be taking off at dawn on Tuesday.'

'That's right,' said Mr Adams. 'We'll be having the test run on Monday. Then if everything's all right he can take me home again.'

'It doesn't give much time,' agreed the captain.

The second mate said, 'Jack Donelly.' There was a little ripple of laughter round the table. Only the captain remained serious. 'I wouldn't think of it,' he said.

The first officer took him up. 'Nor would I, sir, for myself. But I don't want to get to Tahiti as much as Mr Stewart. As I see it, it's either him or nothing. Mr Stewart's over twenty-one. I don't see why he shouldn't have a look at him.'

'I wouldn't be any party to it,' said the captain. 'If he ever gets his ship out of hock to the harbourmaster he'll just go off and disappear, and no more heard of him, ever. I've seen it all my life.'

Keith asked, 'Who is this Jack Donelly, anyway?'

The first officer leaned back in his chair. 'He's an American from Oregon or somewhere. Maybe he's a fisherman – I wouldn't know. His ship's a sort of sloop-rigged fishing boat – a sailing boat. He built it himself. Quite small. I should say that he's a half-caste, and I'd guess that his mother was a Polynesian. He's a big chap, though, and he must be a good seaman because he sailed here from the United States alone – single-handed.'

'He's got the mentality of a child of ten,' said the captain.

'That may be, sir. He's so dumb that he can hardly string two words together. But he did get here from the United States, two thousand ruddy miles of open sea, found the islands. You can't get away from that.'

'Yes,' said the captain, 'and you know how he did it.'

'I do.'

Keith asked, 'How did he do it?'

'Got on the air route between here and San Francisco and followed the aeroplanes,' the captain said scornfully. 'There are about ten flights every day, or more. That's a fine way to navigate.'

'Never mind, sir. He got here.'

'He won't get to Tahiti that way,' said the captain. 'There's no air service.'

'Is he going to Tahiti?' Keith enquired.

The captain leaned forward. 'Look, Mr Stewart,' he said. 'I don't want to stand in your way if you want to go and talk to him. But, first of all, I'll tell you about Jack Donelly. He came in here about a fortnight ago and sailed right in to this basin as far as he could go till his bow was practically in the street, and tied up just ahead of us. I'll admit he handled his ship well. He came in under sail – he hasn't got a motor – with his warps all ready fore and aft, got down his main and came in under jib, dropped the jib and came alongside sweet as anything, chucked his warps on to the quay, hopped on shore and made her fast bow and stern in two shakes of a duck's arse. It was pretty to watch. I'll agree with Number One here, he's probably a good seaman.'

He paused. 'Now that's as far as I go. The port authorities were after him as soon as he tied up. He hadn't got permission to berth there, but that was the least of it. He hadn't got any ship's papers at all – no registration, no manifest, nothing. He hadn't got a bill of health and he didn't seem to know what it was. He hadn't even got a passport. I shouldn't think he's got any money.' He paused. 'I think they were pretty kind to him, all things considered,' he remarked. 'They called him a yacht and towed him round into the yacht harbour.'

'How did you come to know about him, then?' Keith asked.

'He came on board,' the captain said. 'He came on board to ask the way to Palmyra and half a dozen other places. He's got no charts. He wouldn't know how to use one if he had it. What he's got is a small school atlas with the whole of the Pacific Ocean on one page, and a pretty dirty page it is, I can tell you. He picks the biggest merchant ship that he can see and comes on board to ask the course to the next place. That's why he berthed just ahead of us. We were the biggest ship in harbour at the time.'

Keith asked, 'Did you give him the course?'

'He didn't seem to know where he wanted to go to,' the captain said indignantly. 'He just wanted a course to what he called 'The Islands'. Well, this is an island, but he didn't like this one, apparently. Too civilised, I suppose.'

The Second grinned. 'What he wants is the Huahines. Naked women.'

'That's about the strength of it,' the captain said. 'He's been reading the books.'

'I shouldn't think he can read,' remarked the chief engineer.

'Well, somebody's been telling him stories, then.'

Keith asked again, 'Did you give him a course, sir?'

'I did what I could for him,' the captain said. 'I gave him half a dozen, all magnetic. True courses wouldn't be any good to him, and no good talking about variation being different at the end of two thousand miles. I gave him a mean value for the course to several places. Nukahiva was one, I remember, and Tahiti was another. Of course, ocean currents don't mean anything to him.'

'He can write – just,' the first officer observed. 'He drew a thick line with a stub of pencil on his atlas from here to each place, and wrote the course along the line. I never saw such a mess.'

Keith wrinkled his brows in perplexity. 'But can he find an island two thousand miles away just with a compass course from here?'

'Of course he can't,' the captain said scornfully. 'He'll go off and there'll be no more heard of him. He'll die, and that's the end of it.'

'I'm not quite sure that I agree with you, sir,' said the first officer.

'What don't you agree with?'

'I don't think he'll die. He may get to the wrong place, and he may take the hell of a long time to get there. I talked to him after you gave up, and gave him a beer. I must say, I was rather impressed.'

'What was it that impressed you, Mr Fairlie?'

'Well, for one thing, sir, he knows a lot about birds. Sea birds, I mean.'

The captain snorted. 'What's that got to do with it? Is this Raft Book stuff?'

'Yes, sir, I think it is. Birds fly from A to B just like aeroplanes. What I mean is, if he gets within a hundred miles of land, I think he'll find it.' He paused. 'Swell, seaweed, floating mangrove seeds – all that sort of thing. Things that we don't use.'

The captain got up from the table. 'Well, I've heard everything now, and so have you. Mr Stewart. If you like to go to sea with a bloke that navigates by mangrove seeds, don't let me stop you.' He smiled. 'One of the boys will show you where the yacht harbour is, if you want to go there.'

He went out, and to his cabin. The others all got up from the table. The first officer glanced quizzically at Keith. 'Want to go any further with it?' he asked.

Keith hesitated. 'Well – I don't know. Do you think he's going to Tahiti, for a start?'

'So far as I could gather, he didn't much mind where he went. Footloose, you might say.'

'Do you think he'll get there?'

Mr Fairlie stubbed his cigarette out in the ashtray. 'It's an opinion, Mr Stewart. I've got a better opinion of him than Captain Davies has. In some ways what the captain says is right – he's simple. If you like, he thinks like a child ten years old. But he's certainly a good seaman, and he knows a lot about the sea.'

'You think he'll get there?'

'In the end – yes, I think he probably will.' He glanced at Keith. 'It won't be comfortable.'

'Would you go with him yourself?'

Mr Fairlie smiled. 'If I was absolutely desperate and had to get there somehow, at whatever risk – yes, I think I would.'

There was half a minute's silence in the wardroom. To go back tamely with the aeroplane to Blackbushe, to renounce all chance of getting Janice her inheritance because he was afraid of Jack Donelly, would be cowardice. If he did not at least investigate this line he felt that he would never be able to tell Katie the truth about this journey; at one point he would have to lie, and go on in the same lie for the rest of his life. At the same time, he felt that he was sliding deeper into the mire of the unknown and the fantastically dangerous. Still, there was no need to decide anything until he'd met the man.

'I think I'd better go and have a talk to him,' Keith said at last.

CHAPTER SIX

THE FIRST OFFICER changed out of uniform into linen slacks and a light shirt open at the neck, borrowed Mr Yamasuki's car and driver, and took Keith to the Alawai yacht harbour. They dismissed the car and walked past the rows of sleek motor cruisers till they came to the less opulent end. Mr Fairlie pointed out a vessel with one mast. 'He's still here. I was half afraid he might have left by now.'

The vessel that he pointed out was a white, fishing-boat type, about forty feet long and very beamy. She had one mast and no bowsprit. She had no pretensions to yacht finish; everything about her was heavy and painted; her metal fittings were all of iron. The sail upon the boom was of heavy red canvas, apparently tanned with oil and ochre. There was an appearance of rough efficiency about her, but in the Alawai yacht harbour she looked like a poor relation.

She was moored stern-on to the quay, and a single plank gave access to her deck. Mr Fairlie stood on the quay and hailed. 'Jack Donelly! You aboard, Jack? I've got a friend I'd like you to meet.'

He hailed again, and presently there was movement in the cabin and a man appeared at the hatch. He was a very big man possibly forty years old, olive-skinned, with tousled black hair and a somewhat vacant expression. He was bare to the waist and wore only a pair of very soiled blue jeans. He blinked in the sunlight and muttered, 'Who are you yelling at? I was having a lie down.'

Mr Fairlie said, 'You remember me, Jack? Jim Fairlie, from the *Cathay Princess*, the tanker you came aboard the first day in. We had a beer together.'

'I haven't got any beer,' said the mariner vaguely.

'That's all right,' said the first officer. 'I didn't come for that. I brought a friend along with me to see your ship. Mind if we come aboard?'

'I haven't got any whisky either. Haven't got nothing.'

Mr Fairlie said quietly to Keith, 'Except methylated spirits, I should think.' Aloud he said, 'That's all right, Jack. We'll come down, if we may. I want you to meet Mr Stewart. He's from England.'

Mr Donelly grunted, turned his back on them, and retreated from the hatch into the cabin. 'He may be on the booze,' Mr Fairlie said to Keith, 'and he's very shy. But there's no harm in him. I think he means for us to go on down.'

They walked gingerly down the sagging, teetering plank on to the transom of the vessel, stepped over the horse, ducked under the boom, and stood on deck by the tiller; the vessel had no cockpit. Jack Donelly appeared again at the hatch. 'Guy fell in off that plank,' he muttered. 'Wanted dough for berthing here or sump'n. He got a swim.' He threw back his head and laughed, suddenly and a little shrilly, startling to hear. 'He wanted seven dollars and two bits, and he got a swim.' He went on laughing, and then stopped suddenly. 'Tell you sump'n,' he muttered. 'You tread on the bow warp up forward by the winch,' he said seriously, ''n she goes forward just a tiddy little way 'n then the plank comes off the transom. That's how it's done. But don't tell anybody.'

They laughed dutifully. 'Has he been back again?' asked Mr Fairlie.

Mr Donelly shook his head wordlessly.

'I want you to meet Mr Stewart, Jack,' said the first officer. 'His name's Keith – Keith Stewart. He's from England and he's having a look round. I was telling him how you built this ship yourself and sailed it out here from the States.'

'Keats,' said Mr Donelly.

'No, Keith, Jack. Keith.'

'Keith,' said the mariner obediently. 'Never heard a name like that before.'

'It's a Scots name,' said Keith. 'Did you build this ship yourself?'

Mr Donelly grunted.

'It's a big job,' said Keith. 'Did you have anyone to help you?'

Mr Donelly shook his head.

'How long did it take you?'

''Bout five years. Worked in the lumber mill some of the time, get dough for fastenings and that.'

Keith ran his eye over the ship with a new interest. There was nothing that a patient woodworker could not have done over the years ... except ... his eye fell on the seams of the deck planking. Each plank was twelve or fifteen feet long and tailored in plan form to fit the washboard and the bulwarks at the outside of the deck, the curvature reducing to a straight edge towards the centre of the ship where the hatch and the skylight of the cabin made a line. Keith stooped and ran his finger along the seam. 'How did you get these curves?'

A gleam of interest illuminated the dark features. 'Router.'

'You routed each plank all along its length to fit the next one?' It was not impossible, but it denoted a skill and a love of ships that threw a little beam of light on the character of the man.

The owner grunted in assent. Then he heaved himself out on deck and stood beside them, a massive, powerful man. 'Show you sump'n,' he muttered. He led Keith down the port side to a point about three feet aft of the mast, went down on his knees, and pointed out a blemish on one plank, caulked with a tarry compound. 'That's where my finger come off,' he said seriously. He lifted his left hand and showed that the forefinger of the left hand was missing down to the second joint.

'In the router?'

Mr Donelly grunted. 'Boss said I shouldn't have been using the machinery. But how in hell would a guy do these curves without he had a router? That's what I said to him. He couldn't answer that.'

'How long did it hold you up?' The job was the thing.

'Two weeks, I guess. Soon as it quit bleeding I could work.'

Keith got up from the deck, and the owner got up with him. He looked around, studying everything with a technical eye unpractised in the shipwright's art. 'Where did you get the hull lines from?' he asked. 'Out of a drawing in some book?'

Mr Donelly shook his head. 'Guy gave me a lot of blue papers with white lines,' he said. 'I put my thinking cap on, but they didn't seem to mean nothing.' He paused. 'Got some bits of hardwood 'n made half models over 'n over till I got one right. Took the frames off of that. Got it below still.'

It was the old shipwright's approach. Keith said, 'Can I see it?'

The man turned and made for the hatch; Keith and Mr Fairlie followed him down the ladder. Inside the ship was little but an empty shell. She was fairly new so that the dirt had had no time to accumulate, but she was already dirty. There were rough, unpainted wooden berths to port and starboard, the port one with a palliasse on it that was evidently Jack's bed. There was a cupboard with a deeply fiddled top on which stood a Primus stove and a few dirty glasses and plates. Forward there was a mass of sails and sailcloth and rope in tangled confusion erupting into the living portion of the ship. Aft of the hatch, behind the ladder, seemed to be a tangled mass of nets and cordage. The whole smelt strongly of salt water and of Jack Donelly.

The owner burrowed into the forecastle, treading over sails and rope with his bare, horny, rather dirty feet. He emerged with three half models glued and screwed to pieces of hard, fine-grained planking. He showed them to Keith shyly. 'These are what I made.'

Keith took one from him and examined it critically. Half models of ships were no novelty to him, but he had never examined one that had shown better workmanship. It was about two feet long, made of some hard, dark wood, perhaps mahogany, french-polished. He sat down uncomfortably on the vacant berth to examine it the better, squinting along the lines from bow to stern. 'You certainly made a good job of this,' he said seriously. 'I never saw one better.'

'You want to make them nice,' commented the builder. 'Else you get mad looking at them.' He took the half model from Keith. 'That's the second one you're looking at. This was the first.' He gave him another. 'I looked at it two weeks, maybe more, but it didn't seem right somehow. Looked like she wouldn't rise to a following sea.' He took that model, and gave Keith the second. 'I filled out the buttocks a tiddy bit on this one 'n I didn't like that no better, made her look fat-arsed and slow.' He took that model away and gave the third to Keith. 'So I put my cap on 'n brought the beam back aft a ways, not so much cod's head 'n mackerel tail. Couldn't see nothing wrong with that, so that's the way I built her.'

The process of design by eye was nothing new to Keith. There were very fine lines scribed vertically upon the half model that he handled, at intervals all down her length. 'You took the frames off this?'

Mr Donelly dropped his eyes and shuffled one foot upon the floor. 'You want book learning for that,' he muttered. 'It's not right what I told you, I built her all myself. The schoolmaster at Cushman, he set out the frames. But I did everything else.'

Keith warmed to this uncouth, dirty man. 'You designed her and you built her,' he said. 'Setting out the frames from the half model – that's nothing. How does she behave at sea?'

'Okay. Bit heavy on the helm first go, so I took a tiddy bit off the boom 'n leach, makes her easier to reef anyways, 'n just as fast.'

Mr Fairlie asked, 'You built her at Cushman, Jack? Where's that?'

'Mouth of the Suislaw.'

'That's in Oregon?'

'South Oregon,' the owner muttered. Interrogation seemed to make him shy and resentful.

Keith reached up and ran his finger along the joint between one of the deck beams and the frame at the side of the ship; it seemed to him that it would be difficult to insert a ten-thou feeler in it, and all the others were the same. 'You certainly made a beautiful job of building her,' he said.

The owner glowed with pleasure. 'I kinda liked doing it,' he said. 'It took quite a while, but I kinda liked it.'

'I know,' said Keith. 'I like making things. But mine aren't so big as yours.'

He pulled the little box from his pocket and unwrapped the generator set and gave it to Mr Donelly, who handled it as carefully as an egg in his great horny hands. 'You made this?' he enquired.

'He designed it and made it, electrics and all,' Mr Fairlie said. 'Just like you did this ship.'

Mr Donelly stared at it in wonder. 'I never did see such a tiddy little thing,' he said. 'It doesn't go, does it?'

'It goes all right,' said Keith. He took the little engine, turned it upside down, adjusted the tiny carburettor delicately, and flipped it into life with his thumb. It broke into a roar disproportionate to its size, steadied its note, and the pea bulb lit up. He placed it on the bare wood of the cabin floor and it went on generating steadily.

Mr Donelly went down on his hands and knees upon the floor and studied it, entranced. 'Making the electricity,' he breathed.

'That's right.'

'I seen the big ones,' he said, 'three-cylinder diesels and that, making electricity.' He raised his head. 'Say, Mr Keats, I guess this is the smallest in the world, isn't it?'

Keith said, 'It's not the smallest engine. I think perhaps it might be the smallest generating set.'

Mr Donelly broke into a cackle of laughter, and looked up at Mr Fairlie. 'Well, what do you know?' he enquired. 'There's the smallest generating set in the world running right here in the cabin of the *Mary Belle*! Folks wouldn't never believe me if I went ashore and told them that. They'd say I was nuts!'

Keith leaned down and stopped it with his pencil, fearing that it might overheat if he kept it running too long without a cooling draught of air. Mr Donelly bent closer to examine it at rest. 'Look at all those tiddy little wires,' he breathed as he scrutinised the armature. 'All going the same way, and each to the right place.' He raised his head, 'Mr Keats, did you think out all that, yourself? The way each had to go?'

Keith nodded. 'Everybody to his own job,' he said. 'I couldn't have begun to build this ship. I wouldn't know where to start.'

'You start with the half model. What I showed you.'

'Ah, yes. But if I made a half model, I wouldn't know by looking at it, if it would make a good ship. Not like you do.'

'You wouldn't?'

Keith shook his head. 'Not a hope. You've got to really know the sea for that. You must have been at sea all your life.'

'My old man,' said Mr Donelly, 'he took me off-shore first of all when I was six, long lining. 'Course, I was playing around in scows and that with all the other kids before.'

Keith nodded. 'You build up experience without knowing it,' he said. 'Then when the fit takes you to build a ship like this, or build a generating set like that, it just comes easy.'

Mr Donelly glanced at him with common understanding from the floor. 'Say, you got sump'n,' he said. 'Building *Mary Belle* was just like it was kinda fun.'

Keith reached down and picked up the little generating set, wrapped it up, and put it back into his pocket. Mr Donelly watched him do it regretfully; he got back on to his feet and sat down on his berth. Keith asked him, 'What are your plans, Jack? Where do you go from here?'

'I guess I'm going to the Islands.'

Keith said, 'I've got a reason for asking that. I want to get down to Tahiti, and then out to an island called Marokota. That's somewhere in the Tuamotus. But there's no regular service and no trading schooner, and anyway I've not got very much money. Mr Fairlie here suggested that you might be going down that way.'

There was a long silence. 'Ma came from Huahine,' Mr Donelly said at last. 'She said for me to get back to the Islands where I'd meet up with my own sort. So that's where I'm going.'

Mr Fairlie asked, 'To Huahine?'

'I guess I'll go there some time. I don't know where it is.'

'It's not far from Tahiti. It's in the same group.'

'That's what a guy said one time. Then another guy said it was this place Nukahiva.'

'It's not, Jack. It's nowhere near Nukahiva. It's a bit over to the west from Tahiti. I'll give you a chart.'

'I got an atlas,' said the mariner. He rummaged under the palliasse on the wooden boards of his bunk and produced his one navigational aid. It opened automatically at the map of the Pacific Ocean. 'I looked at all the tiddy little names,' he said, 'but I never see Huahine. I guess they left it out by mistake.'

Mr Fairlie said, 'I think it's probably too small to show on the atlas, Jack. If you're going to take Keith along with you to Tahiti I'll give you a chart that shows every island on the way and round about Tahiti. I know we've got a lot of outdated ones on board.'

Mr Donelly grunted; Keith guessed that he had little use for charts, never having used one. 'You want to get down to Tahiti?' Donelly asked.

'That's right.'

'Got a bed?'

Keith hesitated, somewhat taken aback. Mr Donelly helped him out by lifting the dirty corner of his palliasse; it rustled, evidently filled with hay or straw. 'Like this.'

'I haven't at the moment,' Keith said. 'But I'll get something.'

'There's a bolt of sailcloth you could sleep on but I guess you'd find that kinda hard,' said Mr Donelly.

'I'll get a bed like yours,' said Keith. 'How much money would I have to pay you for the passage?'

'Well now,' said the mariner, 'I'd have to put my thinking cap on for that. The harbourmaster, he wanted seven dollars and two bits when he come on board and had his swim.' He cackled into laughter. 'I reckon he'd want more now, what with drying his clothes. Then there's the eats ...' He sat in evident bewilderment. 'How long you reckon it would take to sail to this Tahiti?'

Keith shook his head. 'I don't know at all.'

Mr Fairlie asked, 'How long did it take you to get here from San Francisco, Jack?'

134

'Three weeks'n two days. I had a fair, reaching wind most of the way.'

'It's a little bit further to Tahiti,' said the first officer, 'and you've got to get through the Doldrums. You'll need food for six weeks at least.'

'I dunno what that would cost,' said Mr Donelly. He lifted his head, and cut the Gordian knot with decision. 'Say,' he asked, 'how much you got?'

'About a hundred dollars,' said Keith conservatively.

'Well then,' said the ship owner, 'the fare's a hundred dollars.' He leaned back with the air of one who has concluded a difficult business negotiation.

'We bake every day,' said Mr Fairlie, 'but we carry a stock of biscuits in sealed tins, twenty-eight pounds. I'll talk to Captain Davies. Maybe we could let you have two or three of those against repayment in England. Save the dollars, anyway.'

'That 'ld be very kind of you,' said Keith.

'I got 'bout half a sack of cornmeal, 'n some grits,' said Mr Donelly. 'I guess we could catch fish a day or two 'n dry some of them, 'n salt down the rest. There's plenty sun here, dry the fish. Not like it 'ld be at home.'

'Where would you put them to dry?' asked Mr Fairlie.

Mr Donelly looked surprised. 'Out on shore some place,' he said.

'I don't think they'd let you do that here, Jack.'

'Huh?'

'They'd get people on the power yachts belly-aching about the smell.'

'They said I was to berth here,' Mr Donelly muttered. 'Got a motor boat 'n towed me round.'

Keith judged it better to change the subject. 'We'll think up something together about the food,' he said. 'When do you want to sail?'

'Most any time,' the owner said.

'And you'd be willing to take me along?'

The other raised his head. 'You get sick?'

It was better to face it. 'I'll probably be sick,' Keith said. 'How long does it go on for?'

'Two-three days. I get sick after a spell on shore. There's nothing to it.'

'I don't suppose I'll be much use to you, at first,' Keith said. 'I'll do the best I can.'

'Can't do better 'n that,' Mr Donelly said. 'You'll be bringing the tiddy little motor along?'

'This?' He fingered the little box. 'Oh yes, I'll be bringing this.'

'Move in when you like,' said Mr Donelly.

They arranged that Keith would go into the question of the food supplies with Mr Fairlie, and presently they left the *Mary Belle* and took a taxi back to the *Cathay Princess*. In the wardroom Mr Fairlie said, 'I think we've earned a beer.' He went and fetched a bottle and two glasses, filled them, and raised his own. 'I think you're a brave man,' he said.

Keith smiled. 'So do I. But I liked him well enough.'

'There's no harm in him,' Mr Fairlie agreed. 'He'll probably get you there. But I wouldn't take any liquor on board.'

'I won't.'

The first officer eyed him speculatively. 'You're technical. Do you know anything about navigation – anything at all?'

Keith shook his head.

Mr Fairlie sighed. 'Well, there's no time to teach you astro-navigation. But I'll look out the charts and a volume of the *Pacific Islands Pilot* for you this evening, and give you an hour on them tomorrow morning. You can read, at any rate, and that's more than Jack Donelly can.'

Keith left the ship soon afterwards and walked back through the town to the Beachcomber Hotel, looking as he walked for a shop that sold a mattress. The prices did not seem to him to be excessive, but they were all far to good to put into the *Mary Belle*. He knew that he was in for an indefinite spell of hard living, and he had no great fear of it. It was many years since he had suffered much discomfort, though as a child and a young man in Renfrew he had known plenty of it; to sleep on a straw palliasse upon bare boards would be no novelty to him. The food was a perplexity. Something better was needed than Jack's cornmeal, grits, and dried fish, but what he needed was to him unknown, or how to buy it. He clung to the thought of the sealed tins of biscuit that might come from the *Cathay Princess*.

In his room at the hotel he found Dick lying upon his bed listening to the radio, and told him all about it. 'I fixed up that I'd go with him,' he said. 'He's not as mad as all that.'

The engineer raised himself on one elbow. 'He's going to Tahiti?'

Keith started to undress, preparatory to a shower. 'He'll go anywhere so long as it's away from here. He'll take me to Tahiti.'

'Sure about that?'

Keith sat down upon the bed. 'I think so.'

'Captain Davies isn't, old man.'

'I know. I've been talking to Jack Donelly all afternoon on board his boat. The boat's quite good, you know. What's more, he built her himself.'

'He did? Without any help?'

Keith nodded. 'Single-handed.'

'That doesn't mean that he can find his way to Tahiti from here, though. It's an awful big place, the sea.'

'I know.' Keith got up from the bed. 'I've never done this before,' he muttered. 'There's no fuel problem anyway, because all he uses is the wind. It seems to boil down to carrying enough to eat and drink for an indefinite time.'

'How much water storage has he got?'

'I saw a forty-gallon drum, up-ended, tied to the mast with rope lashings. I suppose that's it.'

'How long is the trip going to be?'

'Jim Fairlie says at least six weeks.'

'You'll want more than that much water, then, old man.'

Keith went into the shower, and Dick lay back upon his bed in perplexity. What Keith did was no concern of his, really, and yet he felt himself involved. In the world of workshops and of amateur mechanics Keith was a well-known man, and that world was Dick's world also. If Keith were to lose his life at sea with this man Jack Donelly, inevitably Dick King would be involved and charged with some responsibility by other members of their common world, for it would be known throughout that world that he had been with Keith in Honolulu. If Keith were to disappear at sea, as Captain Davies had warned him bluntly might well happen, he, Dick King, would be telling a defensive story of their time in Honolulu in the workshops of England for many years to come, excusing himself, perhaps for all his life. He could hear the whispers: 'He's the bloke who was with Keith Stewart in Honolulu and let him go off with that crazy fisherman. You'd think he might have done something about it ...' He did not like the prospect.

If only Keith knew a little more about foreign countries, about the tropics. If only he wasn't quite so raw.

He said no more, but lay there troubled in his mind while Keith also rested on his bed, letting the cool breeze blow over his bare body. It seemed to Dick that there was no escape from the position he was in. Keith had some compelling reason to get down to Tahiti that was driving him to take the most fantastic risk by going with this half-caste fisherman. If he, Dick King, wished to escape the odium of the future, there were only two courses he could take. One was to talk Keith out of it; he did not think that would be possible. The other was to try to make the journey a success.

Presently they dressed and went downstairs for a beer before dinner. Captain Davies was there in the bar with Captain Fielding. Somewhat the same line of thought may have been running in his mind, too, because he said, 'Evening, Mr Stewart. Evening, Mr King. Beer?'

The engineers said, 'Thank you, sir.'

The captain said to the girl in the cheongsam, 'Two more beers.' Then he turned to Keith and said, 'Mr Fairlie tells me that I've got to provision your ship.'

Keith was embarrassed. 'That's not necessary at all, sir. All he said was that you might let me have some biscuits on repayment in England.'

'To help out the grits and dried fish? I don't know if you've ever tried to live for two months on dried fish. It goes bad, of course. Then the thing to do is to put it in a barrel with some salt. You've got to eat it in the end, of course. Some people like it.' He laughed. 'You'd better come on board tomorrow with a list of what you want, and we'll see what we've got.'

'That's very kind of you, sir.' The aircraft navigator strolled up to them, beer in hand. 'As a matter of fact, that really would be a great help. I was coming on board tomorrow anyway to see Mr Fairlie. He was going to go over the charts with me.'

'Well, that's something, anyway. Bring your list along.'

'Thank you, sir. Here's luck.' He raised his beer.

'You're going to need it,' said Captain Davies grimly.

The air navigator asked, 'Is this Jack Donelly?'

'That's right,' said Captain Fielding. 'Keith's going with him to Tahiti.'

'Can he find Tahiti?'

'That's the sixty-four-thousand-dollar question,' said Captain Davies.

The navigator sipped his beer in thought. 'Has he got a sextant?'

'Of course he hasn't,' said the captain. 'He looks to see which way the aeroplanes are flying. If there aren't any aeroplanes he looks for mangrove seeds. If there aren't any mangrove seeds he follows his compass, and that's probably wrong.' He turned to Keith. 'I was right – he hasn't got a motor in the ship, has he?'

'No, sir.'

'Well, that's something. I don't suppose he's ever had his compass swung. Just watch he doesn't put a bucket down beside it when he needs it most.'

Keith nodded thoughtfully. 'I'll watch that, sir. It makes a big difference, does it?'

Captain Davies laughed. 'Try it and see.'

'Pity about the sextant,' said the air navigator. 'The track must be just about due south. A meridian latitude would give them quite a lot of information.'

'You've got to be able to add and subtract for that,' said Captain Davies.

Mr King drew the air navigator on one side. 'I've been thinking about that,' he said. 'I mean, he's made up his mind to go. A meridian sight for latitude isn't very difficult, is it?'

'It's the easiest sight there is,' said the navigator. 'You want a sextant and a nautical almanac, and a rough idea of Greenwich time. Then you've only got to add and subtract.'

'He could learn to do that, couldn't he?'

'Jack Donelly?'

'No, Keith. Keith Stewart. I mean, look at the things he does in the shop with mikes and sine bars and all that. He'd learn to manage a sextant in five minutes with somebody to put him in the way of it.'

The navigator stood in thought. 'It's an idea ... where's the sextant coming from?'

'I think I know where one could pick up one second-hand,' said the engineer. 'You know where King St crosses Nuuanu?' The navigator nodded. 'Well, coming this way, second or third side-street on the right, there's a Chinese shop – sells everything, you know. Old clothes, lacquer screens, Bali heads, all sorts of junk. I'm pretty sure I saw a sextant there.'

'This trip?'

'This afternoon. I was poking around, get something for the wife.'

The navigator stood in thought. 'It's an idea. There's not much time to teach him. We could write it all down for him, of course – just what you do. And it should be possible to pick up an old sextant in this place.' He stood in thought. 'Pity it's got to be this time of year,' he said at last. 'The sun 'll be pretty near the zenith when they get down to Tahiti.'

'That makes it less accurate?'

'More difficult, anyway. I tell you what I'll do. I'll slip down to the ship after dinner and have a talk to Jim Fairlie – see if it's worthwhile trying to stuff something into him.'

Keith spent the evening cogitating in his bedroom, pencil and paper in hand. He had no wish to provision the *Mary Belle* with expensive delicacies to which Jack Donelly would be unaccustomed. He knew that if he were to live harmoniously with this man for six weeks in the close association of a very small sailing vessel he must adapt himself to Jack Donelly and live as he did. That did not trouble Keith; what troubled him was that he had little idea what Jack was in the habit of eating. He did not know what cornmeal tasted like or how you ate it, and grits were a sealed book to him, but they were what Jack seemed to eat. It was pretty certain that he would like sweet things, though. He headed his list with – Sugar, 30 lb; and added – Jam.

He was certain of nothing else, and at the end of half an hour he had only six or seven items on the list. His mind drifted to the navigation hazards that they all seemed so concerned about. He got out the chart that Mr Sanderson had given him in Ealing, Ealing that now seemed so far away. There were certainly a lot of islands to be passed on their course southwards to Tahiti. They had names that he had never heard before, Malden and Starbuck and Flint, and many others. He supposed they would be coral islands, similar to that which had destroyed *Shearwater*. If John Dermott, who was an experienced navigator, could not sail through this archipelago in safety, could Jack Donelly?

His hand drifted to his pocket, and he sat in perplexity fingering the case-hardened grey steel egg that he had made for Janice. Presently he got a scrap of paper and measured the distance between these islands. He had a hazy idea that the vertical graduations on the side of the chart gave you some measure of the scale, and by that the closest of these islands were two degrees apart. But how far was a degree? He sat in thought. Anyway, the earth was twenty-two thousand miles round at the equator. He figured with a pencil on the chart. If that was right, the closest of these islands were over a hundred miles apart, about as far as it was from Ealing to Weymouth. That didn't seem so bad. There was a lot of sea to sail on in between.

The difficulty might lie, as the ship's officers said, in finding one of them at all. It was very different in the Tuamotus where *Shearwater* was lost. There the islands all seemed to be on top of each other.

He went to bed before Dick King got back from exploring the nightlife of Honolulu, and slept fitfully, uneasy and worried. Next morning he was on board the *Cathay Princess* by half-past eight. He found Jim Fairlie and showed him his inadequate list. The first officer took it, summoned the third, and told him to get out a mess list for two men for eight weeks, able seamen's scale, biscuit instead of bread.

'We'll compare his list with yours and see how they match up,' he said. 'There's one thing, though. If you're going to provision the ship, you don't have to pay Jack Donelly a hundred dollars.'

He took Keith up to the chartroom on the bridge behind the wheelhouse. 'I've got one chart,' Keith said diffidently. He unfolded the one that Mr Sanderson had given him.

'Oh, good. You've got seven eight three.' Mr Fairlie slipped a chart back in the drawer. 'Now you want seven eight two and nine nine two.' He opened a volume of the *Pacific Islands Pilot* and showed Keith the chart index. 'These two – and that one you've got.' He paused. 'I'd have liked you to have three o four five as well in case you get set over to the west, but I haven't got it. Maybe you could get one in the town – Yamasuki would tell you where to try. Now look. I'm going to put these two together and pencil in your track. Do you know what I mean by compass variation?'

They worked on together. 'Well, there you are,' Jim Fairlie said presently. 'Your track is one six six degrees, and, in theory at any rate, you don't hit anything. You don't have to sail over any dry land. You're in the clear the first part of the passage. Then you come to all this over to the west – Christmas Island and all that. Keep away from that – they let off atom bombs from time to time. Then you've got to go between Flint Island and the Carolines. They're about two and a half degrees apart – call it a hundred and fifty sea miles. If you're on course you probably won't see them. After that there's nothing till you hit Tahiti.'

They stood examining the charts and the *Pilot* for the best part of an hour, Keith making notes busily. In the middle the air navigator came in, greeted them, and stood listening in silence. They turned to the predominant winds, and studied the picture for January. 'You should have a fair wind all the way, easterly.' The first officer laid his finger on the page. 'A bit irregular on the Equator, in the Doldrums, but steadying again as you get further south. All easterly. I don't know how much leeway that ship makes, but just watch out you don't get set over too far to the west. Jack knows about that, I think. I'd keep edging up to windward, ten degrees at least. You're very unlikely to go much east of track, but you might get down a long way west of it.'

They stood in consultation, Keith scribbling down notes. At last he said, 'Well, that's pretty clear. It's very kind of you to take all this trouble.' He smiled. 'The only thing remaining is to know how far one's gone.' He laid his finger on the line that marked the track.

From behind them the air navigator remarked, 'You've said it, chum.'

Jim Fairlie said, 'Jack Donelly would probably say he knows how fast he's going from the look of the water, how many miles he does in a day. Take note of that, and jot down what he says for each day. He may not be so very far wrong when you tot it up. But don't depend on him.' He paused. 'You could trail a log, but then it's not your ship. He might not take to it – probably wouldn't.' He paused. 'The proper thing for you to do would be to take a noon sight for latitude each day. As a matter of fact, we were talking about this last night.'

The air navigator said, 'It's dead easy, Mr Stewart. You'd better let us show you how to do it. Once you've got your latitude upon this course you know how far you've gone, and no argument. Have you ever handled a sextant?'

Keith shook his head.

'Well, you're going to handle one now.' The first officer was opening a polished wooden box upon the chart table.

Keith was torn between technical interest and practical considerations. 'I haven't got a sextant,' he said, 'and I'm sure Jack hasn't.'

'You can probably pick one up second-hand quite cheap,' the air navigator said. 'As a matter of fact Dick King's off looking for one now, with Captain Fielding. Look, Mr Stewart. We don't want to read in the newspaper one day that you're dead. This latitude sight's easy for a man like you. You'd better let us put you in the way of it, and then go off and buy a sextant.'

They settled down to show him how the sextant worked. He was accustomed to precision instruments and had no trouble with it upon the stable deck of the fifteen-thousand-ton ship in harbour. In half an hour he was able to bring the sun down on to the horizon and read off its altitude with some accuracy. 'You'll find it a bit more difficult on Jack's ship because of the motion,' the first officer said. 'It's a matter of practice on a ship like that. Or any other ship, for that matter.'

They took him through the relevant part of the nautical almanac, and drew a little diagram for him to show what declination meant. 'You're behind Greenwich time,' they told him. 'When you're taking your noon sight you want to use the declination for ten o'clock at night on the same day. Twenty-two hundred. Look, I'll underline it for you each day so you won't go wrong. You can take this copy and we'll get another for the ship.' The air navigator bent to the task.

At a quarter to twelve they took him out on to the bridge and made him start taking the altitude of the sun on the horizon over Sand Island. 'Never go back,' Mr Fairlie said quietly. 'Maximum altitude is what you want.'

When they were satisfied that he had got it they took him back into the chartroom to do the figuring. 'Height of eye here is about thirty feet,' they told him. 'With you – take about five feet.' They underlined the correction for him. 'Now – away you go.'

He did the sum. 'That seems to come to twenty-one degrees twenty-three minutes,' he said diffidently.

'North or south?'

He studied the figures. 'North'.

'Quite sure?'

'I think so.'

'Okay. Now put a horizontal pencil line on that latitude, on the chart.' He did so. 'Not too bad,' the air navigator remarked. 'You're about three miles north of where we are, up in the suburbs somewhere. Still, it's not too bad.'

Keith stared at them in wonder, and at his pencil line. 'Is that all I'm wrong?'

'That's right. Twenty-one twenty is the right answer. I told you it was dead easy.'

He was amazed and naïvely pleased that he had done this thing, that he, Keith Stewart, looking at the sun through a precision instrument had established the position of Honolulu on the surface of the earth. He said something of the sort to his instructors. 'You're forgetting about longitude,' Jim Fairlie said. 'I'd like to teach you that, but there's not time. Anyway, it needs a watch and a wireless set and tables. It's not practical, I'm afraid. But learn this thoroughly, and you'll be all right – on the way to Tahiti, anyway.'

That afternoon he went off with Dick and the air navigator and bought a second-hand sextant for twenty-seven dollars and a depressed looking flock mattress for six fifty. Back to the ship to show his sextant to Mr Fairlie, who spent an hour trying to get out the index error and reduced it to about three minutes, and to have a session with the third officer about provisioning. Subject to the captain's approval, he found that the ship could provide practically everything that they would need on board the *Mary Belle* in the way of food. He mentioned an extra forty-gallon drum for water; the Third said that if he got the drum they could steam it out for him. He went and called Mr Yamasuki, who agreed to find a second-hand oil-drum and get it to the ship.

It was Sunday evening. He was tired by the events of the day, but he did not dare to let a day go by without visiting Jack Donelly, lest he should forget about his passenger. He gave the sextant to Dick King to take back to the hotel and went on shore and found a taxi. He picked up his mattress at the Chinese shop and drove to the yacht harbour. Jack Donelly was sitting on the bow of his ship fishing over the side with a hand line; six or seven small silvery fish lay on the deck beside him in the evening light.

'Evening, Mr Donelly,' Keith said. 'I brought my bed. Can I come on board?'

The owner grunted. Keith took this as assent and ventured cautiously down the plank, the mattress on his shoulder, keeping a wary eye on Jack Donelly as he went. But the owner went on fishing. Keith carried his mattress below and laid it on the vacant berth, and then went up on deck and forward to his host. 'What are you using for bait?' he asked conversationally.

'Maggots,' said Mr Donelly.

Keith sat down on the deck beside him, watching the line. 'Where did you get them from?'

'Out the cornmeal sack. There's just a few in there. Don't make any difference.'

Keith swallowed spasmodically. 'How long did it take you to get these?'

'Not long.' He jerked the line sharply, there was a flurry in the water, and he pulled another little fish on board. 'They come in here after the muck the boats let go, toilets and that.' He baited the hook with another maggot. 'You staying to supper?'

'I can't tonight, Jack. I've got things to do back at the hotel. I was thinking I'd move in tomorrow, if that's all right with you.'

'Cornmeal fritters 'n fish. Get a few more, 'n there'll be plenty for two.'

'I'd like to, but I can't tonight. Look, we'll want another oil-drum for water, won't we?'

'What for? We wouldn't be having baths.'

'How much did you use coming from San Francisco?'

The owner ruminated. 'I guess I filled it last at Sausalito. There's still some left. I'd better get a hose 'n fill it up before we go.'

'Think you'd have used half of it? On the passage, I mean.'

'Might have done. There was plenty left when I came in.'

'There'll be two of us this time,' Keith said patiently, 'and the trip's a longer one from here down to Tahiti. I've got another oil-drum if you want it.'

'You have?' The owner considered this proposal. 'It might be a good thing to have it along,' he admitted. 'Always use a barrel.'

'Where would you put it? Forward by the mast, with the other one?'

Mr Donelly sat in thought. 'Have it aft under the ladder, if you want it full of water,' he said at last. 'Make her a bit lighter on the helm. I'll have to make some chocks.'

Keith nodded. 'It's getting steamed out tomorrow. I'll get it on board soon as I can.'

'Say,' said Mr Donelly with enthusiasm, 'that's a good idea. The one I got had kero in it one time. Been better, maybe, if it had been gas.' He paused. 'Kero kinda makes you feel sick in the stomach,' he explained.

Keith nodded. 'They're steaming it on board the tanker,' he remarked. 'They might do the other if we asked them – the one you've got now. There's another thing, Jack. They've got out a list of food they think we'll need for the trip to Tahiti, basing it upon the seamen's scale. I've got to see the captain, but I think they'll let us have the stuff. They say that I can pay for it in England.' He pulled the list out of his pocket on two sheets of paper. 'That's what they suggest.'

Mr Donelly took the list and glanced at it, uncomprehending. 'You read it out,' he suggested.

148

Keith started to do so. Mr Donelly sat watching him, bemused, while the words flowed past him. Presently he stopped Keith. 'Jam, 'n butter, 'n currants,' he said. 'Kinda rich chow for a ship. We haven't got all that dough.'

'It's what they give the seamen on the tanker,' Keith explained. 'They have to, by law. If you signed on on the *Cathay Princess* that's what they'd give you to eat.'

'That so?'

'That's right. I was going to pay for it myself and take it out of the hundred dollars, if that's all right by you.'

Mr Donelly looked at him vacantly. 'What hundred dollars?'

'The hundred I was going to give you for the passage. I could buy the food for us both from the *Cathay Princess* if the captain agrees, and take the cost of it out of the hundred dollars.'

'You got two pages there,' Mr Donelly objected. 'A hundred bucks wouldn't buy that much.'

'I think it will, and leave a good bit over,' said Keith, who had already been roughly through the costs with the third officer.

'Huh,' said Mr Donelly.

Keith turned to the list again. 'Is there anything that you don't like that I've read out?' he enquired.

'Turnips,' said Mr Donelly.

Keith wrinkled his brows, and turned over the two pages. 'There aren't any turnips on the list,' he said.

'That so? I never did like turnips.'

Keith nodded. 'I'll look out and see that we don't get any.' He put the list back in his pocket, assuming correctly that Jack Donelly would eat everything else. 'When do you think we ought to sail?'

'Most any time. Tomorrow, if you like. Sure costs the earth in this place.'

'I don't think we'll be able to sail tomorrow, Jack. We've got to get this food on board from the *Cathay Princess*, and the other barrel. I tell you what – I'll probably move in tomorrow, and sleep on board, if that suits you. Then maybe we could sail on Tuesday.'

'Suits me,' said the owner. He jerked another little fish on board, rebaited the hook with a maggot from a tin, and lowered the line again. 'I been thinking,' he said presently. He paused a long time after that alarming statement. Then he said, 'See that three-stick schooner at the end?'

Keith followed his glance. Lying at the end of the seaward jetty there was a fine three-masted schooner yacht. She lay almost in the deep water channel because there was no room and no depth of water for her closer in. She carried a big crew all dressed in whites; her decks were white, her polished brass gleamed in the setting sun. She wore the flag of the United States, and one of the white-clad seamen was standing by the halliard ready to lower it at the sunset gun. Even Keith was impressed by her.

'I see her,' he said.

'She's built of wood,' said Mr Donelly. 'I guess we'll go aboard her before sailing, 'n check up on the course.' He struggled to give voice to what was in his mind. 'Ships built of iron,' he explained, 'they go a different way upon the compass to what ships do if they get built of wood. That *Cathay Princess*, she's built all of iron. I guess she'd go quite a different way to get to this Tahiti than what that schooner would, because she's a wooden ship. She's a wooden ship, and *Mary Belle*'s a wooden ship, so they'd go the same way. I guess we'll go aboard before we sail 'n check up with the captain.'

Novice in navigation though he was, Keith suspected that Jack Donelly hadn't got his theory of compass deviation quite right. Still, any second check upon their course was good, and it might be that from the captain of a sailing ship Jack could pick up information about getting through the

Doldrums which he would not have learned on the seventeen-knot tanker. 'That's a good idea,' he said amiably.

He left the *Mary Belle* shortly after that, and went back to his hotel. He found most of the aircrew drinking beer with the officers of the *Cathay Princess*, and joined them. Captain Davies said, 'Mr Fairlie tells me that you've turned into a navigator.'

'He was very kind,' Keith said. 'He showed me how to get the latitude.'

The captain nodded. 'Think you'll remember how to do it?'

'I think so. I made a lot of notes. I'll have another go at it tomorrow, at midday.'

'Jack Donelly's in luck. I don't suppose he knows it. But he might get there, now.' He took a drink of beer. 'Mr Fairlie show you the victualling list?'

Keith took it from his pocket. 'I've got it here. He said I was to see you and ask if I could have the stuff.'

'You can have it if you sign a pretty detailed letter saying where and when you'll pay for it,' remarked the captain.

'That's very kind of you, sir. Payment in England would be all right, would it?'

'I think so. You'd better come on board tomorrow morning and I'll draft the letter for you to sign while the Third gets the stuff on deck. How are you going to take it round to the yacht harbour?'

'I'll have to get a taxi.'

'Make Yamasuki take it. He's got nothing else to do.' Beside them Dick King said, 'Give you a hand with it, if you like. I've got nothing else to do, either.'

Presently they went in to dinner. At the table Keith said to Dick King, 'You're still taking off on Tuesday morning?'

The flight engineer nodded. 'Seven o'clock take off for Vancouver.'

'You're going back the same way?'

'That's right. Vancouver, Frobisher, Blackbushe.'

'When will you be back in England?'

'Thursday midday if the fans keep turning. We'll have been away a week.'

Keith said, 'I wonder if you'd take a letter back with you, and post it in England? It's just to tell my wife what's happening.'

'Why, sure. She should get it Friday morning.' That evening Keith went up to his bedroom after dinner and sat for an hour with his sextant and his nautical almanac and his notes. He rewrote the notes into a progressive and coherent form while the subject was still fresh in his mind, pausing from time to time to draw little diagrams around the outline of an English penny. It was when you came to the Equator that you needed a clear head, or when the sun went over the zenith … Still, if you followed the rules exactly it would probably come out all right. The thing was to practise.

Presently he left the navigation and started a letter to Katie. He could not make it very detailed because he did not want to worry her; the details of his passage to Tahiti were not such as would create confidence. In consequence, his letter consisted mainly of a description of the flight to Honolulu and the installation of the rotor in the ship; his future plans and movements were dealt with in one sentence at the end, in which he said that he had got a passage on a ship going to Tahiti and he hoped to be there by the end of February. He sealed it up and gave it to Dick King to post in England.

Next morning he went with the flight engineer to the ship, signed a letter drafted for him by the captain, looked in on the generator trials, inspected the oil barrel newly steamed out and free from taint, and took another noon sight. They lunched on board, telephoned for a taxi truck, loaded the oil barrel and the stores into it, and set off for the yacht harbour.

Dick had not seen the *Mary Belle* before nor met Jack Donelly, and he was filled with misgiving. He knew about sailing boats in theory, at any rate, and he had little confidence in them. They depended solely on the fickle and the vacillating wind; if the wind didn't blow in the right direction they couldn't go. They were archaic survivals of a bygone age. It was true that the wind, their motive power, was free, but what did that matter in an era of government subsidies? The right way to get from Honolulu to Tahiti was in a Douglas with twelve or fifteen thousand horsepower pushing it along. It was penny-pinching to think of going by the wind because the wind was free. It was thinking small, and there was no future in that in these modern times. You wanted to think big.

He was deeply concerned when he went on board the *Mary Belle* with Keith. There was not so much as a wheel to steer by, nor any seat on deck for the pilot of the craft. A sort of stick stuck forward from the top of the rudder, which came through the deck, and you steered by pushing this stick from side to side so that the ship went the opposite way to what you pushed. He knew of this arrangement, of course, but had thought that it had gone out with the dodo. There was, of course, no engine. He was prepared for that, but the total absence of all mechanical contrivances shook him badly. Even the bilge pump was a crude affair, square section in its bore, built up of wood.

It was a hot, humid day. When they arrived the owner was below making the chocks for the new oil-drum; because he was below and out of sight and because it was hot he was working without any stitch of clothing on his burly frame. He had a woodworker's vice arranged upon the side of Keith's bunk, and the deck of the cabin was a litter of shavings as he formed the floor chocks curved to the radius of the drum, using a spokeshave. Keith went on board with Mr King and called to him down the hatch. 'Afternoon, Jack,' he said. 'I've brought the grub.'

The woodworker looked up. 'Get the barrel?'

'We've got that with us, too.'

'Huh.' Mr Donelly stood in thought. 'Better bring the barrel down 'n see if these chocks fit,' he said at last. 'It's going here.' He indicated a spot behind the ladder, which seemed to have been moved forwards.

'We might need a hand getting it on board,' said Keith. 'It's an awkward thing to handle.'

Mr Donelly laid down the spokeshave and started up the ladder. Keith checked him. 'What about a pair of trousers, Jack?' he said. 'There's ladies about.'

'Huh.'

Mr King said, 'They'll put you in quod if you come out on deck without your trousers on.'

'This place makes me sick,' said Mr Donelly. 'You see some of the girls on these hooch ships. They don't wear practically nothing.' Grumbling, he turned and pulled on his soiled trousers, and came out on deck.

They got the drum on board, Jack lowering it quickly and expertly from the quayside with the two ends of a warp around it, and lowered it down through the hatch into the cabin. Dick King and Keith carried all the rest of the stuff on board; there was no room to stow anything below till Jack was finished with the oil-drum, so they stacked it all by the tiller. There was little more then that they could do till Jack had finished except watch him through the hatch, which they did for a time. He worked on oblivious of their presence. Both Keith and Dick King were impressed with the quality of his woodwork; he worked accurately and quickly, putting a loving finish with a few strokes of glass-paper on each chock before laying it aside. Presently Keith leaned down the hatch and told him that he was going on shore to say goodbye to the ship's officers and to the aircrew, but would be back later. Mr Donelly only grunted in reply, intent upon the job.

CHAPTER SEVEN

KEITH MOVED INTO the *Mary Belle* that evening. The installation of the new oil-drum was finished when he arrived and it was ready to be filled with water in the morning. There had been no opportunity to get Jack's drum steamed out, that had once held kerosene, for the *Cathay Princess* was due to sail for Yokohama in the morning. Keith was to regret most bitterly that he had not taken action upon that earlier, when he drank his first cup of coffee.

They stowed the tins mostly beneath the bunks, the tins of biscuit going in the forecastle and the perishables in the one cupboard. The cooking equipment of the *Mary Belle* consisted of a frying-pan and two battered saucepans; there were two chipped enamel plates and an inadequate supply of knives and forks. Keith found them sufficient for his needs, however, because Jack Donelly ate mostly with his fingers.

They supped off tinned sausages and beans, cooked by Keith, followed by a half loaf of stale bread that he discovered in a locker, and a tin of jam. As he had suspected, Jack Donelly was a voracious eater; he ate everything in sight and then leaned back with a contented sigh. 'You cook good chow,' he said. 'What you got in that wood box?'

'A sextant,' Keith said. 'I've got some charts here, too.' He opened the box, took out the sextant carefully, and gave it to his captain, who handled it gingerly.

'I seen them in shop windows,' he observed presently. 'Marine stores and that. You know how to use it?'

'Not very well,' Keith said, 'They put me in the way of the noon sight on board the tanker.'

'Huh.' Mr Donelly handed the mystery back to him. 'Tells you where you are, don't it?'

'Not quite. Not unless you're better at it than I am, but I think it may tell us how far we've gone.'

Jack Donelly said, 'Well, I can tell *you* that.' He turned to the soiled wooden bulkhead at his side and showed a long vertical line of pencil-scrawled figures. 'That's how far we went each day coming from San Francisco.'

Keith got up and examined the record with interest. 'How did you know how far you went each day?' he asked.

Mr Donelly said, 'Well, each day after sunrise I'd sit down and put my thinking cap on and reckon we were doing five knots yesterday morning say four hours – well, that makes fifteen knots.' He paused in thought, and then started counting on his fingers rather expertly. 'No, that makes twenty.' He went on, 'Then around midday maybe it fell light and then I'd reckon up that. Then maybe I'd heave to in the night, catch up a bit on the sleep, 'n reckon on a knot or maybe a knot and a half. So then I'd tot it up for the day 'n write it down up there.'

Keith was deeply interested. 'How did it come out?' he asked. 'I mean, how did it compare with the real distance when you got here?'

'I never got it added up,' Mr Donelly admitted. 'Sometimes I'd try adding all those figures up, but it always came out something different to last time.' He reached for his atlas and scrutinised the dirty page of the Pacific Ocean. 'It says here two thousand and ninety-eight,' he remarked. 'A guy came on board one time, said he was from a newspaper. He added it up and wrote it underneath.'

Beneath the horizontal line, written neatly in another hand, was the figure 2237.

'That makes it about a hundred and fifty miles too much,' said Keith in wonder. 'Less than that – about seven per cent.'

'You don't go straight all the time,' said Mr Donelly. 'You get way off course 'n then that makes it more.'

Keith nodded. 'I think it's very good indeed,' he said. He sat in wonder for a moment. If you took off a bit, say four per cent, for course deviations, then Jack Donelly's estimate of the distance made good was only three per cent in error, and that error was on the safe side. 'How do you know how fast the ship is going through the water?' he asked.

'My Dad taught me. He used to know.'

'Do you look at the waves she leaves behind, or something?'

'I dunno. Just how she goes.'

He could not explain himself, and Keith did not pursue the subject. Jack's dead reckoning was clearly most important to them; Jim Fairlie had warned him that at that time of year the skies might well be overcast as they got further south, making the noon sight impossible. If he could only get an occasional sight as a check on their progress they might well depend more on Jack's estimates than on his sights. 'We'll do this again,' he said.

Mr Donelly ran a dirty finger down the woodwork. 'Put another lot of figures right alongside, there,' he said. He was seized with doubts. 'Think you can add them up right, all those tiddy little numbers?' he asked.

'I can have a try.'

'Huh.' There was a pause, and then the captain said, 'You bring the little motor along, what makes the electricity?'

Keith nodded. 'I've got it here.' He reached into his suitcase and pulled out the box, unwrapped the model, and set it going with a flick of his thumb. He placed it on the floor, and Jack Donelly got down on his hands and knees and gazed at it, entranced. 'Smallest in the world,' he breathed. He looked up. 'That's right?'

'I think so.'

A disturbing thought crossed the captain's mind. 'How long does it go on one fill of gas?'

'Ten or twelve minutes.' He added. 'I've got a bottle with me.'

'A bottle of gas?'

Keith nodded.

'We could run it every day?'

'I think so.' He let it run until the miniature tank was dry and it stopped, and then put it in its box on the fiddled top of the cupboard. 'We'll keep it there.'

He washed the dishes, a proceeding which his captain obviously considered to be quite unnecessary. The cabin was dimly lit by a kerosene lamp in gimbals, too dark for reading if there had been anything to read. They sat on deck for a while, smoking and listening to the radio music from the yachts in the row, brought to them by the cool, scented breeze. 'Get the hose along first thing, 'n fill the barrels,' said Jack Donelly. 'Then we're all set to go.'

Keith thought about ship's papers and the strange thing called a bill of health, and decided that they were matters which concerned the captain of the ship, and not himself. He asked, 'How much paraffin have we got – I mean, kero?'

'Kero? There's a jerrycan. I guess it's still about half full.'

'I'll get it filled up tomorrow.' Four gallons, he thought, should take them to Tahiti, since there was only one Primus stove and the cabin lamp. 'I saw a store at the end.'

'I wouldn't buy nothing there. They'll skin you alive.'

'Is there any other place I could buy kero?'

'I dunno.'

They retired to bed soon after. Keith found that Jack's preparations for the night consisted simply in taking off his pants and lying down upon his dirty mattress with a soiled blanket ready to pull over if he felt cold. Keith followed his example, having made a pillow of some of the clothes from his suitcase, and put out the lamp. He was tired, but for a time he was kept awake by the strangeness of his surroundings, the hardness of his bed. The wind blowing steadily from the east kept the main halliards tapping rhythmically against the mast, the water lapped against the ship's side by his ear with little liquid noises; from time to time as the ship moved in her moorings the rudder in its pintles made a clunking sound. He did not know what any of these noises were except the lapping water, but Jack Donelly was already asleep, so they were probably all right.

This was Monday, Monday night. It was only on Thursday morning that he had left his home in Ealing, but how far away it seemed! Even Katie seemed distant and remote, and Janice, in whose interest he was here, hardly more than a little wistful dream. He tried to reckon sleepily how many thousand miles he was away from his workshop in Somerset Road, and gave up the attempt. Eight or ten thousand miles, perhaps. But he still had the case-hardened egg that he had made for Janice, the grey egg, safe in a little box within his suitcase.

The warm wind blew softly through the cabin, scented with frangipani and salt water. Presently he slept.

He woke in the dawn to the sound of Jack Donelly getting out on deck and the sound of a thin stream of water falling by the ship's side, and realised that he was out on deck without a stitch of clothes on. He got up, put on his trousers, and put his head out of the hatch. 'Are you allowed to do that here?' he asked mildly.

'Morning,' said his captain. 'Isn't nobody around. Cleaner 'n doing it in the bucket.'

Since there was only one bucket on board to be used for washing and all other purposes, Keith could not but agree. 'I think I'll go ashore,' he said.

159

'Up the end there, by the store. How you sleep?'

'Fine.'

Keith put his shoes on and took a little walk. Returning to the ship he asked, 'What would you like for breakfast?'

'Cornmeal fritters,' said Mr Donelly.

'You'll have to show me how to do that,' Keith said. He received his lesson over the Primus stove, Jack picking the maggots expertly out of the cornmeal and putting them in a tin for future use as bait. He had a dirty tin of fat smelling strongly of fish, carefully hoarded and poured back after the fry. Keith added some bacon rashers and a loaf of bread that he had bought at the store. To his surprise the cornmeal fritters were very good if you could forget about the maggots, and the coffee brewed by Jack was excellent but for the kerosene. All told, he didn't do too badly, and sat for a while smoking before washing the two plates.

He went off after breakfast with the jerrycan for kerosene while Jack looked for a hose along the quayside that he could borrow without permission. The can had only a little kero in the bottom, and though it seemed to Keith that there must be sufficient in the drinking water to get them to Tahiti it was as well to fill the can. He did so at the store and bought a few tinned delicacies that took his fancy, and walked back heavily laden to find Jack with a hose watering the ship.

'I let the forward barrel overflow a little, get rid of some of the kero,' he said. 'She might need pumping out now, if you've nothing else to do.'

Keith bent to the bilge pump, a crude affair with a straight pull upon the plunger, awkward to the novice. It worked well, however, and a steady stream of dirty water flowed out on the deck and away by the scuppers, gradually becoming clearer. Jack finished filling the barrels below and put the running hose on the deck in the warm sun, turned it off upon the quay and returned it to wherever he had got it from while Keith continued his back-breaking work. Finally the pump sucked, and Keith rested his aching muscles.

'Guess we're all set to go,' said Jack. 'You don't know of anything we might want?'

Keith shook his head. 'I can't think of anything.'

Jack went below and fetched up his atlas, which opened at the soiled page of the Pacific. 'Captain Davies, he said to steer one five three,' he said, looking at the scrawled pencil figure on the smudged line. 'He said that was the same as south twenty-seven east on the compass, but the real course was sump'n different.' He sat in puzzled silence, the thinking cap firmly on his head. 'I guess we'll go on board the three-stick schooner,' he said at last. 'She's a wooden ship, same as *Mary Belle*.'

Keith asked, 'Do you think it would be a good thing if I brought the charts along?'

'Sure,' said Mr Donelly affably. 'Can't do no harm.'

They set off for the schooner, Jack Donelly clad in pants alone and Keith in trousers, cricket shirt, and braces crowned by the somewhat crumpled Panama hat that he wore on holidays in Cornwall. He seemed pale and fat and undersized in comparison with the magnificent torso of the man beside him, and he was very conscious of his physical deficiencies. Whatever one might think of Jack Donelly's mental ability, and Keith was now beginning to differ from Captain Davies, there was no denying that he was a fine figure of a man.

They walked round the head of the yacht basin and down the long tier of vessels to the immaculate schooner yacht at the end. As they approached her Keith's heart sank. She exuded wealth at every glance, from the polished bronze cap on the end of her bowsprit to the gilt emblem on the top of her ensign jackstaff at the stern. Her paintwork, her varnished brightwork, were spotless and brilliant; her halliards were of stainless steel wire rope running to hydraulic winches at the foot of each mast, her sheets of gleaming white nylon. A wireless aerial ran from the truck of the mainmast to the mizzen and down to the wheelhouse and deck lounge at the stern, from which a television aerial and a direction-finding loop protruded. A deckhand in immaculate white overalls lounged by the varnished gangway leading to the deck. Keith would never have dreamed of setting foot on such a ship himself; he decided that negotiations here were his captain's responsibility.

No such qualms beset Jack Donelly. He marched down the gangway to the deck, Keith following behind. The lounging sailor stood erect. 'What can we do for you, brother?' he asked.

Jack said, 'See the captain.'

'What do you want with him?'

'None o' your business. Just tell the captain I got sump'n to talk to him about.'

'You got to say what you want. The captain's busy.'

Jack flared into a quick anger that Keith had not seen before. He advanced a threatening step towards the man. 'You go tell him.'

The deckhand stepped back hurriedly. 'Okay, Superman, okay. But he won't see you till he's finished breakfast. Just wait up on the jetty.'

'We'll wait right here.'

The man hesitated, and then went towards the wheelhouse door. He almost collided with a woman who came flying out on deck. 'Who's that?' she asked him urgently.

'Coupla guys want to see the captain, lady,' he replied. 'They won't say what they want.'

She hesitated, and then brushed past him and walked quickly to Jack and Keith by the gangway. 'You haven't come from Manuel?' she asked. She had bright auburn hair, almost red in the Honolulu sunlight, that probably owed something to art. Keith judged she might have been about thirty years of age.

Jack looked at Keith blankly; the situation was beyond him. Keith said, 'We've come to see the captain.'

'Oh.' She was plainly disappointed. 'I was expecting somebody else.'

'We just want to see the captain.'

She looked them up and down. 'Want a job?' She said to Jack, 'You're a sailor by the look of you. He might have one for you. I don't suppose he'd have one for your friend.'

'We don't want no job,' Jack Donelly replied. 'Just want to see the captain – ask him about the course down to the Islands.'

She stood in silence, her lips drooping. Keith had a queer feeling that at any moment she was likely to start crying. 'You're nothing to do with Manuel?' she asked dully.

Jack looked blank, and Keith shook his head. 'We've never met him, I don't think,' he told her. 'Who is he?'

'At the Royal Waikiki Hotel, with his orchestra,' she said. '*Music with Manuel*, every Thursday evening on CBS. You must have seen it. Everyone knows Manuel.'

Jack Donelly said, 'We just want to see the captain.'

She turned away from them and walked slowly to the deckhouse door, and vanished inside. They stood in the sun at the end of the gangway, waiting. Jack smiled thoughtfully. 'Like to see her with no clothes on,' he remarked. 'She'd peel off nice.'

Keith laughed. 'You're not likely to get the chance.'

The deckhand reappeared. 'Captain, he's at breakfast,' he told them. 'He said to tell you to wait, or else come back again in half an hour.'

'Guess we'll wait,' said Jack patiently.

They waited for a quarter of an hour or twenty minutes. Then the captain came out of the deckhouse door and walked towards them, a tall, bronzed, efficient-looking man

163

in naval whites and a white-topped naval cap. 'You want to see me about something?' he asked. 'I'm Captain Petersen.'

Jack said awkwardly, 'I was wondering if we could check a course with you down to the Islands. I'm Jack Donelly, and this is Mr Keats, sailing with me.'

'Sure,' said the captain. 'There was a piece about you in the paper. You came from San Francisco single-handed, didn't you?'

'Piece about me in the paper?' asked Jack vaguely.

'In the *Post-Journal*, nearly a column about you and your ship. One day last week. Didn't you see it?'

Jack shook his head.

'I'll get the steward to look through the papers in the cookhouse. Maybe we've got it still. That's your ship up at the end? The white sloop?'

'That's right.'

'Where are you bound for now, captain?'

'Going south to this place Tahiti,' Jack Donelly said. 'Mr Keats's got business to do there.'

'Quite a way,' said the captain, 'but you should find a fair reaching wind, this season of the year. It might fall light and variable when you get down about five north. Then after the Equator it might steady up again, still from the east. You haven't got a motor?'

Jack shook his head.

'Oh well, I think you'll be all right. You may get a few days slamming about in the Doldrums. Come into the charthouse and we'll have a look at the course.'

They went with him towards the deckhouse door. Keith asked, 'Have you got a motor, sir?'

'Oh, sure. We've got a big main diesel and a smaller one for starting and battery charging. The engine room is quite a show place in this ship.'

'How many hands you carry?' asked Jack.

'Nine deckhands,' said the captain, 'two engineers, one cook, two stewards, boatswain, mate, and me. Seventeen all told.'

They entered the wheelhouse and stood by the chart table. The captain pressed a bell-push and a buzzer sounded below; a steward appeared. 'Sam,' said the captain, 'chase around the ship and see if you can find a copy of the *Post-Journal* about the middle of last week, Wednesday or Thursday, with the column in it about Captain Donelly and the *Mary Belle*. If you find it, bring it here. And – hold it.' He turned to Jack and Keith. 'Cup of coffee? Right. Three cups, Sam.'

They turned to a consideration of the course. Keith was surprised and pleased by the consideration that the American captain of this very fine yacht gave to Jack Donelly's problems. A dumb fisherman from Oregon was clearly no novelty to him; moreover, he had probably been briefed by local gossip in the yacht harbour. He examined Jack's smudged atlas page with interest and with care and turned to Keith's charts with tact, ran out the course for them, and curiously enough arrived at exactly the same magnetic course as Captain Davies had in the *Cathay Princess*. 'Guess I needn't have troubled you,' said Jack at last. 'I thought maybe it would be something different, the tanker being an iron ship.'

The captain shook his head. 'That's compass deviation. You don't want to stow anything made of iron near your binnacle – an anchor, or anything like that. Take it up forward.' They went on to discuss the probable winds, two men of the same country talking the language of sail. They went on talking for half an hour, sipping the cups of coffee, smoking as they stood over the charts. Keith showed his newspaper cutting about the loss of *Shearwater* and the death of Jo, and told this pleasant man the purpose of his journey. The red-headed woman came up from below dressed for the shore and passed them by, walked with quick steps up the gangway, got into a car upon the quay, and drove off.

'You won't have any trouble,' Captain Petersen said at last. 'A good, reaching wind most of the way, unless you're very unlucky. You should make better than a hundred miles a day, average. Add a week in the Doldrums. I'd say you'll be in Papeete in thirty days.' He paused, and then said, 'Wish I was coming with you.'

Keith asked, 'Have you been here long?'

'Too long,' the captain said. 'Nearly four weeks. We came here from LA bound for Tokyo and then Manila with the owner, his daughter, and some friends. Four months' cruise, it was to be. But soon as we got here he was talking on the telephone to New York and then to Cincinnati where the plant is, and he left and flew back east. He'll be back again some time, but Lord knows when. In the meantime there's just the daughter living here on board, and she's doing no good.'

'That's the lady who went on shore just now?' Keith asked. 'She came and spoke to us while we were waiting.'

The captain nodded. 'Mrs Efstathios,' he said. 'At least – I always call her Mrs Efstathios. I don't think the decree's gone through yet.'

Jack said, 'She was asking sump'n about a guy called Manuel. Seemed to think we ought to know about him.'

The captain nodded. 'Manuel de Silva,' he said reflectively. '*Music with Manuel*. He was born Mike Simmons, but that was in Puerto Rico so I suppose he felt he'd got a right to a Spanish name. Looks like he's going to be Number Four if we stop here much longer.' He stood in thought for a moment. 'Gee,' he said, 'I wish that I could jump this ship and come down to the Islands with you boys.'

They thanked this competent man and said goodbye, and went on shore, and started to walk back towards the *Mary Belle*. 'Fine ship,' said Jack Donelly.

'She was beautiful,' Keith said. 'I've never been on board a ship like that before. Do you know her name?'

'*Flying Cloud*. Registered in Seattle.' He walked a few steps in thought. 'She costs somebody plenty.'

They walked back to the *Mary Belle* and went on board. In the cabin Jack tucked the school atlas away under the mattress of his bunk, and Keith wedged the roll of charts behind the locker. Jack looked around the cabin. 'You think of anything we need we haven't got?' he asked.

Keith thought, and shook his head. 'We've got food, water, and kero,' he said. 'I don't know about the ship.'

Jack grunted. 'You ever been in a sailing craft like this before?'

Keith shook his head.

'Just keep out of my way, 'n don't do nothing 'less I tell you.'

He busied himself for the next half hour about the deck while Keith stood on the ladder in the hatch and watched. He set the jib in stops, made halliard and sheets ready, set up the main boom and removed the crutch, made fast the main sheet and removed all but two tie-ers from the sail. The wind was blowing from the east down the fairway of the yacht harbour towards the entrance. He took in the leeside bow and stern warps and led the doubled end of the bow warp from the weather bow pile to the stern. Then everything happened in a rush, so quickly that Keith had difficulty in appreciating what was going on. Jack cast off the weather stern warp and then he was everywhere at once, a big, nimble man stripped to the waist, hauling on ropes and casting them off. The *Mary Belle* moved forward smoothly from her berth into the fairway, turned as the jib broke out, and then she was sailing quietly down the middle of the rows of yachts towards the entrance, trailing a long rope in the water from her bow, Jack at the helm. 'Just gather that rope 'n put it on the deck beside the mast,' he said.

Keith did his best with this, and got it all on deck. They turned by the *Flying Cloud* and headed out to sea under jib alone, the wind a little aft of the beam. As they passed the schooner yacht Captain Petersen came out and waved to them from the deckhouse door.

They carried on southwards down the channel till Jack judged that they were well outside the reef. Then he told Keith to get down below out of the way. He loosened the main sheet, cast off the tie-ers from the main, put the ship up to the wind, and ran forward to hoist both peak and main halliards. The big tanned sail slammed and banged about as Keith crouched down below it in the hatch and Jack worked like a demon at the mast. Then suddenly it was over, and they were sailing quietly again, Jack at the helm, the big sail billowing above them. They were sailing much faster now, a little heeled to starboard, making about five knots.

Keith sat in the cabin hatch enjoying the smoothness of the motion in the lee of the land. As he looked around he saw a white launch come out of the harbour behind them. Presently he noticed it was closing up upon them fast, making about twenty knots, a white plume under the raised bow that grew and spluttered as she slammed each wave.

He said, 'There's a boat coming out behind us.'

Jack turned and looked at it. 'Always sump'n,' he grumbled.

The launch ranged up alongside them and slowed to their speed. A uniformed man in the stern spoke through a megaphone. 'Say, Captain,' he said, 'you better heave to.'

Grumbling beneath his breath Jack Donelly pulled the foresheet up to weather, slacked the main, and put the helm down; the *Mary Belle* came up into the wind and lay quietly with little forward way. The launch ranged up beside her on the lee quarter only a few feet away. The uniformed man appeared by the coxswain. 'Where are you bound for?' he shouted.

Jack Donelly answered, 'Hilo.'

'You're not going any further?'

'Just to Hilo.'

'You've got to get clearance if you go outside the group.'

'Don't need no clearance for Hilo.'

'No,' the officer admitted. 'All you need is just pay fourteen dollars and fifty cents.'

'What we got to pay that for?'

'Harbour dues, Captain.'

'Jeez. I wasn't in the harbour more 'n a week.'

'Nine days,' the officer said. 'Your size makes one fifty each day, plus tax. Makes fourteen dollars fifty.'

'I dunno as I've got it.'

'Then you'll come right back and tell the Judge about it. Come on, Captain – I got things to do.'

Grumbling, Jack left the helm and went below and from some secret store unearthed the money. The officer reached out a little fishing net on a bamboo for it and passed back the receipt in the same way. The launch sheered off, put on speed, turned around, and made off back towards the harbour.

Keith asked timidly, 'Where's Hilo?'

'On Hawaii. They make all kinds of trouble if you say you're going foreign.'

He let draw the jib and the main, and got the vessel on her course again. 'You sick yet?' he asked.

'Not yet,' said Keith.

'Come 'n take the helm a while and I'll show you.'

Keith came to the tiller, held by a turn of light rope round it from a cleat upon the bulwark, the rope held in the hand.

He sat down on the deck as he had seen Jack sit. 'Keep looking at the card,' he said. He laid a dirty finger on the glass of the binnacle. 'That black line, that's the lubber line 'n that goes with the ship. The card, with all them black marks on it, that moves against the lubber line the way you pull the tiller. You see the big thin diamond? Well, not that one but the one next to it; the tiddy little triangle. Not the big triangle, the tiddy little 'un. Keep her about there.'

Keith put on his glasses to inspect the binnacle and picked out the tiny numerals, remembered from his navigational instruction, and so identified the tiddy little triangle. He settled down to try to steer the ship, and became engrossed in it. Jack watched him for a time, and then went down and lit the Primus stove. He made a jug of coffee while Keith steered and the island of Oahu grew less distinct behind them, and presently passed up on deck a cup of coffee, a great hunk of corned beef out of a tin, and two inch-thick slices of bread. 'You okay?' he asked.

'So far,' said Keith.

Jack Donelly grunted. 'Guess I'll have a bit of a lie down,' he said.

Keith was alarmed. 'What will I do if anything happens?' he asked.

'Aw, nothing's going to happen,' said the captain. He sat by the galley at the foot of the ladder contentedly eating bread and beef. Then, without ever looking out on deck, he went forward and lay down upon the lee berth, which was Keith's, and went to sleep.

Keith sat at the helm, terrified. He had never sailed a ship of any sort before. Now he was in sole control of this rushing, heaving monster which towered above him in a mass of brown sails and rope whose very function was a mystery to him. He had mastered only one small element of the seaman's craft, that of keeping the appropriate compass mark upon the lubber line, and that only within the last half hour. He did not know what disaster would ensue if he should let it stray either way. The wind seemed to be increasing and the sea rising as they cleared the land, and the ship was heeling noticeably more. He was scared stiff. He sat there in his cricket shirt and braces with Panama hat upon his head under the brilliant sun of the Hawaiian Islands, the bread and the corned beef untasted on the deck beside him, concentrating on doing the one thing that he had been taught, keeping the tiddy little triangle upon the lubber line. Presently his cup of coffee, now quite cold, left him and slid down into the lee scuppers, still upright.

An hour later he was still sitting in the same position, the ship still rushing along in much the same way under the steady beam trade wind. He was hungry and thirsty, and very sore from sitting motionless on the hard deck. He was less frightened now and his arms were getting tired. He began to experiment with the rope lanyard which assisted him to hold the tiller. If he took another turn around the tiller it eased the grip of his hands. He still had to steer, but if he tied it, the ship would probably go straight enough for ten or fifteen seconds while he retrieved the cup of coffee from the scuppers. He made a couple of trials, and then, greatly daring, lashed the helm and slithered down the deck upon his bottom to retrieve the cold cup.

By the middle of the afternoon he was taking things more easily. He ate his lunch about three o'clock, and sat on at the helm growing steadily more sunburnt and tired. Below, he could see Jack sleeping peacefully upon the lee berth. Tired as he was, he realised that this made sense since for the next month they would have to sail all night. He could not sail the ship at night; Jack would have to do that, or they must heave to as they had done when the harbourmaster's launch had overtaken them. He must stick it out and call Jack at sunset, which seemed to come at about six o'clock.

171

When the sun was about an hour above the horizon he couldn't stand it any longer, and called Jack. The big man stood up in the cabin, yawned, and came on deck. 'You done a good spell,' he said. 'Everything okay?'

'I think so,' said Keith. 'I haven't touched anything.'

Jack Donelly took the tiller. 'I got her now. Get down and rustle up some chow. I'll heave her to 'n pull a reef down case it gets up in the night.'

Keith got up stiffly and went down below, regardless of what was going on on deck. He lit the stove to make some coffee and got out a tin of pork and beans to heat up for their supper. He had got as far as getting out the bread when he suddenly felt dizzy and faint; the fumes of the stove were nauseating, the motion of the ship intolerable. He struggled on for a little, unable to focus his eyes on anything. Then he was overcome and dashed up on deck to be sick over the lee rail.

He moved back to the hatch when it was over. Jack was tying down the reef points at the boom, and paused in his work. 'Gets you, down below,' he said affably. 'Stay out on deck a while. I'll get the chow.'

'I can manage.'

'You'll get sick again. Stay where you are.'

Keith obeyed him and sat on the deck by the hatch, gradually recovering. Jack finished his chores on deck and went below. Presently he handed up a dirty plate with a great mess of steaming pork and beans on it, a huge hunk of bread, and a cup of coffee. 'I don't want anything,' said Keith faintly.

'Go on 'n eat it.'

'I'll be sick again.'

'Sure you'll be sick again. Go on 'n eat it.'

Keith took the path of least resistance, and ate most of it, and felt the better for it for the moment. Jack took the dirty plates and cups, wiped them with a filthy rag, and put them back ready for use again. He took the bucket with the lanyard on the handle and sluiced it over the side, left a little sea water in it, and placed it on the deck below, beside the head of the lee berth. He lit the cabin lamp and turned it low, then came on deck and took the tiller, let draw the sheets, and got the vessel on her course. It was now nearly dark.

'Get on down 'n get some sleep,' he said. 'Don't go standing up – lie down right away. You got nothing else to do till daylight.'

'You can't sail her all night.'

'Aw, if I get sleepy I'll heave to.'

Keith took off his shoes, went down below and stretched out on the berth. Somewhat to his own surprise he fell asleep at once. He slept for five or six hours, woke up feeling sick, and got out on deck to vomit over the rail. Jack was sitting smoking at the helm, and the ship going smoothly over the long ocean swell. 'Just take her while I get some chow,' he said.

Keith took the helm in the bright moonlight and struggled to keep the vessel on her course in the faint light of the oil-lit binnacle. Presently Jack passed him up a mug of coffee and a great hunk of bread spread with jam, and sat below himself finishing up the tin of cold pork and beans. Then he came on deck again. 'Guess I'll take her now.'

So the night passed for Keith, in alternate vomiting and sleep. He took the helm again at dawn while Jack Donelly slept. In general he was well enough on deck while he concentrated on the sailing of the ship, and he was ill directly he went below. They sailed on all the day under a blue sky flecked with cloud. Once in the afternoon when Keith was lying dozing and exhausted on the lee bunk he opened his eyes to see Jack Donelly wedged upon the other bunk, and realised that there was no one at the helm. To his enquiry Jack said, 'She goes by herself okay with the wind forward of the beam. Won't be no harm if we get up a tiddy bit to weather.' He pointed at the bulkhead at his feet. 'I reckon we made ninety-five miles yesterday, up till dawn today. See where I wrote it down?'

Later that afternoon when Keith was at the helm and Jack below, beginning the preparations for supper, he happened to glance up through the hatch. Immediately he stopped what he was doing and came out on deck, and stood looking at the sky. Keith asked him what he was looking at.

'Frigate bird,' said Jack. 'That's the third I've seen.' Keith followed his arm pointing and saw the bird, very high, flying or gliding on a straight course. 'That's a gull, isn't it?' he asked.

'Frigate bird,' said Jack. 'Much bigger 'n a gull. See his forked tail. He's going home some place.'

'How do you know that?'

'That sort don't spend nights at sea. They go way out, but they go back to land each night. He'll be down by sunset.' He glanced at the sun. 'Hour 'n a quarter, hour 'n a half. There's land that way, forty, fifty miles. That's the third I see, all going the same way.' He laid a horny, dirty hand vertically across the binnacle, looking up at the flight of the bird and down at his hand. 'Just a tiddy bit south of east,' he said. 'Get them charts of yours 'n see what land that is.'

Keith went below and got the chart and brought it up on deck quickly before he was sick. He put the *Pacific Islands Pilot* down on it with the edge pointing a little to the south of magnetic east. 'Must be Hawaii,' he said. 'If we're on course that should be about sixty miles away.'

Jack thought about it, watching the bird now disappearing to the east. 'I dunno as he'd fly so fast as that,' he said. 'Reckon we're up to windward just a tiddy bit.'

CHAPTER EIGHT

THE DC6B FLOWN by Captain Fielding landed back at Blackbushe about midday on Thursday, just a week after leaving for Honolulu. They could have flown to Speke from Frobisher, which would have been more convenient for Mr Adams, but the landing fees for the aircraft at Speke far exceeded Mr Adams' fare by rail from London to Manchester, so they took him to Blackbushe with them. They landed back into the cold foggy drizzle of a January day in England; after the languorous sun and warm trade winds of Honolulu the change was little to their liking. 'Half-inch thick underwear, fires in the living-room, and hot buttered crumpets for tea,' said the navigator thoughtfully. 'Well, I dunno. I suppose there's something to be said for it.'

The crew were tired and ready for a rest. They had flown the best part of their maximum permitted allowance of flying for a month in one week, finishing up with thirty-six hours on end. For most of them there was employment or instruction on the ground in the installations of Blackbushe until they were rostered for another flight, but all were entitled to three days of rest. Dick King would start again upon the overhaul of engines in the shops on Monday morning, but having turned in his log books and written his report he was free to go home.

He telephoned his wife, Ethel, to bring the car to Blackbushe to fetch him. He lived at Egham in a house off Stroude Road convenient both for Blackbushe and for

London Airport in case he wanted to change his job, and convenient for Ethel for shopping in Staines. He had brought back little gifts from Honolulu for his wife, a lei of frangipani blossoms in a polythene bag and a bracelet of coloured tropical nuts, unusual in Egham. 'I haven't got anything particular for tea,' she said as he got into the car. 'Anything you fancy?'

He shivered a little in the unaccustomed, raw chilliness of the early dusk. 'Sausages,' he said. 'Pork sausages and fried potatoes.' He thought of the navigator. 'And crumpets. Let's have lots and lots of crumpets. Got the fire lighted?'

She looked surprised. 'I didn't light it yet – it's not very cold. Are you cold?'

'A bit. We'll light it when we get in.' Halfway home he thought of Keith Stewart's letter in his pocket, and they stopped and posted it, and bought sausages and crumpets.

When they got home he gave her his presents, and she exclaimed with pleasure at the bracelet and the lei, which was satisfactory to him. While he was lighting the fire and putting the car away she picked the lei to pieces and put the flowers in water in an endeavour to make them last a little while in January England, and then she started to cook the potatoes and the sausages and crumpets. 'I never asked if you had a good trip,' she said.

'Pretty fair,' he replied. He paused, and then he said, 'You remember me telling you about Keith Stewart of the *Miniature Mechanic*, who was coming with us?'

She nodded. 'I remember. Did you bring him back?'

'No. He got off in Honolulu. Tell you all about it after tea.'

He did so as they washed the dishes in the kitchen, and as he recapitulated to her what had happened in Honolulu the unease grew on him again. It was absurd, of course, and that he realised, because Keith was his own master and if he chose to go to sea with a man like Jack Donelly in a ship like the *Mary Belle*, well, that was that. Moreover, it was all ten thousand miles away, and no concern of his. Yet he was still worried.

Something of his unease communicated itself to her as they sat before the fire. 'We got him fixed up with a sextant and the ship's officers showed him how to use it to take a latitude sight,' he said. 'I hope to God it's going to work out all right.'

'Doesn't the captain have to do that?' she asked, puzzled.

'This one couldn't. He was just a sort of fisherman. American,' he added, in ultimate disparagement.

'Doesn't the captain of a ship have to pass exams, like in an aeroplane?'

'I don't know,' he replied. 'Maybe if the ship is small enough you don't. I shouldn't have thought that this chap could read or write.' He thought for a moment. 'He was a good woodworker.'

'However small the aeroplane, you've got to have a licence and pass exams before you can fly it anywhere, haven't you?' she asked.

'That's so. It may be different with ships. This chap couldn't navigate at all. He got to Honolulu from San Francisco by following the aeroplanes.'

She was puzzled. 'But they fly to all sorts of places, don't they? How would he know that any aeroplane he saw was going to Honolulu?'

'It's the only place they can go to,' he said. 'They all put down at Honolulu to refuel. You get out in the Pacific west of San Francisco and you see one flying to the west, it's going to Honolulu.' He sat in brooding silence.

Presently she asked him kindly, 'What's the trouble, Dick? Are you afraid that they won't get to this place he's going to? What's the name?'

'Tahiti,' he said. 'That's about the strength of it. It's the hell of a long way – more than two thousand five hundred miles of open sea. Nearly as far as from here to New York.

And at the end of it, to find one tiny little island in among a lot of coral reefs you could get wrecked on, like his sister was. To think of starting off upon a trip like that in a sailing ship without an engine, with a skipper who can't navigate!'

'There's nothing you can do about it,' she said at last.

'No …' He turned to her. 'I was with him all the time in Honolulu. We shared a room in the hotel. I've never shared a room with someone who was somebody before – I mean, well known. *You* know.' She nodded. 'He'd never been outside England before,' he said uncomfortably. 'For so famous a man – he didn't know a thing, really. Never seen a shower before, or foreign money. He didn't even know how to sleep properly in hot weather.'

'Was he nice?' she asked curiously.

'Just like you or me,' he told her. 'We got on fine.' He sat in an uncomfortable silence. 'I ought to have stopped him going on that ship,' he said at last. 'I didn't quite know how.'

She comforted him. 'It'll probably turn out all right,' she said. 'You see.'

'I hope it does.'

He spent a restless night, much to her discomfort, weighed down by a sense of imminent disaster. He did not know what to do, but he knew that if Keith were to lose his life he would be associated with the tragedy in some small measure. Towards morning it occurred to him that anyway he should not keep his grim forebodings to himself. Two heads, or several heads, were better than one. If he shared his apprehensions with other people someone might pull some rabbit out of an unthought-of hat, might make some suggestion that would somehow make Keith's journey to Tahiti safer. But who to talk to?

He talked to everyone that he could think of over the weekend, and he talked to all and sundry at Blackbushe when he started work again on Monday, but no rabbit was extracted from any hat. On the Wednesday, when he had been back in England for nearly a week, he took a batch of exhaust manifolds for repair to a firm in Croydon, travelling with them to suggest a welding modification that would prevent certain cracks from starting. He rode with the driver in the truck, arriving in the middle of the morning. He did his business in the welding shop and had lunch in the firm's canteen.

By the time he had disposed of his lunch and his work it was getting on for three o'clock. There was little sense in going back with the truck to Blackbushe for at most an hour of work before knocking-off time, and Keith Stewart was still uneasily in his mind. He rode with the truck driver to Croydon station and took a train to Victoria. An hour later he was walking into the editorial offices of the *Miniature Mechanic* in Victoria Street.

It was not a large office, and it was not modern or well furnished. In the outer office there was a girl and a young man, and two vacant desks littered with bits of miniature machinery, photographs, and pulls from blocks. He asked the girl if he could see the editor.

'Who shall I say?' she asked.

'Mr King,' he said a little awkwardly. 'Mr King of Albatross Airways. He won't know me. Tell him it's about Keith Stewart.'

She went into the inner office, and came out followed by the editor. He went up to the engineer. 'Mr King?' he said with outstretched hand. 'My name is McNeil. You've come about Keith Stewart?'

'That's right. I thought you might like to know how he's getting on.'

'Come into the office. Like a cup of tea?' He turned to the girl. 'Make us two cups, Daphne.'

They went into the office and the editor gave him a chair. Dick King said, 'I'm the flight engineer of the crew Mr

Stewart went to Honolulu with. We left him there when we flew back last Tuesday. I thought you might like to know how he was getting on.'

'I certainly would. He told me he'd got a flight with you to Honolulu and he wanted to get down to Tahiti. He had to go there to see about his sister's death.'

'That's right.'

'Did he manage to get a passage on to Tahiti? He wasn't quite sure about that when he left.'

Dick King said, 'He did get a passage, of a sort. That's what I wanted to tell you about, really and truly. He was going on a sort of fishing boat. She hadn't got an engine even – just the sails.'

Mr McNeil opened his eyes. 'That doesn't sound like Keith. Couldn't he get anything better?'

'Apparently not. We were all a bit worried about it, but he made up his mind, so there wasn't anything that we could do.'

'It's a very long way, isn't it?'

'About two thousand four hundred miles.' He hesitated. 'Sea miles, that would be – knots. Close on three thousand land miles, I suppose.'

'And he's gone on that in a fishing boat – sailing?'

'That's right.'

The tea came. When the girl was out of the room the editor said, 'Tell me just what happened, Mr King.'

The engineer considered how to tell his story. 'Well,' he said, 'it was like this. There was this crew of the *Cathay Princess*, the officers, I mean, the ship we took the generator rotor to.' Launched on his story he had little difficulty in going on in his own way, and the editor had little difficulty in getting the essentials of the tale. 'The chap was kind of simple,' said the engineer, describing Jack Donelly. 'He built the boat himself and made a good job of her. He's a woodworker by trade, or else a fisherman. He could be a bit of both. But I don't think he can read or write, and he certainly can't navigate.'

Mr McNeil was puzzled. 'If he can't navigate, how's he going to find Tahiti?'

'That's the trouble,' said the engineer. 'Captain Davies – he's the captain of the tanker we took the generator rotor to – he said they wouldn't get there at all. The first officer, he said he thought they'd get there in the end, but they'd take the hell of a long time.' He paused. 'It was all a bit of a mess-up, if you get me,' he said unhappily.

'But he went off on this ship, did he?'

'I suppose he did,' said the flight engineer. 'We took off at dawn last Tuesday and they were going to sail the same day. I don't know for sure that they went, but I suppose they did.'

'How long was the voyage to take?'

'Mr Fairlie said six weeks. You'd make it in ten hours in a DC6, but that's the time he said it would take.' He paused. 'He did teach Mr Stewart how to take a latitude sight, and we got him a sextant. And Captain Davies, he fixed them up with food and that.'

The editor pursed his lips. It sounded absolutely crazy, and it probably was. He had private troubles of his own that concerned Keith Stewart. It was barely a fortnight since he left England, but already his absence had been felt very much by the staff of the *Miniature Mechanic*. Every other day a batch of letters arrived from Katie that Keith normally would have answered, and which now had to be answered by the editor himself. They were letters from all over the world. Jim McNeil had not fully realised till he had the job of answering these letters from Edmonton and Bulawayo, from Gateshead and Hong Kong, how widely Keith's influence had spread, in what high regard he was held by modellers all over the world. He was uneasily conscious that Keith's salary was perhaps too small; after all, it was only

181

one third of his own, yet which of them did more for the circulation of the magazine? The overseas subscriptions were increasing every day. The air fare from Honolulu to Tahiti might not be more than the book could stand, a hundred or a hundred and fifty pounds. Keith had been on the staff now for twelve years. It might be reasonable to stand him that.

He asked the engineer, 'How could we find out if he's actually left?'

Dick King rubbed his chin. 'Well, I don't know. I think he probably *did* sail the day we left.'

'I'd like to know for certain.' The editor paused. 'If I'd known that he was in this difficulty we'd have given him some help, I think. I'd have to put it to the Board, of course. But I think we'd have helped him with the air fare, rather than see him get into a mess like this.'

'You can't fly direct,' said the engineer. 'You've got to go by Samoa.'

'Have your firm got an agent in Honolulu that I could cable to?'

'Not that I know of,' replied Mr King. 'There's Mr Yamasuki. He was agent for the ship, the *Cathay Princess*.'

'Any good?'

The engineer thought for a minute. 'I don't think he'd do much for a stranger unless there was money in it for him,' he said at last. 'He didn't seem to want to be mixed up in it at all. It might be worth a try ...'

'I'll think it over for an hour or two,' said the editor. 'I might think of something better.' He took Mr Yamasuki's name, talked to the engineer for a few minutes longer, and thanked him for coming in. Finally Dick left the office to catch a train to Staines and so to Egham.

Back in his office after seeing the engineer off the premises, Mr McNeil sat deep in thought, smoking pipe after pipe. Something would have to be done about Keith

Stewart; he should have realised that earlier. He should have realised when Keith first proposed his most improbable journey that his value to the magazine was such that he must be assisted to complete it quickly and get back to work again. True, he had made a half-hearted offer of an advance payment if Keith should be in any difficulty; it now seemed to him that in view of his very small salary that offer had been quite inadequate.

He should have offered him assistance with the airline fare to Tahiti and return – especially the return, because he wanted Keith back at work. It would have been quite a shock to his Board, but he could have pushed it through. Indeed, he would have to push it through now, whether the Board liked it or not. The effect of his penny-pinching was that his best contributor, the man who attracted correspondence to the magazine from all over the world, had had to go off on a crazy trip in the Pacific, on a fishing boat sailed by a skipper who didn't know how to navigate.

If Keith Stewart were to lose his life, the effect upon the magazine would be disastrous.

He sat in brooding silence. No good crying over spilt milk now. Constructive action was required; the first thing was to find out whether Keith was still in Honolulu or whether he had in fact left upon this fishing boat. Whom did he know or correspond with in Honolulu? He searched his mind. There was nobody he could think of. There must be modellers in Honolulu; probably the mail department of the printers could produce half a dozen subscribers to the *Miniature Mechanic* in Honolulu if you included the armed forces. But he knew none of them.

Well then, Americans … Americans who might have contacts there. Professor O'Leary leaped to his mind. Professor O'Leary was Professor of Mediaeval Literature at Ann Arbor University in Michigan, just outside Detroit. Perhaps as a reaction from the mediaeval literature, he made models. They had published an article by him once – was it in 1952? – on the construction of his 4³/₄ inch gauge locomotive model of one of the old wood-burning 4-4-0 engines of the Northern Pacific railroad of 1880. Two years ago he had visited England and Mr McNeil had lunched with him and with Keith Stewart. He was then completing a model of a Case traction engine, acknowledging a considerable debt to Mr Stewart for his articles upon the Burrell. He had shown them photographs of a very well equipped workshop in the basement of his home in Ann Arbor with the oil-fired air-conditioning plant in the background, which had interested them as much as the model. Mr McNeil and Keith had kept in touch with this pleasant reader, who was now engaged on the construction of Keith's Congreve clock. A Congreve clock is an antique clock mechanism in which a steel ball rolls upon a zigzag path down an inclined plane and takes half a minute to do so, when the incline of the plane reverses and the ball rolls back again.

Professor O'Leary was the man. He had been in Honolulu lecturing, probably more than once. He must have numerous contacts on the academic staff. Indeed, with his engineering hobby he might well know other modellers in Honolulu or members of the faculty of engineering at the University, to whom the name Keith Stewart would be known. In the professor the editor felt he had a sympathetic contact in the United States who would exert himself to the utmost to find out what had happened to Keith Stewart in Honolulu.

His staff were all departing or had gone by the time he reached that conclusion. He reached for the telephone and rang up his wife in Finchley to tell her that he would be a bit late, and went out into the deserted outer office. He sat down at his secretary's typewriter, put an air-letter form and carbon into the machine, and began to type.

He wrote:

Dear Professor,
You will remember lunching with Keith Stewart and myself when you were last in London, when you showed us the photographs of your Case traction engine and your workshop. I am a bit concerned about Keith Stewart, who was recently in Honolulu, and I have wondered if you have a friend there who could assist me in an enquiry.

The circumstances are as follows ...

He wrote on, putting the case clearly and concisely, explaining about Keith's sister, about his financial inability to pay for his extensive journey, about his free flight to Honolulu, about Jack Donelly and the *Mary Belle*. He ended with a few words of apology:

I feel we are to blame in some degree in not assisting him with the expense of this journey in view of his long service with the magazine, but you will appreciate that we do not make great profits. We did not think that he would become involved in such difficulties, and we would assist him now if we could get in touch with him. Do you know anyone in Honolulu who could cable us, at my expense, to tell us what the position is? Or who could get in touch with him if he is still there, and ask him to cable us?

Yours sincerely,

James McNeil.

He folded the air letter and sealed it. He glanced at his watch; there was still time to catch the airmail to New York if he took it to the Charing Cross post office. He put on his hat and coat, turned out the lights and locked the door, and went out into the chilly January night to catch a bus to Charing Cross.

Cyrus Shawn O'Leary got that letter on the Friday morning at his home in Ann Arbor near Detroit. He had no formal lecture on that day though he had essays to correct. On Monday he was lecturing upon the debt owed by the Elizabethan lyric-writers to the early English mediaeval poets, and on that morning he was engaged in tracing a comparison between *Piers Plowman* and the work of John Donne. He had strayed a little from his line to consider Thomas Campion, the graceful reprobate, and the mail lay unnoticed at his elbow, and he smiled as he read, for he was still young at heart:

> *I care not for these ladies,*
> *That must be woode and praide:*
> *Give me kind Amarillis,*
> *The wanton country maide.*
> *Nature art disdaineth,*
> *Her beauty is her owne.*
> *Her when we court and kisse,*
> *She cries, Forsooth, let go:*
> *But when we come where comfort is*
> *She never will say, No.*

Perhaps there was enough of that in Ann Arbor; he had better not stress it to the sophomores. Better to stick to the religious angle, to the soul-searchings that had followed the Reformation. He laid Campion aside, and turned back to John Donne. Outside, the snow lay deep; the cars passing in the street made a whisper and a rustle. It was overcast outside with heavy, lowering clouds presaging more snow. Spring with flower-decked meadows was the time for Thomas Campion. Winter was the time for John Donne, and for the workshop …

He resolutely turned his mind away from his hobby. John Donne was his business, and he turned to him again, endeavouring to regain the train of thought from which he had been side-tracked. He read the passage again which seemed to him to reflect the Plowman:

> *Thou hast made me, and shall Thy work decay?*
> *Repair me now, for now mine end doth haste;*
> *I run to death, and Death meets me as fast,*
> *And all my pleasures are like yesterday ...*

That echoed something, surely?

> *On your midnight pallet lying,*
> *Listen, and undo the door:*
> *Lads that waste the light in sighing*
> *In the dark should sigh no more.*
> *Night should ease a lover's sorrow;*
> *Therefore, since I go tomorrow,*
> *Pity me before.*

No, that was Housman, much, much later. His mind was wandering today: he could not concentrate. Pallets – he was worried about the method of machining the pallets of his clock – but then that was a different sort of pallet. He did not see how he could hold them in the four-jaw chuck to bore and ream the axis hole, and Keith Stewart had not explained that in the serial. He must be being stupid; there must be some simple way to do that job which every modeller would know. Perhaps if he went down to the basement and had another look ...

No. He never went down to the workshop in the morning. Get thee behind me, Satan – he must work. If the work would not flow, at least there was the mail to go through, and the essays to correct. He picked up the pile of letters and furtively looked through to see if the new issue of the *Miniature Mechanic* had arrived. It hadn't, but there were two heavy-looking archaeological journals, three local letters, one air letter from his married daughter in Colorado Springs, and an air letter from London, England.

He opened the one from his daughter first and skimmed it through. It was all about the baby and not much else; his wife would be interested. He put it down and picked up the one from London. The back showed it to be from J McNeil; the name rang a faint bell, but he could not place it.

He opened it, and sat riveted in his chair as he read. This was really serious, very serious indeed.

He read the letter again and then sat deep in thought, *Piers Plowman* and John Donne and the remainder of his correspondence unnoticed on the desk before him. The direct appeal stirred him deeply. He was an engineer at heart; if things had broken differently for him he might have been one. He had money; that was the trouble. His grandfather, Shawn O'Leary, had been a railway contractor in the palmy days of expansion; in reaction his father had become a minister in Boston, Massachusetts. Cyrus had been directed to the academic life and he had not resisted; a year at Oxford had followed four at Harvard. Research had come after that, and academic appointments. He did not regret his life, but the urge to make things had been strong in him all the time, inherited, perhaps, from his grandfather who had made the iron roads towards the West. His workshop meant a great deal to Cyrus O'Leary.

He enjoyed his literary work, but the high spot of his visit to Europe two years previously had been the lunch with Keith Stewart and his editor. He had subscribed to the *Miniature Mechanic* for nine years, and in that time he had come to have a deep regard for the design engineer whose lucid, modest, and well written articles had taught him so much. They did not seem to breed that sort of writer in the United States, and he had wondered why his country with so much engineering achievement did not throw up people of that sort. When he had met Keith Stewart he understood a little better. He had thought from the pleasure that the engineer had given to so many modellers that he would be in the twenty to thirty thousand dollars a year income bracket. When he had met him his regard for Keith was, if anything, increased, but he now realised that his income was three to four thousand, or even less. Few people of such ability in his own country would be content with so modest an income, and perhaps no engineers. The devotion to an art inherent in Keith Stewart's circumstances flowered more prolifically in Europe.

He sat wondering how to deal with this appeal, how best he could help. He did know Honolulu; he had lectured there three times, but the people that he knew there were all literary people. Mr McNeil had been in error when he had assumed that Professor O'Leary might know members of the engineering faculty in Honolulu University. It was the professor's habit to conceal his workshop hobby from his colleagues, even in Ann Arbor. He did not display his locomotive or his traction engine to his fellow professors, fearing that if he did so he would not be taken seriously when he spoke on mediaeval poetry. He would not have dreamed of talking about engineering matters when visiting another university. In consequence the only associates that he had in Honolulu were serious and somewhat unpractical students of mediaeval history. He did not know one person there to whom he could turn for an account of the movements of a fishing boat in the harbour.

He left his study and went down to the basement of his house, to the workshop. He had a special bookshelf down there for the copies of the *Miniature Mechanic*, not caring to display them in his study. The row of little magazines was now seven feet long, extending every week; presently he would have to put up another shelf.

He had abstracted from the series the issues of the magazine dealing with the construction of the Congreve clock, and these lay in a little pile upon the drawing bench. He turned them over thoughtfully; it was incredible that a man who could write stuff like that should be so short of money ... He turned to the bench, deep in thought, and fingered the tilting platform of the clock already assembled in a trial erection in its trunnions. He had made that first, thinking it to be the most difficult part; in fact, it had proved to be the easiest. Who could he turn to for help in this affair? Who else in the United States was an admirer of Keith Stewart? Who else was making a Congreve clock to his instructions?

There was that dairy farmer down in Maryland – he wouldn't be much help. There was Dave Coulson in Indianapolis – he was an accountant. There was the chap that he had met at the Brotherhood of Live Steamers in Detroit, the stockbroker's clerk in Toledo ... Then – wait a minute, out on the West Coast ... lumber and pulp mills ... what was his name? Hirzhorn – Solly Hirzhorn. Solly Hirzhorn had attended a meeting of the Brotherhood last year, and nobody had realised who he was till after the meeting a week later. Solly Hirzhorn was building a Congreve clock, and he had all the money in the world, and all the contacts, too.

He picked up the tiny pallet that he could not think of how to hold for machining and stood fingering it absently. He should have bored and reamed it first before shaping it to that rather complicated form. Perhaps if he put it in a tin and melted lead all round it he could hold the lead – but then, how would you line it up? There *must* be a simpler way than that. He wondered if Solly Hirzhorn had been caught that way, or whether he hadn't got as far as making the pallets.

As he stood there at the bench of his workshop it seemed to him that Solly Hirzhorn was the one person to whom he could turn. He did not know the lumber tycoon well. He had been introduced to him at the meeting of the model engineering society, the Brotherhood of Live Steamers, and they had talked enthusiastically together about the Congreve clock for nearly a quarter of an hour. Both had then been starting on the project and had been drawn to each other by their common interest, the fat, unwieldy magnate sixty-eight years old and the lean professor of fifty-two. In that quarter of an hour they had become friends, though it was only when they came to exchange addresses at the end of it that each learned who the other was. That was a year ago; they had exchanged cards at Christmas but they had not met again, nor were they very likely to do so.

He glanced at his watch. Half past eleven – that would be half-past eight in Tacoma. Not a very good time to call a tycoon upon a personal matter, when he would just have arrived in his office perhaps. He went up to his study again, closed the door, lifted the telephone, and spoke to the long-distance operator. 'I want to call Mr Solomon P Hirzhorn, person to person,' he said. 'This is Professor O'Leary. I don't know the number, but it's in Tacoma, Washington. It's Hirzhorn Lumber Enterprises Inc., or something.'

'It's *the* Mr Solomon Hirzhorn, is it?' she asked.

'That's right, if you get through to his secretary, tell her it's about a clock. I'll take the call at any time convenient to him.'

He hung up; five minutes later the operator called again with news from fifteen hundred miles away. 'Mr Hirzhorn is dealing with his mail right now,' she said, 'and after that he has to fly to a conference at one of the plants. He could accept your call best at his home at five o'clock tonight. That would be eight in the evening of our time. I was to ring her back and tell her would that be okay.'

He said that would be fine, and put the receiver down. He could not work that day. Against all his rules of routine, he went down again to the workshop and stood turning over the work of Keith Stewart. So much pleasure given to so many people, in all walks of life. And yet the man was short of money – worse paid than a professor! It didn't seem right, but that was evidently the way it was.

At eight o'clock he was speaking to the magnate on the telephone. 'Say, professor, this is a real pleasure,' said Mr Hirzhorn. 'How are you making out with the clock?'

'Not too bad,' said the professor. 'I got the tilting table and the escapement made all right, but now I'm finding the clock motion to be quite a job. However, I'll get over it all right. What I wanted to talk to you about was Mr Keith Stewart.'

'He's a great guy,' said Mr Hirzhorn. 'Whenever I get in a difficulty I write to him and he comes right back with the answer.'

'He's in a little trouble. I thought you might like to know. He's been in Honolulu, but he's probably somewhere in the Pacific at present.'

'In Honolulu? What's he doing there? If I'd known I'd have flown across to meet him.'

'I got a letter from his editor. Shall I read it out?'

'Sure, professor. I'm sorry if he's got in any trouble.'

Professor O'Leary started to read the letter from Mr McNeil. When he was halfway through, Mr Hirzhorn stopped him. 'Say, professor,' he said, 'this is interesting, but I'd like to see a copy and consider it. Mind if we put it on the tape?'

'By all means.'

Mr Hirzhorn laid down the receiver and called to the next room. 'Julie! Say, Julie!' A handsome Jewish-looking girl appeared at the door. 'Get this on the tape, the letter that Professor O'Leary will be reading out. Get the conversation, too – all of the call.' In a moment he spoke again. 'We're all set now, professor. If you wouldn't mind starting the letter again.'

When that was over he said, 'Well, professor, that'll need some thought. I'll have it copied and think about it, and call you again.'

'Can you find out whether he's left Honolulu?'

'Oh, sure. I'll call Honolulu right now. If I can contact him, I'd better speak to him myself and read him out this letter.'

'That would be a good idea. His editor, this Mr McNeil, he's evidently prepared to help him with the fares. He'd better cable his office. But I'm afraid that he'll have started already.'

'Well, we'll find that out. Say, if we can locate him I'd be mighty glad to have him visit with me for a day or two on his way back to England. There's one or two things on the clock that I'd like his advice on, and he might be interested to see some of the plants. Would you be able to come over and join us?'

Professor O'Leary said, 'Not till the end of May. I've got things I must do here each day.'

'Too bad. Well, anyway, professor, I'll be calling you again.'

Mr Hirzhorn put down the receiver and called for Julie. When she came he said, 'Give me all that in type, soon as you can. And say, what's the name of the guy that runs our business in Honolulu, making monkey-pod wood bowls and dishes?'

'Setches, Mr Hirzhorn. Setches and Byrne, Incorporated.'

'That's right. Paul Setches. Well, get that tape in type and let me have it. After that I may want to speak with Paul Setches.'

She went out, and he sat on alone in his study, a glass of rye and water with a little ice beside him. He sat, as was his habit in the evening, in front of the great picture window facing to the west. He lived not far from Wauna on an inlet off the Puget Sound ten miles from his office in Tacoma. The east side of the house looked out over the inlet, his private airstrip, his boathouse, and his moored motor cruiser; the west side looked over many miles of forest to the snow-capped Olympic range. Here he would sit on the evenings when he had the leisure, and rest a little and watch the sunset light beyond the snowy forests. He had been born a lumberman, and he loved forests.

He lived very much alone, devoted to his business. His two sons lived in suburbs of Tacoma more convenient to schools and to the main Seattle-Tacoma airport where the executive aircraft of the corporation were housed and maintained. His wife liked Florida and was frequently away there in the winter. He liked Florida well enough and sometimes spent a day or two there with her in the sun, but he could not live for long away from his business and his forests. The girl Julie Perlberg lived in the house with him and managed the servants and worked as his secretary at home. She was an illegitimate daughter of his oldest son, Emmanuel, who had found a job for her in the office of the plant at Marblemount on the Skagit River when she was fifteen years old, conveniently tucked away in the mountains at a discreet distance from Tacoma. She had the Hirzhorn blood in her, however, and by the time she was eighteen she was virtually running the Marblemount plant. There had been little option but to transfer her to the head office in Tacoma if they wanted to keep a man as manager in Marblemount. There the old man had met her and had taken a fancy to his grand-daughter, largely because of her encyclopaedic knowledge of the business. As he found less room for detail in his mind he had taken her as his personal secretary; his sons approved of this, because they were a closely knit family and theirs was a family business.

His father had emigrated to Seattle from Austria in the early years of the century. Solly had been an enormous, powerful young man who liked work in the woods. He had been a hand faller at the age of twenty and a high rigger when he was twenty-five; he saved his money and at the age of thirty-two he had taken his own lumber concession and had become an employer of men. From that time he had never looked back. Forest after forest had been added to his empire, mill after mill to his payroll. His writ now ran from Bellingham to Eugene, from Cape Flattery to Spokane. He employed rather more than forty thousand men in the various businesses under his direct control; he owned logging railroads, bulldozers by the score, trucks by the hundred, and many lumber mills. At sixty-two he had a coronary, and his doctors told him bluntly that he must do less work. He must acquire a hobby and live quietly at home for a portion of each day, or of each week.

He had seen this sentence coming, and he knew what he would do. As his business had grown he had bought huge varieties of engineering products, but he had never been an engineer. He had never formed a thread upon a bolt, though in theory he knew how it was done. He had concealed his lack of engineering knowledge all his life by virtue of his native wit, but always he had been uncertain in the background of his mind. If now he had to stay out of the office for a portion of his life he would devote that portion to learning something about engineering, the craft that impinged so largely on his business. He set to work to organise a very spacious workshop in the basement of his house at Wauna where he could learn some engineering quietly and secretly, away from the eyes of the engineers that he employed. Very soon he found out about the English magazine, the *Miniature Mechanic*, and had it sent to him by airmail every week with several other, and lesser, American publications. In a short time he became completely absorbed in his new interest, to the satisfaction of his sons and of his doctors.

He became conscious of a considerable debt of gratitude to the little magazine, the *Miniature Mechanic*. All his life he had heard his engineers speaking casually of milling, and he had not known what the process was. The magazine taught him in the first few issues that came to hand. He consulted with the engineer who maintained their three executive aircraft at the airport, and went with him to a machinery store in Seattle and bought a bench milling machine with a variety of cutters. He got his airplane engineers to install it in his workshop beside the lathe and drill press that he had already bought, and learned to use it; thereafter he could talk on equal terms on milling with his engineers and once or twice was able to correct them, which gave him immense pleasure. In lathe work it was the same.

Of all the contributors to the magazine he held Keith Stewart in the highest regard for the lucidity of his descriptions and his comprehension of the difficulties of the tyro. Once, in a difficulty, which he later realised to be due entirely to his own stupidity, he had dictated a letter asking for advice, hardly expecting to receive an answer. He had got one promptly, brief but helpful; the letter of a friendly man. Encouraged, he had written again some months later, and again, and help had never failed to reach him by return airmail.

This was the mental climate in which he received the sheets of typescript from Julie ten minutes after the call from Professor O'Leary in Ann Arbor. He sat in front of the big picture window in the sunset glow. The girl switched on a standard lamp and moved it to throw the light over his shoulder. He thanked her absently as he refreshed his memory of the call by glancing over her typescript.

'Say,' he said at last, 'he's got himself into a real jam. I wonder where this fisherman came from?'

'Would you like me to try and find out, Mr Hirzhorn?'

'No, leave that be. What time is it in Honolulu now?'

'Half past three.'

'Well, get me a call to Paul Setches. If he's not in the office, give his girl hell 'n tell her to find him and tell him call me at once.'

Ten minutes later he was speaking to the president of Setches and Byrne Inc. 'Say, Paul,' he said, 'this is Sol Hirzhorn. I want you to see if you can contact a man called Keith Stewart for me. He has been staying at the Beachcomber Hotel, but it may be that he's living on a fishing boat called the *Mary Belle* in the yacht harbour or someplace.' He went on to describe the situation, and read out the letter from Mr McNeil. 'The message is, tell him to contact his editor before going any further, and especially before sailing for Tahiti. After he's done that, ask him if he would call me. I'd like to speak with him. He can do that from your office if he's short of money.'

Mr Setches said that he would make some enquiries and call him back. Mr Hirzhorn laid down the receiver, and heaved his bulk up out of the chair. He went to the door of the next room, furnished half as sitting-room with a log fire and half as office. He said to Julie, 'I'm going down into the workshop. If Paul Setches calls again I'll take the call down there. Tell me when it's half an hour before supper, 'n we'll have a drink.'

'Okay, Mr Hirzhorn.'

He lumbered off, and went down to his workshop and stood fingering the tilting table of the clock that he had made and burnished with such loving care. He was a slower worker than Professor O'Leary, partly from inexperience and partly from age; on the other hand he was lavish with equipment and spared no expense in providing machine tools for the workshop. He stood fingering the half-machined bronze trunnions that would support the table, his mind far away.

Ten or eleven days had elapsed since the *Mary Belle* had been due to sail for Tahiti; there was little chance that Paul Setches would find her still in the yacht harbour. She could be half way to Tahiti by this time. But how to find a fishing boat in the wastes of the Pacific Ocean, a boat that had no radio?

Chuck Ferris had a yacht, and – yes, it was a yacht in Honolulu. He had been on a world cruise, and had interrupted it to fly back to New York or some damn place. Paul Setches had entertained Chuck Ferris and his party at the Royal Hawaiian, on the old man's instructions, and he had written later to say that the cruise had been interrupted. Sooner or later Solly Hirzhorn meant to fit Ferris hydraulics as a trial installation in one of his mills, on all of the conveyors. Amongst the many accidents that happened in the lumber business a man caught in the flying chains and sprockets of the conveyors was the most horrible: it always made the newspapers in all its gory detail. It created too much adverse comment. Sooner or later he would have to fit a trial mill with Ferris hydraulics throughout, and cut out every chain. It would be expensive; one million seven hundred thousand bucks was the Ferris estimate for the Flume River mill. Manny was for it, Joe said that it would never pay. His son Joseph was the treasurer of Hirzhorn Enterprises. It was for the boys to decide, but he thought it ought to be tried out one day, in one mill.

He started work upon the backplate of the clock, a thick sheet of brass which involved little but simple cutting and filing. He was, as yet, nowhere near the difficulties which had beset Professor O'Leary. He did not strain his dubious heart by cutting the thick metal with a hand hacksaw, as the Professor did; among his many machine tools Mr Hirzhorn had a little bandsaw powered by an electric motor which did the job for him in no time. He worked on happily for an hour or so and made good progress, till the telephone rang on the corner of the bench. He switched off the machine and picked up the receiver.

'I have Mr Setches on the line,' said Julie. 'Will you take his call down there?'

'Sure,' he said. 'Get it on the tape.'

A minute later he was speaking to Honolulu. 'Well, Mr Hirzhorn, I'm sorry to say he's gone. He sailed in this fishing boat, the *Mary Belle*, on Tuesday of last week.'

'Where were they going to?'

'Well, they told the harbour launch that they were bound for Hilo. That's on Hawaii, in the group of islands. But they never turned up at Hilo, and the gossip on the waterfront says they were bound for Papeete, in Tahiti. That checks with the letter that you read me out.'

'Why would they say that they were going to Hilo, then?'

'I'd say they were afraid of the formalities, Mr Hirzhorn. They'd have to have a French visa on their passports, for one thing, and the French don't like immigrants that haven't any money. That could be the reason. I wouldn't know.'

'What's going to happen when they get to Papeete, then? If they get there.'

'They'll find themselves in trouble, Mr Hirzhorn.'

There was a long silence. Paul Setches said, 'You still there, Mr Hirzhorn?'

'Okay, okay. I was just thinking. Did you hear anything about the captain of this fishing boat?'

'Well now, that's another thing, Mr Hirzhorn. The Customs officers say he's nuts. The yacht-owners down in the yacht harbour, they say he's a good seaman, but kind of simple. They don't any of them think he'll find Tahiti. You see, he's got no radio, no DF loop, no echo sounder, no Iron Mike – nothing. The ship hasn't even got an engine – no engine at all, not even an outboard. And the captain certainly wouldn't know how to use a sextant if he had one.'

It was bad. 'You're sure Keith Stewart sailed upon this boat?'

'Sure thing, Mr Hirzhorn. I spoke with the Customs officer that went after them in the harbour launch. They left without paying harbour dues. He said Keith Stewart was on board. That's when they said that they were bound for Hilo.'

'There wouldn't be any way to get in touch with them, would there?'

'Not that I know of. You see, they've got no radio.'

There was another silence while the old man's mind reviewed the situation. 'Tell me,' he said at last, 'is Chuck Ferris' yacht still in the harbour?'

'The *Flying Cloud*? Sure, she's still here. Mrs Efstathios, Chuck's daughter, she's living on board. Making quite a fool of herself with a band leader, Manuel de Silva. You know – *Music with Manuel*, on the TV.'

There was another pause. 'Well, thanks, Paul. Thanks a lot for what you've done. I'll have to think this over. Maybe I'll be in touch with you again, but that's all for the present.'

'Okay, Mr Hirzhorn. It's been a pleasure.'

The old man stood by the bench for a few moments. The conversation had interrupted the thread of thought connected with his work, and now he could not take up his enthusiasm again. He took off his working apron and hung it on the hook on the door, put on his jacket, and went up again to the big sitting-room with the picture window. Julie had drawn the curtains to shut out the darkness; she came in from her own office in surprise, for she had expected him to stay down in the workshop much longer. 'Will you have the drinks now?' she asked.

'Not yet,' he said. 'Say, that engineer Chuck Ferris keeps at Boeing – the one who came with him last time, Jim Rockingham ...'

'Rockawin, Mr Hirzhorn.'

'That's right. You know where he lives?'

'It's somewhere out by Renton,' she said thoughtfully. 'Elliott, or Maple Valley, or some place like that. I can find out easy enough. Do you want to speak with him?'

'It's more than I can do upon the telephone,' he said. 'What I'd like him to do is to come here right now and visit with me for a little while. See if you can get him at his home. If so, I'll speak with him myself.'

She went into her office and closed the door, and he sank down into his chair before the fire. Seventeen hundred thousand dollars was a lot of money, and on top of that they'd lose at least a fortnight of production from the mill while the conversion was going on. In terms of cash Joseph was probably right; hydraulic operation would put up their costs. But Emmanuel had the right idea. The day was passing when such ghastly accidents could be tolerated in the interest of cheap lumber. People thought much more of human lives now than they used to do. They must convert the Flume River mill for a trial of the Ferris system, but if they were to do that he would see that Chuck Ferris lent his yacht for a few weeks. Chuck had been trying to get his hydraulics into the lumber business for years.

Julie came in again. 'I called Mr Rockawin at his home,' she said. 'He left this afternoon to spend the weekend with his family at the Mount Rainier Mountain Lodge. Skiing.'

'See if you can get him there,' he said.

He sat on by the fire. Presently Julie came in again. 'Mr Rockawin is on the line right now,' she said softly. She moved the table with the telephone upon it closer to his side.

He said, 'That Jim Rockawin? Say, Jim, this is Sol Hirzhorn here. I'm speaking from my home at Wauna. I been thinking a lot about our Flume River mill. I'd like you to drive over 'n have a talk, if you can make it.'

It was a royal command and must be obeyed, but it was also dark and snowing at the Mountain Lodge, and fifty-five miles to go. 'I'd be happy to do just that, Mr Hirzhorn,' he said. The skiing with his family must be abandoned. 'Matter of fact, it's snowing pretty hard up here right now and I'm not too sure I'd make it down the road to the highway. I'll come now if you say, but I'd as soon start with the first light 'n be with you by ten o'clock.'

'Okay, Jim. I wouldn't want you to go and break your neck. Come over soon as you can make it in the morning. Meanwhile, I'll be talking with the boys.'

They hung up, and Jim Rockawin stood in deep thought by the row of telephones in little counter booths. He was a man of about thirty-five, dressed in ski trousers, slippers, and an ornamental pullover. This was business; he sensed it. This was the culmination of three years of patient, tactful work. He did not know exactly what would happen in the morning, but he knew this very certainly: Ferris Hydraulics was about to break into the lumber business.

His wife, pretty and kittenish, came downstairs from the bedroom floor, with their two daughters, twelve and ten years old. 'Who was that, hun?' she asked.

'Sol Hirzhorn,' he replied. 'I'll have to go and see him in the morning.'

'Oh, honey! Won't it do on Monday?'

He shook his head. 'I'm afraid not. Not when Sol Hirzhorn takes the trouble to find me here and ring me personally.'

She sighed, but she did not complain further. Men were like that, always putting business first – but after all, Sol Hirzhorn was Sol Hirzhorn. To her, born and bred in the state of Washington, the name was a household word, and she shared in the reflected glory of her husband's coming visit to Sol Hirzhorn in his fabulous home at Wauna. She said, 'Well, come and eat, anyway.'

'Just a few minutes,' he replied. 'I'll have to call Chuck about this.'

'Oh, honey!'

'He'll be going to bed,' he explained. He glanced at the watch upon his wrist. 'It's ten o'clock right now in Cincinnati.'

She left him, and took the children into the dining-room. He turned again to the telephone, and presently he was speaking to his employer in his home. 'I don't know what it is he wants, Mr Ferris,' he said. 'But it's about the Flume River mill, and it's business.'

'Say, that's great news,' said Mr Ferris. 'What was it that we quoted for the whole job? Just under two million, wasn't it?'

'Seventeen hundred thousand and some odd dollars,' said his representative. 'What will I say if he only wants to do a part of it?'

'String him along, 'n call me soon as you can. In that case I'd not go back to New York. I'd fly right out and be with you Sunday afternoon. He shouldn't split that job. I'd try to talk him out of it. It's not giving the system a fair trial.'

They talked a little longer. 'I guess I'll call you anyway, soon as I get away from him,' Mr Rockawin said. 'You'll be home tomorrow?'

'Sure I'll be home,' said Mr Ferris. 'This is big news. I'll just sit right here looking at the television, waiting for your call.'

Mr Ferris was a small, dynamic man with auburn hair, fifty-three years old. The war had made him what he was. In 1934 he had been a draughtsman in an aircraft drawing office, specialising upon undercarriage legs and on aircraft hydraulics generally. He had considerable inventive genius and even more business acumen. With the growth of aviation he had left the drawing office and had started a tiny specialist business in Cincinnati, working on a shoestring, getting all his machined parts made out by sub-contract. He had never looked back. His business had grown astronomically with the war; by 1945 he was the president of a twenty-million-dollar corporation, with a business that was comparable with that of Solomon P Hirzhorn.

For years he had wanted to get his finger into the lumber industry, which he considered to be antiquated in its equipment, judged by aircraft standards. Moreover, although his business was doing well, there was little doubt that rockets and guided missiles would replace the manned aircraft in the future to a large degree. Guided missiles were not well suited to hydraulic units, and even piloted airplanes were now flying at such altitudes that special precautions, with increased complexity, had to be taken to prevent the hydraulic fluid boiling in the pipes. He had already switched a considerable proportion of his manufacturing capacity to the automotive industry; the lumber business was another one. As a hydraulic engineer, he was turning his attention more and more to things that stayed on the ground.

He did his best to delegate authority, but his business grew too quickly; as soon as he found a man to take one section off his shoulders another enterprise was starting up, needing his guiding hand for the first year or so. In 1952 he had a nervous breakdown and spent three months in a very expensive home. He came out mentally refreshed and fit as a flea, divorced his wife and married another one, and began working sixteen hours a day again. In 1956 he had another breakdown, and went back into the home. This time his doctors impressed on him that he really must do less work and find more interests. They suggested a long sea voyage.

He did not want to die, and so he bought a large schooner yacht, the *Flying Cloud*, that had been built for a cinema magnate who committed suicide for an unmentionable reason. He had actually voyaged in her on his second emergence from the mental home across the Pacific and as far as Sydney. By that time he was so bored that he left her and sank into the deep chair of a Pan American airliner with an audible sigh of relief; in two days he was back in his office at Cincinnati and at work. Since then he had conscientiously tried to use his big yacht as his doctors had recommended, and he was actually on board her two or three times a year; each time intending a month's cruise or longer. Each time the office drew him back as with a magnet, because he had no other interest in his life except his very fleeting loves.

He sat in his home on Paxton Avenue between the Observatory and the Country Club, and waited for the call from Jim Rockawin. It came at about three in the afternoon, noon on the West coast. 'Look, Mr Ferris,' said his representative, 'this isn't just what I thought.'

'No business?' asked his employer sharply.

'I think he's going to order presently, but he's not ordering just yet. Emmanuel was there, the eldest son. They wanted to know if they could use the existing power house with the steam plant in it – throw out the steam plant and put our diesel motors and hydraulic generators in it. It's three hundred and eighty feet from the first conveyor. It's not a proposition, really, but I said that I'd go over Monday and take a look at it with them.' He paused. 'What Sol Hirzhorn really wanted was something different.'

'What's that?'

'He wants to borrow your yacht.'

'For crying out loud!' said Mr Ferris. 'What does he want with that? Go for a sail in it?'

'No. He wants to use it. Say, Mr Ferris, this is going to be mighty difficult to explain over the long-distance line. You got a tape machine there, so you could read it over later and make up your mind?'

'Sure I've got a tape. Wait while I fix it up.' There was a pause, and then he said, 'Go ahead.'

The representative had been collecting his thoughts during the pause and when he spoke it was clearly and lucidly. 'Some years ago Mr Hirzhorn had a bad spell with his health, and his doctors told him he must get himself a hobby in his home. Well, he started a workshop – not a wood workshop like the rest of us, but a real engineering workshop with lathes, milling machines, shapers, a drill press, oxy-acetylene welding, and God knows what. He took me down and showed me. I never saw anything like it. That's where he spends most of his spare time now. He's making some kind of a clock.'

The tape reel rolled slowly, steadily, as he spoke. He told the whole story, reading out the carbon copy of the letter from Mr McNeil to Professor O'Leary at Ann Arbor that he had got from Julie. 'Well, that's the way it is, Mr Ferris,' he said at last. 'He wants to borrow the *Flying Cloud* to go down to Tahiti and pick up these boys on their fishing boat, and do whatever this Keith Stewart wants to do, and bring him back to Tacoma so that Sol Hirzhorn can talk to him about his clock before he goes back to England. He'll pay you charter money, of course. I know this all sounds screwy, but that's the way it is.'

'You think he's going to convert that mill, Jim?'

'I'm sure he is, Mr Ferris.'

'Is he dickering with anybody else?'

'I don't think so. I don't think he'd do that. When the time comes he'll try and beat us down on the price.'

'Sure, sure.' That was a commonplace. 'Well, he can have the yacht, of course. Tell him that right away. Regarding charter money, it won't cost him a cent if he puts an order with us, otherwise – oh, tell him that we'll let him know. I've never chartered it before. No – tell him he can have it free, as long as he likes.'

'Whether he puts an order with us or not?'

'That's right. I shan't be using it.'

'I think that's very wise, boss, if I may say so. Sol's going to be very pleased.'

'Okay, okay. I'll play this tape back and call Captain Petersen. Now, you go over Monday and string them along. Better call me again Monday night, around six o'clock your time.'

Keith Stewart sat on the deck of the *Mary Belle* that Saturday afternoon twelve days out from Honolulu, while Jack Donelly slept below. He was very different now from the fat, rather unhealthy little man who had sailed upon the *Mary Belle*. Five days of seasickness had made him noticeably slimmer and more competent in his appearance. That had been over for a week. He now knew the sails and ropes by name and what they did. He could not yet pull down a reef alone, or he had never done so, but he knew how it was done. He still wore the tattered Panama hat as a protection from the midday sun, and he still wore the cricket shirt at night and when the sun began to burn, but most of the time he went clothed only in a pair of bathing shorts, and barefoot; from frequently stubbing his toes he had charted the position of every eyebolt in the deck and now avoided them. He was a very different man from the Keith Stewart who had boarded the aeroplane at Blackbushe.

By his noon latitude observations and by Jack's dead reckoning he judged that they were now about two degrees and forty minutes north of the Equator, about abreast of Christmas Island and probably two or three hundred miles to the east of it. Jack thought that they were closer than that. They had seen a patch of floating seaweed early that morning, and he had viewed it with concern. 'It could have come from anywhere,' Keith had protested.

'Not from the east it couldn't,' Jack grumbled. 'Seaweed don't last more 'n a few weeks in the sea. I never seen seaweed more 'n three hundred miles from land, 'n that

207

only when there's been an offshore gale. Want to put the thinking cap on for this.'

Later, in the *Pacific Islands Pilot*, Keith had found some evidence of an east-going current in the vicinity of Christmas Island at that season of the year. Jack grunted when he told him. 'I guess we're well away down to leeward,' he grumbled. 'Give me a shake up if you see any birds.' He went down below to sleep.

Later that afternoon Keith saw something better than a bird; he saw the smoke of a steamer. It appeared broad on the starboard bow on the horizon and grew fairly rapidly. It was the second ship that they had seen since leaving Honolulu, and Keith watched it with interest. Presently he could see the hull above the horizon, and realised that it was going to pass fairly close to them.

He called Jack Donelly from his sleep.

The captain put his head out of the hatch and studied the position. 'Bear up a little,' he said. He pointed with the flat of his hand at the direction he wanted Keith to steer to intercept the steamer, or pass close to her. Keith put down the helm and pulled in the main sheet and then the foresheet. 'That's okay,' said Jack. 'Keep her as you go.'

'What are you going to do?' asked Keith.

The captain looked at him in surprise. 'Why, stop her 'n ask where we are,' he said. It seemed the most natural thing to him. To Keith it seemed an appalling thing to do; this was a big ship, costing millions of pounds. But he was new to the sea, and he said nothing.

Jack said, 'We'll need a board.' He thought for a moment, vanished down below, and reappeared with the lid of the locker under his bunk, and, mysteriously, a piece of chalk. 'I'll take her,' he said, going to the helm. 'You write better 'n what I do. Put, W A N T P O S I T I O N.' A sudden doubt assailed him. 'Suppose they give it on a board in this latitude and longitude. You know how to put that out upon the chart 'n say where we are?'

Keith said, 'I can do that.' He bent to his task, making the letters as bold and clear as he could, and adding the word P L E A S E, which seemed quite unnecessary to his captain. Then he took the helm again while Jack went below, and reappeared with a large flag of the United States, which he bent on to the burgee halliards and hauled to the masthead upside down. He viewed it with satisfaction. 'It's a great thing to belong to a wonderful country like the ole United States,' he remarked. 'I mean, you Britishers, nobody wouldn't know if your Union Jack was upside down or not. But with Old Glory, there's no mistaking.'

The ship drew nearer on an intercepting course. She was a tanker, light in the water, painted grey all over like a battleship, and wearing the Blue Ensign. In fact she was a Fleet oiler that had discharged her cargo at Christmas Island and was now on her way back to England through the Panama Canal, but they had no means of knowing that. When she was less than half a mile away and they could hear the noise of her engines above the noises of their own passage they held up their board. Her engines slowed and stopped. Jack took the helm and put the ship about to windward, and let all sheets draw, and sailed down the length of her, Keith holding up their board. From the bridge an officer scrutinised it through glasses, waved to them in acknowledgement, and vanished inside. At the stern of the tanker Jack gibed the mainsail and sailed up the length of her again.

Two officers appeared upon the bridge holding a blackboard. The figures on it read, 'Lat. 02° 50' N, Long. 156° 55' W.'

Keith copied the figures down carefully, and went below and set them out upon his chart. He reappeared at the hatch. 'We're only seventy-four miles from Christmas Island,' he said.

'How far ought we to be?'

'About two hundred and fifty.'

Jack waved a salutation to the officers on board the tanker, and they waved back; they heard the engine room telegraph bells jangle and the big propeller turned in a flurry of foam under her counter. They sailed clear of her stern and got on to their course.

'Guess we'll put her up a point to windward, maybe a point and a half,' said Jack Donelly. 'I knowed that we was getting down to leeward by that patch of weed.'

That afternoon Mr Ferris called Captain Petersen from Cincinnati. 'Say, Captain,' he said, 'I was hoping to have joined you again before now, but I don't seem able to make it. I got a job for you to do, though. You know anything about a fish boat called the *Mary Belle*, been in the yacht harbour recently?'

'Sure, Mr Ferris,' said the captain in surprise. 'They sailed for Tahiti, maybe two weeks ago.'

'How many people were on board her when she sailed?'

'Two, I think. There was the captain, a guy by the name of Jack Donelly. The other was a kind of passenger. English, he was. Flew out here in an airplane from England, and wanted to get down to Tahiti. They came on board here to ask about the course.'

'They did? What was the passenger's name?'

The captain rubbed his chin. 'Well now, Mr Ferris – I'll have to try and think. It might have been Keats.'

'Keith. Keith Stewart. Say, he's a friend of Sol Hirzhorn and Sol's all het up about the risk he's taking going to Tahiti in that way.'

'He is?' The captain's jaw dropped. He knew all about Sol Hirzhorn and his empire of the forests. 'He hasn't any money,' he remarked weakly. 'That's why he went with Jack Donelly.'

His employer replied, 'Sol Hirzhorn hadn't any money when he started, nor had I. Now look, captain, I want you to get going right away 'n follow down the route that he'd have taken to Tahiti. If you catch up with him, that's fine. If you don't, then when you get to this place Papeete, 'n he's not there, you start looking for him back along the track. If you reckon they've got wrecked upon an island, visit every island they could be on. But find Keith Stewart.'

Captain Petersen's heart rejoiced; he was sick of Honolulu. This was a job after his own heart. 'What will I do when I find him?'

'You'll put the *Flying Cloud* at his disposal,' Mr Ferris said. 'Keep in touch with me by radio. His sister got wrecked in the Tuamotus or something, so he wants to go to one of the islands.'

'I know about that,' the captain said. 'He told me. He had a newspaper clipping about it.'

'Fine. Well, put the ship at his disposal for whatever he wants to do. But when that's over, I want him back in Seattle or Tacoma. You'd better come right back to Seattle with the *Flying Cloud*, 'n mind you bring Keith Stewart with you. Sol Hirzhorn wants to see him, and I've got a big deal on with Sol.'

'You shall have him, Mr Ferris.'

'Okay, then, for now. I'll maybe meet you in Seattle when you arrive, or else it might be Jim Rockawin. You know Jim?'

'Sure, I know Jim, Mr Ferris.'

'Well, keep me informed by radio, every two, three days, how it's going on.'

'There's just one thing, Mr Ferris.'

'What's that?'

'About Mrs Efstathios. Will she be coming along with us?'

There was a momentary silence. 'Gee,' said Mr Ferris, 'I forgot all about Dawn. She with you now?'

'She's on shore some place. I wouldn't know. Maybe the Royal Waikiki Hotel. *Music with Manuel*, Mr Ferris.'

'I know, I know.' There was a pause. 'What time is it with you?'

'A quarter of three, in the afternoon.'

'It's a quarter of eight with us. The doctor says I got to be in bed and asleep by ten. Say, if she comes within the next two hours, ask her to call me. Otherwise, tell her how things are yourself.' The captain made a slight grimace. 'She isn't Mrs Efstathios any more. The decree went through. She can move into a hotel on shore, or she can go along with you, or she can come right home. Tell her that – with love and kisses from Daddy. But you sail for Tahiti first thing in the morning.'

'Okay, Mr Ferris,' said Captain Petersen.

CHAPTER NINE

THE *MARY BELLE* made a quick passage to Papeete, covering the two thousand four hundred nautical miles in twenty-five days. They carried a fair beam trade wind all the way but for one day of slamming about in the light airs of the Doldrums on the Equator. They never made quite enough allowance for leeway and passed within five miles of an island which from the latitude they assumed to be Vostok; they bore up two points and passed close to Flint Island. Thereafter they had no difficulty. They sighted Tahiti with the last of the light one evening, hove to for the night and went to sleep, and sailed into the harbour of Papeete next morning.

They had need of all their sleep, because in Papeete every man's hand was against them. On their non-arrival at Hilo the French officials had been fully informed by Honolulu over the radio of their suspected destination, and there was quite a reception committee waiting for them on the quay. The harbourmaster in his launch directed them where to drop their anchor and took a stern warp to the quay. As soon as the vessel was made fast a gangway was put down on to their stern and the reception committee came on board. There was the harbourmaster, an official in plain clothes from the Bureau de l'Administration, an official in plain clothes from the Banque d'Indo-Chine, the Port Health Officer, and three gendarmes in uniform armed to the teeth.

There followed the most unpleasant hour that Keith Stewart had ever had to undergo. Jack Donelly could produce no ship's papers at all and no *carnet*, and was told that import duty would be due upon the value of his vessel on entry into French Oceania, probably at thirty per cent; he was also liable to a considerable fine. He had no bill of health. They would therefore be put in quarantine for thirty days and refused permission to land during that time; they would have to pay for the visits of the Port Doctor to inspect them each day, and would be fined for that as well. He had no passport and no visa to visit the islands; that merited another fine. Keith Stewart had a passport, which the police immediately confiscated. He pointed out that no visa was required for France; they said that a visa was required for French Oceania, and he would be fined. They were forced to produce what money and travellers' cheques they had, which the official of the Banque d'Indo-Chine immediately confiscated, giving them a receipt and stating that accounts would be opened to their credit, a first charge on which would be their liabilities to the Administration. After that the ship was searched very comprehensively by the gendarmes, who left everything in confusion. The party then departed, leaving one of the gendarmes as a guard at the head of the gangway. They were given to understand that they would be towed to the quarantine anchorage later in the day.

Jack Donelly was dazed and bewildered by this rude reception. 'I don't see why they want to be so mad about these tiddy little things,' he said. 'We haven' done nothing wrong.'

'I suppose we set about it the wrong way,' said Keith. He thought deeply for a few minutes while putting the nets back into the stern locker from which the gendarmes had dragged them. 'I think the thing to do would be to ask to see the British consul. Your consul, too.'

'I dunno,' said Jack. 'I never had no truck with one o' them. You ask to see yours first, 'n see what happens.'

Keith went to the gangway and spoke to the gendarme. He knew no French and the gendarme knew no English, so they did not get very far. 'British consul,' he said.

The man shook his head. Actually he was trying to convey the information that there was no British consul in Tahiti. Failing to get his message through, he tried again. '*Sous-officier viendra*,' he said. '*Après le déjeuner.* Spik English.'

Keith said, 'I *am* speaking English.' He tried to move past the man to find someone on the quay who would interpret, but the gendarme barred his way with his rifle. Keith returned disconsolate to the deck of the *Mary Belle*. 'I suppose we've just got to wait here till something happens,' he said.

There was a strong smell of vanilla in the port, and very soon little black iridescent beetles started to descend upon the ship in hundreds; they were everywhere. 'They'd be copra beetles,' Jack observed. 'Ma used to tell me about them, when we were little nippers. They can bite.' He shook himself. 'Let's have some chow.'

They went below and cooked a meal upon an even keel for the first time in nearly a month. Jack was depressed and uneasy. 'They couldn't take the *Mary Belle* away, could they?' he asked. 'I haven't got no thirty per cent. That wouldn't be thirty cents, would it? I mean, it's something more?'

'It means about a third of what the ship's worth,' Keith said. 'But don't worry about that. It's just a try-on. The consuls will put that right for us.' To console and amuse his captain he got out the little petrol generator set and started it with a flick of his thumb; there was still a little petrol left in the bottle. Jack Donelly got down on his hands and knees to watch it running. 'Smallest in the world,' he breathed, entranced. He raised his head. 'Those folks who came on board, the guy from the Banque and the guy from the Governor's office and all – they'd have been mighty interested to see this. Maybe we oughta showed it to them …'

They lay moored stern-on to the quay for most of the afternoon while Papeete slept; the sunlight on deck was torrid and they sweated it out upon their berths. At half-past three there was a step on deck, and Keith got up. It was the *sous-officier*, very smart; he held two folded papers in his hand, and gave one to each of them. '*Citation*,' he said. 'What you say – summons. To the law court, the Judge. On Monday, at eleven hours in the morning. I will come to fetch you.'

Keith opened the paper, but it was all in French. 'Can I see the British consul?' he asked.

'There is no British consul in Tahiti,' said the man. 'He comes sometimes from Fiji.'

'Ask about the American consul,' growled Jack.

'There is no American consul,' said the *sous-officier*. He eyed Jack, puzzled. 'You are American?'

'I'm a US citizen,' said the captain truculently. 'You better watch your step.'

Keith said, 'If you're going to take us to court we'll have to have an interpreter. We neither of us speak French.'

The man nodded, not unfriendly. 'There is here an Englishman, Mr Devenish, who was consul many years. I will ask him to come and talk to you.'

'Will there be an interpreter in court?'

'The Judge speaks good English. Perhaps Mr Devenish also, he will come.'

'Will we get fined?'

The *sous-officier* shrugged his shoulders. 'Perhaps.'

'What happens if we haven't enough money for the fine?'

The man smiled. 'You will have to get some. Sell the ship, perhaps. Otherwise, there is the prison.'

He left them with that to think about and walked up into the town. They sat in the cockpit, dejected, waiting for something to happen. 'I don't like all this talk about going to prison,' Keith muttered. He had an idea that a permit from the Governor would be needed before he could visit Marokota Island, and prison didn't seem the best place from which to forward an application.

'I'd rather go to prison than have these Frenchies steal the *Mary Belle*,' said Jack. 'I haven't got no thirty per cent. What they making such a fuss about, anyway? We done nothing wrong.'

'I haven't any money to pay fines,' said Keith. 'But they can't put us in prison. There must be some way out ...'

'Aw, that's nothing,' said Jack, comforting him. 'I been in prison. There ain't nothing to it.'

Keith raised his head in curiosity. 'What did you go to prison for?'

'Rape,' said the captain. He struggled to explain himself. 'Gloria didn't make no trouble about it. She'd ha' come with me again. But then her Ma turned nasty and she got a lawyer, 'n he said it was rape, 'n they made Gloria say all kinds of things in court. The Judge asked me why I did it 'n I didn't know what to say except that I just naturally wanted to. So he said it was rape too, 'n give me three months.' He stared out over the rippling, sunlit waters of the harbour. 'It was worth it,' he said simply.

Keith didn't know what to say to that. He grinned, and asked, 'What was it like in prison?'

'Okay,' said his captain. 'Good chow, 'n not much work. They got the radio in every cell so you can lie and listen to it all the time. Television twice a week, 'n a movie every so often. It's okay.' He paused in reminiscent thought. 'Gloria would have liked it fine,' he said.

Towards evening the harbour launch came back and towed them out from the quay to the quarantine anchorage.

They were sitting disconsolate on deck next morning, awaiting the arrival of the Port Health Officer, hoping to negotiate with him for supplies of water and fresh vegetables, when the *Flying Cloud* sailed in. She came from the north, and she came very quickly, for it was one of Captain Petersen's principles in making a passage that he carried sail all the time but whenever the speed dropped below about ten knots he put on his big diesel to help her along. In consequence he made good more than twice the speed of the *Mary Belle*; he had sailed from Honolulu thirteen days behind them, but arrived in Papeete only a day later.

He sailed into the harbour, for he liked to display his huge ship and the seamanship of his crew, the big diesel ticking over with the exhaust muttering beneath the counter ready to pull him out of trouble if the unexpected happened in the narrow waters of the harbour. But nothing did so. He rounded up neatly into wind heading for a vacant mooring buoy, a dinghy splashed into the water by her side, the square yards on the foremast came down together, the mizzen swung free above the wheelhouse and deck cabin, and in a couple of minutes a coir hawser had been passed through the eye of the buoy and returned on board.

Jack watched all this, entranced. 'Gee, that's pretty to watch,' he said. 'That Captain Petersen, he handles her fine. Great big ship she is, too.'

'You're sure that's the same one?' asked Keith. 'The one we went on board to ask the course? The *Flying Cloud*?'

His captain turned to him with scorn. 'Sure it's the same one. Think I wouldn't know her? See, she's got one topping lift rigged to the end of the mizzen boom. I never see that before. More often they have twins, rigged about two thirds the way along. 'Course she's the *Flying Cloud*.' He turned to Keith, a brilliant thought fresh in his mind. 'Maybe he'll come off and talk to us. He was real nice that day. Suppose he does, let's you and me show him the generating set. Smallest in the world. I bet he's never seen anything like that.'

He did not come that morning. They thought they saw him on deck inspecting the *Mary Belle* through field glasses, but the ships were nearly a mile apart and it was difficult to say. They thought they saw the woman on deck, too, though they could not be very certain about that either. Sails were furled quickly and neatly, a derrick was rigged and lowered a big motor pinnace into the water, and the captain went ashore to the Customs House Quay.

There was nothing to be looked at any more. 'Let's have some chow, 'n then lie down,' Captain Donelly said. 'I wish that red-head would get in one of them boats 'n come on over.'

The remains of the cornmeal in the sack was now a festering mass of maggots which neither of them had eaten for the last fortnight. Keith persuaded Jack to let him drop it overboard, which Jack did with regret. 'Cornmeal fritters are good chow,' he observed. 'Maybe we can get another sack here someplace.' He scooped up a double handful of the maggots for use as bait and put them in a tin, and consigned the sack to the deep. They had a meal, and lay down to sleep away the heat of the afternoon.

It was about three o'clock when the launch from the *Flying Cloud* came alongside. Captain Petersen hailed them. '*Mary Belle!* Anyone aboard?'

Jack stuck his head up out of the hatch. 'Sure,' he said. 'They won't let us go any other place.'

'Mind if I come aboard?'

'Okay.'

219

The launch drew alongside. Keith joined Jack on deck. 'We're supposed to be in quarantine,' he said. 'Is that all right?'

'That's okay,' said Captain Petersen. 'I've just come from the Harbour Office.' He swung himself over the bulwarks on to the deck of the *Mary Belle*, and turned back to the coxswain of his launch. 'Lay off a cable or so, or else make fast astern,' he said. 'I'll give a hail when I'm ready to go back.'

The launch sheered off, and he turned to the mariners, smiling. 'Well,' he said. 'You boys have certainly got yourselves a mess of trouble here.'

'Aw,' said Jack, 'that doesn't amount to anything. It's only paper stuff. We haven't done nothing wrong.'

There was a momentary pause. 'Well,' said Captain Petersen thoughtfully, 'that's certainly one way of looking at it. It may be the right way.' He sat down on the bulwark. 'Anyway,' he said, 'you aren't in quarantine any more. You can move into the quay now any time you like. I'll get my launch to give you a pluck in later.'

They stared at him, dazed. 'How come?' asked Jack Donelly.

'I got a bill of health for you in Honolulu and brought it along, and put it in with mine,' said Captain Petersen. 'It's only a sort of letter saying that there wasn't any cholera in Honolulu on the day you sailed. I told the Port Health Officer here that you'd left it in the office by mistake, and they asked me to bring it along.' In fact he had had to exercise a good deal of personal charm to soothe the ruffled feelings of the Port authorities in Honolulu, but he had got what he wanted in the end. He had been equally successful that morning in Papeete.

In fact he was a frequent visitor to Papeete in the *Flying Cloud* and had built up an enduring friendship with the Chef du Port over the years. The *Flying Cloud* was a large and an important yacht whose owners expected the captain to avoid irritating delays caused by minor French bureaucracy. There was only one berth in the port that had water and diesel oil piped alongside and from which a telephone connection could be made, at the Grand Quai, used by mail steamers at infrequent intervals. On his first visit to Papeete he had taken the Chef du Port out to lunch, and the Chef had mentioned the great interest that he took in the affairs of the St Xavier Hospice des Orphelins. Orphan asylums, said the Chef, with tears in his eyes, were usually short of money and this one was shorter than most, but they all did what they could to help the little homeless children of Papeete. Captain Petersen reckoned that he knew the form and he was duly touched, so deeply that he had pulled out his wallet there and then and had given the Chef two notes of ten mille francs for him to take up to the Mother Superior as a contribution, and that afternoon he had moved the *Flying Cloud* into the berth at the Grand Quai. He had been stunned that evening to receive an envelope delivered by hand containing a note of thanks from the Mother Superior and a receipt for the full amount. Out of curiosity he had walked up the mountain next morning and had found that the St Xavier Hospice des Orphelins was a real place, complete with nuns and children. Since then he had repeated this donation on every visit that he had made to Papeete, with the result that he had always got the best berth in the harbour and had had no trouble at all.

He squatted on the bulwark of the *Mary Belle* in the warm sunlight, a resplendent figure in a clean white uniform. He dealt first with Jack Donelly. 'They tell me that you're having trouble over no Certificate of Registration, and no clearance from Honolulu, captain,' he remarked. 'Cigarette?' He proffered an opened packet.

Jack Donelly took one and the captain lit it for him. 'I
didn't know you had to have them things,' said Jack.
'Nobody ever told me. Papers, aren't they?'

'That's right,' said Captain Petersen. He turned to the
man beside him. 'Tell me – are you Polynesian?'

'I'm a US citizen,' said Jack. 'I got born in Reedsport,
Oregon, 'n lived there all my life. Eleven of us there was –
eleven that grew up, that is. Seven boys 'n five girls. Dad
met Ma around these parts someplace 'n settled down at
Reedsport. They got married there, I guess.'

'Your mother came from round about these parts? From
these islands?'

'Ma came from a place called Huahine,' Jack said. 'She
was always telling me to get down to the islands and I'd be
okay. I guess she didn't know.'

'Let me get this straight,' said Captain Petersen. 'Your
mother was born at Huahine. She must have been
Polynesian?'

'I'd say she was. She was always kinda dark, darker than
the other women in our street. Not nigger dark, of course.
Just kinda brown.'

'Is she still alive?' asked the captain gently.

Jack shook his head. 'Ma died last year. She was always
wanting to get back to the islands, but she liked the
television too, so she was pulled both ways.'

'Did you tell them you were half Polynesian when you
got here yesterday? That your mother came from Huahine?'

Jack shook his great head. 'I didn't think of it. Nobody
ever asked.'

'Have you got anything to show your mother was a
Polynesian? Any birth certificate, or anything like that?'

'That's papers?' Captain Petersen nodded, and Jack shook
his head. 'I got my Navy discharge paper someplace,' he said
vaguely. 'Maybe I left it back home. But there wasn't
anything about Ma on that.' He hesitated. 'I dunno that

Dad and Ma were ever married, not in church, I mean. But they stuck together over forty years. That counts for something, don't it?'

'Sure,' said Captain Petersen. He turned to the man beside him. 'Look, Captain,' he said. 'They can't do a thing to you down here. You're half a Polynesian. The French run this colony for the Polynesians, not for the whites. They'll have to give you back your money. You won't come into court on Monday – they'll withdraw all the charges against you. They won't try and take your ship away from you. They won't expect you to have any papers for the ship. They'll forget about the passport. You rate down here as Polynesian, and this is your country.'

'I'm a US citizen,' said Jack. 'They won't take that away?'

The captain hesitated. 'No. But don't talk about it, just at first. Let things get settled down.' He paused, 'I'll see the Chef du Port soon as we go on shore,' he said. 'He'll fix everything for you.'

Jack was very pleased. He nudged Keith beside him, and said in a hoarse whisper, 'Show him the little generator. Smallest in the world.'

Keith nodded. 'You tell him,' he said.

Jack Donelly turned to the officer beside him. 'Say, Captain,' he said, 'Mr Keats's got something down below we'd like you to see. Smallest motor in the world, it is.'

'I'd certainly like to see it,' said Captain Petersen politely. They got up from the rail and Jack led the way down below. The captain touched Keith on the arm before going down the ladder. 'Would you be Mr Keith Stewart?' he asked.

Keith smiled. 'That's right,' he said. 'He always calls me Keats. He got it wrong first day.'

'Nice guy?'

'One of the best.'

'I'd say so, too.' He paused. 'I'd appreciate a bit of a talk with you later on, Mr Stewart.'

Keith glanced at him in surprise. 'Of course.'

They went down into the cabin after Jack Donelly. Captain Petersen took a quick glance around the stark bareness of the ship's interior. There was not even any varnish – just the bare wood, getting a bit dirty. There was a minimum of bulkheads and cupboards; the ship was little but an empty shell, devoid of any comforts. Yet she was efficient; the two forty-gallon barrels of water were properly chocked and stayed in place, and the very emptiness of her, the absence of tables, doors, and bulkheads, made it possible to get about inside her in a hurry. He knew fishing vessels, and he liked this one.

Jack lifted the little generator set reverently down from the fiddled shelf. 'Take a look at this, Captain,' he said. 'Smallest generator set in the world. Mr Keats here, he designed it all, 'n made every bit of it.'

The captain of the *Flying Cloud* took it in his hands and examined it with interest and growing respect. He lived at Midlake, close outside Seattle. Here his small son had several model aeroplanes fitted with mass-production compression ignition motors, and he had spent many hours contracting a sore finger twiddling the props to try to make them go. He was very familiar with small motors of that sort. This, which he now held cradled in his hand, was something totally different. It was a four-cycle motor, for a start, with tiny valves and valve springs and push rods, beautifully miniaturised, superbly made. The generator was, to him, a little wonder, with its delicately worked commutator and tiny brush gear.

'Does it go?' he asked in wonder.

'Sure it goes,' said Jack. 'Let's show him how it goes.' Keith filled the little tank with a drain of petrol, inverted the model to prime the carburettor, and flicked it into life with his thumb. The pea bulb lit, the note steadied as the governor came into action, and the model ran on steadily.

'Gee!' said Captain Petersen quietly. 'I never saw anything like it.'

He sat watching the model, deep in thought. He was one of the few people of the West Coast of America who knew anything about Sol Hirzhorn's secret hobby. His wife's youngest sister was engaged to a boy called Pete Homer who worked in a minor capacity upon the maintenance of the Hirzhorn executive aircraft at the Seattle-Tacoma airport. Pete had actually worked upon the installation of the machine tools in the basement workshop of Sol Hirzhorn's home at Wauna, and he had made several visits to the house since then to service minor defects or to take in stocks of materials. He had been warned not to talk about these matters because Mr Hirzhorn valued his privacy, but inevitably he had told his girl about these visits to the Hirzhorn home, and so they had become known in the family. Captain Petersen had heard that Sol Hirzhorn in his later years had taken to making small engines and clocks in the privacy of a fabulous workshop in his home. He had paid little attention to the rumour, but now it came back to his mind most forcibly.

He watched the little motor till it ran out of fuel and came to a standstill. 'Say,' he remarked, 'isn't that just dandy? I never saw anything like it. Is that right, that you designed it all yourself, and made it?'

Keith nodded. 'It's what I do,' he said, a little apologetically. 'I make things like this, and write about them in a magazine.'

'In a magazine?'

He nodded. 'The *Miniature Mechanic*. It's an English magazine.' He reached over to the foot of the bunk and opened his suitcase, rummaged in it, and produced a couple of copies of the little magazine. 'This is it,' he said. He gave one copy to the captain, who examined it with interest, and

NEVIL SHUTE

leafed the other through himself. 'This is the serial I've just finished now,' he observed. 'How to make a Congreve clock.'

'A Congreve clock?' Captain Petersen was puzzled.

'It's a clock that keeps time by a steel ball running on a zigzag track down an inclined plane,' Keith told him. 'Only it doesn't keep very good time. It takes thirty seconds for the ball to run down one way – then the plane tilts and it runs back again. It's quite fascinating to watch. Look – there's a picture of it, here. That's the one I made.'

Captain Petersen examined it with interest. 'You make these things, and then write about them, telling other people how to do it?'

'That's right.'

The captain glanced at the date of the issue; it was only six weeks old. 'Does this come weekly?' he asked.

Keith nodded.

'Does it circulate in the United States?'

'I don't think you can buy it on the bookstalls,' Keith told him. 'A good many copies, thousands, I believe, go to the States by post to subscribers.'

The captain sat in thought. Two days before he had left home in Midlake to come upon this cruise, Yvonne had brought Pete Homer in to supper. Some time in the evening Pete had mentioned that Sol Hirzhorn had started to build some kind of a clock; there had been an order for planished brass sheet five thirty-secondths thick that he had had to chase all round Seattle for, and take out to Wauna.

He raised his head and looked at Keith. 'Say,' he remarked, 'would you by any chance know a man called Sol Hirzhorn?'

In the hot cabin of the *Mary Belle*, with the strong scent of vanilla all around them and copra beetles everywhere, Keith's mind went back to Ealing nearly ten thousand miles away, to the long hours spent after Katie had gone to bed, answering the correspondence in his 'dirty' workshop in the basement, with Janice sleeping in the room next door converted from a scullery. 'I've had some letters from a Solomon PHirzhorn,' he said thoughtfully. 'Lives somewhere in Washington. That's the capital, isn't it? Somewhere south of New York?'

'That's Washington DC,' the captain told him. 'Sol Hirzhorn lives in the state of Washington, in the north-west. I live there myself. Do you know anything about Sol Hirzhorn?'

Keith smiled. 'He's got a secretary with an electric typewriter,' he said, 'I should imagine he dictates to her, from the length of his letters. He's building one of my Congreve clocks following the serial, and he's not very experienced, so he writes me a lot of letters, all of which need answering.'

'You answer them?' the captain asked.

'Oh yes. If people can't understand the serial and take the trouble to write to me about it, I always send them an answer.'

'You must have quite a correspondence,' said the captain.

'I have,' said Keith with feeling.

Captain Petersen sat in silence for a moment. 'I see I'll have to start and tell you things,' he said at last. 'The first is this. Sol Hirzhorn might be one of the wealthiest men in the United States. I wouldn't know about that. What I do know is that he's the biggest noise around our parts.'

Keith stared at him. 'What does he do?'

'Lumber,' said the captain. 'He's the biggest lumberman on the West Coast. He started off from scratch, working in the woods like any other guy. I'd say he's close on seventy years old now, and his sons have taken over the executive side of the business, it's a family concern. God knows how many mills they have, or how many forests they control. I'd simply be guessing if I tried to tell you how many hands they employ in Washington and Oregon, but it's an awful lot. They're quite a family.'

'The old man, Solomon P Hirzhorn – he's the one that's making my clock?'

'That's right. He thinks an awful lot of you, Mr Stewart. He got all het up about the risk that you were taking sailing from Honolulu to Tahiti in a fishing boat.'

Keith's jaw dropped. 'How on earth did he hear about me being here at all?'

The captain smiled. 'I wouldn't know. He wants you to go visit with him for a day or so on your way back to England, 'n help him with his clock, I suppose. Anyway, he wants to meet you.'

'I'd be very glad to meet him,' said the engineer. 'That clock's quite a tricky piece of work for somebody who's not very experienced. But how did he know I was here?'

The captain leaned forward. 'See here, Mr Stewart,' he said. 'Guys at the head of a big business with plenty of money and plenty of contacts all over the world, anything they want to get to know about they get to know. Now that's a fact. I don't know how Sol Hirzhorn got to know that you were here. But I do know this.' He paused. 'He's pretty well out of the business now. He only goes to the head office in Tacoma two or three times a week, they tell me. Other days he might fly out and visit one of the mills, or else fly in the helicopter to one of the clearings where they're cutting. He don't work much. Most of what work he does, he does at home. He's got his grand-daughter working for him as a secretary, a girl called Julie Perlberg. But I tell you, Mr Stewart, there's not a cat kittens in the State of Washington but those two know about it.'

Keith said weakly, 'I never knew that he was anything like that. I thought he was the ordinary sort of man who makes models in the evenings – like a dentist or a bank manager.'

Captain Petersen nodded. 'I guess you did. You made yourself a good friend when you answered all his letters. He got real worried about you, coming down this way. Of course,' he remarked, 'he knows why you came. He knows all about your sister and the wreck of the *Shearwater*.'

'For God's sake!' said Keith.

'There's one more thing I'll have to tell you,' said Captain Petersen evenly, 'and that's why I'm here. My boss is Chuck Ferris, of Ferris Hydraulics, Cincinnati. Mr Hirzhorn got so worried about you that he borrowed the *Flying Cloud* from Mr Ferris to put her at your disposal. My instructions on leaving Honolulu were to find you wherever you were and put the ship under your orders to take you to your sister's grave on Marokota Island and anywhere else you want to go. After that, if you're going back to England, Mr Hirzhorn suggested I might take you to Seattle in the *Flying Cloud* in order that you might visit with him for a day or two and help him with his clock.' He paused. 'I guess this is where I start to say "sir" when I speak to you, Mr Stewart.'

Keith stared at him, dazed. 'But that's fantastic!'

'It may seem so to you. It did to me, at first,' Captain Petersen admitted. 'But I'd say the way to look at it is this. You took a lot of trouble answering letters from a stranger, and maybe some of them were rather stupid questions. I wouldn't know. The fact is that you made a friend, and now this friend's going to a little bit of trouble to help you. That's fair enough. Look at it that way.'

Keith sat in silence for a minute. 'Could you take me to Marokota?' he asked at last.

'Sure. Take us about four days to get there. Spend as long as you like.'

'Would I get a permit from the Governor to go to Marakota? I mean, after all this trouble?'

Captain Petersen said, 'Forget it. We took the Governor to Bora-Bora one time. I've been to the Tuamotus six or seven times with the *Flying Cloud*. Romantic coral islands – that's what a party always wants to see. Lousy, dangerous places – I wouldn't want any part of them. You'll see more grass skirts in Honolulu than ever you'll see in the Tuamotus. But sure – we can go there.'

'It wouldn't be any danger to the ship?'

The captain shook his head. 'Not a bit. I'd take a pilot from here, somebody who knows the islands. There's no lagoon at Marokota that would take the *Flying Cloud*. We'd have to lie off under the lee, and send you in with the launch. But there's no difficulty about it.'

'Is it inhabited?'

'Probably not. It's got a few palms on it – coconuts. I think they come over from Kautaiva in the copra season – gather the nuts. I don't think anybody lives there permanently.'

'Do you think I could get a headstone for the grave made here, and take it with us?'

'Why, yes. There's a Chinese stonemason in the town, does that kind of work.'

'Would that take long?'

'A day, maybe. Suppose we get on shore before so long, and give the order tonight, he'd have it finished by tomorrow night.'

'How much would that cost?'

'I wouldn't know. You'd have to argue that one out with Mr Ferris and Mr Hirzhorn.' He turned to Keith. 'See here, Mr Stewart, sir – I know the way you're fixed. Mr Hirzhorn knows that, too. I got a radio from Mr Ferris that all expenses, of whatever nature, go on the ship. I'll give you an account of what you might call personal expenses when you leave the ship, and you can settle it with them.' He paused reflectively. 'You might have quite a job.'

230

They went up on deck and he hailed the launch. 'I got a cabin ready for you, Mr Stewart,' he said. 'When will you be moving in?'

'I'll stay here tonight,' said Keith. 'I've got a lot of things to fix up with Jack. Would it be all right if I come on board tomorrow?'

'Sure,' said the captain. 'I'll be moving in to the quay tomorrow; we'll need water, and top up with diesel fuel. Come aboard any time you say.'

The launch came alongside. He turned to Jack Donelly. 'How would it be if we give you a pluck in to the quay right now, Captain?'

'Suits me,' said Jack. 'Say, would there be any place where I could get a sack of cornmeal here? We've run out.'

Captain Petersen thought for a minute. 'Lim Hung Foo,' he said. 'He's your best chance. He's a marine store, nearly opposite your berth, but he sells everything. I think he might have it.'

Half an hour later the *Mary Belle* was berthed again stern-on to the quay with the Chef du Port smiling all over his face, and Keith was walking up with Captain Petersen to see the Chinese stonemason. He printed the simple inscription on the back of an envelope; the old stonemason took it and read it carefully, letter by letter. 'Understand,' he said '*parfaitement. Demain, le soir*. Will be finished.'

They walked back to the quay, and met Jack Donelly on the way to his ship carrying an enormous sack of cornmeal on his back as though it had been a feather. 'Bit coarser 'n the last sack,' he said. 'I like it that way. And not a maggot in it!'

'That'll be a change,' said Keith.

'Good thing we saved some maggots from the last sack,' Jack said practically. 'Else we wouldn't have no bait. A bit of fish goes good with cornmeal fritters.'

Keith arranged with Captain Petersen that he would move into the *Flying Cloud* when she berthed in the morning; the captain got into his launch and went off to the schooner, and Keith went on board the *Mary Belle* with Jack. After depositing the sack of cornmeal in the forecastle, Jack came and stood in the hatch looking at the big yacht at the mooring buoy. 'Captain Petersen, he didn't say nothing about that red-head coming ashore tonight, did he?'

Keith laughed. 'No, he didn't. I don't even know if she's on board. She probably stayed in Honolulu.'

'She's on board,' said his captain positively. 'I seen her.'

Keith had expected him to have bought a bottle of whisky with the sack of cornmeal but he did not seem to have done so; alcohol was not his major weakness. To take his mind off other matters Keith went below and started up the little generator set, and with the noise of the engine Jack joined him at once, and sat looking at it entranced. 'Smallest in the world,' he breathed. 'Captain Petersen, he liked it fine. But then, he's a seaman. He handled that schooner beautiful coming up to the buoy – just beautiful. I never seen it done better. Stands to reason that he knows a thing or two. He knows when something's worth looking at. Smallest in the world!'

Presently Keith said, "I'll be leaving you tomorrow, Jack. You heard what he said? I'll be moving into the *Flying Cloud* in the morning.'

'Fine ship,' said Jack. 'You make him learn you how to sail her, like I learned you how to sail the *Mary Belle*.'

'I'll be sorry to leave you,' Keith said. 'Where will you go now?'

'I guess I'll head for Huahine. Over to the west, ain't it? Shows on them charts of yours?'

'That's right. It's only about a hundred miles away, a little bit west of north-west on the compass.' He paused. 'I'll leave you the charts. They might come in handy.'

'Say, thanks.' The captain took them gingerly. 'These things take a bit of understanding,' he remarked. 'Just show me where it says Huahine.'

'There.'

'Oh, I see.' He pointed to the compass rose upon the chart. 'Is that what tells you which way to go?'

'That's right. See, a little bit west of north-west.' He traced the course with his finger.

'They don't put that on the atlas,' Jack observed. 'Wonderful the way they think of things, ain't it? Something new each year.'

He rolled up the charts presently and put them away. 'There's one more thing,' said Keith. 'I'll be moving out tomorrow. We'd better do some settling up.'

'What's that?' asked Jack.

'You remember I was going to pay you a hundred dollars for the passage, when we talked about it in Honolulu? Well, then there was the cost of the food.'

'That's right,' said his captain. 'You bought all the chow except the cornmeal, which was mostly maggots anyway, which didn't cost me nothing. That squares it off.'

Keith said patiently, 'The chow didn't cost a hundred dollars. Most of it came from the *Cathay Princess* at English wholesale prices. There's a good bit owing to you.'

'Aw, forget it,' said his captain. 'You sailed the ship half the time. I didn't pay you no wages.'

Keith stared at him helplessly; he knew better than to cross this man. 'That's not right,' he said. 'We agreed I'd pay a hundred dollars for the passage. The food came to about forty dollars. There's about sixty dollars due to you.'

'I got plenty to be going on with,' said Jack. 'I got forty, fifty dollars to get back out of that bank tomorrow.'

'I'd like to pay you what we said,' said Keith. 'Honestly I would.'

'Okay,' said his captain amiably. 'You pay me sixty dollars when the bank let go of it. Then I pay you seaman's wage, sixty dollars a month and keep. You give it me if you can get it from that bank, 'n I give it back to you. Then we'll be all square.'

His mind was made up and there was no use arguing with him; Keith had had this before. 'I tell you one thing,' he said presently. 'I'll leave the little generator set here, in the *Mary Belle*.'

Jack stared at him. 'Leave that here, with me?'

'That's right. This ship hasn't got a motor. She ought to have one.'

'Gee, Mr Keats, I couldn't take that!'

'I won't want it, Jack. I'd like you to have it.' He did not have much difficulty in persuading his captain to accept it. The big man held it reverently in his great hand. 'Smallest in the world,' he breathed. 'Say, I wonder what they're going to think of this in Huahine!'

Keith glanced at the bottle, which was practically empty. 'I'll get another bottle of petrol tomorrow sometime, and some lubricating oil, and a little oil-can. Then you'll be all fixed up.'

They slept presently, and in the morning Keith spent a couple of hours cleaning up the ship, which certainly needed it. Then he went up to the bank with Jack Donelly and, somewhat to his surprise, they were both repaid their dollars in full; he was not to know that Captain Petersen had been active in the city before him. In the bank he went through the ceremony of paying Jack Donelly sixty dollars for his passage and Jack counted it out carefully and paid it back to him as wages. They then went back to the *Mary Belle* and Keith picked up his suitcase.

'I'll be back on board this afternoon,' he said. 'I'll bring that bottle of petrol and the oil-can.'

He set off, carrying his suitcase, towards the *Flying Cloud*, now moored at the Grand Quai taking on water by a hose. A white-clad sailor from the yacht came hurrying to meet him, and took the suitcase from him.

He walked down the gangway on to the deck of the *Flying Cloud*, an incongruous figure perspiring in his rather inexpensive blue suit purchased in Ealing and suitable for the English climate. Captain Petersen came out of the wheelhouse and welcomed him aboard. 'I'll show you your cabin,' he said. 'It's the one that Mr Ferris uses normally, with a private bath. I think you'll find it comfortable.'

In the luxury of the cabin Keith said diffidently, 'I think I'll have to get something lighter to wear – tropical clothes of some kind. This suit's too hot altogether, and I can't go round this ship in a pair of bathing trunks, like I did with Jack Donelly.'

'Lots of them do that,' remarked Captain Petersen. 'You'd be surprised. Middle-aged women, too, in not much more.' He glanced at the blue suit. 'That suit will be fine for Tacoma in the winter, and we'll probably be there before so long. Clothes are a problem on this kind of trip.' He opened the door of a big wardrobe. 'Say, Mr Ferris, he leaves quite a bit of stuff on board, and you're much the same build. I'd pull out some of these suits, see if they will fit you, before buying anything. It's not worth it, just for a few days.'

Keith glanced at the array of gleaming Dacron and silk tropical suits, the white neckties, the white shoes. 'Are you sure that will be all right?' he asked.

The captain nodded. 'Sure. I'll get everything washed and cleaned before he comes again. He'd want you to have the use of the things, and there's no sense in buying anything.'

He left Keith in the cabin. He had a very welcome shower, his first for a month, and dressed in the soft linen and the light hot-weather grey suit of a wealthy American. He went out a little self-consciously and up into the deck lounge, where he ran into the thirty-year-old red-headed woman that he knew as Mrs Efstathios. She got up to welcome him,

'Say,' she said, 'you must be Mr Keith Stewart. I've heard such a lot about you. My name's Dawn Ferris, and my Pop owns this ship. He never uses it, but he just likes to have it around. Aren't those his clothes you're wearing?'

Keith was embarrassed. 'I hope it's all right,' he said. 'Captain Petersen told me it would be.'

She laughed. 'Sure. Everyone that comes on board uses Pop's clothes. He's never here to use them himself. Say, I remember when you came aboard in Honolulu, only I didn't know who you were then. When did you arrive here?'

'We got in the day before you. The day before yesterday.'

'You must have made a quick trip – we didn't waste any time. Mr Hirzhorn, he got really worried about you going in that little boat, without any motor or anything. Say, that big ape who came on board with you – I forget his name – is he here, too?'

'Jack Donelly? Oh yes, he's here. The *Mary Belle*'s moored further up the quay, that way. You can't mistake her; she's the only boat that's got tanned sails.'

'Is that so? I got some shopping to do presently; I'll take a look and see. Captain Petersen was saying we'd be leaving in the morning for the Tuamotus.'

Keith nodded. 'I've got to go there to see about my sister's grave. I'd like to leave as soon as the headstone's finished. That's supposed to be tonight. Will you be coming with us?'

She said, 'Well now, I don't know. I've seen the Tuamotus so many times, and it seems like this would be a kind of private party. The Captain says he'll have to come back here anyway to bring the pilot back before leaving for Seattle. I was thinking maybe I'd move into the hotel for three or four days while you're away, and explore the island.'

'I should think that would be very interesting,' said Keith.

'It might be,' she said doubtfully. 'They all speak French here and I don't, which makes things kind of complicated.'

They chatted together for a little in the deck saloon. Then she said, 'Time I went on shore if I'm going. Say, if I'm not back on board for lunch, tell the captain not to wait. If I find a decent-looking restaurant that can understand what I'm saying, I'll eat there.'

She picked up a broad-brimmed sun hat with a gaudy ribbon, and went off, and up the gangway to the quay. Keith went out on deck and started to explore the polished cleanness of the ship, an entrancing occupation. The boatswain found him and showed him the anchor winch forward and the winches at the foot of each mast. 'All hydraulic from a central power generator in the engine room,' he said proudly. 'Used to be manual, except the anchor winch, which was a great big electric cow of a thing. When Mr Ferris bought the ship, first thing he did was rip all that lot out and send down his engineers from Cincinnati to make a proper job of her. She's all hydraulic now, steering and all. Ferris Hydraulics.'

Keith was very interested indeed, and spent some time examining the winches and their reduction gears, which evoked his admiration for their clean and efficient design. From the deck the boatswain passed him on to the chief engineer, who took him down into the spotless engine room to show him the power generator, the main diesel, and the stand-by diesel. He spent an hour of sheer delight down there, and was finally discovered there by the steward, telling him that lunch was ready. He had spent the morning with machinery so clean that he hardly had to wash his hands.

He sat down happily to lunch with Captain Petersen, and gave him the message from Mrs Efstathios.

On shore Dawn Ferris wandered through the town, looked unintelligently at the big cathedral, wandered back to the waterfront and looked at the French frigate with the sailors with red pom-poms on their naval caps, and wandered along the quay looking vaguely for a restaurant, past rows of native fishing boats and yachts. Near the end of the row she came upon the *Mary Belle*, which she recognised by the tanned sails. Jack Donelly was sitting on the foredeck with his legs dangling over the side, fishing with a hand-line; a little pile of small, silvery fish lay on the deck beside him. He did not believe in buying food when there was food in the sea. He wore a pair of old blue jeans and nothing else; with his deeply bronzed torso he was a fine figure of a man.

Dawn stopped, and said, 'Hullo, big boy!'

Jack looked up, replied, 'Hullo,' and went on fishing.

She asked, 'What are you catching?'

He jerked a little fish out of the water and added it to the pile. 'These.'

'Are they good to eat?'

'I guess so. They look all right.'

'Are you having them for dinner?'

The conversation was taking his mind off fish, but anyway he had enough. Enough, maybe, for two. 'I guess so,' he said. 'Fish fried with cornmeal fritters are good chow.'

She was suddenly weary of the sophisticated meals on board the *Flying Cloud*, and she had difficulty in under-standing the French writing on the restaurant menus. 'Cornmeal fritters!'

He raised his head. 'Say, can you cook cornmeal fritters?'

'Can I cook cornmeal fritters! Try me and see.'

He got to his feet, an amiable giant about six feet four in height in his bare feet, all bronzed. 'Come on down, 'n let's see how you can do it. I'll fetch the sack aft into the cabin.'

In the *Flying Cloud* Keith Stewart was enjoying his first civilised meal for a month, not altogether sorry to be relieved of the somewhat monotonous diet of the *Mary*

Belle. Over lunch he told Captain Petersen that he had given the little generator set to Jack Donelly in lieu of passage money. 'He's a nice kind of guy,' said the captain. 'He may not know much navigation, but he seems to get from A to B without it. Did you help him much upon the way?'

Keith shook his head. 'I learned to take a noon sight for latitude. The officers of the *Cathay Princess* taught me. But the course was only a point or two east of south, and there was never much more than a hundred miles difference between my sight and his dead reckoning. He'd have got here perfectly all right without my sights.'

The captain laughed. 'Takes us all down a peg or two. It's wonderful the way they do it.' He paused. 'Make a good boatswain,' he said thoughtfully. 'I'd rather have him in the ship than some of the ones we got.'

He sat smoking with the captain for a time, and then went on shore and bought a little oil-can at a hardware store, with an empty bottle, and took them to a filling station to get filled with petrol and oil. With these in hand he walked along the quay to the *Mary Belle*. Jack Donelly was sitting in his blue jeans in the companion, looking at peace with the world and very pleased with himself.

Keith went down the gangplank to the aft deck and stepped over the tiller. 'I brought the gas and oil for the little motor,' he said. He showed them to the captain.

'Gee, that's real nice,' said Jack. 'Right kind o' gas and right kind of oil?'

Keith nodded.

Jack was very pleased; everything in the world was rosy. 'That'll keep her going a long time.'

'I'll just take them down and put them on the shelf,' said Keith. 'Then you'll be all set.'

Jack did not move his big frame from the companion. 'Don't go down just yet,' he said in a low tone, but distinctly. 'Wait while she gets her dress on.'

Keith stared at him in horror. 'Wait while *who* gets her dress on?'

'The red-head,' Jack informed him. 'Some foreign name I forget. But she don't talk foreign.' He added thoughtfully, 'or act foreign, either.' He broke into a happy smile.

Keith thought only of escape from this situation. He thrust the bottle of gas and the oil-can into Jack Donelly's hands. 'Here, take these,' he said. 'I'll come over and see you later.'

'Okay,' said Jack phlegmatically. 'Be seeing you.' Friends and women, he knew, never really mixed.

Keith fled up the gangplank and walked rapidly away up the quay towards the *Flying Cloud*. On deck he passed Captain Petersen and said something incoherent about going to lie down in his cabin, and went and hid himself below. His first instinct was to keep well out of sight and avoid a meeting with Dawn Ferris. Whatever her problem was, he didn't want to get mixed up in it.

He lay on his bunk petrified with terror, waiting for the storm to break, till the steward tapped on the door and entered at about five o'clock. 'Captain says he's sending up a boy with a hand-truck to fetch the gravestone,' he said. 'He wanted to know if you'd like to walk up with him, see the stone before it leaves the yard.'

He ought to do that. Apparently the storm hadn't broken yet. 'Tell the captain I'll be with him in a minute,' he said. 'I'll just put on my shoes.' As he sponged his face he thought of the gravestone and of Jo, his sister, and he thought of how she would have laughed, for her sense of humour had been broad. He was smiling, a little furtively, himself as he left the cabin to meet the captain up on deck.

As they strolled up the hill he asked casually, 'Is Miss Ferris coming with us to Marokota?'

'Not this time,' said Captain Petersen. 'She's seen it all before. She packed two suitcases and moved into the hotel

240

while you were resting. We'll pick her up when we come back here with the pilot, Thursday or Friday.'

'She won't be on board for supper?'

'I don't think so. She said not to disturb you, but just tell you hullo, till Friday.'

They walked into the stonemason's yard. The stone lay upon the bench all ready for delivery, a slab of purple-coloured slate engraved with the simple inscription that he had chosen. He passed his hand over it; when he had done this for Jo and seen it erected there was no more that he could do for her, except to look after Janice. He would see this stone set up above the grave and then he would go away; it was very unlikely that he would come back to see it again. Still, it was something to have got this far; when he had walked out of Mr Carpenter's office in Bedford Square he had intended to try and make it but had never really thought he would succeed.

The captain was talking to the old Chinese stonemason, who was drawing a little diagram for him upon the back of an envelope to show him how to set up a gravestone so that it would not fall over as the years went by. He arranged that the boy with the hand-truck should bring a bag of cement down with the gravestone to the ship that evening, and he paid the stonemason in American dollars to his great content. Then they were walking down the hill again towards the quay in the soft tropical dusk, through the myriad evening smells of Papeete.

On deck the captain turned to him. 'I never drink at sea, myself, or in harbour before sunset. But this is after sunset, sir.' He smiled. 'Would you join me in a highball?'

Keith wasn't quite sure what a highball was, but he appreciated the offer. 'Have you got any beer?' he asked diffidently.

'Sure we've got beer. We've got pretty near every kind of liquor in this ship. We've got dark beer, and we've got a kind

241

of lager beer.' It was still hot in the harbour and Keith chose the lager; they sat down in the long canvas chairs on the aft deck and the steward brought them iced beer and rye on the rocks.

Presently Keith asked, 'What time are we going off in the morning?'

'Any time you say,' Captain Petersen replied. 'Have you got any more to do on shore?'

'No. I'd like to get away as soon as possible.' Before the Dawn Ferris storm blew up, he thought. He found it impossible to imagine what was going to happen to Jack Donelly, or himself. If he were to complete his mission to Marokota, however, the sooner he put a considerable distance between Dawn Ferris and himself, the better. 'Sail tonight if you like,' he said.

'I've got it all fixed for tomorrow morning first thing,' said Captain Petersen. 'Hands to breakfast at six, pilot on board at seven and get under way. Then we have breakfast about half-past eight, when we've got sail set and all clear.' A sudden thought struck him. 'Would you be likely to feel sick? We could have breakfast here any time you say, and get under way after.'

'I shan't feel sick,' said Keith. 'Not after a month in the *Mary Belle* with Jack Donelly. At least, I don't think so. No, that would suit me fine.'

He spent that evening with the captain, dining with him quietly in the big saloon, sitting with him on deck in the vanilla-scented tropical night, watching the reflections on the water. He heard a good deal about Captain Petersen's family and home at Midlake, and the captain heard a good deal about Keith's home in Ealing, and about Katie, and about Janice, and about the wreck of *Shearwater*. Captain Petersen had already picked up local information about that in Papeete. 'They had bad luck, Mr Stewart,' he said simply. 'When that hurricane blew up they were in just the worst possible position they could be in, with no sea room for the change of wind.' He sat in thought for a minute. 'I believe in that position I'd have turned right round and headed back to the south-east with the engine at full power, and chance it turning south before it got to me. I think that might have been a better bet, but it's hard to say. But anyway, they'd only got a little motor, hadn't they?'

Keith nodded. 'That's another thing,' he said. 'From what I hear, the motor was taken on shore from the wreck and covered up. It's probably worth something. If I could get it back to England I could work on it myself and recondition it. Do you think we could get it on board and take it with us to Seattle, and ship it home?'

Captain Petersen considered the matter. 'We can't berth there to get it on board,' he said. 'We've got to lay off shore while you're on the island, and send the launch into the lagoon. It won't be much good now, you know. Not after being in the sea.'

'I'm not so sure,' said Keith. 'Things like that often look a fearful mess with external damage and corrosion, but when you strip them down, they're not so bad. It's got wet liners to the cylinders, so they're replaceable quite easily in England. New pistons and liners, and a coat of paint. It might fetch a couple of hundred quid by the time I've done with it.' He paused. 'Enough to pay my passage back to England,' he said smiling.

'Oh, sure.' It was difficult to keep remembering that this intelligent little man, who had travelled half across the world and who was thought of so highly by so many influential people, had practically no money at all. 'How much do you think it would weigh?' he asked.

'Three or four hundred pounds. I shouldn't think it could be more.'

The captain nodded. 'I should think that's about it. We can do that, Mr Stewart, if that's what you want. I'd beach the launch in the lagoon. Then we'd need six or eight hands ashore and some baulks of timber, get it in the launch and rig a wire strop round it.' He thought for a minute. 'Bring it off to the ship – that's easy. Then to get it on board from the launch to the ship in the open sea ...' He thought deeply. 'I'd make up special coir bolsters, four of them, pretty thick and about eight feet long, for the launch to ride against while we lift the motor on board with the launch derrick. That'll be okay. We can fix that for you, Mr Stewart.'

'There wouldn't be any risk of damage, would there?'

'Only paintwork, at the most.' He thought again. 'We can fix that when we come back into harbour here at Papeete before sailing for Seattle. Get some planks when we get back here, too, and knock up a packing case for it, so it'll be all ready to ship back to England from Seattle.'

'That would be fine,' said Keith. 'I'd give it a bit of first aid before closing up the case. Wash it well out with fresh water, crankcase, cylinders, and all, and leave it to dry in the sun and wind. Then pour a lot of oil into each cylinder and fill the crankcase up with oil. I don't think she'll have come to much harm.'

'Maybe we're too apt to scrap things in the States,' said Captain Petersen. 'The engineers can lend a hand with that.'

They sat in silence for a time. 'There's just one other thing,' said Keith. 'Marokota is uninhabited at this time of year, isn't it?'

'So they tell me,' said the captain. 'There's no regular settlement upon it. The people come there every now and then to pick up the nuts, but they make the copra upon Kautaiva. They happened to be there when *Shearwater* got wrecked, but of course they couldn't do anything.'

'I know ...' He hesitated. 'Would it be very difficult for me to spend twenty-four hours alone upon the island, after we've set up the gravestone?'

The captain turned his head. 'There's no difficulty in that from my point of view, if that's what you want to do. We shall be standing off and on offshore. We can do that for a week if needs be. But there's nothing there, you know. I don't know even if there's any water.'

'I could take that with me, with some sandwiches ...' He turned to the captain. 'I don't suppose I'll ever come back here again,' he said simply. 'I don't suppose that Janice – Jo's daughter, who's going to live with us – I don't suppose she'll ever come here. I want to take a lot of photos – an awful lot of photos, from all kinds of angles, and that'll all take time. I'd rather not be hurried by having other people about. I'd like to have your little rowing boat and go out to the wreck and take some photos of that. And – well, she was my only sister. I'd just like to be there alone for a bit.'

'Sure,' said Captain Petersen, a little huskily. 'I'll get a pack made up for you – blankets. It could be cold at night. Beer, water, sandwiches. What we could do is, go in in the launch with the gravestone, towing the dinghy behind. Set up the gravestone and leave you with the dinghy, go back to the ship. Then come off again next day and load up the engine into the launch, and pick you up. How would that be?'

'That would be grand,' said Keith. 'I could make a good inspection of the engine in an hour or so and decide if it's worth taking back to England. If the engine room could let me have a few spanners it might help.'

'Sure. You got plenty of film?'

Keith nodded. 'I've got three new rolls, over a hundred exposures. I got them here today. I'll be all right for film.'

He went to bed soon after that and slept soundly in Chuck Ferris' cabin, the first night that he had had in comfort for about a month. He wondered, as he went to sleep, about Dawn Ferris; no complaint had come from her, or, if it had, Captain Petersen had not told him. Perhaps the omnipotence of Sol Hirzhorn could protect him, even against that. In any case, apparently they were leaving in the morning. He must take things as they came. He slept.

He was roused by the bustle on the decks at dawn, had a shower and dressed in an open-necked shirt and slacks, and went up on deck. The steward found him and brought him coffee and biscuits, and he stayed on the aft deck out of the way of the seamen, watching the processes of getting the ship to sea. It was all very different from the *Mary Belle*, a matter of ordered movement controlled by an occasional whistle from the boatswain. The pilot came on board, dark-skinned and French speaking, and was welcomed by the captain. Then the main diesel started below his feet with a rumble that steadied to an even purr. The springs were taken aboard, bow and stern lines singled up and brought back on board by a harbour boat. Captain Petersen moved into the wheelhouse, the stern lines were cast off, the engine room telegraph bell sounded, and the *Flying Cloud* moved forward from her berth into the main waters of the harbour. She turned and made for the entrance, hoisting the mainsail as she went, followed by the foresail and the mizzen, causing Keith to retreat into the deck saloon.

From Tahiti to the Tuamotus is a dead beat into the easterly trade wind at that time of year. Captain Petersen put his vessel under all plain sail and kept his engine going hard, taking in the mainsail for the hours of darkness. The distance to Marokota is about three hundred miles, and it took them four days of hard slogging against the wind, a restful and invigorating four days for Keith. He learned a good deal about the management of a large schooner yacht, and took the helm for several spells, to the interest and amusement of the captain. He found that sailing the big schooner was not very different from the sailing of the *Mary Belle* once you had got accustomed to the wheel instead of tiller, and the size of her, and the speed.

They were approaching Marokota Island on the evening of the fourth day. Captain Petersen hove to at sunset, unwilling to venture in among the reefs in the hours of darkness, and they lay hove to all night with the engine stopped so that they could hear breakers but with an engineer on watch ready to start up if necessary. With the first light they got under way again, and by ten o'clock they were hove to under the lee of the island, on the west side of the encircling reef.

Captain Petersen stood at the door of the deckhouse staring at the reef through glasses. He lowered them and handed them to Keith. 'That's the wreck,' he said. 'She went on from this side. Just past that grey coral, where you see those timbers sticking up. That must be *Shearwater*.'

Keith stared at the timbers, washed by the sea. It seemed incredible that this should be all that remained of the yacht that he had been on board in the Hamble River, only six or seven months before. He lowered the glasses. 'Would I be able to get near her from the other side?' he asked.

The captain lifted the glasses again. 'I should think so, in the dinghy. it's on the lee side of the island, so there's not much sea.' He lowered the glasses. 'It looks quite calm in the lagoon.' He hesitated for a moment. 'Like me to come with you in the dinghy?'

Keith shook his head. 'I'd rather be alone.'

'Okay.'

They rigged the launch derrick, put the coir bolsters over the lee side, and, steadying the big launch with guy ropes, watched their opportunity and put her in the water. They lowered the gravestone cased in a wooden frame into the launch with the sack of cement, a breaker of water, a pick, and a couple of shovels. Then they lowered down Keith's pack for the night, and dropped the ten-foot dinghy into the sea with a small davit. The captain got down into the launch with Keith, four seamen joined them, and the launch cast off and made for the narrow passage through the reef into the lagoon, towing the dinghy behind.

The chief engineer leaned upon the rail with the Second, watching the boats as they went in to the shore. 'If he comes off with that engine in the morning we'll have to carry it on deck,' he said. 'Get Sammy to lash a tarp down on the deck, somewhere there.' He jerked his head. 'Don't want to get the deck messed up with oil and rust.'

'Okay,' said the Second. 'I'll see Sammy. Beats me what he wants with all those tools.'

'Going to examine it,' he said. 'See if it's worth salving.'

'With a hammer and cold chisel and a hacksaw?'

'Loosen off the nuts that got rusted up, or cut them off. That's what he said.'

The Second turned from the rail. 'Shouldn't think the engine would be worth the salving, after treating it like that.'

*   *   *

In the sunset Keith Stewart sat alone a little distance from the grave. He had done all that he had to do, and he had taken a good many photographs of the grave, the island, and the wreck out on the reef. He had turned the motor on its side, and he had taken off the sump, cleaned out the interior, and put it back again, replacing all the bolts and screwing them up tight. Darkness was approaching and he had finished all the major jobs. He sat eating his sandwiches upon the beach, and drinking his beer. In the morning he would take a few more photographs, and then he would be ready to return to England.

The gravestone stood erect behind him, set in a wide box of semi-liquid concrete, stayed upright with ropes to pegs driven into the coral sand. They would leave it so. The concrete would set into a solid mass when they had gone; the ropes would slacken off and rot away in time, but the stone would stay erect to mark the grave with its simple inscription to be read by any who should come to Marokota.

He finished his meal and sat looking out over the tropic sea in the fading light, a little sadly. This was the end of it. This was the end of something that had begun in a slum street of Renfrew near to Glasgow on the far side of the world, through the joys and tears of childhood, the Tiller Girls, John Dermott and the naval life, and Janice. Who could have thought that it would all end here, on an uninhabited island in the Pacific Ocean?

He got to his feet and moved over to the grave. He took the steel egg from his pocket, the grey, case-hardened egg that he had made for Janice back in Ealing, on the evening he had told her of her mother's death. 'Jo,' he said quietly, 'this is one of the eggs I made for Janice to go with the duck. It's the only thing I've got of hers to leave with you. And, Jo – I'll do my best.'

He scraped a little hole before the gravestone, and buried the egg in the sand.

CHAPTER TEN

THE *FLYING CLOUD* sailed back into the harbour of Papeete three days later, having made the voyage downwind under sail alone. For much of the time Keith Stewart had been working on the engine secured on deck upon a tarpaulin, assisted by one or other of the engineers. They had removed the cylinder head and washed out the cylinders with fresh water and had hosed out the crankcase, Keith rejecting a proposal that they should take off the sump again as being quite unnecessary. They had dismantled the magneto in the engine room and discovered that all that it required was a new contact breaker; they had assembled everything again and filled the crankcase and the cylinders with oil. By the time they sailed into the harbour the engine was ready for crating for shipment to England.

They approached the harbour in the late afternoon. In the wheelhouse Keith asked Captain Petersen, 'How long will we be here?'

'You got anything you want to do?'

'No. The sooner I start home the better.'

The captain nodded. 'It's too late to go into the quay now – it'll be dark. If there's a buoy to spare I'll lie on that for the night. Go into the quay first thing in the morning. We'll want to top up with diesel oil and water, and a few stores. Get some planks and timber for the packing case, put a little paint on the ship's topsides where the coir mats rubbed, pick up Miss Ferris, get a bill of health and clearance, and send a radiogram to Cincinnati. It ought not to take us longer than a day. I'd say that we'll be on our way day after tomorrow.'

Keith nodded. 'Say goodbye to Jack Donelly.'

'Sure. See if you can find out where he's heading for, and if we can do anything.'

They sailed into the harbour before sunset with the motor ticking over, and rounded up to a vacant buoy. When the bristle of mooring and stowing sail had subsided a little the captain came aft, to find Keith on the aft deck with the glasses in his hand. 'Funny,' he said. 'I can't see the *Mary Belle* anywhere. She's not in the place where she was.'

The captain scanned the shore line and the moored vessels, then took the glasses from him and searched with them. 'She's not there,' he said positively at last. He must have sailed someplace.'

Keith was disappointed. 'I didn't think he'd have done that. I wanted to thank him, and to say goodbye.'

'Maybe he's gone out fishing, be back tomorrow,' said the captain.

The men were putting the launch into the water with the derrick. 'Guess I'll go ashore and take the pilot.' said the captain. 'See the Chef du Port and tell Miss Ferris that we're back. You like to come along?'

They went in in the launch and stepped out on to the concrete steps that led to the Customs House quay. Here they said goodbye to the pilot and shook hands with him: he went off up an alley in the dusk. There was a light on in the office of the Chef du Port and they went in. The Chef was still there, and he got up to greet them.

'Well, we're back, *monsieur*,' said Captain Petersen. He offered cigarettes and lit them for the Chef and Keith. 'We're at the buoy right now, but tomorrow I'd like to move in to the quay.'

'*Certainement*,' said the Chef. 'Tomorrow at what hour?'

'Eight o'clock?' The Chef made a note upon his pad and they went on to discuss the refuelling of the *Flying Cloud* and her clearance for Seattle.

A quarter of an hour later, business concluded, the captain asked casually, 'What's happened to the *Mary Belle*?'

'She has depart,' the Chef said. 'Sailed.'

'Sailed? Where for?'

The Chef shrugged his shoulders. 'Who can say? Native boats, they do not need clearance. They come, they go. Some say Huahine, but that I do not know. In the *Iles sous le Vent* – anywhere. Raiatea, Tahaa, Bora Bora – anywhere. Perhaps even to Samoa in the end. That one, he makes long voyages.'

They stared at him. 'I didn't think he'd have gone off like that before we got back,' said the captain.

The Chef shrugged his shoulders. Then he glanced at Captain Petersen, a glint of humour in his eye. 'We have many years been friends,' he said, 'and we have laughed together. I hope you will laugh now.' He hesitated. 'He took a passenger.'

A terrible thought occurred to Captain Petersen. 'Who was that?'

'A lady from your ship, Mademoiselle Ferris, *avec la tête chataine*.'

The captain stared at him aghast. 'For the Lord's sake!' he said quietly. 'Well, what do you know!'

'The more I see of women the less I know,' replied the Chef du Port. 'At my age it is better to stick to wine.'

'When did they sail?' asked the captain.

'Two days after you,' replied the Chef. 'One night only she stayed at the hotel. Then she moved into the boat. They bought many *choses de cuisine*. Then they sailed the next day.'

'Over to the west? On a westward course?'

'That is true.'

They stood in silence for a minute. Then the captain turned to Keith. 'I guess this is just a bit outside my province,' he said. 'I'll have to put this to Chuck Ferris in a radiogram. Where do we go from here?' He stood conning the words over. 'It's going to be a mighty long one, too.'

They left the Chef du Port and went up to the hotel, hoping to find that Dawn Ferris had left a suitcase there, indicating an early return. The captain went in to enquire at the desk, and came out in a minute or two. 'No suitcase, and no note,' he said shortly. 'Too bad.'

He led the way to the Bureau des Postes et Télégraphes. The office was closed, but there was a light inside and he hammered on the door. A half-caste clerk came at last and told him that the office was closed. A *mille* changed hands and opened it, and the captain stood in worried thought writing three pages of a radiogram to his employer. He made a copy, paid the charge, and went out into the dark, vanilla-scented street with Keith. 'I don't know what we do now,' he said, worried.

'Go back on board, sit down, and have a drink,' said Keith.

'I guess that makes sense.'

They walked back in silence to the steps, hailed the motor launch, and went off to the schooner in her. On the aft deck the captain rang for the steward, ordered the evening drinks, and they sat down in the long chairs in the warmth of the tropic night, looking at the lights reflected in the dark waters of the harbour.

At last the captain broke the silence. 'If I'd thought a million years,' he said, 'I'd never have thought of this one.'

'I would,' said Keith. 'Knowing Jack Donelly.'

'I guess you know him better than I do.'

They drank. Then Keith asked, 'Has she ever done this sort of thing before?'

'I wouldn't know – well – yes. I'd say she must have done. She's been married three times. There must have been – incidents.'

'What did her husbands do?'

'I think the first one was a college boy in Cincinnati. He went into real estate. The second was a rancher somewhere near Helena, Idaho. That lasted quite a while – she had two children, but I guess the country got her down. Then there was Efstathios, but that didn't last long.'

'What did he do?'

'Oriental rugs and carpets in New York City. They called him Count Efstathios, but I don't think he was a count at all.'

'Nice chap?'

'Small guy with black hair and a little black moustache,' said Captain Petersen noncommittally. 'Good dancer, I should say. He wore brown patent-leather shoes. I never saw shoes like that before.' He paused. 'They didn't go with the ship,' he said.

Keith laughed. 'And now it's Jack Donelly. Well, he'd go with the ship.'

'Berthing with the seamen,' said the captain. 'But – I don't know. The rancher, Gort or Grant, some name like that, he was a great big guy and pretty dumb. Maybe that's the way she likes them, after all.'

They sat in silence for a time. 'What worries me,' the captain said at last, 'is, where do we go from here? My last orders were to sail for Seattle, taking you along to meet Mr Hirzhorn. Well, that's right the opposite way to Huahine and Bora-Bora, and there's hundreds of islands down that way, all the way through Samoa and Tonga to Fiji and New Caledonia.' He paused and took a drink. 'If I'm supposed to go and look for her,' he said, 'it could take the best part of a year. And what about you?'

'Don't worry about me,' said Keith. 'I could get back from here some other way.'

'I do worry about you,' said the captain practically. 'I've got a home at Midlake just outside Seattle, and I want to see my wife and kids. I'm not losing any sleep over Dawn.' He paused, reflectively. 'I bet she is.'

There wasn't much that they could do about it except to await an answer to the captain's radiogram. They sat in the warm darkness drinking rather more than usual in their perplexity, and then went down to dinner. They came up on deck again later and sat in the long chairs on the aft deck smoking Chuck Ferris' cigars till it was time for bed. Keith went down and slept well, a little amused, but Captain Petersen spent a bad night.

They moved in to the quay next morning and began to take on diesel oil and water. In the middle of the morning a radiogram arrived in answer from Mr Ferris. It was refreshingly direct:

KING-SIZE DEAL PENDING WITH SOL HIRZHORN SO SAIL IMMEDIATELY FOR SEATTLE BRINGING STEWART ALONG STOP KEEP CONTACT WITH ROCKAWIN AND BE SURE ADVISE HIM DATE ARRIVAL TIME AND BERTH STOP YOU WEREN'T HIRED TO MONITOR DAWN'S LOVELIFE BUT APPRECIATE YOUR CONCERN LEAVE HER SETTLE IT HER OWN WAY STOP AM ARRANGING CREDIT FOR HER WITH THE BANK OF INDO-CHINA PAPEETE SUGGEST YOU TELL HARBOURMASTER ASK HIM TO INFORM HER AS OPPORTUNITY OCCURS.

FERRIS.

The captain showed this telegram to Keith, who read it with interest. 'Well, that's the way it is,' Petersen said. 'We kiss Dawn goodbye, and she goes sailing out into the far blue yonder with Jack Donelly.' He stood for a minute in thought. 'I guess I'll go on shore and take the Chef to lunch, 'n show him this,' he said. 'It's time Chuck Ferris gave a bit more to the Orphelines, anyway.'

Keith asked, 'What's this about the king-sized deal with Sol Hirzhorn? Am I in on that?'

'I wouldn't know,' said Captain Petersen. 'Maybe I ought not to have shown you that.' He paused. 'One thing,' he said. 'Sol Hirzhorn's getting an old man, but he still owns the business. It's quite clear that he thinks a lot of you – as an engineer. My boss – Chuck Ferris – he sells engineering. Maybe Sol Hirzhorn's looking to you for a fresh mind on his problem, whatever that is. Maybe Chuck Ferris knows it. I wouldn't know. It's just an idea I got.'

'I see,' said Keith thoughtfully.

'Anyway,' said the captain briskly, 'we sail for Seattle in the morning.'

'How long will that take?'

'About three weeks. It's quite a way from here.'

'Will we be going into Honolulu?'

The captain shook his head. 'I'll have to do some figuring this afternoon, but I can tell you right now what the answer will be. North from here until we're clear of the Tuamotus at Mataiva. Then make all the easterly we can while we're in the south-east trades. Cross the line about longitude 145, maybe. Then a thousand or twelve hundred miles of beating up against the north-east trades, tracking due north – if we're lucky. After that, gales and fog and rain and radio bearings to Cape Flattery – all kinds of rough stuff. Then home, and a few days skiing on the spring snow. Just lead me to it!'

He went on shore to lunch with the Chef du Port alone and to get the necessary clearances. Keith lunched alone in the saloon and strolled along the quays. He bought a tinted coral necklace for Janice and a bracelet of polished beans and shells for Katie, souvenirs of his travels that did not cost too much because he still had no idea how he was to get back to Ealing from Seattle. The one thing that seemed clear to him was that he hadn't got enough money for the fare, however he might travel. Still, he was getting a good lift on the homeward track by going in the *Flying Cloud* to Seattle. He was not very worried now about the homeward journey; one way or another he would make it.

Twenty days later the *Flying Cloud* entered the Juan de Fuca strait in a rainstorm at about ten o'clock in the morning, running into relatively sheltered water before a strong westerly wind. They drove in with the mizzen furled, the mainsail close-reefed, and the fore topsails doing most of the work, an engineer on watch beside the motionless diesel. They passed, by radio bearings, about four miles north of Cape Flattery and never saw it, and carried on down the strait all day, gradually coming into calmer water. On deck they carried the engine from *Shearwater* in a packing case constructed in the first days of the voyage, one side secured by screws for the benefit of Customs, lashed down on deck beneath two thicknesses of tarpaulin.

In the early afternoon they passed Port Townsend and entered the calm waters of the Puget Sound. The rain stopped and the clouds lifted to a thin, watery sunset light as they ran down past Edmonds, heading south under mainsail and jibs, the topsails furled. With the last of the light they approached Seattle, furled the main and started the diesel, and finally dropped anchor in the quarantine section of Elliott Bay just north of Duwamish Head.

The captain came out of the wheelhouse as the chain rattled out. "We'll be staying here all night,' he said. 'It's a bit late now. Harbourmaster, Port Health Officer, and Customs – they'll be off about eight in the morning. I reckon we'll have breakfast half-past seven. Then after that we move into a berth.'

'What about this chap Jim Rockawin?' asked Keith. 'We had to let him know.'

'That's so. I sent him a radiogram four days ago via San Francisco. I've got a shore connection now on VHF. I guess that this might be as good a time as any, try and get him at his home.'

Ten minutes later he was speaking to Jim Rockawin, who in turn rang Julie at the Hirzhorn home near Wauna. 'Oh, fine,' she said. 'I'll tell Mr Hirzhorn. He's down in the workshop right now. Can I fix everything, or would you like it if I put you through?'

'I don't want to disturb him unless you think he'd like to speak to me.'

'I don't think that there's anything that we can't fix between us, Mr Rockawin. Mr Hirzhorn has been looking forward to Mr Stewart visiting with him for a few days, and he'd like you to bring him right out here, with his suitcases, as soon as you can get him off the yacht. He's kept the next four days free of all appointments. He thought perhaps Mr Stewart might care to take a look around some of the plants with him.'

Jim Rockawin was deeply impressed. He knew that Sol Hirzhorn thought a lot of this British engineer; he had not realised that his regard went so far as to allocate four days of his time to him. The thought flashed through his mind that, inevitably, in that four days they would discuss the Flume River mill, and the proposal to convert it to Ferris Hydraulics. Keith Stewart was important to Chuck Ferris, and Chuck ought to know about it.

He said, 'It would probably be midday before I get him off the yacht, past Customs and all the rest of it. Suppose I give him lunch in the city and bring him out to Wauna in the afternoon?'

She said evenly and directly, 'Mr Hirzhorn doesn't like secret handouts, Mr Rockawin. What's more, he always gets to hear about them in good time, or else I do.'

'Say,' he expostulated weakly, 'we wouldn't think of anything like that.'

'That's fine,' she said. 'I'll expect you in the middle of the afternoon, and we'll get the room made up. Mr Hirzhorn will be very pleased when I tell him. He's very grateful, very grateful indeed, to Mr Ferris for lending his yacht. Don't go and spoil it.'

'I won't,' he said thoughtfully. 'The job's good enough to stand on its own feet.'

'I'm sure it is,' she said. ' 'Bye now.'

Jim Rockawin put down the telephone and sat in thought for a few minutes. His first reaction had been that if Sol Hirzhorn was going to take this British engineer all round his plants and talk to him about the Flume River mill, they should get hold of him at once. He should call Chuck immediately. Chuck would probably drop everything and fly out to Seattle to meet Keith Stewart at lunch tomorrow; Chuck could be pretty impetuous at times. Now, after talking with Julie, he was not so sure that that would be a very good idea. He had a notion that nothing he or Chuck might say to Keith before he got to Wauna would remain long unknown to Julie or Sol Hirzhorn; in Seattle they were playing on their own home ground. Better, perhaps, to take the matter straight, and leave Chuck out of it.

He did not call his boss.

He was on the quayside when the *Flying Cloud* berthed at about ten o'clock next morning. He knew Captain Petersen well, and greeted him cheerfully as he went up the gangway. 'Hi, Joe,' he said. 'How's everything?'

'Good and bad,' said Captain Petersen. 'Jim, this is Mr Stewart.'

'Glad to know you, Mr Stewart.' They shook hands. He turned again to the captain. 'What's bad, Joe?'

'Dawn,' said Captain Petersen. 'You know she skipped it?'

'I did hear something,' Mr Rockawin admitted. 'Got another guy?'

'And how. Is Chuck mad with me?'

'I don't think so.'

'He will be when he hears the whole of it,' said the captain apprehensively.

'He knows most of it already,' said the engineer. 'He did get a bit upset after he got your radio, so he called Sol Hirzhorn and told him all about it. They're pretty thick, just now. Sol put Julie on to find out what she could about this Jack Donelly. She got a line on him from the manager of the forest down on Taylor Butte, and then she called a guy they've got called Paul Setches out in Honolulu to get a line on him from there. I'd say Chuck knows most of it now.' He smiled. 'The worst that Julie managed to find out was that he got in prison once three months for rape, and she reckoned that was a put-up job.'

'That's one I didn't know about,' said the captain. 'Three months isn't much for rape.'

'It wasn't much of a rape, according to Julie,' said Mr Rockawin. 'She says the girl's been giving her mother hell ever since.'

Captain Petersen was immensely relieved. 'Well – gee, I'm thankful that I haven't got to tell Chuck much.'

'He's not worrying. She's left three husbands and she'll leave this one if she wants to. But ... you never know. This one might stick.'

He turned to Keith Stewart. 'Say, Mr Stewart,' he said, 'Sol Hirzhorn's looking forward to you staying with him a few days before you go back to England. He wants to talk to you about a clock he's making, and he wants to take you round and show you something of the Hirzhorn enterprise. Is that okay with you?'

'Of course,' said Keith. 'I'd like to meet him. I had some letters from him back in England.'

'Well, that's fine. If you can get packed up I've got my car right here. What I thought we could do is drive around a bit so you can see Seattle, and then have lunch, and then drive out to Wauna in the afternoon. That's around fifty miles, to where Sol Hirzhorn lives.'

'That sounds fine,' said Keith. 'There's just one thing. This case has the engine from my sister's yacht in it, that got wrecked in the Tuamotus. I want to get it shipped back to England.'

'Perkins and Durant,' said Mr Rockawin. 'They'd be the best shipping agents to handle that. It's passed Customs inwards?'

'That's right,' said Captain Petersen. 'We took the top of the case off for them this morning. There's their mark.'

'Oh well, then, it won't have to go in bond. I'll get a truck along and take it to their warehouse. Leave it to me, I'll bring you out the documents to sign.'

The steward brought Keith's suitcase up on deck. Keith turned to Captain Petersen. 'I don't know if I'll be coming on board again,' he said, 'but I suppose I shan't. I'd like to say thank you, for all you've done for me.'

The captain said, 'It's been a real pleasure having you aboard, Mr Stewart, and having your company. And say, that trip down to Tahiti was a pleasure too, not to mention ending up back here at home. I'd have cut my throat if I'd been stuck in Honolulu for much longer, acting as a houseboat while Dawn made eyes at Manuel.' They shook hands. 'I'll be seeing you one day.'

Keith went down the gangway with Jim Rockawin to the car, the steward following with the suitcase. 'I guess we'll go up through the city first of all so you can see the sort of town it is, up by Lake Union, across the canal, take a look around the university, then back down Lake Washington Boulevard so you can see Lake Washington. Then back by Boeing Field and have lunch in the city.' He paused. 'Say, if you could get Sol Hirzhorn to spare you for a day, I'd like to take you into Boeing. There's stuff there classified you couldn't see, of course, but there's plenty that you could. And there are engineers in Boeing know about your writing in the magazine. They'd be real glad to show you around.'

They drove round for an hour and a half, and finished up in the grillroom of the Olympic Hotel for lunch. Keith was a little daunted by the magnificence of the hotel and completely overawed by the prices on the menu, far from his Ealing way of life. He was equally astounded by the size of the spare ribs when they were placed before him; it seemed impossible that he should eat all that, as indeed it was. Towards the end of his meal, he said to Mr Rockawin, 'Tell me, Mr Rockawin –'

'Jim,' the other interrupted smiling. 'We get pretty quickly here to where it seems kind of formal, even rude, if you keep on using the surname. That's unless there's a good big difference in rank. I don't suppose I'll ever get around to calling Mr Hirzhorn "Sol".'

'All right, Jim,' said Keith. 'Tell me – what does Mr Ferris do?'

The representative brushed the ash off his cigarette, which gave him a moment for thought. 'Hydraulic engineering,' he replied. 'Ferris Hydraulics Incorporated of Cincinnati. Ever heard of them?'

Keith nodded. 'Is that the same Ferris?'

'There's only one Chuck Ferris,' said his representative. 'He's my boss.'

Keith searched his memory. 'Aviation mostly – and motor cars?'

'Well, that's the way it used to be,' said Mr Rockawin. 'Automotive products are up each year, both in the United States and on the Continent of Europe from our Laeken plant, in Belgium. But aviation products are declining – they're way down from what they used to be. That's general in the industry, on account of airplanes flying higher. But we get by.'

Keith thought for a minute. 'I'd like you to know that I'm very grateful to Mr Hirzhorn and to Mr Ferris for sending the *Flying Cloud* down to Tahiti,' he said. 'It was a tremendous help. We were really in trouble – quite bad trouble – when Captain Petersen turned up. I don't think I'd ever have got out to see my sister's grave or to set up a stone without his help. It meant a lot to me.'

'Well, that's real nice to know,' said Mr Rockawin. 'Mr Hirzhorn, he'd be glad to know that, if you tell him.' He paused. 'I think when people get older,' he said, 'they kind of get more mellow. They kind of like to give help in return for help they get. And Sol Hirzhorn, he's mighty interested in that clock.'

Keith nodded. 'It was very good of Mr Ferris, too, to lend his yacht.'

'Oh, sure,' said Mr Rockawin. 'But Chuck's not building a clock. He lent the *Flying Cloud* just in the way of business. It's Sol Hirzhorn that you want to thank.'

'Captain Petersen showed me a telegram he'd had from Mr Ferris,' Keith remarked. 'It was in Papeete, when we were so worried about Dawn. It was all about Dawn. But Mr Ferris did say one thing. He wanted the *Flying Cloud* to come straight back to Seattle with me on board, because he said he had what he called a king-sized deal pending with Sol Hirzhorn.'

'He said that, did he?' Mr Rockawin sat in thought for a moment, wondering if it was wise to take a line so very different from that which his employer would have taken.

'Well, that's true enough, Mr Stewart,' he said at last. 'There *is* a contract pending between Mr Ferris and Sol Hirzhorn. You know that already.' He paused again. 'Whether you come into it or not, I wouldn't know. In any case, I'm not going to tell you a thing about it. You'll be staying with Sol Hirzhorn for the next few days. If he likes to tell you about it, well, it's his business and that's okay with me. But I'm not telling you about Sol Hirzhorn's business from this end.' He smiled. 'Julie would know all about it by the time we get to Wauna.'

Keith asked, 'Who is this Julie? Captain Petersen said something about her once.'

'Julie Perlberg,' said Mr Rockawin. 'She's a Jewish girl, I think – quite young. Twenty-five, maybe. She's the old man's private secretary, sharp as a needle.' He paused. 'I've heard it said that there was some kind of a tragedy, I don't know. In any case, that's only rumour. If true, she'd be his grand-daughter.' He paused. 'She lives at Wauna in the house with him – his wife's away in Florida most winters, so she runs the house servants. She goes to conferences with him, taking shorthand notes. You might say she's his eyes and ears right now.' He laughed, 'And say, they're mighty sharp eyes and mighty long ears.'

Keith smiled with him. 'Long enough to hear what's going on in here?'

'She's quite capable of having someone put a mike into that bowl of flowers,' said Mr Rockawin. 'Although I don't really think she works that way. She'd know by just looking at us if we'd talked about the deal.' He paused. 'She's sharp, like all her family.'

'We'd better not talk about it, then,' said Keith.

'I'm not going to,' said Mr Rockawin. 'I told you that.'

He paid the check and they went out of the hotel to the car at the parking meter, where the policeman was just making out a ticket for staying too long. Rockawin talked him out of it by introducing Keith Stewart as an English visitor, which so intrigued the policeman, who had been in England in the war, that he forgot about the ticket. They got on the road for Tacoma and on southwards down the fringes of the Puget Sound. It was the first time that Keith had been in the United States and he was amazed by the high standard of living, at any rate in visible, material things. The size and beauty of the motor cars, the number of them, the size and quality of the roads, and the enormous number of great four-wheeled trailer caravans: these things impressed him very much indeed.

They drove through the industrial city of Tacoma at the head of Puget Sound and over the toll bridge across the Narrows out into the country again. Presently they left the road and turned into an inconspicuous lane or drive marked only by stone pillars by the roadside, and went on winding up the hill through a forest of fir trees. After half a mile they came out on to an open hillside, a place of grass and granite outcrops with a little snow upon the ground, and with a magnificent view over to the snow-covered Olympic Mountains to the west. There stood the house, a long, low stone building, two-storeyed in the front and single-storeyed at the back by the slope of the hillside, a house very much larger than appeared at the first glance. Below it lay an inlet of the sound with boathouses and a moored motor yacht, and by the water's edge there was a long airstrip with a hangar by the road that led down to it.

Jim Rockawin drove up to the front door behind the house and parked the car. A manservant in a green baize apron came out and took the suitcase, and they went towards the house. A stout, elderly man came forward to meet them. 'Mr Stewart, isn't it?' he said. 'This is a real pleasure. We've exchanged letters, but we've never met before. Say, take off your coat and come right in.' He paused. 'I'm Sol Hirzhorn.'

They went into the huge living-room with the great picture window looking out over the Olympics. 'Mr Stewart, would you like a cup of tea?' he asked. 'I know you Englishmen drink tea in the afternoon.'

Keith said, 'Don't bother about that for me, Mr Hirzhorn. I've been away from England long enough to get out of English ways.'

'We often have a cup of tea around this time,' said Mr Hirzhorn. 'It's getting so it's quite a habit in the office.' He raised his voice. 'Say, Julie!' She came into the room. 'Mr Stewart, I'd like you to meet Julie Perlberg. She does all my letters to you. Julie, this is Mr Stewart. Say, would you tell Jake to get us English tea, with cookies or sump'n?'

'I'm glad to know you, Mr Stewart,' she said quietly. 'I'll see about that right away, Mr Hirzhorn.'

Keith walked over to the big window. 'What a wonderful view,' he said. 'I've never seen anything like it.'

'I built the house for it,' said Mr Hirzhorn simply. 'I saw it first when I was quite a young chap and I used to go all over for the cutting. Lumber – that's my business – you know that.' Keith nodded. 'Nineteen twenty-two – or twenty-three would it have been? I can't just remember. I'd have been thirty years old or so about that time, and married about five years. I thought then that I'd like to have a summer camp up on this hill. Well, then that wasn't hardly practical with a young family and not much time to spare, but I never forgot about it. I got to realise that it would take a lot of money to live here and work at the same time. But anyway, I couldn't get it out of my head, and in 1936 things got so I could buy the land as an investment, so I'd got it, anyway.'

'How much land is there, Mr Hirzhorn?' Jim Rockawin asked.

'Twelve hundred acres. A little more, I think – twelve hundred and thirty-six, far as I remember. Sarah said it was a silly thing to do because we'd never live there – it would cost a fortune.' He laughed. 'Well, then the fortune came, 'n I never wanted to travel or go horseracing or anything – just build the house and live in it, 'n go on working. And that's just what I did.'

Julie came into the room behind them. 'Tea will be here in a minute,' she said softly. She went through into her own room, leaving the men talking.

She closed the door, and went to a tall cabinet of steel drawers. She selected a file marked STEWART and took it to her desk, and opened it again to refresh her memory.

One of her jobs was to protect her employer, who was also her grandfather. She never sought to influence his judgment; she worked rather to get him the maximum of information with the least effort on his part. They had few contacts in England, but she quickly discovered that there was an agency in London which specialised in finding out particulars of individuals in connection with hire-purchase credit. The first document that they had sent her read:

KEITH MALCOLM STEWART. Born, Renfrew, Scotland, 1915. Lives now at 56 Somerset Road, Ealing, Middlesex, a four-storey, ten-roomed house which is his property. The house was purchased for £3,200 in 1943 by Mr Stewart and subdivided. The top two floors are let at a rental of £2 15s 0d per week. There is a mortgage of £2,200 on the property at $5^{1}/_{2}$%. Mr Stewart is married and has no children of his own but has one daughter apparently adopted recently.

Mr Stewart worked as a fitter in the aircraft industry till 1946. He then became a freelance technical journalist working principally for a magazine called the *Miniature Mechanic*. His income is estimated at about £700 per annum. His wife works whole time as a shop assistant in Ealing. With the rental of the leased portion of the house, the family income appears to be about £1,100 per annum.

Mr Stewart does not bet or drink to excess. He does not own a car. He appears to live within his means, and has a good reputation in the neighbourhood.

This report reached Julie while Keith was on his way from Honolulu to Tahiti with Jack Donelly, and she was amazed. First she was surprised by the invoice sent with the report, which was for twenty-five shillings, only about three and a half dollars. Secondly, she was staggered by the smallness of the income, only about three thousand dollars from all sources, including the wife's earnings. And then, to go and adopt a child, upon an income like that!

She had taken the report at once to show to Mr Hirzhorn. He had read it with interest. 'A guy with his ability, he could earn a better wage than that,' he remarked presently, 'even in England. I guess it's just he kind of likes his work better than making money. There's nothing wrong with that.' He handed back the report to Julie. 'You know sump'n? I'd like to see some photographs. Photographs of the wife, of the adopted kid, of the house, of the street, of the garden of the house, so I can see if he keeps it clean or not. Photographs of anything that you can get.'

'Okay, Mr Hirzhorn,' said Julie. 'We'll have to have them here within two weeks or so. They should be able to do that. I'll write today.' She paused in thought. 'I'll say we want it in a hurry. I think I might put three ten-dollar bills in with the letter. Kind of help things along.'

Four days later a pavement photographer took a picture of Katie in Ealing Broadway as she went into the shop, in spite of her smiling denials. Janice got photographed by a strange man on her way home from school, to her surprise, and the house and street were taken from all angles, including the back garden. A week after that a sheaf of photographs arrived on Julie's desk at Wauna in the state of Washington. By the time Keith Stewart got there his hosts knew quite a lot about him.

She put the file back into the steel cabinet and locked it up. The little man looked like what the file and photographs had told her, added to what she had gleaned from sundry issues of the *Miniature Mechanic*: an honest little man of lower-middle-class suburban type, content to go along upon a miserable salary for the sake of doing the work he loved, with a wife who was prepared to work in order that he should maintain that way of life. There was no deceit about this man.

That was important, for she had little confidence in Chuck Ferris. He was too anxious to sell his hydraulics, to get in to the lumber industry. Jim Rockawin was better, but not much. Seventeen hundred thousand dollars for the conversion of the Flume River mill was quite a contract, in anybody's language. She knew that production at the Cincinnati factory was declining on account of the reduction in aviation contracts; she knew that they laid off a thousand hands last month. Ferris Hydraulics had indulged in too much salesmanship, and made Julie suspicious. This lending of the yacht ... Seventeen hundred thousand dollars was a lot of money.

She had not mentioned her misgivings to her grandfather. Her business was to take his orders, take the load off him where she could, and get him information. She knew, however, that the same misgivings had occurred to him; there had been too much salesmanship. Chuck Ferris would have done better to have charged a charter fee for the *Flying Cloud*. His refusal to do so had undoubtedly held up the contract for the Flume River mill; the old man smelt a rat. He had delayed a decision till a fresh mind was brought to bear upon the problems of the mill, for fresh advice. He had been waiting for Keith Stewart, to see if this insignificant little engineer from England could say anything useful.

She got up from her desk. She had decided in her own mind that he was honest; that was where she stopped. Whether he was competent was a matter for her grandfather to decide.

She went out into the living-room. The men seemed to have finished drinking tea, and Jim Rockawin was getting up to go. She went through to tell the houseman to clear away the tea, and came back to the hall in time to bid Jim Rockawin goodbye. She went on into the living-room to pull the curtains over the great picture window and to light the lamps, for dusk was falling now.

Sol Hirzhorn came back into the room with Keith. 'Like to have a look at what I'm doing with your clock, downstairs?' he asked.

'I'd like to very much, Mr Hirzhorn,' he said. They moved towards the door.

Julie said quietly, 'Drinks will be on the table here at seven o'clock, Mr Stewart, and dinner is at seven thirty. Mr Hirzhorn usually goes to bed at nine.'

'You see how she keeps me on a string,' said the old man.

'That's what I'm here for,' she said equably. She smiled. 'I generally go down to the workshop about ten minutes of seven, and chase him out. Otherwise he'd be there all night.'

The two men went down to the workshop in the basement. It was a long room, more than forty feet long, but only eight or nine feet wide. There was a long workbench for the full length of it lit by windows in the outer wall, and these windows looked down the hill over the sea inlet and the airstrip. The back wall was of light construction, separating the workshop from the heating plant and from the laundry of the house.

In this long shop was every machine and hand tool that a modeller in metal could desire, from lathes and a milling machine to oxy-acetylene welding and soldering irons. Keith stood and took it all in with a practised eye, from the clock parts laid out on a white cloth at the end of the bench to the racks of raw materials on the back wall. He had never before seen anything like it in a private house, and not in many institutions; its completeness staggered him. He turned to the old man by his side. 'You've certainly got a beautiful set-up here,' he said. 'Did you do all this yourself?'

'No,' said Mr Hirzhorn. 'I'll be straight with you. When I first got interested eight years ago I had the bench put in, and got the South Bend lathe, and fixed that up myself. Well, then when I got going and got really stuck into it I decided on a whole raft of things I ought to have. I was new to it, you see, and the lathe took me a month to get fixed up the way I wanted it. So then I figured by the time I got the shop fixed up I'd probably be dead, and nothing done. So then I got along Clem Harrison, who runs our aviation section, and told him what I wanted, and he made the plan and got the things for me, and put it all in with his boy, Pete Homer. I wouldn't like you to go thinking that I did all this for myself, with my own hands.'

'Very sensible,' said Keith. 'You've certainly got a fine shop.'

'You like it?'

'It's the best I've ever seen, in any private house. That's the clock, over there?'

'On the cloth. That's as far as I've gone so far.'

Keith moved over and picked up the tilting table. 'You've made a good job of that,' he said, examining it. 'A beautiful job. How did you get the burnishing so flat and even?'

'Lapped it on a sheet of plate glass with oil and fine grit carborundum,' said Mr Hirzhorn. 'Then I finished off with metal polish.'

271

'On the plate glass?'

'That's right. I thought this was the part folks would be always looking at, so it ought to be finished good.'

Keith nodded. It was better finished than on most of the examples of the clock that he had seen. He picked up the trunnions and the rocking arm, examined them, and laid them down. 'You're getting on quite well,' he said. 'These are the four plates?'

'That's so. They've to be burnished, but I won't do that till all the holes are drilled.' He hesitated. 'They don't get seen so much,' he said. 'I thought I'd do them on a polishing mop.'

Keith nodded. 'That's quite good enough. These bevels – did you make them yourself?'

'No,' Mr Hirzhorn admitted. 'I got Clem Harrison to have them made for me. I do spur wheels, but I never did a bevel wheel.'

'They aren't so difficult,' Keith said, 'but they do take time. I often get mine made in a shop where they've got proper tools for it.' He turned over the parts. 'You're getting on quite well,' he said. 'I should think you must be about halfway through. What's the next part to be tackled?'

'Bobbins and armatures,' said Mr Hirzhorn. 'I never wound a coil before, and I don't know how I'm going to make out. Forty-six gauge is mighty fine wire to handle when you can't see so well.'

'I know,' said Keith. 'It's better not to handle it at all. It's so easy to get kinks. I made a coil winder for mine. It's quite a simple thing. The wire passes from the spool through softwood grips tightened by a spring, to give the tension. Then that traverses along the slow feed – the pitch just bigger than the wire diameter. Reverse direction with the tumbler reverse at the end of each row. Like this.' He seized a piece of paper and began to sketch, Mr Hirzhorn watching intently. Suddenly he stopped drawing. 'Look – you don't have to make one. Get on with the 95- and 20-tooth wheels next, and the maintaining gear. As soon as I get back to England I'll put my coil winder in the post to you, airmail.' He moved to the South Bend lathe and examined it. 'You'll have to make a little plate fitting and put it on the tool post, here. I shan't be using it. You can post it back to me when you've done with it.'

'Say, that's mighty kind of you,' said Mr Hirzhorn. 'I've been kind of frightened of those coils, and yet I want to learn to do them. You know how it is.'

Keith nodded. 'They aren't difficult,' he said. 'Use the coil winder, and pick a gauge of wire to suit a slow feed on the lathe, and run in back gear at your slowest speed. There's no magic in forty-six gauge.' He examined the gearbox on the lathe. 'Look, this one here gives an advance of four thous per rev. Forty-four gauge is 3.2 thousandths diameter. I should use this gear with forty-four gauge wire. You won't have any difficulty. Mine took about an hour to make each coil.'

An hour later Julie came down to the workshop. She came in unnoticed by the men and stood behind them for a little, watching and listening. The visit of this English engineer was a good thing; there was no doubt of that. She had been troubled from time to time that the circumstances of his life compelled her grandfather to pursue his hobby and his interest alone. Every evening he went down into the workshop alone. She could not share his interest with him, nor could his wife. It seemed all wrong to her that he had nobody to play with, but that's the way things were. She knew it for a solitary occupation, in that he wanted to make the whole clock himself, but his pleasure in Keith Stewart's visit pleased her very much indeed.

She said quietly, 'Drinks are on the table, Mr Hirzhorn.'

The two men started, and turned to her. Sol Hirzhorn said, 'They can't be,' and looked at his watch. 'Oh, well ...'

They went obediently upstairs with her and washed their hands in the cloakroom. Over the drinks before the big log fire Sol Hirzhorn said, 'I was wondering if you'd care to take a look at one of the mills tomorrow, Mr Stewart. Ever seen a lumber mill in operation?'

'I don't know anything about the lumber industry at all,' Keith said. 'It's all new to me. I'd like to very much indeed. But I don't want to take your time.'

The old man shook his head. 'I want to go and see this mill myself. We've got an engineering problem there needs sorting out. I think we'll go into the office first of all while I look through the mail, 'n you can meet the boys – my two sons, Emmanuel and Joseph. They do most of the work now. And then we'll go on to the mill. Julie!'

'Mr Hirzhorn?'

'Julie, we'll want the car half after eight tomorrow, for the office. You'd better come along. Then ring the aviation section, say I'll be coming to the airport and I'll want the helicopter at ten o'clock for the Flume River mill. Maybe we'll drop in at the Eight Mill Cut in the afternoon, so Mr Stewart sees the whole process.'

'Okay, Mr Hirzhorn. Will you want Jim Rockawin along?'

'No. We'll leave him out this time. But say, if Manny's free I think he might come. Call Manny after the airport, and if he's home I'd like to speak with him.'

She moved the telephone to the small table by his side and put it by the glass, and went into her office, closing the door. Five minutes later the buzzer sounded quietly, and the old man picked up the receiver. 'The helicopter will be ready at ten o'clock,' she said. 'I have Mr Emmanuel on the line now. Will I put him through?'

'Sure.' There was a click and Mr Hirzhorn said, 'Manny? Say, Manny, I've got Mr Stewart with me now, the British engineer that I was telling you about. That's right. I'm coming in the office, see the mail first thing and let him meet you and Joe. After that I'm taking him to see Flume River. Would you be able to come along?'

'I think so, Dad.' There was a short pause. 'Bill Schultz of Euclid, he's coming in the morning about the new trucks, but it's all financial. It's more up Joe's alley than mine. I'll call Joe presently. If that's okay with him, I could come.'

'That's fine,' said Mr Hirzhorn. 'I'd like you to be there if you can make it. Time we made up our minds. I kind of thought that telling Mr Stewart all about it might help to make up our own minds. You know what I mean?'

'Sure, Dad. I'll call Joe, and if he doesn't think he'd like to handle it I'll maybe call Bill Schultz and put him off a day. It's not that urgent.'

'Okay, Manny. Give my love to Rachel. See you in the morning.' He put down the receiver.

They dined simply in a great dining-room rather too ornately furnished, full of oil paintings and clocks, served by the manservant, Julie dining with them. 'My wife, Sarah, she'll be sorry to miss seeing you,' said Mr Hirzhorn once. 'She gets this sciatica each winter in the cold and wet, and nothing seems much good except the sunshine and the warmth. She used to go down into California, but she likes Florida best. I go and see her there once in a month or six weeks, but there's nothing to do there.' He smiled. 'No business and no workshop. I like it here. She likes it, too, excepting when it's cold. She'll be back around the end of April, soon as it fines up.'

They went to bed early, and Keith slept well in the deepest, softest bed that he had ever slept in, in the intense stillness of Wauna. By ten minutes to nine next morning he was in the head office in Tacoma meeting the two sons, Emmanuel and Joseph, treated as a very honoured guest. They left Julie in the office and went on at half-past nine to the Seattle-Tacoma airport; by ten o'clock they were outside the private hangar labelled HIRZHORN ENTERPRISES INC.

with the helicopter standing on the tarmac in a little drifted snow, saying good morning to the pilot. 'We'll want to go to the Flume River mill,' said Mr Hirzhorn. 'We'll be there for lunch. Then if there's time we'll look in at the Eight Mile Cut. We'll be going back to Wauna after that, but it might be close on dark. Maybe we'd better go home in the Cessna.'

'Okay, Mr Hirzhorn,' said the pilot. He spoke to a ground engineer and the father and son got into the machine in the back seat, putting Keith beside the pilot. The pilot got in after them, the doors closed, the engine started, the rotor revved up. Presently the pilot moved the big lever in his right hand gently up and they were in the air and moving ahead slowly. He put the helicopter in a climb and they set out towards the east and north.

The flight was a delight to Keith, who had never been in a helicopter before. It took about fifty minutes over mountains and up shallow valleys filled with the unending forest. In the end a river showed up ahead of them and buildings marked by a great plume of smoke and steam, a railroad, and a small town beside. Mr Hirzhorn reached forward and touched the pilot on the shoulder. 'Circle round a bit,' he said. 'I want Mr Stewart to take in the whole set-up before we land.'

The pilot nodded and put the aircraft into a right-hand turn around the plant at about a thousand feet, while Manny explained the lay-out to Keith; the logs coming down the river, the log pond, the jack ladder from the log pond to the mill, the drying kilns, the lumber stores along the railroad tracks. Then they had seen all that was to be seen from the air, and they came in to land softly on an open space reserved in the car park.

They spent two hours in the sawmill seeing the whole process as the logs four feet in diameter were sawn into planks and taken away for kiln-drying or stacking, while the offcuts were turned into pulpwood for newsprint. The

Hansel debarker, ripping the bark off the logs by jets of water, interested Keith very much. The saws, both bullsaws and bandsaws, were well within his experience though on a vastly larger scale than any he had seen before. He spent some time in the saw-sharpening shop talking to the head sawyer about set and cutting angles for the various types of wood to be cut, information that he stored away in his mind. The flying carriages operated by four-inch roller chains running over great sprockets appalled him, but he did not say so at the time.

They lunched with the manager and the secretary at a table reserved for them in the canteen. No drinks were served, for the whole plant was dry. Emmanuel apologised to Keith for this omission. 'We're kind of strict on that,' he said. 'This is a company town. We've got most everything else that folks would want – a dance hall and a movie theatre and eight stores – but not a liquor shop. We find that liquor and a sawmill don't go well together.'

'Do you have many accidents?' Keith asked. He had been shown a very comprehensive little first-aid room.

'Not more than what's average to the industry,' Manny replied. 'You get gangs felling the tall timber in the forests, or walking around on logs in the log pond, or dealing with quick-moving saws like what you saw – you'll get more accidents than in the automotive industry, for example. We try and keep them down.'

'There hasn't been a fatality in this plant since it was set up,' said the manager. 'That's seven years.'

'That's so,' said Manny. 'That's partly due to Lou here. But he's got a modern plant to help him. We had three at Viper Bend in the last year.'

Sol Hirzhorn leaned forward, and they all deferred to him. 'Say, Mr Stewart,' he said. 'You've been around a bit. What do you think of safety in this plant, coming to it fresh? Now that you've seen it?'

Keith paused before answering, thinking over all that he had seen that morning. 'I don't think you could do much better with the saws,' he said at last. 'With big saws running at that speed, you'll always get the bloke who gets careless as the years go by, and puts his hand in one. You can't help that – except by cutting out the drink, as you do. The thing I didn't like were all those chains.'

Emmanuel and Lou glanced at each other. The old man asked, 'You mean the roller chains that work the carriages?'

'That's right. I saw that they were well lubricated. How do they get greased? You don't keep stopping the plant?'

'They get greased nights and midday when the plant's stopped for dinner,' said Lou, the manager. 'They'll have greasers working on them now. In between, a guy goes around with a slush-can and a brush upon a five-foot stick, and puts it on with that.'

'Does that stick ever get caught up? Some of those chains were going thirty miles an hour.'

'Sometimes. Not very often.'

'Does the greaser ever get caught up with it?'

'Not here,' said Lou definitely. 'Not in the seven years that I've been manager.'

Sol Hirzhorn said, 'Say, Mr Stewart, do you know anything about Chuck Ferris? Ferris Hydraulics, in this mill?'

Keith faced him. 'No, I don't,' he said. 'I know that Mr Ferris has a contract he's negotiating with you. I asked Mr Rockawin if he'd tell me what it was, in case I put my foot in it and said the wrong thing. But he wouldn't tell me. He said it was your business.'

There was general laughter. Sol Hirzhorn said, 'Good for Jim. Manny, would you be able to come back to Wauna this evening? I don't think we'd lose anything by telling Mr Stewart what's proposed, now that he's seen the plant.'

'Sure, Dad.' He thought for a moment. 'I'll call the office, and have them send the plans out to the house. They can call Rachel, too – tell her I'll be late.'

They left in the helicopter after lunch and flew for twenty minutes eastward up the river. They came to the Eight Mile Cut, a timber camp, and put down on a level platform built of logs with a plank decking specially for the helicopter. They got into a truck with the young manager and were driven a mile or two through the devastated forest to where the felling was going on.

This was wholly strange to Keith; he could make no useful comment and he said so, though he found it full of interest. He watched a couple of Douglas firs about a hundred and fifty feet tall as they were felled, watched the branches being lopped off by men standing on the trunks working with axes. He tested the edge of an axe and found it as sharp as a razor. He watched the bulldozers pulling the logs down to the lake and rolling them in, to be made up into rafts by the boom-men and floated down the river to the log pond at the mill.

The work seemed to him to be excessively dangerous, but on enquiry he found that the Hirzhorns were not worried by accidents in the forest cuts. They said that the accident rate was lower than in the mills, possibly through the average age of the men being lower; most of them were unmarried anyway, so that accidents made less trouble. Keith thought that the monotony of work in the mills might have something to do with it. In factory work when men get thinking of other matters than the job in hand accidents are apt to happen, but out in the forest where no two jobs were ever quite alike men kept alive to the chance of a tree rolling over and crushing them.

They drove back to the helicopter in the truck and took off for home. They landed at the Seattle-Tacoma airport as cars on the main highway were beginning to put on their lights, changed into the Cessna waiting for them on the tarmac, and landed on the strip below the house at Wauna a quarter of an hour later. The car was there to meet them and take them the few hundred yards to the house, Sol Hirzhorn being forbidden to climb hills. An hour and twenty minutes after leaving the forest cut a hundred miles away they were seated with cups of tea and cookies before the fire in the great living-room at Wauna.

Julie had come back to Wauna from the head office in Tacoma in the car, and had brought with her a great packet of plans and specifications from Ferris Hydraulics, a file of correspondence, and a sheaf of photographs. She had laid these out upon the table in the middle of the room; she showed them to the men and retired to her own office. When they were warm and comfortable before the fire Sol Hirzhorn said, 'I'd like you to know the way things are at the Flume River, Keith.'

'I'd like to hear it, Mr Hirzhorn.'

The old man paused in thought. 'It started over a year ago,' he said. 'I got an invite to attend a demonstration of rockets at this place Cape Canaveral in Florida, Thor and Atlas and things like that. Well, I don't know anything about rockets or satellites or space vehicles, or what you call them, and not much interested either, but an invite like that don't come very often and I was taking Sarah to Palm Beach, so I decided to go. I didn't understand much of what I saw or what they told me either, but one thing did interest me. They had one of these things lying horizontal on the launching base while they serviced it and did things to it. Then they had to lift it up into the vertical position for fuelling and firing. It was eighty or ninety feet long, and they put it up vertical with two great hydraulic jacks, one on each side, all in next to no time. Those jacks must have been thirty feet long, the extension, I mean, and I never saw jacks go so fast.' He paused. 'Well, you know how it is. You know at the first sight it might be useful in the business but you don't know what it is you've got in mind. So I asked the officer showing us around who made the jacks, and he said, Ferris Hydraulics.' He paused again.

'It wasn't till the middle of the night I thought that if those jacks could push at that speed they could push our carriages in the mill just the same, 'n cut out every chain. I don't suppose you ever saw a man caught up in a four-inch roller chain that runs over a sprocket, Mr Stewart?'

'No,' said Keith.

'Well, you don't want to, either. I got in touch with Ferris Hydraulics, and Chuck Ferris he came down with his engineers, and left them with us for a week. I guessed it would be best to try it out in the one mill for a start, and we picked on the Flume River. Well, what they proposed was that we didn't stop at the carriages but put hydraulic motors on the saws as well, worked off the same hydraulic mains, from the same plant. Well, that's attractive in some ways although it's a big increase in the costs. I don't care about high-voltage electric motors in a sawmill much more than the chains. Six hundred volts can kill a guy quite quick, and you take an eight-foot bull-saw, that'll take close on two hundred horsepower. You get a saw break and hang up and things are apt to happen.' Keith nodded. 'Well, with the hydraulics they just put a sort of safety valve across the mains and noone's likely to get hurt, no damage to the motor either. I don't care about high-voltage current in the mill, any more than the chains.

'Manny's got the drawings and the specifications on the table there,' he said. 'I wondered if you'd care to take a look at them.'

'I'd like to very much,' said Keith. 'I don't know that I'd be able to help much, you know. It's not as if I was a consulting engineer.'

'No. But you've been around a bit. I'd appreciate it if you'd look the scheme over.'

Keith crossed to the table with Emmanuel and they started to discuss the scheme, while Sol Hirzhorn sat on in his chair before the fire. They started on the plan of the mill, then turned to the Ferris drawings and the specification. It was all straightforward enough to an engineering mind, a well prepared scheme, easily comprehensible. It was good, too; Keith Stewart liked the look of it. It was one which would remove most of the apprehensions which had troubled him that morning in the mill. It would certainly make the work safer.

'What happens to the waste heat?' he asked Emmanuel at last.

'What's that?' asked the mill-owner.

Keith turned to the specification. 'The power going into the hydraulic system is the brake horsepower of these diesel motors, the prime movers,' he remarked. 'Six thousand five hundred horsepower.'

'That's so.'

'That's the power going into the mill when everything's going at full blast. Well, of course, nothing works at hundred per cent efficiency.' Emmanuel nodded. 'I don't know what the efficiency of these hydraulic rams would be,' said Keith thoughtfully. 'The motors might be ninety per cent. Suppose we guess that as the figure for the whole mill – ten per cent power loss. That means that when the plant is going at full blast, six hundred and fifty horsepower has to be got rid of as waste heat.'

'Seems a lot,' said Emmanuel.

'I don't know that it is,' said Keith reflectively. 'Not in the scale of the whole job. I suppose it goes into the hydraulic fluid. I saw something about that.' He turned over the pages of the specification. 'Here it is. Maximum temperature of the fluid, 110°F.'

'That's what these intercoolers are for, I think,' said Emmanuel. 'They've got them stuck around behind each motor and each ram, with water from the river running through them. Here's the drawing of the water mains and pump.'

'I see.' Keith took the drawing and studied it. 'That's all right. This is the drawing of the intercooler ... in two sizes.' He studied the dimensions. 'It's not very big ...'

'I wouldn't know,' said Emmanuel.

Keith smiled. 'Tell you the truth, I don't know either.' He sat in thought. 'How hot does it get there at the mill?' he asked. 'Outside, I mean – on a fine day in summer?'

'Oh, it gets quite hot,' said Emmanuel. 'The guys outside, they work in pants and singlet. Eighty degrees, I'd say – maybe eighty-five. It's right down in the valley, so you don't get much wind.'

'That'd be the inlet temperature of the hydraulic fluid by the time it got from the power plant into the mill,' said Keith thoughtfully. 'It must go in at around about air temperature.'

'I guess it would,' said Manny.

Julie brought the tray of drinks into the room, and the two men crossed over to Sol Hirzhorn by the fire. 'How did you make out?' he asked.

'I'd like to think about it just a little bit,' Keith said. 'The trouble is, I don't know much about hydraulics, and they know just about everything there is to know. There are one or two things I don't understand, but that's probably my fault.' He paused, and took a drink. 'I'd like to read that specification through quietly after dinner, by myself.'

'Do that,' said Mr Hirzhorn. 'I'll be down in the workshop starting work on the gear wheels.'

'Not after nine o'clock you won't,' said Julie firmly. 'You've had quite a day.'

Keith settled down after dinner at the big table in the middle of the room, while the old man retired to his workshop and Emmanuel sat in a long chair before the fire smoking a cigar. He read the specification through twice and did a little figuring on the back of one of the drawings. At the end of it, when Julie went downstairs to flush Sol Hirzhorn from the workshop, Keith was as much in the dark as ever.

He got up as the old man came into the room. 'I'm sorry,' he said simply, 'but I still don't understand these intercoolers. I'd say they were too small and they should be about three times the size. There's almost certainly some factor here that I don't understand.'

'Could be,' said Sol Hirzhorn briefly. He turned to his son. 'Manny, how would you like to take a run up to Cincinnati with Mr Stewart, show him the hardware 'n talk to the engineers?'

'When, Dad?'

'Tomorrow, I guess.'

Emmanuel reflected for a moment. 'I could do that,' he said. 'Go in the office first and catch the United plane midday, Flight 183, thirteen zero five. Gets in around nine o'clock their time, sleep in the hotel 'n see them in the morning. Back here next night. We could do that if you like, Dad.'

'I'd be kind of happier, now this has been raised,' the old man said. 'If we don't get it cleared up we might be worrying about it all the time.' He turned to Keith. 'Could you do that for us?' he asked. 'It seems asking rather a lot.'

'I'd be very pleased, Mr Hirzhorn,' said Keith. He smiled. 'I'd be very glad of the chance of walking through the Ferris works.'

Sol Hirzhorn turned to Julie. 'Better call United now and make the reservations. Make them for the return flight too.'

'Okay, Mr Hirzhorn.'

The organisation went smoothly into effortless action. Keith spent the next morning in the workshop going over all the details of the clock with Sol Hirzhorn. At twelve-thirty the Cessna was waiting on the airstrip to take him across the water to the airport. At twelve-fifty the pilot escorted him to the booking hall and handed him over to Emmanuel. Ten minutes later he was sitting in the DC7, and at nine-thirty that night he was in his bedroom at the hotel in Cincinnati over two thousand miles from Wauna.

He had a morning of absorbing interest in the Ferris plant next day, and finished up with considerable admiration for the design and manufacture of the hydraulic motors. The morning ended with an office conference presided over by Chuck Ferris, a small, dynamic red-haired man that Keith had no difficulty in recognising as Dawn's father. The chief engineer was present with one of his aides, a Mr Monnington.

Keith said he didn't quite understand the intercoolers. 'That's all right,' said the chief engineer patiently. 'The cold river water comes in here from the main, picks up heat, and comes out here, and back into the river. The oil comes in here, and goes out here, a whole lot cooler.'

Keith said he understood that. 'What puzzles me is the heat transfer balance,' he said. 'I take it that the hydraulic fluid goes into the intercooler at a hundred and ten degrees? That's the maximum temperature you work at?'

'That's so,' said the chief engineer. 'In the case of the biggest motors that would be the outgoing temperature.'

'And it goes into the power generator about eighty degrees?'

'More or less.'

Keith stared at the drawing, still puzzled. 'Well, what's the temperature rise in the cooling water, then?'

The chief engineer glanced at his aide. Mr Monnington said, 'Fifty degrees. Fifty-five under extreme conditions.'

Puzzled, Keith said, 'It can't go higher than the temperature of the oil, or it couldn't do any cooling. What's the inlet temperature of the water?'

'Fifty degrees,' said Mr Monnington. Emmanuel stirred, but left the talking to Keith.

'That seems on the cold side for summer temperature,' said Keith.

'It's general in these rivers,' said the engineer. 'Maybe you don't get the same conditions in England. This is snow water, made by melting the eternal snows upon the Glacier Peak.'

Emmanuel leaned forward on the table. 'That's baloney,' he said candidly. 'Flume River doesn't rise from Glacier Peak. Flume River rises in the Troublesome Mountain, not much higher than five thousand feet. All the snow's gone from Troublesome by the end of April, most years.'

He paused, and then he said, 'Tell you sump'n. I went fishing up the Flume two years ago, in August, ten or fifteen miles above the Eight Mile Cut. Trout fishing. We didn't catch anything because the water was too hot, the fish wouldn't stir. So there was only one thing to be done, see? We stripped off, 'n went in for a swim. Real warm it was – I stayed in half an hour or more. I guess the water in that river, in the Flume, the one we're talking of – I guess it was seventy-five degrees or more, that day.'

There was a dead silence in the conference room of Ferris Hydraulics, Inc.

Sol Hirzhorn took his call to Chuck Ferris next morning in Julie's office because he didn't want Keith Stewart to hear what was said. The girl started the tape recorder as he lifted the instrument and stood back in the room.

He said, 'That Chuck Ferris? Morning, Chuck. The boys tell me they had quite a party with your engineers.'

'That's right,' said Chuck cautiously. 'About the intercoolers. There was a difference of opinion on the inlet temperature of the water.'

'Manny tells me that he's putting on a swimming party at the mill next August. Girls and all.'

'I know, I know,' said Mr Ferris. 'Quit ribbing, Sol. My boys had the rivers mixed up. We're redesigning the intercoolers for your plant right now. That won't hold up the job, and our quotation stands. There's quite a bit more copper will be needed, but that's our mistake and we pay for it.'

'That's fine,' said Mr Hirzhorn. 'Mr Stewart that I sent with Manny, he was very impressed with what he saw.'

'Well,' said Mr Ferris, rather relieved, 'that's nice to know.'

'Really impressed, he was. He had a long talk with Manny on the plane on the way back. They didn't put much importance on this intercooler business, now that's all cleared up. They advised me to go right ahead and sign the Heads of Agreement so the attorneys could draw up the contract. There's only one point to be settled now.'

'What's that?'

'Who's going to pay Keith Stewart?'

There was dead silence on the line. The tape rolled on.

'He's not on your payroll and he's not on mine,' said the old lumber-man. 'He isn't going to be on mine, either. I asked him to look over the scheme as a friend. He said he didn't understand why the intercoolers were so small, so I sent him up with Manny to see your boys. Well, they found that there'd been a mistake in your office.'

'I know, I know,' said Mr Ferris. 'You think he ought to get something?'

'I sure do. Kind of a consultant fee.'

'What were you thinking of?' asked Mr Ferris cautiously.

'One per cent on the contract.'

Mr Ferris leaped in his chair. 'Jeez!' he exclaimed. 'That's – that's over seventeen thousand dollars! He's not a guy that's in that sort of money!'

'See here, Chuck,' said the old man evenly, 'a guy's worth what he earns. If he'd not spotted that the intercoolers were too small they'd have gone into the plant the way they were. Next July or August we'd have had to stop production for a month or more while you put the job right. Maybe we'd have had a lawsuit over it. There's big money involved. Do you know what one day's production from that mill is worth?'

'I know, I know,' said Mr Ferris petulantly. 'Still – seventeen thousand dollars! That's three Cadillacs!'

'If we'd had a lawsuit over this, 'n you lost, it would have cost you fifty Cadillacs,' said Mr Hirzhorn.

'Sure. But there isn't going to be a lawsuit. We've got the new design laid out in the drawing office right now. I was in there just a few minutes ago.'

'Sure there isn't going to be a lawsuit,' said Sol Hirzhorn. 'Maybe there isn't going to be a contract either. My son Joe, he said right from the start we should have had some competition in on this.'

There was a pause. 'You really feel that this guy's contribution rates seventeen thousand dollars?'

'I certainly do,' said the old man. 'If those intercoolers had gone in as the old design we'd have been up for ten – fifteen times that amount. And it wouldn't have been me who paid it.'

Mr Ferris threw in the towel. 'Okay,' he said. 'If that's what you think right, well, that's the way it is, Sol. That'll be okay with us at this end.'

'Well, that's fine,' said Mr Hirzhorn. 'Jim Rockawin, he's got the Heads of Agreement typed out ready. If he brings them to the Tacoma office tomorrow morning I'll sign up, and he can sign for you. Then we'll get them right over to my attorneys. There's just one clause needs adding: seventeen thousand dollars payable to Mr Keith Stewart for consultant services. Oh – one thing more. Mr Stewart will be leaving for England day after tomorrow, so Jim Rockawin had better bring the cheque along with him, with the Heads of Agreement. Seventeen thousand dollars.'

He put down the telephone and leaned back, a little weary. Julie came forward from the back of the room. 'He won't know if he's coming or going,' she said softly. She turned off the tape recorder. 'Shall I do a transcript?'

'May as well,' he said. 'We'll have it at the office in the morning, in case they have second thoughts.'

'They won't do that,' she said. 'They want this job too much.'

He got up from her chair. 'He's earned it,' he said. 'The guy has a right to be paid for the job he gets mixed up in, whether he's accustomed to that scale of dough or not.' He smiled. 'Pay off his mortgage.'

'It'll do more than that,' she said. 'It's three times the value of his mortgage.'

'Well, he'll have a little bit of loose change, then.'

'Is he going back to England day after tomorrow?' she asked.

'That's what he wants to do.'

'Had I better get busy with the reservations for his trip?' she asked.

He nodded. 'Yes, do that.'

'On the office?'

'Why, certainly. On the travelling overhead.'

'Okay,' she said. 'I'll see him presently. I've got the mail right here, Mr Hirzhorn, if you'd like to see it now.'

Half an hour later while Sol Hirzhorn was getting ready to go into Tacoma for a business lunch appointment she called Keith Stewart to her office. 'There's two or three things,' she said, businesslike and efficient. 'First, Jim Rockawin called yesterday. He's got some shipping documents he wants you to sign, about the engine salvaged from your sister's yacht.'

Keith nodded. 'He was going to get those.'

'Well, you've just got to sign and it's all through. The engine will be shipped upon a British ship sailing Thursday of next week, the *Clan McAlister*, to London docks. He's having it consigned to you, care of Perkins and Durant in London. Is that okay with you?'

'Fine,' said Keith. 'When can I sign the documents?'

'Well now, that's another thing. Mr Rockawin is coming to the head office tomorrow morning to sign the Heads of Agreement for the Flume River contract. Will I call him and tell him to bring the documents along with him then?'

'That would be fine.'

'Okay, I'll do that. Mr Rockawin has been talking with some of the Boeing engineers and they certainly would like to take you through the plant one day. Would you like to do that tomorrow afternoon?'

'I'd like to do that very much, if Mr Hirzhorn can spare me.'

She glanced at her diary. 'He's got a business lunch today, and another one tomorrow. He won't be back here either day till around five o'clock.' She smiled. 'I know that he'd appreciate an hour in the workshop with you then.' She stood in thought for a moment. 'Suppose we fix Jim Rockawin for ten o'clock tomorrow morning. Signing the Heads of Agreement and your shipping documents won't take more than half an hour. He could take you on then to lunch with the Boeing engineers and see some of the plant. Then I'll have the Cessna at the Boeing Field a quarter after four to bring you right back here.'

'Well,' said Keith, 'that'd be grand for me. But it's putting everybody to a great deal of trouble.'

She shook her head. 'The airplane and the pilot would be standing idle in the hangar. Manny's got meetings in Seattle and Joe hardly ever flies. I'll fix that. Now there's another thing, Mr Stewart, and that's about your consultant fee.' One of her duties was to deal with awkward or embarrassing matters for her grandfather.

'My what?'

'Consultant fee, Mr Stewart. Mr Hirzhorn asked you to look the Ferris plans over and you discovered a mistake that had to do with the intercoolers. To check on that you had to go to Cincinnati. Well, the Ferris crowd *had* made a mistake that would have cost both parties a great deal of money if it had gone through. Mr Ferris reckons that your technical services rate a consultant fee, and he called Mr Hirzhorn about it this morning,' she said, lying like a good personal secretary. 'They reckoned that one per cent of the contract would be a reasonable figure – that's seventeen thousand dollars. Is that okay with you?'

Keith was dumbfounded. 'But that's absurd!' he exclaimed. 'It's much too much!'

'It's what's usual in this country,' she said off-handedly. She could lie beautifully, with a perfectly straight, business-like expression. 'If you want to talk Mr Ferris out of it you'll have to go to Cincinnati. But there's no reason for you to do that. It's in line with fees paid every day for consultant technical services.'

'I'll have to think about it,' Keith muttered.

'Jim Rockawin's bringing the cheque out with him tomorrow morning,' she remarked. 'It's probably made out by now. That's because Mr Hirzhorn told Mr Ferris that you're on your way back to England. They fixed between them that would be a reasonable fee, and there's a clause in the Heads of Agreement about it.'

'It's much too much for the work I did,' he repeated.

'That may be so in England,' she remarked. 'I wouldn't know. I can tell you one thing, though. If you want those Heads of Agreement altered in the morning, Jim Rockawin will have to call Mr Ferris in Cincinnati and you won't get to Boeing in time for lunch. I'd leave things the way they are, if I were you.' She paused. 'There's one more thing. Mr Hirzhorn said you'd be leaving us day after tomorrow. Will you be going straight through to London?'

Keith nodded. 'I've got to hurry home. I've been away too long.'

'Too bad that you can't stay a little longer,' said Julie. 'Maybe you'll be over again. I'll call United and book you on the flight to Idlewild, New York, that connects with the night Pan-Am flight to London. Okay?'

'Wait a bit,' said Keith. 'I don't know that I want to fly. I was thinking that I'd have to go by train and boat.'

She said, 'But you flew out to Vancouver and Honolulu, didn't you?'

'I got that free,' he said. 'At home – well I don't live like you do here.'

She said, 'I know it.' She eyed him kindly. 'You mustn't think that everybody in the US lives like Mr Hirzhorn,' she said. 'One day, maybe, I'll get married, and then I'll come down with a bump. Mr Hirzhorn has a right to live like this. He's built up a great industry, and that's about the only real interest he has, except the workshop.' She paused. 'I asked him about the reservations and the tickets,' she remarked. 'He said to put them through the office account.'

Keith paused for a moment, untangling her unfamiliar words. 'You mean, he wants to pay my airline fare back to London?'

She smiled. 'Not personally, of course. He said to me to put it on the travelling overhead at the office. But that's what it adds up to.'

'I can't let him do that,' Keith said. 'Not with seventeen thousand dollars of Mr Ferris' money in my pocket.'

'You want to learn arithmetic,' she said. 'If this goes in the office overhead it gets deducted from the profit before tax is charged. Mr Hirzhorn won't pay twenty per cent of these fares. If you pay, you'll pay it out of your net income, one hundred per cent. That doesn't make sense.'

She paused. 'Don't refuse him when he wants to do this little thing,' she said gently. 'You've given him a lot of pleasure with your letters and the clock. Let him do this for you.'

CHAPTER ELEVEN

KEITH STEWART LANDED back in England at London Airport three days later, eighty days after he had left England from Speke. He passed through Immigration and Customs and took the airline coach for London. He stopped the coach and got off at the end of the South Ealing Road and got on a bus. Shortly before lunchtime he arrived at his house in Somerset Road, carrying his suitcase. It looked a little small now, and a little tawdry, but he was very, very glad to be back.

He let himself in with his latchkey, for Katie would be at the shop and Janice would be having lunch at school. For the first time in months he could relax. He put his suitcase down, took off his coat, and went down to the basement. His clean workshop was untouched, the machines bright and shiny, ready for work. In the dirty workshop there was an enormous pile of correspondence on his desk, but outside the daffodils were nodding in the sunshine and the wind. He looked into Janice's room, that once had been the scullery. The plastic duck still sat upon the four eggs, multicoloured, in the basketwork nest upon the table by her bed.

It was very good to be home.

He made a cup of tea and a couple of pieces of dripping toast. There was one job that must not be delayed. He put on his coat after the little meal and went out again. He walked a quarter of a mile to the shops of West Ealing, and into the local branch of the Westminster Bank. Before the eyes of the astounded cashier he endorsed a cheque for seventeen thousand dollars, and paid it into his account.

He walked back to the house and let himself in. He took his coat off and went down to the workshop, and stood for a time in thought. He had brought back with him a few of the Ferris drawings of the hydraulic installations at the Flume River Mill, and his mind was playing upon those. The hydraulic motors might not be too difficult to make in model scale ... and would be something new and up to date for readers of the *Miniature Mechanic*. Suppose he took the 20cc Gannet engine as a basis, or any engine of about that power. Suppose he coupled the power generator on to that, aiming to deliver a quarter of a horsepower, working at a pressure of 300lb per square inch, as a first guess ... Then a miniature hydraulic motor driving something or other – a small bandsaw, for example – a tiny replica of the great bandsaws he had seen in the mill ... Start off with a bronze casting, like this ... He seized a pad of paper on the desk and began to sketch.

An hour later he heard the gate clang and heard Janice's footsteps on the path to the front door. He went upstairs and let her in before she could open the front door with her key. She dropped her satchel of schoolbooks and flew into his arms. 'I'm glad you're back,' she said.

He hugged her clumsily. 'Miss me?' he asked.

She nodded. 'Mm.' And then she said, 'It's been dull, not having anything made.'

'You been all right at school?' he asked.

She nodded. 'I'd have come home early if I'd known you'd be here,' she said. 'We play hockey for the last hour now, Mondays and Thursdays. This is Monday, so we've been playing hockey. But if I'd known you were here I could have come home after school.'

'Like hockey?' he asked.

She nodded again. 'Aunt Katie bought me a lovely hockey stick with a green and yellow handle, new. Diana's got a new one, too. She's awfully good at hockey.' She struggled out of her coat. 'I must put the kettle on because Aunt Katie will be coming home.'

He glanced at his watch. 'She won't be home for an hour.'

'She gets off an hour earlier now,' said Janice, rushing to the kitchen to fill the kettle. 'She started doing that when you went away because she said she ought to be at home when I get back from school because you weren't here, but I'm a big girl now, aren't I? And then they started taking eight and tenpence from her pay packet each week because she left an hour early. Wasn't that mean of them?'

Together they laid the kitchen table and put the macaroni cheese in the oven to heat, and got out the bread and the butter and the jam and the cherry cake. Across the table she asked suddenly, 'Did you go to where Mummy and Daddy were buried?'

'Yes, I went there,' he said. 'We had a stone made and put it up to mark the grave. I took a lot of photographs for you, but I haven't had them developed yet. I'll take them up to London, to Kodak, tomorrow or the next day. Better not trust them to a local photographer.'

'Were they buried on the island?' she asked.

'Yes,' he said. 'On the island with the sea all round. Nobody lives there. You see, it's only a little island, and there isn't any water for people to drink, so nobody else can live there.'

She stood looking at him. 'Can you hear the sea from the place where they're buried?'

'Yes,' he said. 'You can hear the sea all round.'

'I think that's nice,' she said. 'They always liked the sea.'

'I left the grey egg with them,' he said, 'because I thought they'd like to have something that was yours. I buried it just underneath the sand.'

She nodded. 'They'll like that.'

That was the end of it. She did not speak about her father or her mother again till they showed her the photographs ten days later.

Katie came in before the kettle boiled. 'Keith!' she said. 'Why didn't you let us know? I didn't really think that you'd be home for another month. Where have you come from?'

'There wasn't really time to write,' he apologised. It was out of their economic way of life to send cables about the world. 'I came from the other side of America, right through. I left there … yesterday morning, I suppose. Times get a bit mucked up.'

She wrinkled her brows. 'Flying?'

He nodded. There was much to tell her, but it would have to wait till Janice was in bed. 'You've got so *brown*,' she said in wonder. 'Whatever have you been doing? Out in the sun?'

'That's right,' he said. 'I'll tell you about it later.'

Janice said, 'Diana went to Bournemouth with her Mummy and Johnnie, and they all came back ever so brown. Can we go to Bournemouth some day, Aunt Katie?'

'We'll go there one day, dear. Perhaps next summer.' Then they went in to tea.

After tea Keith unpacked his suitcase and got out the little presents he had bought for them in Honolulu and in Papeete, and gave them to Janice and to Katie. There was so much to tell them that Katie allowed Janice to stay up for half an hour longer, but it was a school day next day, and Katie took her off to see she washed her ears and neck properly in the bath after playing hockey and to see that she brushed her teeth and said her prayers and went to bed without reading.

Keith washed the dishes while all that was going on, and when Katie came up from the basement room where Janice slept they were free to talk. 'First thing,' she said practically, 'have you got any money, Keith?'

He nodded. 'I was trying to sort it out on the plane,' he said, 'but it's all foreign, so it wasn't too easy. I didn't have to spend very much.' He pulled a muddled sheaf of notes from his breast pocket, with a black wallet of travellers' cheques. He shuffled the pack. 'There's a pound note,' he said, pulling it from the mess. 'And there's another. These things must be francs. You see what you can make of it.' He passed the lot to her.

She opened the little wallet. 'There's forty pounds here that you haven't used!' she exclaimed.

'Is there? I knew there was a good bit left.'

'Well, thank the Lord for that,' she remarked.

'Are things tight?'

'Not worse than they've been before. We don't owe anything. I've got a little over three pounds in my purse. But there's ten guineas to pay next month for the school. Still, this will put us right. I think we've got about eight pounds in the bank.'

'We've got more than that,' he said comfortably. 'I paid in a bit over six thousand pounds this afternoon.'

'That's Janice's money,' she replied. 'We can use that for her school fees, but we can't use it for living on ourselves. We'd better open another account for her money.'

'It's not her money,' he retorted. 'That's coming along later. This is ours.'

It was midnight before they went to bed.

Next morning he wrote a letter of thanks to Mr Hirzhorn and packed it up with the coil winder in a little box to go to him by airmail. He spent most of the rest of the day in sorting out his vast pile of letters and answering the most urgent ones, thinking regretfully of Julie in her office in the house at Wauna and how she would have made a meal for them. Perhaps, he thought idly, one day Janice would become a secretary and would be able to help him. He gave up the correspondence early in the afternoon, and turned for relaxation to the design of the hydraulic models.

Next day, rested and refreshed, he took his hydraulic sketches up to Mr McNeil in the office of the *Miniature Mechanic*, and told him most of what had happened on his journey, and about Sol Hirzhorn and his Congreve clock. They lunched together at a nearby Lyons, and talked about the serial that Keith proposed for the hydraulic mechanisms. 'We've got quite a few subscribers in the Seattle and Tacoma district,' he told his editor. 'They told me that there are six or seven in Boeing alone.'

'I'll get hold of the subscription figures,' said Mr McNeil thoughtfully. 'I think a serial on model lumber mechanism is a good idea – especially if you incorporate the bandsaw. After all, that's useful in the workshop, too. Besides being something really up to date for the Canadians and the Americans ...'

Keith stayed quietly at home for the next six weeks, catching up with his work, developing the hydraulic models, and writing the serial. Then the *Clan McAlister* docked, and he was called down to the docks to see his packing case through Customs. Presently it was delivered to the house in Somerset Road upon a truck. He got the truck driver to help him roll the case on short lengths of steel bar from the workshop through the front gate and the front garden, and down beside the house to the back garden, where they left it in the middle of the garden path. Keith gave the driver five shillings for his help.

Next morning, after Katie had gone to the shop and Janice had gone to school, he unscrewed the sides of the packing case. The engine seemed in fair condition, though a good deal of external corrosion was evident all over it. He got an enamel basin from the kitchen and drained the oil from the crankcase, spilling a good deal on the garden path to Katie's subsequent annoyance. She wasn't too pleased about the condition of the basin either, which she used for washing vegetables.

He had no chain blocks to lift the engine with, nor any ropes or tackle. He undid the main holding-down bolts from the wooden bearers, put a couple of coal sacks where the head would hit the ground, and turned it rather roughly on its side, using a length of one-inch round steel bar as a crowbar. In that position he could undo the bolts holding the sump in place.

That afternoon he rang up Mr Carpenter, the solicitor, at his office in Bedford Square. 'This is Keith Stewart speaking,' he said. 'You remember? Commander Dermott's brother-in-law.'

'Of course I remember, Mr Stewart. You've been away, haven't you?'

'Just a short holiday.' Keith said. 'You know those diamonds that we were looking for?'

'I do.'

'Well,' said Keith. 'I believe they've turned up. My wife Katie – she was turning out the boxroom yesterday and she found a suitcase that she didn't think belonged to us, full of clothes. She showed it me when I got home and they were uniforms and things like that, and books and things. It must have been one that John left behind that he hadn't told us about, or we'd forgotten. Anyway, there was a little box in it full of white stones, cut like jewels, if you understand me. Do you think they'd be the diamonds?'

'Did you count them?' asked the solicitor. 'How many of them are there?'

'Half a minute, and I'll count them now,' said Keith. There was a pause. 'Forty-seven,' he said.

'That is the number of the stones that Mr Franck sold to John Dermott,' the solicitor replied. 'I should think you probably have found them, Mr Stewart. That's very fortunate, very fortunate indeed.'

'What had I better do with them?'

Mr Carpenter thought for a moment. 'They'll have to go back to Mr Franck as soon as possible,' he said, 'to be sold for the benefit of the estate. We shall have to reopen the matter with the Estate Duty Office – but that comes later. I'll ring Mr Franck at once. Could you bring them up to my office tomorrow morning, if I ask him to come round? Say about ten-thirty?'

'That's all right for me,' said Keith.

'You'll have to be careful of them tonight,' said the solicitor. 'If they're the diamonds, they're worth twenty-seven thousand pounds. It's just like having so much cash in the house with you. Does anybody else know about them?'

'Not a soul,' said Keith. 'I haven't even told Katie. And there's no one in the house now, to hear us talking.'

'Well, be careful of them, and don't tell your wife or anyone. You'd better take a taxi in the morning, straight from your house right up to this office. I'll expect you at ten-thirty.'

Keith walked into the solicitor's office next morning, dressed in his soiled old raincoat and holding his dirty old felt hat in his hand. There was a florid man with Mr Carpenter, with curly black hair, middle-aged. They both got up when Keith came in. The solicitor said, 'Good morning. Mr Stewart. Mr Stewart, this is Mr Franck, of Rosenblaum and Franck, the diamond merchants.'

Keith said, 'Good morning,' and shook hands.

Mr Carpenter asked, 'Did you bring those stones up with you, Mr Stewart?'

'I've got them here,' said Keith. He pulled a little cardboard box out of his jacket pocket and gave it to the solicitor. Mr

Carpenter opened it, glanced inside, and handed it to Mr Franck.

The diamond merchant took it, glanced at the contents, and frowned. He took a monocle magnifying-glass from his waistcoat pocket and fitted it in his right eye. Then he selected one of the largest stones and carried it to the window for a better light. He stood in silence for a minute scrutinising it. Then he scratched it with his thumbnail and examined it again.

'What's this yellow stuff all over them?' he asked.

'I don't know,' said Keith. 'That's how I found them. Is there something wrong?'

'There's this yellow, gummy deposit on them,' said the diamond merchant. 'Have they been stored in oil?'

'Not since yesterday,' said Keith truthfully. 'That's all I know.' He paused, and asked a little anxiously, 'Would it matter if they had?'

Mr Franck shook his head. 'It'll polish off. I can scratch it off with my nail. They're diamonds all right,' he said. 'At least, this one is.'

He came back to the desk and put the stone in the box with the others. From his attaché case he took a little black leather case, opened it on the desk, and erected a tiny set of scales with minute weights handled by a pair of forceps. He weighed them all together, very carefully, then he pulled a typed list from his pocket and consulted it. 'Ninety-seven carats,' he said thoughtfully. 'The diamonds that I sold Commander Dermott totalled ninety-two carats. But then, they've got this deposit on them now ...' He took the two largest stones and weighed them carefully, and the two smallest stones, again consulting his list. He counted them for number.

Finally he put the lid on to the cardboard box and put away the scales. 'I think there can be very little doubt that these stones are the stones I sold Commander Dermott,' he said. 'I can't be absolutely sure until we have them polished and examine each stone individually. I should like to take them and have that done, giving you a receipt for them, of course. Then I suppose that you would want them to be sold?'

A few minutes later he left the office, taking the diamonds with him, asking the office girl to call a taxi to the door. Keith said, 'Well, I'll be getting along. You'll let me know what happens?' He got up and reached for his old, shabby hat.

The solicitor got up with him. 'You're looking very well,' he remarked. 'Much better than when I saw you last. You must have been out in the sun.'

'I had a bit of a holiday,' said Keith defensively.

'A very good thing to do,' said Mr Carpenter. They moved towards the door. 'Tell me,' he said, 'did you ever do anything about the engine that was salvaged from your brother-in-law's yacht?'

'I had it shipped home,' said Keith. 'I've got it in the garden. But it's not much good, not really.'

The shadow of a smile appeared on Mr Carpenter's face. 'I don't suppose it is, not now,' he said. He moved to the door with Keith. 'I wish some of my other clients took their trusts as seriously as you have done,' he said. 'I think Commander Dermott made a very wise choice of a trustee.'

Janice still goes to Miss Pearson's school in West Ealing, but she is entered for the Royal Naval School for Officers' Daughters at Haslemere and she will go there next year. After that, Katie would like her to go to Oxford or to Cambridge if she can get in, and Miss Pearson thinks she probably will. Katie says that that's what Jo would have wanted for her, and she may be right.

Jack and Dawn Donelly are married in a kind of way, though there is still a little doubt about Jack's marital status.

They live on Raiatea Island in the *Iles sous le Vent*, at the south-east corner, on Baie Hotopuu. They lived first on the *Mary Belle* at anchor in the bay, mostly on fish and cornmeal fritters, but presently Chuck Ferris sent the *Flying Cloud* to Raiatea with a prefabricated house for them broken down into small sections for deck cargo, and Captain Petersen helped them to put up the main structure before sailing for home. The completion of this house has kept Jack busy woodworking, which he does very well, and he in turn has kept Dawn busy for she had three children in one calendar year, twin girls in January and a boy in December; I believe there is another one on the way. Of course, she lives some distance from a pharmacy. Chuck Ferris is sending out another house to them, to make a bit more room.

Sol Hirzhorn has just finished the Congreve clock and is thinking about starting off on the hydraulic models in Keith's serial. Julie still works for him and looks after him in the winters when Mrs Hirzhorn is in Florida. He would like Keith to come out to the West again and bring Katie and Janice with him for a few weeks' holiday. Keith has deferred this until Janice is a little older, but Julie writes privately that Sol really means it and that Joe says that in view of Keith's professional services the fares would certainly be chargeable to Hirzhorn Enterprises Inc., so Keith will probably accept the invitation in a year or two.

Keith finally sold the engine salvaged from *Shearwater* for sixty pounds, but it took him six months to do so. It cost him fifty-nine pounds eight shillings and tenpence in shipping charges from Seattle, so that he made a profit on the transaction.

Katie no longer works in Buckley's drapery shop in Ealing Broadway. They discovered that the interest on the sterling equivalent of seventeen thousand dollars just about equalled her wages at the shop, and that all Janice's expenses were amply covered by the interest from her own money, relieving them of the burden they had willingly assumed. At the same time Keith's correspondence throughout the world was growing to such an extent that some days he did nothing but write letters. So Katie gave up her job and bought a typewriter and a tape dictating machine, and took charge of the letters. She is not a Julie Perlberg and she never will be, but Keith by sitting in his chair and talking into the microphone can clear the heaviest mail in an hour or so, and the letters get done somehow.

If you happen to be in the trolley bus from Southall or from Hanwell at about nine o'clock on a Friday morning, you may see a little man get in at West Ealing, dressed in a shabby raincoat over a blue suit. He is one of hundreds of thousands like him in industrial England, pale-faced, running to fat a little, rather hard up. His hands show evidence of manual work, his eyes and forehead evidence of intellect. A fitter or a machinist, you think, perhaps out of the toolroom. If you follow him, you will find that he gets out at Ealing Broadway and takes the Underground to Victoria Station. He comes up to the surface and walks along Victoria Street a little way to an office block, where he climbs four flights of stone stairs to the dingy, old-fashioned office of the *Miniature Mechanic* to deliver his 'copy'.

He will come out presently and take a bus to Chancery Lane, to spend the remainder of the day in the Library of the Patent Office. He will be home at Somerset Road, Ealing, in time for tea. He will spend the evening in the workshop, working on the current model.

He has achieved the type of life that he desires; he wants no other. He is perfectly, supremely happy.

NEVIL SHUTE

Trustee from the Toolroom

NEVIL SHUTE

THE FAR COUNTRY

The Far Country relates the story of a young English woman's holiday in the Australian outback just after World War II. Travelling from a cold, rainy country she finds a land of plenty and falls in love with Australia's wild countryside. She meets an older doctor, a displaced person from Europe and their friendship begins to teach them about themselves and their adopted home.

IN THE WET

Stevie, an ex-pilot, ex-ringer, drunk and drug addict lies dying in a remote hut in the Australian outback in the wet season. His passing is witnessed by an old Episcopal priest. As he lays dying, he dreams of his future incarnation as a pilot in the Queen's Flight. The priest shares his dream, and wonders if a corner of the veil has not been lifted for him.

NEVIL SHUTE

LANDFALL

Jerry Chambers is a coastal patrol pilot in World War II; Mona Stevens is a barmaid at the Royal Clarence Hotel where Jerry drinks and dines with his friends. They meet and fall in love. All looks fine until Jerry is accused of making a terrible mistake in combat, and only Mona may be able to save his career.

ON THE BEACH

Australia is one of the last places on earth where life still exists after nuclear war started in the Northern Hemisphere. A year on, an invisible cloak of radiation has spread almost completely around the world. Darwin is a ghost town, and radiation levels at Ayres Rock are increasing.

An American nuclear-powered submarine has found its way to Australia where its captain has placed the boat under the command of the Australian Navy. Commander Dwight Towers and his Australian liaison officer are sent to the coast of North America to discover whether a stray radio signal originating from near Seattle is a sign of life...

Nevil Shute

Pied Piper

Elderly John Howard goes off to the Jura in France on a fishing trip, except this is no ordinary time. Germany is at war with Europe. Friends at his hotel ask him to take their children back to England with him to safety as Germany is poised to invade France. Their harrowing journey begins by train and then proceeds on foot.

'Mr Shute not only writes vividly and excitingly of occupied France, but with a delightful understanding of children.' – *The Sunday Times*

A Town Like Alice

Jean Paget survived World War II as a prisoner of the Japanese in Malaya. After the war she comes into an inheritance that enables her to return to Malaya to repay the villagers who helped her to survive. But her return visit changes her life again when she discovers that an Australian soldier she thought had died has survived. She goes to Australia in search of him and of Alice, the town he described to her.